HANDBOOK
OF
FOAMED PLASTICS

RENE J. BENDER
ENGINEERING CONSULTANT

LAKE PUBLISHING CORPORATION
LIBERTYVILLE, ILLINOIS

Opinions and data presented in this Handbook are believed to
be a true representation of the state of the art in the opinion
of the authors. Neither the publisher nor the authors can be
responsible for any liability that may result from any of the
information published.

FOREWORD

It took a little over two years to put together this first "Handbook of Foamed Plastics," and over thirty authors have collaborated for its preparation. Who they are, why they were considered worthy of undertaking this work can be found in the brief biographies which follow. These people have cooperated in a remarkable manner to cover as completely as possible the subjects treated in their respective sections. To my co-authors, and co-authoress, I wish to express my sincere gratitude.

The Handbook is offered as a handy reference to readers engaged in the widest scope of activities: the designer looking for the most effective way of insulating a building, packaging a new product, introducing a new dimension in decoration or comfort; the chemist; the engineer, seeking accurate data on a specific foam; the professor; the student writing an essay on plastics; the bank economist describing a rapidly growing industry; the editor who writes about it.

An effort has been made to subdivide the presentation as clearly as possible, so that no time will be wasted in finding the information desired.

Obviously, there is a certain amount of repetition: equipment needed to manufacture or fabricate a certain foam may be described briefly in the Section pertaining to that foam and, at greater length, in the Section on Equipment. This, also, should save time and effort, when data must be put together with a minimum of delay. What is not discussed in detail in the text, but may be of interest to an engineer or a scientist, can be found with the help of the comprehensive bibliography at the end of the Handbook.

The experts who have written this Handbook are connected with leading companies in the field of foamed plastics. But these are only a fraction of the many manufacturers of raw materials and equipment, fabricators, processors, technicians, engineers and users of foamed plastics, who have supplied information and illustrations and, in a hundred ways, have supported and encouraged the publication of this Handbook.

RENE J. BENDER

CONTENTS

MEET THE AUTHORS

GEORGE MICHAEL, without whose untiring efforts and guidance this Handbook could not have been published, is chief editor of PLASTICS DESIGN & PROCESSING. He has a B.S. in chemical engineering (Northwestern University, 1951) and his experience includes R and D in chemicals and editing divers technical publications.

RENE J. BENDER is a graduate engineer from Ecole Centrale des Arts & Manufactures of Paris, France. For twenty-five years, he was associated in various engineering and executive capacities with Sinclair Oil Corp. in the U.S. and abroad. During the First World War, he served in the French Army; during World War II, he was Lt-Cmdr in the U.S. Navy, in the African and European theaters of operations. He is now an associate editor of the McGraw-Hill magazine POWER, and the U.S. correspondent of the French PLASTIQUES INFORMATIONS. Bender is a member of the ASME, the ACS, the SAE and the SPE. He is currently president of French Engineers in the U.S., Inc., and chairman of the lecture committee of that Society.

BETTY LOU RASKIN has been head of plastics research and development at the Carlyle Barton Laboratory of The Johns Hopkins University since 1954. She attended the Western College for Women in Oxford, Ohio, was graduated from Goucher College, and received her master's degree in chemistry from Johns Hopkins. Miss Raskin has invented several commercially-used processes concerning glass fiber-reinforced plastics and has made significant contributions to the foamed plastics field. On Sept. 15, 1954 in Minneapolis she presented the paper "Foamed plastics—A New Field of Chemistry" at the 128th national meeting of the American Chemical Society. This was the first paper ever given before any scientific organization on foamed plastics as a versatile new family of materials. Miss Raskin is the inventor of foamed plastic smokes and the particles collected from them. She has served as a consultant on foamed plastics to several governmental agencies and industrial firms and for five years was secretary of the American Society for Testing and Materials' Subcommittee XX on Cellular Plastics. She has been elected a Councilor of the American Chemical Society and a Fellow of the American Association for the Advancement of Science and is the recipient of several national honors for her plastics work.

DR. SAMUEL STEINGISER is a native of Springfield, Mass. He received his B.S. degree from The City College of New York in 1938, his M.S. degree from Polytechnic Institute of Brooklyn in 1941, and his Ph.D. from the University of Connecticut in 1949. From 1941 to 1950 he was associated with Rockefeller Institute for Medical Research, the Atomic Energy Commission working on the Atom Bomb Project, Publicker Industries, Research Associate of the Office of Naval Research, and a fellow of the University of Connecticut. Dr. Steingiser was Group Leader and Research Scientist with the Central Research Department of Monsanto during the period of 1950-1954. He joined Mobay in 1954 as Group Leader of the Evaluation Group. Dr. Steingiser brought to Mobay a wide and varied background in the fields of mass spectroscopy, nuclear chemistry, magneto-optics, high vacuum phenomena, and high polymer physics. He was promoted to the position of Assistant Director of Research in May of 1959. Dr. Steingiser has worked extensively with trade organizations such as the SPI, ASTM, SAE, and ISO. He is at present Chairman of the Cellular Plastics Division of the SPI and a member of the Board of Directors of the SPI.

DANIEL P. SHEDD attended Purdue University and the University of Rochester, majoring in Chemical Engineering and Organic Chemistry. His industrial experiences encompass twenty-two years in the chemical industry where he has been primarily concerned with problems of chemical marketing and market development. Since joining Arthur D. Little, Inc., in 1960 as a senior staff member, he has been project manager on studies involving chemical marketing, diversification and acquisition covering a wide range of products including thermoplastic and thermosetting foams, their raw materials, processing and marketing. He is a member of the American Chemical Society.

HERB BRABANDT, JR. graduated from the University of Louisville with a B.Sc. in Physics. His experience in foam processing equipment started in 1957 as a designer with Martin Sweets Co., Inc. In 1960 he joined the development division of Olin Chemical Co.—then Olin-Mathieson—in Brandenburg, Ky., where he contributed to a testing program related to urethane foam. He returned to Martin Sweets as a development engineer, and held that position until 1963. Now he heads a consulting firm of his own, in Louisville, dealing in the design of process equipment for urethane and other plastic foams. He is a member of the SPE.

STANLEY SZELWACH is vice president and general manager of Miller & Van Winkle Co., Paterson, N. J. Prior to joining that company, he was plant manager for the Roto Bag Machine Corp. After graduating from Adelphi College, he has been actively employed in the production and engineering field for over 25 years. Mr. Szelwach, a well-recognized designer, holds many patents on devices of his own invention, and has currently applied for one on the slide mold filling technique.

GEORGE E. MURRAY was born and reared in Michigan. He served in the U.S. Army in Europe, then in Korea. After graduating from Flint Jr. College he received a B.Sc. degree in architecture from the University of Cincinnati in 1955, then a Masters degree in architecture from Rensselaer Polytechnic Institute. He joined The Dow Chemical Co. in Midland in 1956 in the Plastics Development and Service Department, devoting his efforts toward research and development of new construction concepts and the application of plastics as building materials.

RONALD H. HARDING was born in Chicago, Ill., obtained his B.Sc., and Ph. D. from Purdue University, where he worked as research assistant and residence hall counselor from 1953 to 1957. He then joined the R.&D. department of the Chemicals Division of Union Carbide Corp., was research chemist from 1957 to 1962, is now a group leader. He has published research papers on paint films and rigid foamed products in many technical publications, and has lectured at Purdue Paint & Varnish Technology Short Course, and at the Building Research Institute Conference. He is a member of the AIChE, the ACS and the AAAS.

THOMAS J. MAHONEY is a native of Brooklyn, N.Y. He got his B.Sc. in Chemistry from Manhattan College, 1950, his M.S. and his Ph.D. from Carnegie Institute of Technology, 1953 and 1954. He is a member of the ACS. He has been with Union Carbide Corp. since 1953, in the Silicones Division, then the Chemicals Division and is now manager of market development, dealing mostly with the intermediates for urethane foams.

ROBERT A. STENGARD was born in Fitchburg, Mass. in 1923. He received both B.Sc. and M.Sc. degrees in Chemical Engineering from Worcester Polytechnic Institute. Positions held before he joined DuPont include teaching at the University of Massachusetts, process engineer at M. W. Kellogg Co., chemist at Hood Rubber Co., sales engineer with F. S. Gibbs Co. and process engineer

with National Research Corp. In DuPont's Elastomer Chemicals Department, he has been working on sales service and control on neoprene, development and sales service on isocyanates, principally as applied to rigid urethane foams. He has written several publications for E. I. duPont.

PAUL G. GEMEINHARDT was born in Saint Louis, Mo., schooled at Rolla School of Mines Extension of University of Missouri, Washington State College, Pullman, Wash., Central College, Fayette, Mo., and Northwestern University, Evanston, Ill. He has a B.Sc. in Chemistry with honors, and did postgraduate studies in chemistry. He has been a research chemist for Monsanto Chemical Co. Now, he is Senior Research Group Leader at Mobay Chemical Co., administering studies in urethane foams. He has a number of patents, issued and pending, and has written many technical papers in the field of polyurethanes.

GUY A. PATTEN got his B.Sc. in Chemical Engineering from Iowa State University, is now employed as a plastics development specialist at The Dow Chemical Co. He is chairman of several committees and subcommittees of the SPI, the NFPA and the ASTM, and a member of the ACS. The articles he publishes deal mostly with the heat resistance, the flammability tests and the heat conductivity of plastics.

ROBERT E. JONES was born in Madison, Wis., in 1926. He received a B.S. in Mathematics and Physics in 1949 from the University of Wisconsin and an M.S. in Physics in 1950. He joined the Forest Products Laboratory (of the Government) in 1952, and was employed there until 1955 when he went to Nopco Chemical Co. In charge of Plastics Division Physical Laboratory from 1955 to 1962; since 1962, Assistant Director of Laboratory. He has published articles in the fields of package cushioning and urethane foam. Currently he is chairman of ASTM D-20 Sub XX on Foam Plastics, as well as being on the Policy Committee for the Cellular Plastics Division of the SPI.

ROBERT G. HANLON received his B.Sc. degree from Michigan State University in Packaging Technology, and served several years as Packaging Specialist in the U.S. Air Force. He is now Plastics development engineer with The Dow Chemical Co., Midland, Mich.

ROBERT N. KENNEDY, a B.Sc. graduate in Chemical Engineering of Michigan State University, is Section head of the Construction Materials Group in the Plastics Development and Service Section of The Dow Chemical Co. Prior to this, he worked with Anderson Prichard Oil Co. and Wilcox Gay Corp. He is a member of ACS, ASHRAE and the

Cellular Division of SPI. He has authored several articles on Plastic Foams.

ARNOLD C. WERNER was born in New York City, graduated with an M.E. degree from Stevens Institute of Technology in 1950, did postgraduate work in coating resin technology at Brooklyn Polytechnic Institute. After a short time with United Lacquer Mfg. Corp., and Metal & Thermit Corp. on organic coatings development and production assignments, he joined the Naugatuck Chemical Division of U.S. Rubber Co., is now Senior Group Leader for plastisol resin product development and technical service. Werner is a member of the SPE, the Society of Rheology and the ACS. He has written many authoritative papers on plastisol resin technology.

MICHAEL W. SEELE is product manager of the polyethers section, Urethane Chemical Sales Department, of National Aniline Division of Allied Chemical Corp. He was born in New York City and studied at Saint Michael College in Vermont.

JON S. LAING holds a B.Sc. degree from Michigan State University. He is Plastics Development Engineer with The Dow Chemical Co. The youngest of our co-authors, he has prepared an excellent chapter on low-density polyethylene foam.

WILLIAM R. CUMING, a graduate from Stevens Institute of Technology, is vice president and chief engineer of Emerson & Cuming Co. He is a specialist in the application of plastics as dielectric materials, holds a number of important patents in this field. He is a member of the ACS and SPE. He served in various engineering capacities with the U.S. Navy during World War II.

JOHN DELMONTE obtained his B.Sc. from New York University, College of Engineering, and his M.Sc. from Massachusetts Institute of Technology in 1934. Following several engineering and executive connections, he is now president and general manager of Furane Plastics, Inc. He has published several technical books on plastics and adhesives, presented many papers. Mr. Delmonte is a member of SPE, SPI, ASTM and the ACS.

FRITZ HOSTETTLER is the only Swiss citizen who contributed to the Handbook. He was born in Berne, got both his M.S. and his Ph.D. at the Swiss Federal Institute of Technology. He has been with Union Carbide Corp. since 1953, in the Research & Development Laboratories of the Elastomer Chemicals section of the Chemicals Division. He is a member of the ACS.

H. J. PAZINSKI, a 1954 graduate of Rutgers University, is engaged in product development and technical service of extrusion compounds at Union Carbide Corp., Plastics Division, Bound Brook, N.J.

M. N. PAUL is another of our Canadian-born co-authors. He obtained his B.S. and M.S. from the College of Forestry of Syracuse (N.Y.) University, with five years in the U.S. Infantry intervening between these two degrees. He is now Market Manager of the Bonding Resins Section of Union Carbide Corp., Plastics Division, a company with which he has been connected for 14 years.

VERN L. GLINIECKI, born in Bay City, Mich., is a graduate of University of Michigan, and has been with The Dow Chemical Co., since 1952. He is now Technical Representative, designing equipment for extrusion of expandable polystyrene.

REID G. FORDYCE is a naturalized U.S. citizen born in 1914 in Regina, Saskatchewan, and educated in Canada; he got his B.S. and M.S. at the British Columbia University, his Ph.D. at McGill University in Montreal. He has been with Monsanto Chemical Co. for the past 20 years, holds now the position of Director of Research & Development in Springfield, Mass. He has to his name several patents in the field of vinyls, polystyrene and laminates, and is the author of many technical papers, particularly a series on copolymerization.

GEORGE C. KIESSLING is a graduate from Rensselaer Polytechnic Institute (1947). He was first employed as a plastics development engineer with the Tek Hughes division of Johnson & Johnson, Inc. in Watervliet, N.Y. Since 1952, he has held positions with the Plastics division of Koppers Co., Inc., and is now technical director, expandable polystyrene, Product Development Dept. He is a member of the ACS, the SPE and the Packaging Institute. He is, with W. C. Teach, co-author of a book; Polystyrene (Rheinhold 1960), He lives in Sewickley, Pa., with his wife and five children.

HAROLD L. VINCENT, a native of Midland, Mich., graduated from Michigan State University with a B.Sc. degree in Chemistry in 1954. After serving two years in the U.S. Army Chemical Corps, Mr. Vincent made his career with Dow Corning Co., where his is currently Senior Project Chemist in Advance Product Development. He is a member of the SPE. He holds several patents and has written many technical papers, mostly on Silicone and Silicone foams.

WILLIAM M. SMITH is responsible for all technical services for B. F. Goodrich Chemical Company's polyvinyl chloride plastisols and solution resins. He came to BFG Chemical in 1955 as a development engineer at the company's Avon Lake, Ohio, Development Center. In 1959, Smith was transferred to the Cleveland home office as a product engineer, and was named senior product engineer, his present position, later that year. Smith attended Case Institute of Technology, is a member of the Society of Plastics Engineers and is BFG Chemical's representative to the vinyl dispersion division of the Society of the Plastics Industry.

INTRODUCTION

An undertaking such as this Handbook represents a degree of maturity for the Cellular Plastics Industry. The time had arrived for the critical examination of the multitudinous scientific data developed during the last decade and for the compilation of such information in a readily accessible form. Much thought had to be given to a judicious selection of what was to be included as well as to what one could afford to omit. In a collaborative effort such as this Handbook, the ability to select experts in each field covered is of basic importance to its value and success. The editor then serves the purpose of integrating the diverse parts into a well-rounded, easily readable and scientifically detailed entity.

The Cellular Plastics Industry has grown by leaps and bounds in recent years. Market forecasts have prophesied sales anywhere up to billions of pounds in the next decade dependent on various factors. It is apparent that such growth must be based upon the technical competence of the industry. The basis for this competence is the technical information made available. Much of it is developed by raw material suppliers, some of it by foam producers' research efforts. Industry-wide cooperative efforts by such trade organizations as the Society of the Plastics Industry, Inc. (SPI), and the American Society for Testing and Materials (ASTM) have also resulted in making available a considerable amount of technical information.

Having gathered all this information, both from individual companies and from printed scientific literature, this Handbook serves as a compendium of practical technical data that one needs to conduct a technically sound business.

A look at the table of contents of this Handbook indicates its wide scope. It covers all the presently known cellular plastics. The technique of multiple authorship has enabled this book to be written in the shortest possible time and thus to be as up-to-date as can be. In a fast-changing technology, this is most important. It is hoped that, as our industry grows older, future editions of this Handbook will keep pace with its technical growth to keep reflecting what is up-to-date in the industry.

The editor and each and every contributor are to be commended for their efforts in a difficult task. The value of such work in critically recording our permanent technology is never to be underestimated. It is the building block upon which each next step is to be taken.

SAMUEL STEINGISER, Chairman
Cellular Plastics Division
Society of the Plastics Industry, Inc.

Section I—FOAMED PLASTICS: A YOUNG, VERSATILE AND GROWING FAMILY

By Betty Lou Raskin

Foamed plastics comprise a versatile new family of low density, cellular materials, which are made in a variety of processes remotely resembling the making of bread. These synthetic materials are polymers which have been expanded by a gas in volume so much that they have a uniformly cellular structure which can look like an extremely fine honeycomb or a mass of very tiny ping-pong balls fused together. The cells of some foamed plastics are large enough to be seen; cells in others are so fine that a microscope is needed.

All polymers can be expanded by a gas, some much more readily than others. There is no single all-purpose plastic foam, but there are a seemingly infinite number of resinous compositions from which foams can be made. These compositions can be tailored chemically —that is, they can be designed, synthesized, processed, and fabricated—to meet the requirements for innumerable types of end-use applications. Among those may be a sheet of vinyl foam which only a trained eye could distinguish from top-grade cowhide, a fluffy piece of urea-formaldehyde foam which looks like dry whipped cream, a plank of timber-like rigid urethane foam, a powder-puff made from a very resilient urethane foam, a slab of polystyrene foam like that used to insulate a new office building in Pittsburgh, a chunk of phenolic foam for keeping cut flowers in place and moist, and a length of cellular poly-ethylene wire-covering which looks like the unfoamed type, but weighs half as much, costs less, and has better electrical insulation properties.

Although they are being used more and more in place of metals, concrete, paper, wood, asbestos, glass fibers, foam rubber, cork, wool, and leather, foamed plastics are definitely not substitutes for conventional materials. Most plastic foams have unusually low densities, high strength-to-weight ratios, and many are excellent thermal and electrical insulators. Some of these properties are comparable to or better than those of non-foamed natural and synthetic materials. Plastic foams have other advantages, like good X-ray, radio, and radar transmission, and resistance to abrasion, vermin, and chemicals. The aircraft industry is using plastic foams for radar receivers, vibration damping, potting electronic components, acoustical insulation, upholstery, fume-filters, crash-padding, and as reinforcing cores between plastic or metal skins in structural parts.

Also known as *expanded* or *cellular* plastics, these materials come in a variety of consistencies ranging from that of raw cotton to hard wood. Flexible, semi-rigid, and rigid foams are available in densities of about 0.1 lb per cu ft to 80 lb per cu ft. As a result, we have structures of radically new design; more efficient production techniques; and items which are adding immeasurably to the comfort, convenience, and safety of everyday living. Already we can wear, live in, walk on, ride in, float on, fly in, houseclean with, sleep in, drink from, bathe in, play golf or tennis with, and even be buried in products which have been improved by some kind of plastic foam. On land, sea, and in the air, civilians and military personnel are using expanded plastics in such diverse fields as packaging, construction, low-temperature insulation, crash-padding, electronics, marine life-saving equipment, filtration, comfort-seating, bedding, clothing, display, prosthetics, and sculpture. From bassinets to ballistic missiles, from trucks to Telstar, in virtually all industries and fields of technical endeavor, engineers are either using cellular plastics or investigating them for particular applications.

Recently a urethane foam was used in a nocturnal experiment so unique that a motorist a few miles away reported having seen a miracle. The liquid components for the foam were put through a gas turbine-powered smoke generator and produced a white cloud of microscopic-sized, gas-filled particles of plastic. That "holey smoke" cloud floated hundreds of feet above ground and served as a projection screen when some color slides were focused on it from an enormous slide projector called Skyjector. The smoke puff had enough depth to it to make the images look three-dimensional—as if they had been carved out of colored marble with the velvet-black sky as a backdrop. More than just a spectacular new technique for advertising purposes, pictures-in-the-sky on projection screens made of foamed plastic smokes may become an important aid to education in areas deprived of teaching facilities. A teacher could lecture into a loudspeaker, illustrate his lesson on the "holey smoke" screen overhead, in an outdoor night school for thousands of students.

The sky is no limit for expanded plastics. At the Fels Planetarium of the Franklin Institute in Philadelphia there is a Moon Room in the new space science section. Constructed and furnished almost completely with a foamed plastic, the room is a sample of the type of housing which our explorers might establish in a cave on the moon. With chemicals for producing the plastic taken to the moon, the pioneers could fabricate their own insulation and furniture on the spot. As Dr. I. M. Levitt, director of the Planetarium said: "Foamed plastics may provide the key to the establishment and perpetuation of a civilization on the moon."

The Hughes Aircraft company has developed a one-part, completely solid type of foamable urethane for use in space applications. Discs of the powdered solids were cemented to a wire chair-frame and to the surface of a seven-foot diameter balloon. When exposed to infrared lamps in a vacuum chamber, conditions simulating those of a space environment, the discs foamed into a rigid material which had a density of only two to five lb per cu ft, but was strong enough to support a man on the moon.

There is even a "space parachute" under development at the General Electric Company's Missile and Space Vehicle Department in Philadelphia. Engineers there are working on a way for an astronaut to foam a protective chute around himself, like a cocoon, in case he has to abandon ship.

The originator of this idea, John H. Quillinan, explained how the chute would work. To return to Earth, the astronaut would step out of his ship, taking along his retro rockets, oxygen supply, recovery aids, and survival gear. Over his space suit, he would wear a plastic bag shaped properly for re-entry; it would have tanks of foamable plastic and a mixer attached. To foam himself home, he would first fire the rocket to head earthward. Then he would inflate the bag, and fill the space between himself and the bag with the foamed plastic. During re-entry into the atmosphere, a hard dense foam would serve as a heat shield and a more sponge-like foam would form a shock-absorbent landing-cushion. At about 30,000 feet, a parachute would release and, at the same time, pull cords which would strip the foam from around his hands and arms. After landing, he would free himself completely from the foam and remove his embedded survival kit. If he landed on water, the foam would also serve as a raft.

Because of cellular plastics, we now have family-size sailboats which two children can carry, gasoline which can be stored in "brick" form, featherweight winter clothing, a spongy, dirtless, plant-growth medium, mines which are more comfortable to work in and less prone to cave-in than ever before, shoes for walking on water, paperlike wrappings which keep chocolates from melting, and picnic coolers which can retain heat so well that they have carried Chesapeake Bay crabs, piping hot, from Baltimore, Maryland, to London, England.

Sculptors also are benefiting from foamed plastics. At a recent American Bowling Congress in Detroit there was a 15-foot, 120-pound statue of a giant carved from slabs of plastic foam and covered with a layer of gold-painted plaster. This was the most inexpensive way of producing a figure of this size and complexity.

Expanded plastics are being used to package all kinds of fragile items. Boeing Aircraft Co. used to deliver a delicate missile part by human courier. Now the part is packed in a slightly resilient, polyethylene foam and shipped by air parcel post. Reusable, molded containers of expanded polystyrene are being used to house spare electronic components for the Navy's new Polaris Mark 84 fire-control system. Each foamed plastic container takes up only 30% as much space as the original aluminum package, cuts the weight by 98% and the cost by about $35. Polystyrene foam, the least expensive of the impact-resistant cellular plastics, is one of the most widely-used for packaging applications. In 1963, 12 million pounds of polystyrene foam in many different forms were used for that purpose. By 1968, this will double.

A typewriter firm is now packaging its product in urethane, foamed right in the corrugated shipping carton. The typewriter is put into a plastic bag and then into the carton. When the foam-making ingredients are poured into the remaining space, the foam billows up, fills the box and rapidly hardens. Cost of this package is about one-fourth that of wooden containers.

Mattresses is another example of how the properties of these new synthetics are used to advantage. A crib mattress of urethane foam weighs less than the average newborn baby; a double-bed size weighs 16 lb, about one-third the weight of an inner-spring mattress. Economical (about 40% less expensive than foamed rubber) and easy to turn, these urethane mattresses are made to controlled degrees of firmness, have excellent chemical resistance, are long-lasting, and sterilizable.

Largest use for flexible vinyl and flexible urethane foams is for furniture and automotive cushioning. Fabrics coated with calendered or cast vinyl foam have the look and feel of fine leather—at about one-third the cost—are used for handbags, shoes, jackets, belts, gloves and upholstery. In 1958, 20,000 yards of this type of material, 54 inches wide, were sold in the U.S. In 1963 the amount had risen to more than 50 million yards.

Garment interlinings of urethane foam are also popular. Made of about 97% air and 3% plastic, they are being laminated to almost any material—even jerseys and lacy knits. Foam-backed fabrics are soft, comfortable to wear, wrinkle-resistant, and keep their shape well. They provide so much extra warmth that now almost any material can be used in outerwear—even light-weight cottons. Foam backings are also used for winter underwear, shoe linings, slip covers, sleeping bags, and rugs.

Automobile manufacturers, already using plastic foams for cushioning, crash-padding, gaskets, and filters, are trying them out in door panels and roofs of cars to cut down noises and vibrations, to make the cars warmer in winter and cooler in summer, and more impact-resistant.

The first train made largely of a foamed plastic was recently built in Germany. Operated between Cologne and Leverkusen by Farbenfabriken Bayer for its 40,000 Bayerwerk employees, this train contains prefabricated, quickly replaceable parts made from a laminate of urethane foam and aluminum.

The United States Rubber Company's new expanded acrylonitrile-butadiene-styrene (ABS) laminate is another promising new plastic foam being developed for use in the vehicular construction field. Made from calendered plies of a modified ABS which are laminated together and the core expanded, this rigid, but slightly resilient plastic "foam" can be rapidly produced in a wide variety of shapes by conventional thermoplastic sheet-forming techniques—in epoxy molds which usually cost only 1/100th as much as the dies and tooling required for steel parts. For example, one-piece automobile bodies made from this foam, without the reinforcements and bracings required for conventional materials, are quiet, light-weight, (the one-piece body for an experimental Ford car weighs only 120 lb) and well insulated; they have exceptional impact-resistance, require virtually no upkeep, and can be sold at reasonable prices.

Another spectacular application for foamed plastics is in the low-temperature insulation field. This use is expected to consume 30-million lb per year of these materials in 1965 —almost triple our present output for that purpose. Part of this anticipated growth is due to the code proposed by the Associated Food and Drug Officials of the United States (AFDOUS). It recommends that frozen food products be kept at 0°F or below during all phases of handling including shipment. Some states already have adopted this code; others are contemplating doing so.

Rigid urethane foam containing a volatile fluorocarbon is considered to be the best available type of insulation in equipment for transporting frozen food. For example, a closed cell urethane foam containing trichlorofluoromethane has a k-factor of 0.14 or less, whereas fibrous glass used in refrigerators has a k-factor of 0.22. This means that only about half as much of this cellular plastic is needed to produce the same insulation as glass fibers. The result is about 25% more storage space in present-size refrigerators and, of course, greater payloads in commercial refrigerators and refrigerated vehicles. During a recent test conducted by the U. S. Department of Agriculture, a reefer-van insulated with a urethane foam kept 18 tons of grapefruit in prime condition during a 4,000-mile, 19-day trip from Florida to Switzerland.

Marine applications for foamed plastics run the full gamut from life-saving gear to impact and moisture protection for the Navy's sonar equipment. Each of our nuclear submarines was constructed with thousands of pounds of weight-saving expanded plastics. Other marine uses include the fabrication of swimming pools, pleasure boats, floating toys, docks, rafts, and buoys which can be shot at by pranksters or rammed by boats without sinking.

Microwave equipment for the national defense program is being measured and calibrated in radar-test-chambers, made usually from blocks of polystyrene foam. This plastic absorbs electromagnetic energy so well that the room is "echo-free" and therefore simulates the non-reflective outdoors in which the equipment is to be used. There are more than 250 of these cost-saving test-chambers in the U.S. A flexible silicone foam with a melting point of 500°F was recently found suitable for use as a broadband microwave absorber in high heat environments. Extruded cellular polyethylene and polypropylene containing tiny nitrogen-filled cells have lower dielectric constants and higher tensile strengths than solid polyethylene or solid polypropylene. These materials offer the communications industry a means of reducing the thickness and cost of cable insulation without a change in cable capacitance.

In experimental surgery, some of the uses for foamed plastics include packings of polyvinyl-formal foam, adhesives of fast-foaming urethanes for joining broken bones together, and enemas of foamable, silicones for detecting small cancerous growths in the colon.

The greatest potential for rigid foamed plastics is in the building construction field. Today, only a few million pounds of these foams are going into this field, but it is believed that in 1965, 30-million lb will be consumed for this use, accounting for over one-third of our entire output of rigid foams. The long-range growth of this market could be enormous (perhaps on the order of a billion pounds per year) but it will depend largely on: (1) installed costs of these plastics becoming less than those of conventional materials, (2) acceptance by trade union officials of the changes in building techniques required for these materials, (3) improvements in the fire-retardancy of foamed plastics, and (4) favorable changes in building codes throughout the nation.

In Washington, D.C., the Smithsonian Institution's new $30,000,000 Museum of History and Technology has been insulated with a flame-retardant polystyrene foam in board form produced by the Koppers Company.

Recently a British firm made a hut to house eight people and a laboratory for Sir Edmund Hillary to use on his Himalayan expeditions. Made from about 100 interlocking panels of polystyrene foam covered with plywood, the hut can be erected and dismantled at any location to keep the explorers warm—at well below freezing outside temperatures.

Slabs of expanded plastics covered with reinforcing skins of metal, wood, asphalt, concrete, or plastic are used in the construction of curtain walls, partitions, roofs, floors, siding, doors, and perimeter insulation. Several firms are developing interchangeable panels of this type containing built-in plumbing, heating, and electrical lines.

Spectacular roofs, covering acres of surface area without any interior support, are being made of aluminum-polystyrene foam sandwich panels which are suspended from steel cables. The World of Tomorrow exhibit at the 1962 World's Fair in Seattle was housed in the first building made with this type of roof.

An economical process for using boards of polystyrene foam as a form for concrete in thin shell roof construction involves placing the plastic over sculptured earth; casting reinforced concrete over it, and lifting the finished roof into place. The 268-foot diameter domed roof of the International Convention Building of the Church of God headquarters in Anderson, Indiana, was made by this method and lifted 22 feet into place. Thin shell construction with foamed plastics allows for increased architectural freedom in creating graceful, flowing structures and more spheric or paraboloid shapes.

Resins which can be foamed in-place offer tremendous potential in the construction field. In Canada a three-bedroom house was fully insulated in 5½ hours by a foamable urethane composition which was sprayed into place—in half the time required to insulate the house with stapled batting. At the DuPont Company's Elastomers Laboratory near Wilmington, Delaware, a partially pre-expanded (frothed) urethane foam, which looks like shaving cream coming out of an aerosol can, was poured between two thin four-by-eight-foot aluminum sheets. A few minutes later the foam had expanded to a volume 30 times that of the original components, completely filling the four-inch-wide space, and firmly adhering to the aluminum. Shortly thereafter ten men stood on that panel without deflecting it.

A masonry cavity wall filled with a frothed urethane foam was found to have a bursting strength more than twice that of a comparable unfilled wall. This means that less structural steel will be needed in new masonry buildings using that technique. The savings in steel can be sufficient to offset the installed cost of the foam, which is several times that of the conventional materials used in residential construction. This plastic foam has an exceptionally uniform cell structure and is of special interest for use as insulation in electrically-heated houses, where air-tight construction is essential for economical heating. Expandable urea-formaldehyde and epoxy resins which can be sprayed into masonry wall cavities are also being investigated.

The Army is experimenting with instant housing for field use. In Natick, Massachusetts, at the Quartermaster Research and Engineering Command are some of the so-called "buildings from a barrel." An expandable urethane is sprayed over a large inflated balloon. After the foam has expanded and cured, the balloon is deflated, leaving a structure firmly bonded to the ground and suitable for use as mess hall, barracks or field hospital. Light enough to be picked up and moved to a new site, it can also be cut into pieces and glued back together with more of the same foamable composition. A 10×20×45-foot structure can be built by three men in three hours.

"Buildings from a bag" are also on the way. Made of preshaped flexible skins with foamable components inside, they can be erected in a few minutes after the membrane separating the highly reactive chemicals is broken.

Although all of this versatility is relatively new, the first foamed plastic was made several decades ago. In 1931 Swedish engineers Carl G. Munters and John G. Tandberg invented foamed polystyrene. Independently, The Dow Chemical Co. invented and developed commercially "Styrofoam," the oldest and still one of the well-known cellular plastics in the United States. Americans became familiar with this prefabricated foam because of its widespread use as a decorative material, particularly at Christmas time, but it was used extensively during World War II, in life-saving equipment for servicemen downed at sea. Several of the rubber companies' unicellular vinyl foams were also used for this purpose.

The urethane foams also are an international development. In the mid 1930's chemists at the DuPont Company's Experimental Station discovered ways of using isocyanates in the synthesis of high polymers, and during the period 1937-39 the company was issued basic patents covering reactions of diisocyanates with polyols and with polyamides.

In Germany in the late thirties, Bayer developed rigid urethane foams based on the reaction of tolylene diisocyanate and a polyester, prepared from adipic acid, trimethylolethane, and ethylene glycol. By the end of World War II, the Germans had begun to use these foams in aircraft construction and as insulation in submarines and tanks. Postwar reports from Allied investigators spurred many U.S. organizations to study these foams and to start producing them. In addition to DuPont, other U.S. firms which were pioneers in the field include: Monsanto Company, Lockheed Aircraft, Bell Telephone Laboratories, American Latex Products, and Nopco.

One of the earliest uses for a rigid urethane foam was in radomes. During 1947-48 Lockheed chemists developed and patented a technique for foaming a rigid urethane in place. Later on, DuPont developed lower cost rigid and semi-rigid urethane foams based on castor oil and tolylene di-isocyanate.

By 1951, flexible urethane foams had become a commercial reality in Germany as a result of Bayer's research. In the United States, DuPont and Monsanto had built pilot plants for producing diisocyanates and other firms were starting research on urethane foams. In 1954 Bayer and Monsanto formed the Mobay Chemical Company, the first chemical company jointly owned by a U.S. chemical firm and a foreign one. Subsequently many firms became foam-producers by licensing the Mobay, Lockheed or DuPont patents, and before long large quantities of resilient urethane foams were on the market.

One of the earliest examples of a large-scale foaming-in-place operation occurred in midwinter of 1949 at the Philadelphia Navy Yard on the aircraft carrier USS Cabot, where an acid-catalyzed phenolic foam completely filled 8100 cubic feet of blisters, which are empty spaces along the water line. Compared to the cost of the balsa wood originally used for that purpose, the savings were $169,000 worth of labor and 97 days of dry-dock time.

In the 1950's, foams made from expandable polystyrene beads, cellulose acetate, epoxy, polyethylene, silicone, and urea-formaldehyde became commercially available. The largest single use for any of these was in the 1956 motion picture, "War and Peace." All of the artificial snow used on the sets was made of the urea foam.

Now there are about 350 U.S. firms which either produce plastic foams or supply the basic raw materials. A Who's Who of the industry would include tire and rubber manufacturers, oil companies, meat packers, drug companies, glass firms, paper companies, metal fabricators, clothing manufacturers, and all of the major chemical companies.

Announcements about new technical developments concerning plastic foams are almost a weekly occurrence. The patent literature is becoming prolific and sophisticated. Standards for all major types of these synthetics are being evolved by the International Standards Organization, the American Society for Testing and Materials, the Society of the Plastics Industry, and other groups. At the same time, millions of advertising dollars are being spent by processors of leather, wool, and other natural materials in an effort to combat plastic foams.

Like all materials, cellular plastics have their strong points and their limitations. Although virtually all of them have high strength-to-weight ratios, some lack sufficient mechanical strength for special applications and therefore must be used with reinforcing skins. Some phenolics and silicones have excellent heat resistance but crumble when subjected to intense vibrational stress. Others, like polystyrene and polyethylene foams, have excellent thermal insulation properties at low but not at high temperatures. No foamed plastic is fireproof, but many of them can be made flame-resistant; that is, they can be chemically formulated or coated with a mastic so that they will not support their own combustion or add fuel to the flames. Toxic fumes evolved during the expansion reaction can also be a problem, especially in the case of urethane foams. Therefore, protective clothing and fume exhausts should be used indoors.

From the chemical point of view there are also limitations. Some low density foams contain large blow-holes, instead of a uniform distribution of cells of given size and shape. The molecular structure of some cellular polymers may deteriorate with age. Some foams are decomposed by solvents; others, like cellular polytetrafluoroethylene, are so solvent-resistant that it is difficult to find a solvent for them when it is necessary.

The relatively high cost of some foamed plastics prevents them from being used in applications for which there are less expensive materials capable of doing a similar job. For example, cellular cellulose acetate is a structurally strong insulator which is seldom used in the construction field, because it costs about $8 per cubic foot, uninstalled. However, most plastic foams and the products made from them are becoming increasingly competitive as the cost of their components comes down. Consider the case of the disposable, eight-ounce, hot drink cup. For years this item was made of a paper which was a poor thermal insulator. Now, well-insulated disposable cups of extruded polystyrene foam are on the market at $7.00 per thousand, paper cups are becoming collectors' items—and there are no more burned fingers.

Foamed plastics are relatively inexpensive to ship and store in the unexpanded form; they usually cost less to process, fabricate, and install than conventional materials; they require less material to do a given job than equivalent non-foamed materials. In view of the intense research and development work now underway in all phases of the expanded plastics industry, it can be assumed that the price of these materials will drop markedly in the near future.

Expense-cutting operations in this highly competitive business are in evidence on many fronts. There have been business mergers, especially between raw material producers and fabricators of the foams. Equipment manufacturers are coming out with sophisticated, high-speed machines, some of which are automated, for pumping, metering, mixing, pouring, nucleating, spraying, frothing, pre-expanding, extruding, molding, calendering, and curing large quantities of various foamable compositions.

Chemical modifications are being made in foam formulations so that extremely low density foams, consuming less resin per cubic foot, can be used without loss of functionality. For example, expandable polystyrene beads, (the most widely used and least expensive raw material for producing a rigid cellular plastic) are being molded into densities of 1.5 lb per cu ft for packaging applications and 1 lb per cu ft for insulation boards—and these densities may go even lower as a result of further developments.

Special catalysts are making possible the cost-saving "one-shot" method for producing rigid polyether-based urethane foams. This method eliminates the necessity for manufacturing a prepolymer and is discussed in detail in Section IX. Recently chemists at the U.S. Department of Agriculture's Northern Utilization Research Laboratory in Peoria, Illinois, prepared a rigid urethane foam from glycoside polyethers, which they had synthesized from cereal starch. Other examples of chemical cost-cutting methods include the use of inexpensive nucleating agents like air and carbon black, flame-retardants which are built into the polymer instead of being added separately (brominated epoxy resin, for example), and inexpensive foam extenders, surfactants, and fillers.

Expanded plastics can be fabricated in many different ways, but not all foams can be treated in the same manner, because they vary greatly in resiliency, density, chemical resistance, mechanical strength, melting point, and other properties. The fabrication methods include: heat-sealing, cementing, coating, laminating, thermoforming, embossing, sewing, slicing, nailing, and stapling.

Plastic foams can be purchased in many different forms. There are prefoamed logs, slabs, sheets, rods, tubes, choppings, netting, tapes, and particles. Expandable plastic compositions, ready for on-the-job foaming, are available as molding powders, beads, plastisols, and highly reactive liquids which, when mixed together, literally foam-in-place and cure with remarkable adhesiveness wherever they are poured or sprayed—into odd-shaped containers, into large cavities, or over enormous surfaces. All of these foamable compositions are so adaptable that they are making it possible for foamed plastics to be used in ways and places that were undreamed of only a few years ago. For example, a vinyl plastisol containing a chemical blowing agent can be calendered, extruded, dip-coated, molded, or rotationally-cast. A urethane foam sprayed onto the damp walls of a mine, firmly binds loose rocks, seals air leaks, thermally insulates the mine, and reduces fire hazards—all in one operation. At its Houston, Texas, plant, Shell Chemical Company insulated a 44,000-gallon ethylene storage vessel with a 2.5"-thick, 2 lb per cu ft, sprayed-on, fire-retardant epoxy foam—more effectively and inexpensively than

with any previously-used material. Bridges undercoated with a one inch-thick layer of a sprayed-on urethane foam remain virtually clear of ice, snow, and heavy frost formation during winter months. This point was proved recently in a dramatic experiment in Watertown, New York, conducted by representatives of Allied Chemical Corporation and the New York State Department of Public Works.

As a result of the present enthusiasm for cellular plastics, the production of these synthetics has become one of the fastest-growing industries in the world. In 1953 about ten million pounds of all types of plastic foams were produced in the United States and sales were about $10 million. By 1963 U.S. output of these materials had increased to about 340-million lb, and the sales figure is nearly $300 million. It is believed that in 1968, 860-million lb will be produced and the sales figure will reach $650-million. Total world production outside U.S.A. is close to U.S. production and increasing rapidly. Major foreign producers of plastic foams are West Germany, Great Britain, France, Italy, and Japan. In virtually every part of the world foam-making facilities are springing up, frequently with financial and technical aid from the United States. Some of these new facilities are jointly owned by U.S. and foreign firms. One of the newest foreign plants is in Southern Rhodesia where rigid urethane foams can be turned out at a top rate of 60 lb per minute.

In the United States, until about ten years ago when the flexible urethane and flexible vinyl foams came into prominence for use in comfort-seating applications, polystyrene foam was the most widely used of all of the plastic foams. It still is the biggest seller of all *rigid* foams. In 1963 polystyrene foams were only 27% of the total output of cellular plastics; *flexible* urethane foams alone made up nearly half of the total.

The spectacular growth of the foamed plastics industry in this country is due in large measure to the resilient foams, but now research and development emphasis is on the rigid foams, especially those which can be foamed-in-place. Of these foams, the urethane is the undisputed favorite, but in this rapidly changing business, a versatile new group of foamable polymers could capture the limelight from the urethanes at any time.

The long-range potential for rigid foams is greater than that for flexible ones, but progress on the rigids has been slow because most of the time and capital in the foamed plastics industry has been spent on flexible urethanes. Perhaps the main reason is that years ago manufacturers recognized their immediate sales potential while markets for rigid foams are more expensive to penetrate.

It is possible to get into the business of spray-foaming rigid urethanes with only about $10,000 worth of equipment, but anyone contemplating doing so should remember that research and development costs in this field are high. The field is so new that virtually every type of foaming-in-place application presents problems which must be solved, *mainly by the firm doing the job*. This often means working outdoors, at the job-site. Resin suppliers and spray-gun manufacturers are valuable sources of information for the production of these foams, but no one should expect these firms to solve all one's technical problems.

Even though the equipment for preparing a particular type of plastic foam may involve nothing more than a disposable cup and a wooden tongue depressor, a kitchen-type mixer and a bowl, or a spray-gun, the chemical and physical factors underlying the foaming reaction taking place in that cup, bowl, or spray-gun can be extremely complex. A detailed discussion of the theoretical aspects of the syntheses of each of the different types of foamed plastics currently on the market is found in the appropriate section of this book.

Type of material	Forms available	Standard sizes	Density lb per cu ft	Thermal conductivity Btu /sq ft /hr / °F /in.	Tensile strength, psi	Compressive strength, psi
Cellulose acetate, closed-cell, rigid	Boards and rods	Any length, 1″ x 4″, ¾″ x 6″, ½″ x 8″, 2¼″ dia rods	6 to 8	0.31	170	125
Copolymers: 1. Methyl-methacrylate-styrene	Boards	8′ long 16″ wide up to 6″ thick	1.7	0.50	—	6.5 @ 3.3% deflection
2. Styrene-acrylonitrile expandable beads	Billets	—	1.0	—	—	10
Epoxy: 1. Preformed blocks	Blocks	Up to 1′ x 2′ x 6′	5 to 20	0.25 to 0.30	51 @ 5.6 lb per cu ft 490 @ 17.7 lb per cu ft	62 @ 5.6 lb per cu ft 950 @ 17.7 lb per cu ft
2. Sprayed	Liquid	—	1.7 to 2.0	0.11 to 0.17 @ 75°F mean temp.	26 to 31 @ 77°F mean temp.	13 to 17 @ 77°F (10% deflection)
Phenolic	Liquid resin for foaming-in-place	—	1/3 to 1½ 2 to 5 7 to 10 10 to 22	0.21 to 0.28* 0.20 to 0.22* 0.24 to 0.28* —	3 to 17 20 to 54 80 to 130 —	2 to 15 22 to 85 158 to 1200 300 to 1200
Polyethylene, closed-cell, semi-rigid	Boards, rods, sheet	Wide variety	1.8 to 2.2	0.35 @ 70°F mean temp.	20 to 30	Resilient
Polystyrene expanded	Boards, planks logs	12″ to 24″ wide 8′ & 9′ lengths up to 10″ thick	1.8 2.8 4.3	0.23 to 0.28 @ 40°F mean temp.	55 105 180	30 60 120
Polystyrene, expandable	Beads, boards, shapes	up to 4′ wide up to 12′ long up to 8″ thick	1.25 1.0 2.0 5.0	0.23 @ 40°F mean temp. 0.26 @ 70°F " " 0.24 " " " " 0.25 " " " "	44 33 54 121	16 to 20 14 29 115
Polyurethane, rigid, closed-cell	Boards, shapes	Wide variety	Fluorocarbon Blowing agent 1.5-3.0 0.17-0.12 4.0-8.0 0.15-0.21 9.0-12.0 0.23-0.27	CO$_2$ Blowing agent 0.23 0.23-0.29 0.31-0.35	15-70 90-250 300-400	15-50 70-275 350-550
Polyurethane, foamed-in-place, closed-cell	2-and 3-part systems mixed on job	—	Fluorocarbon 13-18 0.28-0.34 19-25 0.36-0.44 26-40 — 41-70 —	CO$_2$ 0.36-0.40 0.42-0.52 — —	475-700 775-1300 1350-3000 3000-8000+	650-1100 1200-2000+ 2100-5000 5000-15,000+
Polyvinyl chloride: 1. Closed-cell	Sheets, molded shapes	36″×44″ 1/16″ to 2½″ thick	4 to 25	—	—	1.5 to 8 @ 25% deflection
2. Plasticized, closed or open cell	Liquid or paste	Foamed in-place 3 to 30 ft. @ 310-400 ft.	7 to 26	0.36	250-1200	—
Silicone	Powder	Foamed in-place @ 320°F cell size 0.08″	14 16	0.30 0.30	— —	200 325
Urea-formaldehyde	Block, shred	20½″x10½″x4½″	0.8 to 1.2	0.18 to 0.21	Poor	200

Prepared by George Murray. Portions courtesy Modern Plastics Encyclopedia.
*Long term, 100°F mean temperature

Chart

	Coeff. of linear expansion, in./in./°F	Burning rate, in./min	Water vapor transmission, g/hr/sq ft/in./cm Hg	Moisture absorption, % by wt.	Dielectric constant	Dissipation factor	Chemical resistance
	2.5×10^{-5}	4.5	—	13-17 @ 100% RH 1.9-2.5 @ 50% RH	1.12	—	Good
	3.5×10^{-5}	6.0	—	—	1.05	—	Fair
	$3.0\text{-}4.0 \times 10^{-5}$	Flame retardant	—	0.15 lb per sq ft surface area	—	—	Good
	—	Can be self-extinguishing	—	—	—	—	Good
	—	Can be self-extinguishing	0.9 to 1.2 perm/in. @ 75°F, 50% RH	0.03 to 0.05 lb per sq ft, left for 48 hr	—	—	Good
	0.5×10^{-5}	Self-extinguishing	2074 g/day/sq m (2 lb/cu ft) 1844 g/day/sq m (5 lb/cu ft)	13 to 51 @ 100% RH 10 to 15 @ 100% RH	— 1.19 to 1.20	— 0.028-0.031	— —
	—	2.5	0.40 with skin 0.80 exposed cells	One volume % by 24 hr	1.05 @ 10^9 cps	0.0002 @ 10^9 cps	Good
5	3 to 4	Flame retardant	1 to 2	nil	<1.05 @ 10^2 to 10^8 cps	0.0002 @ 10^2 to 10^8 cps	Poor
	2.7 to 4.0	4.5 (can be self-extinguishing)	2.0	nil	<1.05 @ 10^2-10^6 cps	<0.0005 @ 10^2-10^6 cps	Poor
0	$3\text{-}4 \times 10^{-5}$ 4×10^{-5} 4×10^{-5}	Can be self-extinguishing	— — —	4.0 1.8 0.8	1.05 1.10 1.20	0.3-1.3 $\times 10^{-3}$ @ 10^3 to 10^9 cps	Good
	4.0×10^{-5}	Can be self-extinguishing	— — —	0.4 0.2 — —	1.3 1.4 1.5	2.0 $\times 10^{-3}$ 3.0 $\times 10^{-3}$ 4.0 $\times 10^{-3}$	Good
5	—	Self-extinguishing	—	5.0 max	—	—	Good
	—	Self-extinguishing	—	—	—	—	Good
	—	Non-flammable	— —	— —	— —	— —	Good
	—	—	—	—	—	—	Good

Section II—THE PRESENT MARKET AND FUTURE POTENTIAL OF PLASTIC FOAMS

By Daniel P. Shedd

1. GENERAL PROCESS DESCRIPTION

Since World War II an increasing emphasis has been placed on materials which are lighter in weight and more functional. The trend is noticeable today in automobiles and aircraft, housing and architecture, home furnishings and clothing. Foamed plastics have contributed significantly to that trend, and the cellular plastics industry, started in the immediate post-war years has grown to a sales volume of $600-million, at consumer level, in 1962. This spectacular growth was helped by intensive research on the part of chemical material suppliers, foam processors, and foam users, and fields ranging from basic chemical science to refrigeration engineering and architectural design. In view of their success to date, it is anticipated that such research will continue and probably be intensified to develop new, more versatile, less expensive raw materials and processes to yield new and improved foam products.

In considering applications for foamed plastics it is important to understand what they are, how they are made, and what they can do.

Plastic foams are produced from a variety of thermosetting or thermoplastic resins. Currently, the most important classes of foamed thermosetting resins are the urethanes, epoxies, phenolics, urea formaldehydes, and silicones. Of the thermoplastic foaming resins, polystyrene, vinyls, polyolefins, and the cellulosics are the common types.

The properties of the base resin and the choice of foaming agent are important in determining the physical properties of the final foam; the cost of the resin and complexity of the foaming and fabrication process are determinates of the over-all economics of producing the final foam product.

Nearly any resin may be foamed by one or more of the following basic processes: 1) frothing, that is whipping air or other inert gas into a resin dispersion and then fusing the resulting foam; 2) dissolving gases or low boiling liquids in a resin so that they will vaporize at processing temperatures; 3) dispersing in the resin heat-sensitive chemical blowing agents which decompose at processing temperatures and release an inert gas. Modification of these three basic methods and development of new foaming technique are the object of a great deal of research which will yield new processes and products in the years to come.

When properly formulated and produced, foamed plastics are strong, tough and durable, and light in weight. They derive their chemical characteristics from the basic polymer used in their production, but their cellular structure gives them useful physical properties not apparent in the base polymer. The density can be varied from as little as one-half lb per cu ft to as much as 10 or 12 lb per cu ft, but the majority of the commercially important foams have densities of 1½ to 5 lb per cu ft.

The cell structure of a foam may also vary significantly. The cells themselves may be open and interconnected to allow the passage of liquids and gases through the foam, or they may be closed with the membranes of resin forming the cell walls intact, so that they act as barriers to gases and liquids except by diffusion. Commercial foamed plastics are open or close celled depending on the foaming process or the properties desired in the foam. The size and uniformity of the cells themselves may be varied from very fine structures barely visible to the naked eye to coarse foam cells half-an-inch in diameter. The cells may occur on a random distribution of sizes within a given foam, or they may be very uniform in size.

Control of polymer structure is important to obtain final desired characteristics of a foam. If a flexible, elastomeric polymer is used to produce a foam, the resulting product will be soft and flexible. If a highly crosslinked, rigid polymer is used, the resulting foam will be rigid and friable. Since friability is an undesirable characteristic in most applications, tough—rather than brittle—resins are used for foaming whenever possible.

In the foaming of thermoplastic resins, the

Table II-1—Common Methods of Producing Foamed Plastics and Types of Products

	Method of foaming	Blowing agent	Method of Production	Density lb per cu ft	Open celled	Close celled	Flexible	Semi-flexible	Rigid	Forms available
Thermoplastic Foams										
Styrene	low boiling solvent	hydrocarbon (isopentane, n-pentane) methyl chloride	expandable head molding,	1.5-2.5		X			X	board stock, molded shapes.
			extrusion	2-4		X			X	board stock, film and sheet.
Vinyl	frothing a plastisol	air or nitrogen or CO$_2$	pour in mold and heat spread on surface and heat	3-6	X	X	X			molded shapes, slabs, sheets
	chemical blowing agents	azodicarbonamide N,N'–dimethyl-N,N'– dinitroso-terephthalamide	cast plastisol and heat calender sheet and heat	12-25	X	X	X			molded shapes, supported or unsupported sheets.
			extrusion and heat	7-25		X	X			profiles.
Polyolefin (polyethylene)	low boiling solvent	fluorocarbon p,p'–oxybis (benzene-sulfonyl hydrazide)	extrusion	2-4		X		X		boards, round and oval profiles
	chemical blowing agents	azodicarbonamide	extrusion	19-23		X		X		wire insulation
Cellulosic (cellulose acetate)	low boiling solvent	hydrocarbon	extrusion	5-7		X			X	board stock
Thermosetting Foams										
Urethane	chemical blowing agent and/or low boiling solvent	chemically released CO$_2$ fluorocarbon (F-11)	poured in slab poured and molded poured-in-place spray-in-place	1.5-4	X	X	X	X	X	slab stock, molded shapes, sheets, sprayed in place insulation
Epoxy	chemical blowing agent	chemically released CO$_2$	poured in slab poured and molded poured-in-place	4-9		X			X	board stock, molded shapes
	low boiling solvent	fluorocarbon (F-11)	spray-in-place	2-3		X			X	sprayed-in-place insulation
Phenolic	low boiling solvent	water and solvent	poured in slab poured and molded poured-in-place	0.3-4	X				X	board stock, molded shapes, hollow micro-spheres
Urea formaldehyde	low boiling hydro-carbon	hydrocarbon	poured, molded, dried	0.8-1.2		X			X	blocks and shredded material
	frothing	air	poured, molded, dried	1-2.0	X				X	
Silicones	chemical blowing agent	N,N'–dinitroso-pentamethylene-tetramine	poured-in-place poured blocks	14-16		X			X	blocks and sheets molded shapes
	chemical blowing agent	chemically released hydrogen	poured-in-place sprayed-in-place	3.5-4	X			X	X	poured or sprayed insulation
	chemical blowing agent	—	poured-in-place poured and molded	5-30	X	X	X			poured-in-place electrical, thermal, and vibration insulation

polymer structure is unaltered during the foaming process, whereas thermosetting resins are foamed simultaneously with polymer buildup. Thermoplastic resins are generally foamed by the application of heat to the resin in which the foaming agent is thoroughly dispersed. The function of externally applied heat in this case is to activate the blowing agent and to soften the resin so that it will flow or fuse. In the production of thermosetting foams, two or more reactive components (generally liquids) which form the polymer are mixed together with a blowing agent. Minor quantities of catalysts, foam stabilizers, and activators may be added to facilitate processing. The heat generated from the polymerization is used to activate the blowing agent.

Therefore, the choice of the foam for a given use depends not only upon the suitability of the foam's physical and chemical properties and its raw material cost, but also on the foaming techniques and process equipment available and the cost of conversion, when needed. Table II-1 describes common methods of producing foams and types of products made from them. Current and projected markets for foam plastics are based not only upon foam properties but also upon versatility of fabricating techniques available.

2. MARKETS

In making market projections for the consumption of plastic foams by polymer type or by end use, it is important to consider not only the degree to which existing foam products have penetrated a market, but also the maturity of the technology.

It is frequently possible to obtain an accurate estimate of the current position and the potential of a foam, but it is difficult to predict the effect of changes in technology on the long-range market. In discussing markets for foam plastics the importance of the technology is assessed in predicting market expansion.

Table II-2 lists the consumption of cellular plastics in 1962 and projects their growth through 1970. Flexible and semiflexible foams are listed by application and material and are considered apart from rigid foams, since the applications for these two classes of foams are quite different. These projections are for foamed plastics in the density range of 1 to 8 lb per cu ft and do not include cellular vinyl used for garment and upholstery fabrics, polyolefins for wire insulation, or silicone blocks, moldings and sheets. These products are produced in densities of 12 or more lb per cu ft and do not normally compete in the applications described.

3. FLEXIBLE AND SEMIFLEXIBLE FOAMS

By 1970, flexible and semiflexible foams will have increased to more than 2½ times their present volume, with urethanes accounting for most of this growth. Flexible, open-celled urethane cushioning is produced primarily as slab stock from which a variety of shapes are fabricated by cutting and slicing. This procedure yields a high percentage of scrap which, in the production of extremely irregular shapes, may be as much as 30%. The scrap, however, finds a market in the production of stiff cushions, such as for bar stools, for which it is ground and rebonded with elastomeric adhesives. More recently, suitable processes have been developed which allow the economical production of molded shapes, and this method of production of irregular shapes is gaining rapid acceptance. Urethanes offer the widest latitude of processing techniques, and the foams may be produced in a wide range of stiffnesses at a given density. In addition they are the least expensive of the truly flexible foams, and their excellent solvent and chemical resistance contributes to good durability.

Urethane foams have dominated the furniture applications for foamed plastics where they not only supplant foam rubber in seat cushions but also have gained increasing acceptance as padding for upholstered arms and backs. The flexible, low-density, open-cell urethane foams based on polyester and polyether foam systems are available in a wide range of softness so that a furniture manufacturer has great latitude in selecting the proper foam for a certain application. Further increase is expected in usage of urethanes for furniture cushioning as molded urethane foam cushionings become more available and as new urethane foam systems are developed. One new development is the introduction of inert filling materials into flexible urethane foam formulations. These have the effect of increasing density, resulting in a slightly heavier cushion, more like foam rubber, with less tendency to buckle when a person sits on it than the current 1½ to 2 lb per cu ft material. New developments in froth foaming of vinyl plastisols will probably find applications in the production of deep contoured, integrally-skinned vinyl foams but will probably find limited application in furniture cushioning.

The automotive industry uses a substantial quantity for flexible urethane foam as topper pads on seats; a more dense and stiffer product (about 4 lb per cu ft) is molded in vinyl skin materials and used as padding for instrument panels, visors, and arm rests. Smaller quantities of vinyl foam, faced with vinyl sheet

Table II-2—Consumption of Cellular Plastics (in million lbs)

Flexible and Semi-flexible Foam

Applications	1962	1970	Materials
Furniture	80	130	Urethane, vinyl
Automotive	40	100	Urethane, vinyl, polyolefin
Bedding	12	80	Urethane
Clothing interliner	7	20	Urethane
Rug pads	neg.	35	Urethane
Packaging	2	20	Urethane, vinyl, polyolefin
Protective equipment	1	10	Urethane, vinyl, polyolefin
Miscellaneous	10	25	Urethane, vinyl, polyolefin
	152	420	

Materials		
Urethane	140	370
Vinyl	10	30
Polyolefins	2	20
	152	420

Rigid Foams

Applications	1962	1970	Materials
Building trades	20	180–480	Urethane, styrene
Packaging	20	70–200	Styrene
Low-temperature insulation			
Appliances & display cases	10	75	Urethane
Cold storage & process rooms	14	30	Urethane
Transportation	10	40	Urethane, styrene
Buoyancy	10	15	Urethane, sytrene
Military and space	3	10	Urethane, styrene
Miscellaneous	13	25	Urethane, styrene, other*
	100	445–875	

Materials		
Urethane	18	225–475
Styrene	77	200–380
Epoxy	2	10
Phenolic	2	5
Other*	1	5
	100	445–875

*Includes urea, polyamide, silicones, cellulose acetate, etc.
Source: Trade Publications, Industry Sources and Arthur D. Little, Inc. estimates.

material, are used as door liners and kick pads. The market in 1970 will have expanded from the current 4 to 5 pounds of foam per car to about 10 pounds per car with *urethanes* continuing to have the major share. The expansion will come with the increased use of molded flexible urethane foams for bucket seats and other integral seat construction. Further use will be made of vinyl foam and sheet combinations in interior trim, and polyolefin foams will find use as autocarpet underlay. Urethanes are already well established as cushioning materials in aircraft, and this use will continue to grow. Volumes for aircraft and other commercial transportation seating are at present included in the estimates for automotive uses.

Although urethane foam is used currently as a padding for tops and edges of mattresses, the bedding industry offers an excellent opportunity for growth of foams for full mattresses and pillows. Urethanes will dominate this use because of their light weight, soft texture, durability, availability in a wide range of stiffnesses, and their ease of manufacture in large shapes. Supersoft urethane foams are now available for use in pillows, and lightweight fabric covered urethane foam quilts and comforters will increase in usage, further adding to the total urethane foam consumed by the bedding industry.

Applications of foams to clothing and apparel have grown rapidly, in the past few years, to 7- to 10-million pounds and may reach 20-million pounds by 1973, if current estimates of 300 million square yards of urethane foam interliner for outerware are realized. These interliners are formed by combining flexible urethane foam sheets of from 1/8 to 3/32 inch thick to fabric backing materials by use of flame lamination techniques or adhesives. Such foam-fabric combinations are used as lightweight insulating materials for raincoats, snowsuits, topcoats, hunting jackets, and other outerwear. Urethane's breathability, warmth, light weight and ability to be either laundered or dry cleaned are important factors in this use.

The rug cushioning field has not been invaded yet by plastic foams. However, urethanes have the best opportunity in this area, since they can be easily made available in thin sheets; however, the foams to date have been either too soft or, if they have been stiff enough, have failed to recover properly from the high unit loads imposed by furniture. In addition unbacked urethanes tend to stretch and creep out from under the edge of the rug. It is reasonable to believe, however, that improvement in foam systems will occur which will allow the use of urethane for this purpose either as separate pads or as an integral backing to the carpet itself.

The packaging field offers an opportunity for flexible urethanes and polyolefin foams to provide protective cushioning for fragile items subject to repeated shock loads and vibrations. Urethane is provided as premolded cushioning, foamed-in-place around the article to be protected, or in die-cut shapes made from slab material. Such cushioning is currently used to protect missile components and delicate electron tubes during shipment. Polyolefin foams are closed cell and are generally stiffer than urethanes. They can be used where higher loadbearing is required. Currently the only important polyolefin foam, polyethylene, is available as extruded shapes which generally require further fabrication to specific cushion shape.

For protective equipment, urethanes, vinyls, and polyolefins all compete. The choice depends on whether an open or closed cell foam is desirable for a given use. The open-celled foam uses will be dominated by urethanes, whereas vinyls and polyolefins compete where closed-cell foam is desirable. The high loadbearing,

flexible and semiflexible foams will be used for such things as football helmets, gym mats, life jackets, and boat fenders.

The versatility of both closed or open-cell flexible and semiflexible foams make them suitable for a variety of miscellaneous applications, such as sponges, novelties, toys, table pads, paint rollers, etc. These markets should grow to about 25 million pounds by 1970.

4. RIGID FOAMS

Of the rigid foams currently produced, closed cell, foamed polystyrene dominates the market, with urethanes second. Foamed styrene is produced both as an extruded board stock (Dow's "Styrofoam") and from solvent-containing beads which are expanded with heat and then fused in a mold to yield blocks (from which board stock is cut) or molded shapes. Foamed styrene is less expensive than rigid urethane on a board foot basis.

Rigid closed-cell urethanes, despite their generally higher cost, have the following advantages compared to polystyrene: 1) they may be blown with fluorocarbons and retain the high molecular-weight gas, which makes them extremely efficient thermal insulating materials; 2) when foamed-in-place, rigid closed-cell urethanes provide good adhesion to a variety of skin materials; 3) they may be applied as coatings by spraying techniques; 4) their density may be more easily controlled over a wider range; 5) they can be used at higher temperatures and are more solvent and chemical resistant.

By 1970, rigid foams will grow to 4 to 8 times their current volume, exceeding substantially the growth of flexible foams. Foamed polystyrene, in the form of boards or molded products, currently dominates this field, and these products are expected to continue growing. However, production of rigid urethanes should exceed the production of styrene foams by 1970.

In the building trades, polystyrene foam is used for a variety of purposes, such as plaster base, perimeter insulation, and shell concrete forms. Much has been reported about potentials for rigid foams in construction, but the penetration of this market will depend on a number of factors—not the least of which is acceptance and recognition of foams by the various insurance writers, fire protection agencies, building code officials, architects and contractors. In the building trade the factor of performance is particularly important. Stone, concrete, wood, steel and glass have been used for many years, and the designers, architects, and builders know how to handle them, since the limitations of these products have been well established. Plastic foams however should have gained a substantial hold on this market by 1970, particularly if the foam industry continues to work with building industry authorities (through groups, such as the Applications Group within the Cellular Plastics Division and the Manufacturing Chemists Association's Committee on Plastics in Construction) to adapt test methods and standards. These will be recognized in the industry as assurances of the durability and suitability of its products.

Foamed polystyrene will continue to share in the growth of this market in applications where a board form product is needed, because it will continue to have a lower price than rigid urethane board and, in many of the building applications, the added insulation efficiency of a fluorocarbon blown rigid urethane foam board is not of major economic importance. However, the technology for molding, pouring-in-place, and spraying rigid urethane foams will make them the chosen material where on-sight foaming or prefoamed structures will be the most economical construction means.

The packaging industry, currently dominated by styrene foam molded packages or package inserts, will increase substantially. In addition, styrene foam films will account for further substantial growth. The rate of development of foam film and sheet appears uncertain at the present time, but depending upon the technological developments, by 1970 a minimum of 70-million pounds and a maximum of 200-million pounds, mostly styrene, will go to the packaging market.

The low-temperature insulation field will be dominated by rigid urethanes, because of the greater insulation efficiency, which they obtain from fluorocarbon gas (blowing agent) trapped in their cells.

The use of rigid urethane foam insulation in appliances has been frustratingly slow to develop, but will certainly reach its goal of 75 million pounds by 1970; it may even achieve a major portion of this penetration within the next two years.

Cold-storage and process-rooms (including industrial insulation) currently consume 14 million pounds of foam, and will increase this consumption to 30 million pounds, primarily molded, slab, or foamed-in-place urethanes.

The transportation industry, including mobile homes, which currently uses only 10 million pounds of both styrene and urethane, will increase its usage to 40 million pounds, most of which will be foamed-in-place urethane.

The buoyancy market, including boats and floating docks, will achieve a modest increase by 1970. Where flotation is foamed-in-place, urethanes will be used, whereas on floating docks the less expensive styrene board foam will be used unless exposure to oil slicks and other petroleum products is severe. In this case, urethane board or the more newly developed styrene-acrylonitrile copolymer foams (both with added resistance to solvents) will be employed.

In the military and space effort, functionality combined with density makes rigid urethane foams destined to fulfill such applications as insulation for missiles and structures inflated in space. Although these foams will be important to our military and space efforts, they will represent only a small fraction of the total foam consumption and, at this point, must be considered a specialty market.

As in the case of flexibles, the versatility of rigid foams induces imaginative applications which vary from the use of foamed styrene for decorations, to "do-it-yourself" urethane foam molding kits for lobster men making floats of their own design. These miscellaneous applications will account for some 25 million pounds by 1970.

Special attention should be given the polyolefin foams, since they are newcomers in the field and offer the promise of substantial growth by 1970. They are semiflexible, closed-cell products which will find their best uses in life jackets, weather stripping, impact absorption (such as boat fenders), and the like. Epoxy foams are a big question mark. The higher density chemically-foamed epoxies are currently produced in slab form and machined to dimension, for products such as dies and molds used in metalworking; or they are molded or poured in place as potting compounds in electronic applications. Systems have been developed which can be blown with fluorocarbon like urethane systems. If raw material costs and processing techniques for fluorocarbon-blown epoxies can make them competitive with urethanes, the epoxies could capture a significant share of the urethane market. At any rate, a substantial increase in production of foams is expected. Phenolic foams have the advantage of being relatively inexpensive, although friable and with less desirable properties than urethanes, styrenes, or epoxies. Because of their low cost and low density, they are used for void filling, for encapsulating, and as microspheres for syntactic cellular mortars. Their use will continue to expand.

Minor quantities of foams are made (for special properties or special applications) with urea, polyamide, silicone or cellulose acetate resins. We believe there will be further growth of these products in areas where special properties of the polymers are needed. For instance, extremely high-temperature resistant foams are based on silicones; low-cost potting foams are based on urea; extremely tough foams are based on polyamides and cellulose acetate. At this point, however, it is not believed that they will be major factors in the over-all market for rigid foams by 1970.

To achieve the projected growths, the foamed plastics industry has an obligation towards the foam user: improve the properties, performance, and price of its products, in that order of importance. Certain major foam consuming industries, such as automobiles and appliances, can work directly with raw material suppliers and can agree on specifications which will guarantee the performance in their products under conditions of use which are well defined by the industry. In other industries, particularly those consuming flexible foams, marketing channels are so diverse that it is virtually impossible for a foam producer to determine the actual end use to which his product will be applied; hence, industry standards to protect quality are of utmost importance. Here again the Cellular Plastics Division of the S.P.I. has taken the initiative and, in the case of urethanes, has suggested a set of industry standards on the basis of the end-use requirements. In addition, it has established the Urethane Institute, one function of which is to inform the public of the uses for which these foams are suitable and to maintain the quality of consumer products.

Section III—MANUFACTURING EQUIPMENT FOR FOAMED PLASTICS

PART I—MULTI-COMPONENT FOAM PROCESSING

By Herbert Brabandt, Jr.

1. INTRODUCTION

Before undertaking a venture involving the production of plastic foams, one naturally wants to know what sort of processing equipment is involved.

Fortunately a number of basic rules may be established, to form a design criterium. Most all foam applications have certain common denominators, and it is these denominators with which this section is concerned.

Basically, to produce multi-component foams we must convey metered quantities of several ingredients to a mixing chamber, where they will be properly mixed and dispensed. As each component requires a separate pumping and metering unit, the more components to be metered separately, the costlier the equipment and greater the maintenance problems. In some instances, hand-mixing may be sufficient, whereas other applications could not be successful without specialized automatic machinery.

The bulk of the foam machinery manufactured today for multi-component systems is for the production of urethane foams. The basic equipment for many of the other foamed plastics, such as silicone, polyvinyl, and epoxy foams, is just a variation of the equipment used to produce urethane foam. Slight modifications may be necessary to convert a standard urethane machine to another type of foam-producing machine. For example, some of the epoxy foams are processed at around 250° F. The modifications necessary here would be provisions for metering and mixing at somewhat higher temperatures than used in the urethane process.

It is appropriate to point out that certain foams, for example vinyl foams, may be produced by either a mechanical or a chemical process. In either case, the vinyl resin, plasticizers, and other ingredients must be *thoroughly mixed*. Then the plastisol compound may be foamed by either process. Poly-ethylene foam is produced by adding a blowing agent to the resin and then extruding or molding the resin. For extrusion, equipment other than urethane machinery is necessary. With the exception of specialized auxiliary equipment, the basic machinery for producing foamed plastics is versatile and lends itself to many different types of applications.

2. VARIOUS PROCESSES FOR URETHANE FOAM

Total prepolymer process for urethane

In this process, also known as complete prepolymer, all of the hydroxyl compound is reacted with the diisocyanate. The reactions are complex, and the resulting prepolymer is affected by many variables, including temperature and rate of material addition. If a low-equivalent-weight polyol is reacted with diisocyanate, the resulting viscosity may be too high; for these reasons, the total prepolymer method is not as popular as the two following processes.

Quasi-prepolymer process

This process, also known as semi-prepolymer or partial prepolymer, is intermediate between the total prepolymer and the one-shot processes. It is a two-step process. In the first step, the prepolymer is formed by mixing the diisocyanate with part of the polyol. The catalyst, emulsifiers, blowing agents, etc., are blended with the remaining polyol. In the second step, foam is produced by reacting the prepolymer with the polyol containing the other ingredients.

The equipment necessary for use of the quasi-prepolymer system depends largely upon the size of the operation. Large-volume producers of quasi-prepolymer foam may find it more economical to do their own pre-mixing and consequently would need pre-mix tanks and agitators. For a small volume operation, a pre-mixed, two-component, ingredient is often purchased, completely eliminating the first step.

One-shot process

In this process, the raw ingredients are converted to foam in one step. This process offers certain economic advantages over the quasi-prepolymer method, but it is somewhat more complex for a number of reasons. Each component may be pumped separately to the mixing chamber, but in some cases, several ingredients may be combined and pumped as one component. The instantaneous generation of internal heat which results from the exothermic reaction calls for great care to retain control;_however, less external heat is required. In particularly large pours, the exotherm is of such magnitude that scorching may result. Current efforts to reduce exotherm in "one-shot" applications have reportedly been successful.

Another difficulty is the lower overall viscosity. The pumping and metering of four to six separate streams of ingredients having different viscosities, at various flow-rates, emphasizes the importance of properly designed metering equipment. Hand batches are not recommended using the one-shot method. The equipment for handling one-shot will be as complex as the formulation required to produce the foam desired.

Each application must be carefully evaluated so that the right process may be selected to produce good quality foam. Not only formulation, but mechanical variables, contribute to the success of a dependable foam system: formulation and mechanical variables such as throughput, mixer speed, catalyst balances, and temperatures are inter-dependent.

3. PRODUCTION METHODS

Generally, a machine which meters, mixes and dispenses automatically is necessary for the following applications:

1) For large pours such as panels, large molded items, reefer trailers, deep seat cushions, mattresses, filling of boat bulkheads, and numerous others.

2) Where the material must enter an orifice too small to use a bucket pour (batch mixing).

3) In very small pours (100 grams or less) where the amount of waste material in the mixing container might be a large percentage of the total material used.

4) For continuous thin sandwich construction such as insulated cardboard or paper cartons.

5) Where formulation or cream time is extremely short.

Today, the four generally accepted methods used in producing urethane and similar foams are: batch mixing, continuous slab production, on-off or intermittent, and spraying. Frothing, which is a variation of pouring, will be treated as a separate method because of special equipment requirements.

Batch system

In this method, the ingredients are mixed either by hand or with a power mixer in any clean container ranging from a small glass beaker to a large pail or bucket. Hand mixing with a spatula is usually limited to pours of one pound or less It is a "mix and evaluate" type of operation. Large size batches may be 50 lb or more. Ideally, a power mixer should do a thorough job of mixing in 10 to 15 seconds; some of the higher viscosity, slower formulations may require up to 30 seconds for mixing. One of the most popular mixers used is an electric drill motor with various blades fastened on the shaft.

Example of a batch system problem: insulate thermos bottles at a rate of 9,600 bottles per week, or 1,920 per day. Allowing a time cycle (time from pour to release from mold or jig) of 20 minutes per part and a 15-second pour cycle would require at least 80 molds. Without going to a totally automated system, the following equipment would accomplish the job:

1) A metering machine and operator. This machine should meter the correct amount of each component into the mixing container.

2) Some sort of conveyor system to convey the bottles from the metering unit to the mixing station.

3) Two "milk-shake" type mixers and two operators.

4) Two operators to insert and remove thermos bottles from the molds.

5) Conveyor to packaging line.

Installation of a machine which meters, mixes, and dispenses would save two men in this operation; however, the anticipated production figures, the duration of the project, and a number of other factors must be considered before determining whether or not an integrated machine would offset the cost of the personnel saved.

One disadvantage of the batch system is the possibility of non-uniform end products.

The advantage is mainly the elimination of costly equipment. Actually, small production is possible with only a laboratory balance or scales, mixing containers, and an agitator.

Continuous slab production

Continuous slab lines are a high-volume production technique. Flexible slab production is used to make mattresses, cushions, pillows, shock-absorbing packaging materials, peeled goods for laminated clothing, paint rollers, toys and sponges. The rigid slab may be used for panel insulation, flotation purposes, packaging, and numerous other applications.

The process involves continuous delivery of the chemical components, at fixed rates, to a mixing head which moves across a conveyor. It deposits the liquid mix on the conveyor in a pattern of parallel lines, or ribbons. The foam is moved continuously by the conveyor, which is on a slight downgrade to keep the liquid mix from being deposited on top of rising foam and maintain a uniform end product. The liquid mix is dispensed into a continuous mold which is usually roll-paper formed into a trough by the conveyor and adjustable side-boards. Then the foam moves through a curing oven. If it is flexible, it will also be moved through crushing rolls.

Exhaust hoods are properly positioned to remove any irritants which may have volatilized during the foaming. The slab then passes through a series of auxiliary equipment, which may include cut-off saws, horizontal and vertical trimmers, slicing machines, hot-wire cutters, etc., before moving to the storage area.

Slab-line operation requires a considerable amount of floor space, as well as large storage area for raw materials and end-products. A typical slab-line may be from 200 to 400 feet in length. To minimize scrap loss, particularly in the rigids, low surface-to-volume ratios are necessary. The scrap loss in the flexibles may be nearly eliminated by shredding and rebonding.

One of the major losses in slab production results from the removal of a sort of "free-rise" crown that must be cut off. A recent development almost completely eliminates this crown effect. It is termed a *four-sided conveyor;* essentially it restricts the rise to produce an even and flat top surface.

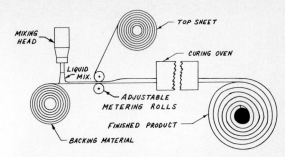

Figure III-1, continuously cast urethane foam system.

The width of the finished bun is determined by the spacing of the adjustable side-boards which back the paper trough. This dimension may be up to 80 inches and, for economic reasons, is usually a multiple of the desired width of the end-product. The height of the bun is a function of throughput and conveyor speed and may be up to 24 inches.

Another recent development in the continuous production of urethane foams has been the making of end-products of exact desired thickness, by applying foam between two continuous layers of surface finish, such as foil, fabric, wood veneer, or metal. This method eliminates the need of slicing equipment (Fig. III-1).

Metering and pumping equipment for continuous production need not be of a recirculating type. Recirculating type mixing heads are more expensive and are not necessary for a continuous type of operation.

The importance of temperature control should be recognized because an entire production run can be ruined if the temperature of one of the materials is allowed to change, causing a pressure change and off-ratio output.

The relationship of the size run (throughput and volume) to the heaters, chillers, and supply tanks must be considered. They must be sized to accommodate more than enough material for the run.

To sum it up, continuous slab production requires a huge initial capital outlay for equipment, much floor space for the work area, and storage space for the finished products. Moreover, a sufficiently large market is needed to maintain economic production.

"On-off," or intermittent operation

The process machinery termed "on-off" or

Figure III-2, small three-component production foam machine with on-off mixing head. Components include: remote variable-speed mixing head drive, scraped-surface chiller unit (left), and automatic solvent-flush system (front). Courtesy Martin Sweets Co.

intermittent equipment (Fig. III-2) may be used in molding, pour-in-place, or interrupted slab operations for flexible or rigid foams.

Molding may be used for manufacturing cushioning for the furniture or automotive industries, pipe insulation, flotation and various other articles. One of the main advantages of molding is the low scrap rate, which is seldom more than 5% to 10%, including over-fill and rejects. In a typical operation, the mold is pre-heated and coated with a mold release agent. A pre-metered amount of liquid mix is then poured into the mold, the mold is closed, and the liquid mix foams to the mold configuration. After curing and cooling, the part is stripped from the mold.

Pour-in-place may include thermal insulation for refrigeration and packaging applications, structural reinforcements, encapsulation, buoyancy and numerous others. Pour-in-place differs from molding primarily because adhesion to the mold is desired, whereas in molding perfect release is desirable. Pour-in-place techniques eliminate joints and lines which tend to fail at low temperature. Also, during the expansion process, a skin is formed next to the surface of the filled cavity, thus eliminating the necessity for vapor barrier materials. Pour-in-place techniques are essen-

tially the same as those used in molding.

Interrupted slab operations may be used where it is not economically practical to produce foam on a continuous slab basis. Resulting slabs or blocks may be 60 to 72 inches wide by 80 to 96 inches long by 12 to 15 inches high.

"On-off" machinery must be very precise. Whereas in a continuous slab operation, the first few feet of material of a run can be sacrificed, such is not the case in molded and pour-in-place applications. There are no intermediate production steps. Every drop of mix which goes into the mold must be homogeneous, or an inferior product will result.

Steps must be taken to insure positive metering, simultaneous valving, thorough mixing, and proper dispensing. The metering should incorporate in-line temperature conditioning equipment for best results.

To guarantee accurate proportioning, it may become necessary at times to incorporate a type of pressure developing device to compensate for difference in the viscosity of the individual components. A recirculating type head can be used because every drop of material (excluding that in porting between valve and mixing chamber) can be conditioned by recirculating and is readily available at the flick of the valve. Simultaneous positive valving is necessary to insure that proper amounts of components enter the mixing chamber over a given time interval. To achieve proper mixing, the mixer should be a high-shear type, and must be self-cleaning.

Other equipment will depend largely upon the particular product to be molded. For example, to establish a particular pour pattern, wet more surface, and refrain from dispensing liquid mix onto rising foam, the mixing head may be mounted on a traversing mechanism.

In pour-in-place operations, where thin sheet metal walls are involved, it is often necessary to back up the thin walls with some sort of re-inforcing jig to prevent them from blowing out as a result of expansion pressures (see Section XI). These jigs may be eliminated when the frothing technique is utilized.

Spraying

Although this is covered in detail in another part of this section a few brief comments are in order. In the urethanes, spray is limited to two low-viscosity component prepolymer systems primarily because of the complexity and bulkiness of multi-component control.

The "spray-in-place" method is used for insulating large chemical storage tanks, reinforcing fiber-glass boats, insulating homes and, in mining, to make a quick urethane insulating wall in tunnels, to seal off mine fire areas. It is also used in other applications, such as furniture, appliances and for rapid panel construction.

Spray equipment should be reasonably mobile, lightweight, compact, and easy to maintain. Generally, the back-up or metering equipment consists of air-driven, dual-piston pumps which can be inserted directly into the raw material containers, which may be 5-gallon buckets or 55-gallon drums.

Spray guns used in conjunction with the back-up equipment may be either the internal-mix or the external-mix type. The internal-mix gun does a more thorough job of mixing and is best suited for the higher viscosity spray formulations. This type may also be adapted to pouring applications. It is somewhat more difficult to keep clean than the external-mix type, but with the proper solvent and air fittings, the cleaning problem is minimized.

The external-mix gun operates on the air atomization principle; i.e. high pressure air atomizes and blends the streams as they leave the gun. Disadvantages of this type are caused by the high atomization pressure: over-spray is high and TDI concentration in the air increases. However, it requires less maintenance, because it does not have to be dismantled after each spraying operation.

Frothing

Frothing is the production of foam in a pre-expanded form by mixing a volatile liquid blowing agent, generally dichlorodifluoromethane (R-12), into the other components under pressure. It is, essentially, a three-step process·

1) The components, including R-12, are metered and thoroughly mixed in the mixing head. All components must be kept in liquid form for the mixing process; therefore to keep the blowing agent from vaporizing, the mixing chamber must be pressurized. This is done with a let-down valve which restricts the discharge nozzle of the mixing chamber, thus creating a back-pressure greater than the vaporization pressure of the R-12.

2) As the material is discharged from the mixing head, it is partially expanded, but actual frothing is caused by the pressure reduction from mixing head to atmosphere. The blowing agent vaporizes in the mix, causes immediate expansion, forming a liquid foam or "froth" which is similar in appearance to shaving cream dispensed from an aerosol can. The amount of expansion and the final density depend on the amount of R-12 metered into the system.

3) The froth itself then expands to the final density, which may be from 2 to 10 lb per cu ft, depending on the amount of other fluorocarbons in the system.

Frothing techniques may be used in vertical pouring applications of rigid urethane foam where the surface-to-volume ratio is high. This may be the insulation of refrigerated railroad cars and trailer vans, large refrigerators, or just the building of panels. Because of the fluidity of the product after dispensing, and its quick curing, frothing is very well suited for continuous production of laminated roll-stock using flexible skin materials such as foil, corrugated paper, cardboard, etc. It may be necessary to use some sort of spreader to insure even spreading of the partially expanded froth.

Froth may also be sprayed. If the equipment is properly designed and adjusted, R-12 pressure reduction may be used, in lieu of air, to propel the material to the surface being sprayed.

The frothing technique has advantages:

● Lower and more uniform in-place densities may be obtained. In high surface-to-volume applications, particularly, because the foam is partially pre-expanded, the shear effects imparted by the mold walls are not as great as in conventional systems. Since frictional forces are not as great as in conventional pouring, the material expands more freely, giving a more uniform density overall.

● Lower foaming pressures are generated since the material is dispensed into the mold in a partially expanded form. This may eliminate the need for jigs and fixtures which are ordinarily used to hold the foamed article to its desired shape.

● Froth may be screeded by methods similar to those used in concrete screeding in the construction industry.

● Another advantage is the realization of more uniform physical properties.

Commercial equipment for frothing is still in the development stage. A number of problems must be overcome to reduce its cost and complexity.

The pumping and metering units for frothing must be able to accurately deliver material against a minimum pressure head of 100 to 150 psi. Otherwise the component feed-lines fill with mixed material and become plugged. Therefore, a pressure-developing system must be used to insure that feed-line pressures exceed mixing chamber pressures. The material may be pumped with a positive displacement rotary gear or vane pump or a reciprocating piston pump.

The R-12 metering system is the most complex part of the frothing system. Mechanical pumps put energy, that is heat, into the system, creating a rise in temperature. When the temperature reaches the vaporization point, flashing may occur and cause cavitation and irregular flow.

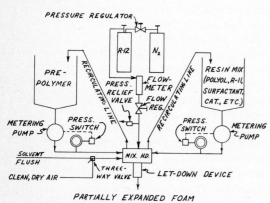

Figure III-3, schematic flow diagram of urethane frothing system.

One of the latest systems for fluorocarbon metering is shown in Fig. III-3. The fluorocarbon, in a special froth-type container, is pressurized by an inert gas, usually nitrogen, well above its vapor pressure at the temperature of the foaming system. The liquid R-12 then travels through a flow meter, which must be calibrated. Regulators insure constant back-pressure, and flow valves introduce R-12 at the desired pressure into the mixing chamber. Since the material is not being pumped, it may be "dead-headed" when the valve is in the recirculating position for the other components.

Seals in the mixing head for froth application are a real challenge. The high pressure requirement adds to the overall complexity. The high-speed shaft seal is the critical area: the slightest build-up of material on the faces of the seals may cause severe leakage under high pressure. It is necessary that the mixing

head be self-cleaning to prevent seal damage from excessive material build-up.

The let-down device is used to restrict discharge of the material from the mixing head. As the mixed material is channeled through the let-down valve, the pressure of the material is reduced, and frothing occurs as it is discharged. A properly designed let-down device should be readily adjustable, easy to clean, and dependable. It may be connected to the mixing head with a hose, possibly several feet long. It must be carefully monitored to prevent clogging.

Depending upon the application and existing equipment, it may or may not be economically sound to convert a pre-designed conventional system to frothing. The following changes are necessary:

1) Pressure inducing devices, of some sort, are necessary to maintain inlet pressure above mixing chamber pressure.

2) The mixing head must be equipped with seals to prevent any leakage resulting from the increased frothing pressures. This may mean an entirely new head, specifically designed for frothing.

3) A let-down device must be added to the discharge end of the mixing head.

4) The entire R-12 metering system must be procured. This includes the frothing type R-12 cylinder, a nitrogen regulator, and metering equipment, control valves, flow meter, etc.

When purchasing or designing equipment for conventional applications it may be well to remember that the system might have to be converted to frothing at a later date.

4. SELECTION AND DESIGN CONSIDERATIONS

Many standard model foaming machines are available. They may be used for various applications as is or with simple modifications. Other models may be highly specialized. Once the objectives are set, one can determine what will be necessary to best satisfy the requirements. The equipment manufacturer, because he is dealing with machinery and related equipment everyday, is in an excellent position to provide very valuable guidance, particularly concerning his own equipment. "Do-it-yourself" attempts may lead to infringing upon certain machinery patents.

Type of Operation

The type of operation—closed mold, slab line, spray, or frothing—must be considered first. The reason for this may be illustrated by the following example: Suppose we start with equipment designed for continuous mixing. If we should convert to a closed-mold operation, we would have to purchase a new "on-off" type mixing head, add recirculating lines, and make other extensive changes. Therefore if there is a possibility that we should convert to closed-mold operation, on-off equipment should be purchased in the first place.

In a like manner, if the initial operation calls for spraying, but there is a possibility of needing pour-type equipment in the future, guns must be selected which are capable of being adapted to a second use. This applies to the internal-mix type. Also, if conversion to froth is anticipated, it is well to incorporate provisions for the high-pressure requirements, and to procure a high-pressure, sealed mixing head.

In short, size up present needs and future possibilities, then decide on an economically happy medium.

Type of operation may also refer to production line or laboratory operation. Generally, in a laboratory where there is much testing of formulations, it is desirable to keep the equipment as flexible and versatile as possible, for running different ratios and different types of materials. On the other hand, if the operation is fairly straightforward (formulation known, throughput established within a certain range, and important variables defined), the machinery may be constructed for this particular operation at a minimum cost.

Size of operation

Along with the type of operation, it must be considered how extensive it is and for how long it will be in existence. It may be of such short life, that purchase of elaborate machinery would not be economical. If the overall project justifies the purchase or construction of processing equipment, then a reasonable budget limit should be set. This limit should be reasonably flexible, because, it may be necessary to acquire machinery for varying requirements.

Ratio variance requirements

Several ratios may be encountered in foam machinery terminology. They are: (1) the ratio at which the various components are run, and (2) the throughput ratio.

Component ratio—A foam system may have from two to six pumping units, depending upon the number of components to be metered individually. Component ratios may vary from 1:1 for a two-component resin-prepolymer system to 100:1 or 100:2 in a six-component, one-shot system. A machine may be designed for specific throughputs at pre-determined ratios; should it become necessary to use a formulation of entirely different component ratios, this could raise a problem. Each pump, particularly the rotary type operates more efficiently over a particular throughput range. If it becomes necessary to change component ratios radically, it means changing one of the component pumps so that it will operate effectively at the new desired throughput range. This is why foresight is important; the design must work for maximum *anticipated* conditions.

Throughput ratio—When a foam machine has a throughput range of from two to twelve lb per min, it is said to have a 1-6 (minimum to maximum) throughput range. The minimum throughput is controlled by the minimum effective operating speed of the pumps on a given unit. Maximum throughput is, in like manner, a function of the maximum effective speed of the pumps under consideration.

A two-component machine may be advertised as capable of handling a ratio varying from 1:1 to 1:25. However, as the component ratio increases, the maximum total throughput will decrease. For example, if the same size pumps used on a two-component foam machine are capable of maximum throughputs of 500 gm per min each, the total maximum throughput would be 1000 gm per min at a 1:1 component ratio; however, should it be desirable to dispense, from the same machine, a formulation with a component ratio of 1:25, the total maximum throughput would decrease to 520 gm per min. This is why it is most important to know all formulations or *component ratios* which may be used on a project, as well as desired rates of throughput, before selecting equipment.

Viscosity

Viscosity of components will affect pump selection and overall machine design, but it cannot be considered independently because throughputs and line pressures are interrelated.

A machine manufacturer knows which of his pumps and mixing heads will handle a material of a given viscosity, for a desired rate of throughput. Viscosity and throughput are among the primary starting points in machinery design. Pumps, drives, line sizes, mixing heads, mixing head drives, and pressure systems are all sized and selected accordingly.

Throughput rating is closely related to viscosity. It is basic in the overall machine design. Many factors must be considered when choosing a particular throughput range:

1) Higher throughput equipment is more expensive.

2) Higher throughput may mean faster production.

3) Cream time, together with shot size, may be a factor in determining rate of throughput.

4) Ability to handle the item in production rapidly after being poured may affect the throughput.

Heating or chilling

It may be necessary to heat or chill one or several components. If the material has a high viscosity, it is possible, and in some cases advantageous, to heat it and bring it to a more reasonable working viscosity.

It may on the other hand be desirable or necessary to chill the material to maintain a blowing agent, such as Fluorocarbon-11, in liquid state. Many problems may result from inadequate or improper temperature conditioning equipment; some of these are discussed in the chapter on "Heaters and chillers." These may be needed to maintain constant operating temperatures, and, in turn, constant viscosity and line pressure. In many of the higher viscosity materials, a few degrees of difference in temperature may result in a difference of thousands of centipoise. If viscosities and line pressures are not constant, the metering will be irregular. Temperature variations in materials may also cause difficulties by modifying pump slippage. Uniform results can be expected and obtained only when temperatures can be maintained within closely controlled limits.

Good reproducibility also may be achieved only by controlling the temperature. Reproducibility is extremely important in production operations, particularly in closed-mold work where the exact amount of material must be dispensed at each cycle. Not only

must there be shot-to-shot reproducibility, but day-to-day consistency.

5. DESCRIPTION AND FUNCTION OF EQUIPMENT

Pumping and metering unit

The pumping and metering unit (Fig. III-4) is the heart of the foam system. Its function is to deliver uniformly, at a fixed rate, a given amount of material.

Some pumping and metering units are commercially available as separate components. Others are incorporated in the overall design of a foam machine as integral parts of a complete unit. The pumping and metering unit consists mainly of a feed tank, a pump, a drive unit, and miscellaneous gages, lines and fittings.

Drives—By drive unit is meant the motor and gear-box or reducer, as most pumps operate at speeds lower than that of the motor. Many gearmotors and variable speed drives are commercially available. Sizing and selecting the proper drive is important and should not be attempted without reviewing several pertinent factors, such as throughputs, viscosities, duty cycles, available power, and budget. Variable-speed-drive units are expensive compared with single-speed gearmotors.

In some applications, one may be able to get by without a gear box to drive the pump. Speed reduction is then accomplished by chain and sprockets, timing belts and timing pulleys,

Figure III-4, large pumping and metering unit with variable-speed pump drive unit.

"V"-belts, "A"-belts, and variable pulleys which produce adjustable speeds.

For a high-speed reduction, a timing belt is often the most effective method. The speed is generally too high for chain-and-sprocket, and "V"- or "A"-belts and pulleys are not considered positive enough.

Chain-and-sprocket combinations are usually preferred for lower speeds such as connecting gearmotors, or low-speed variable-drives, to pumps.

Chains, sprockets, belts, and pulleys are relatively inexpensive but they can be used only as step reductions, since each time a different speed is desired, at least one pulley must be changed.

The drive unit should be positive, able to hold the ratios (variable in some cases) and of uniform speed. Both a-c and d-c motors are used in the design of foam equipment. Each manufacturer seems to have his own preference and as in most issues, there are advantages and disadvantages with each. D-c motors can be affected by line voltage fluctuations. But, since the entire unit is subject to these fluctuations, the ratio of one component to the other will not be affected. However when it is desirable to maintain a certain shot size, particularly in closed-mold applications, there should be no variance in pump speed, which actually controls throughput. Another point in favor of d-c is that pump speeds may be varied without speed-reduction gearbox or variable-drive unit.

The speed of a-c motors does not vary in the same manner.

Speed indicators—There are many different types of speed indicators which may be used to relate pump speed to throughput. The familiar mechanical tachometer may be connected to the pump shaft. There are d-c generator-type tachometers which generate a definite voltage for a given number of rpm, using a voltmeter as a readout. Another type is the magnetic pick-up, which works on the principle of an interrupted magnetic field. Regardless of the type used, for best control and faster metering, the throughput that corresponds to a particular pump speed should be known. These data plotted over a throughput range constitute the metering curve.

Pumps—Selection and sizing of the proper pump is an essential task in the design of foam processing equipment. There are many different kinds of pumps available: one well-

Figure III-5, pre-mix tank with agitator. Tank is insulated and heated by hot-water jacket.

known equipment manufacturer uses approximately 100 different sizes and types.

There is no concrete rule in selecting the proper pump because each application has its own requirements. Factors that must be considered are, for example, maximum and minimum viscosities of materials handled, rate of throughput, amount of heat generated, amount of maintenance required, maximum pressure head against which pump will operate, corrosive nature of material being pumped, and degree of metering accuracy acceptable.

Pre-mix tanks, feed tanks, and agitators

Pre-mix tanks (Fig. III-5) are not necessarily auxiliary equipment. To make high-volume urethane foam by the prepolymer method, a pre-mix tank is used to manufacture the prepolymer.

Tank size is determined by knowing the amount of "mix" consumed over a given period, and the time necessary to insure proper mixing or reaction of the mix. Prepolymer manufacture may require from one hour, for a simple isocyanate-*polyester* rigid foam, to 24 hours for a more complex isocyanate-*polyether* prepolymer.

Feed tanks are those which feed the individual pumps, and are sized according to the particular run and production requirements. Since they are actually a part of the pumping and metering unit, their size should be kept minimum. Most feed tanks may be fabricated from ordinary steel, with the exception of those which are to be used for tin or amine catalysts, or related chemicals. Tanks are usually sized according to formulation: if the ratio of resin to catalyst is 100:3, and a 35-gallon tank is used for resin, then a one-gallon tank would be sufficient for the catalyst.

The distance from a feed tank outlet to the pump inlet should be kept minimum. Especially with high viscosity materials, cavitation may result if the pump cannot get material as fast as it is trying to pump it.

Tanks may be jacketed or insulated to help maintain constant temperature.

Agitators may vary, in type, from low-speed synchronous laboratory models to high-speed production units; they may be powered by electric or air motors.

Important design considerations for agitators are speed, horsepower, and positioning with respect to the mixing vessel or tank. Agitator speed and power consumption are governed by viscosity, size and design of agitator blades.

It is important to refrain from positioning the blades too close to the tank discharge port, particularly in high-speed applications. The agitator should not create too much turbulence at the tank discharge. This could result in cavitation, which would cause inconsistent metering. The agitator should also be positioned in such a manner that air is not whipped into the material, decreasing the density and again causing inconsistent metering. Agitator blades should continuously and completely be covered with material.

Heaters and chillers

There are many methods for heat-conditioning materials prior to mixing. These may range from hot-water jacketing, which might be used in a laboratory, to scraped-surface heat exchangers on large production lines, with temperature controlled automatically.

Methods of heating are by hot water or steam jacket, or by electricity. The hot water-steam method is frequently used, but has temperature limitations; it won't work with materials, such as some epoxies, where high temperatures are necessary. Electrical heating seems to be more trouble-free, can be controlled over a wider temperature range, and has a faster response.

Types of chillers may range from an ice bucket to a large scraped-surface heat exchanger, more commonly used on large production units. In laboratory operation, an ice bucket, or a brine jacket around the feed tank is satisfactory. Shell-and-tube heat exchangers are best suited for lower viscosity materials such as isocyanates. The scraped-surface units, more versatile, are generally used in high viscosity applications.

Chilling equipment design is more complicated than heating equipment because we are dealing with materials which may range from one up to 500,000 or 1,000,000 centipoise. Pressure drops in the lines and in the equipment may double, in some cases, as a result of just a few degrees of temperature change. For a given material, or component, the extreme temperatures (minimum and maximum) obtainable may mean the difference between laminar and turbulent flow, at the same rate of throughput. It is also possible that doubling the throughput may change the type of flow from laminar to turbulent or vice-versa. These situations are not uncommon, and predictions are difficult, if not impossible.

Another point to consider is whether or not in-line cooling or heating should be used in an application. In-line refers to the placing of the heater or chiller directly into the feedline to the mixing head. If the application is one of critical component-temperature control, then an in-line method should definitely be considered. In-line temperature pre-conditioning offers the advantage of conditioning the material just prior to its entry into the mixing chamber. Preheated hoses have been developed, to aid further in maintaining uniform temperatures in very critical operations. Some of the above equipment can be quite expensive, but must be included in the budget when it is required for good results.

Since temperature pre-conditioning may only be necessary for raising or lowering the material temperature from ambient, a careful survey of seasonal ambient conditions might be useful to determine the capacities (Btu transfer) required.

Mixing heads

The importance of proper and thorough mixing cannot be over-emphasized. The extremely wide range of viscosities and the increasing number of components that have to be metered separately make the mixing problem no easy task. Inadequate mixing can produce inferior-looking foam, entirely unsatisfactory from many physical standpoints. However, with a thorough understanding of the problems involved, and a knowledge of what is required to produce a homogeneous, thoroughly blended mixture, the problem is much simpler.

Mixing equipment falls into two major categories: continuous and on-off (or intermittent). A number of considerations apply to the design and construction of both:

(1) *Throughput* may be defined as the total amount of liquid mix dispensed by the mixing head per unit of time. Most applications call for mixing heads ranging in throughputs from 0.25 lb per min to 150 lb per min, although there are special applications outside of this range. Obviously, this range cannot be handled by a single mixing head. Each equipment manufacturer has a number of different models of mixing heads, each designed for a particular throughput range. A typical division of the ¼ to 150 lb per min range may be: ¼ to 2 lb per min; 2 to 10 lb per min; 6 to 36 lb per min; 25 to 100 lb per min; and 50 to 150 lb per min. There would be five different model mixing heads for this range of throughputs and the limits overlap to give adequate coverage.

(2) *Number of components* refers to the number of individual streams which are fed separately into the mixing head. There may be more ingredients than components pumped and metered separately; this is because some of the ingredients are combined and metered as one component. In some cases, pre-mixing of several ingredients simplifies the situation by decreasing the demands on the mixer mechanism. The larger the number of separately metered components, the costlier the mixing head. Pre-mixing of several components may limit the control of the mixing operation; a number of the pre-mixed streams may have a short pot-life. There are advantages and disadvantages in each method. The particular application should be thoroughly evaluated before deciding how many streams to pump and meter. Materials producers are usually glad to assist in making recommendations.

(3) *Absolute stream separation*—If any of the materials are allowed to come in contact with another, prior to their entry into the mixing chamber, some serious problems may result. For example, reaction could take place in one or more of the component lines, resulting in clogging or restricted flow which may cause component ratios to be inaccurate. This may ruin hoses, pumping, and other equipment. Absolute separation of component streams, before they enter the mixing chamber, is most essential.

(4) *Motors and drives*—The type of drive or motor used and its location with respect to the mixing head have direct bearing on the portability and maneuverability of the mixing head. The sizing of a motor plays an important role in the mixing operation. Factors such as throughputs, viscosities, impeller speeds, etc., must all be considered in selecting the proper size motor. If a motor or drive unit is undersized, an appreciable drop in mixer speed will result. The mixing of high viscosity materials, at higher throughputs, requires very high amounts of energy to produce a homogeneous mixture; consequently, power requirements may reach five to ten hp.

Air motors are being used mainly because they are considerably smaller. They do, however, drop in speed when loaded and are quite noisy.

Electric motors are more commonly used; they are more bulky and much heavier. If the weight of the mixing head must be minimized, electric motors and drives may be mounted remotely, and connected with a flexible shaft of various lengths to the mixing head.

It is usually desirable to have a range of mixing speeds available. Variable speed drives or other methods of controlling mixing head speeds from 2000 to 20,000 rpm can be used. (See discussion under "Pumps.")

(5) *Shaft seals*—Somewhere between the motor and the impeller, a shaft must enter the mixing head. Because this shaft must turn freely, and at high speeds, sealing of the mixing head becomes a problem.

In conventional foam systems, the problem is not nearly as difficult as in the case of frothing applications where the pressures are substantially higher (up to 400-500 psi).

For the "froth type" mixing head, there are fewer seals commercially available which may give satisfactory service. The seals which are available are guaranteed by their manufacturers, but the proper locating and positioning of a seal is critical. Improper positioning may cause a minute gap between the seal faces, and this ultimately may cause a blowout. Seal manufacturers will be happy to co-operate and furnish helpful information.

(6) *Other features*—One feature which should be incorporated into the design of the

mixing head is a controlled air inlet, at low volume and pressure. This is to assist in the control of cell size. It may be a single port leading directly to the mixing chamber; but there should be some sort of check-valve, to prevent material from backing into the lines.

It is very important, particularly in the case of on-off mixing heads, that the mixing chamber be as self-cleaning as possible. The design of the impeller and housing actually determines the success of this feature.

No matter how self-cleaning a head may be, a film-coating of liquid mix will remain on all parts which are exposed to the mix, and provisions should also be made for the introduction of a solvent-flush. This may be through a port into the mixing chamber so that a shot of solvent will rinse all parts exposed to the liquid mix.

Shut-down should be simple and require little time. The design of the head should permit rapid disassembly. The mixing head should not only be easy to maintain, but also reliable and easy to set-up.

Continuous mixing heads

Continuous mixing is used primarily for slab production although it may be used for special continuous lay-down applications. Continuous mixing heads are, by far, more compact, less complex, and less expensive. Since the streams of chemicals flowing into the continuous type head cannot be turned off at the

Figure III-6, pin-type mixing impeller. Courtesy Martin Sweets Co.

mixing head, the flow can only be controlled by starting or stopping the material metering pumps or by inserting a recirculating valve somewhere between the metering pump outlet and the mixing head. When this valve is placed close to the pumps, the recirculating of the materials is referred to as *short-cycling*. The location of this valve determines the length of the recirculating lines. Since there is no direct recirculating from the continuous-type head,

no valving is necessary in the head, and the main body of the head is relatively simple to design.

Among the most common and more successful impellers or beaters used in continuous mixing, is the familiar "pin" mixer (Fig. III-6). It is composed of a shaft or rod which has been drilled and fitted with pins located at right angles to each other. The number of pins, their size and spacings, have been experimentally found to be critical. There are a number of other successful designs, yet the pin impeller seems to be accepted as industry's "old faithful."

On-off mixing heads

On-off mixing heads, because of their versatility, may be used for practically any pouring application, but particularly for encapsulating, pour-in-place, and molding.

The most important feature of the on-off type mixing head is the valving. Essentially, this consists of a series of valves which can be actuated simultaneously. When the component materials are recirculating, they enter the mixing head, circulate through the valve, then leave the mixing head and return to the feed tank. When the valve is moved to "mix" position, the materials are channeled to the mixing chamber, at which time they are thoroughly mixed. This valve may be manually or air actuated; the main concern is that each component flow cut-off is instantaneous as well as simultaneous. This sharp cut-off is necessary to insure shot-size reproduction in molded applications; each component must be turned on and off simultaneously to maintain the formulation ratio. In order to accomplish simultaneous valving of each component, it is necessary that the valving be operated off a common shaft, or the component valves should be physically tied together in another way.

Valves should have long life expectancy and should be sealed so that components are not in danger of contacting one another by internal leakage until they reach the mixing chamber.

Once the materials enter the mixing chamber, they are retained long enough to be thoroughly mixed. The period involved from time of entry until discharge may be referred to as transit time. There are a number of factors and variables which affect this transit time, or hold-up, of the materials until thorough mixing is accomplished.

The impeller design may be similar to a

Figure III-7, spiral type mixing impeller. Courtesy Martin Sweets Co.

screw (lan and groove arrangement) such that the mix is, in effect, screwed out (Fig. III-7). The pitch of the lans and grooves is very critical; for example, the pitch could be such that, at a given speed, the impeller's pumping ability might not be sufficient to discharge the material as rapidly as the mixing chamber is receiving it. This would cause a flooding of the mixing chamber which might result in a shaft seal rupture, over-mixing, or any number of malfunctions. The geometrical configuration of the housing and impeller may vary: both conical-shaped and straight cylinder types are available.

The space between impeller and housing is another consideration. This clearance is a high shear area for the liquid mix. The amount of clearance also controls transit time.

Impeller speed is related to transit time, and one can see why some variable speed may be desirable.

Transit time is also affected by viscosity. Higher viscosity materials flow more slowly; therefore, longer transit times result.

Many factors must be considered in determining the design throughput rate of an on-off mixing head:

1) Amount of material which must be dispensed to make one pour, or one part, as the case may be.

2) Minimum and maximum time required to make the pour. This time will be a function of production requirements.

3) Method of pour, that is whether all the material is to be dispensed in one spot, or whether some definite pour pattern is to be used.

4) "Cream time" of the liquid mix. This is very important: it's the time elapsed between dispensing and first signs of cellular formation. This may vary with formulation, component and mold temperatures.

5) "Rise time," which ends when the cellular formation ceases. This must be considered in cases where molds must be closed after the dispensing operation is completed.

In some applications, it may be necessary to dispense from a mixing head which has a housing or discharge diameter larger than that of the mold opening. This may be accomplished by employing a funnel type cone at the discharge end of the mixing head. It should, however, be remembered that with such a restricting device, pressures will be increased in the mixing chamber and may very well cause "flooding."

Traversing mechanisms

Traversing mechanisms are used when it is desirable to uniformly "lay" foam into a mold or slab-line in rows, by mounting the mixing head onto a traversing dolly or carriage (Fig. III-8). These mechanisms may range from a simple dolly manually moved from end to end of a small track, to a large automatically, air-driven unit with adjustable stroke and height, and other custom features.

Generally the hand-operated variety is used on a large molded or pour-in-place application, such as the pouring of urethane foams into the bottom of a small boat.

In slab applications, some of the features which might be required in an automatic traverse mechanism are:

1) *Adjustable traversing speeds*—The rate of traverse will vary with throughput and conveyor speeds, and a certain amount of adjust-

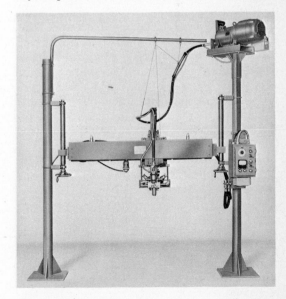

Figure III-8, automatic traverse mechanism with remote drive-powered mixing head and control panel. Courtesy Martin Sweets Co.

ment in the traversing speed is necessary to lend flexibility to this expensive piece of equipment.

2) *Adjustable stroke*—The stroke length is determined by the width of the finished slab; it averages from two to six feet.

3) *Adjustable height*—Some means of controlling the distance between the nozzle of the mixing head and the floor should be built-in.

4) *Jam-proofing*—The carriage on which the mixing head is mounted should not jam, if it should happen to over-ride the limit controls.

Control panels

Control panels, when properly designed, may be worth many times their cost. In certain cases, it is a necessity to have a central control of all the equipment in a foam machinery installation. For example, in a slab-line, one man can supervise an operation which would require several operators without centralized control. All equipment must also be co-ordinated through a single, central control to prevent failure of the entire slab-line operation.

In on-off equipment, the primary function of the control is to monitor the pump and drive settings, the amounts of foam dispensed, and the reproducibility of the shots.

There are several types of controls: direct, that is built into the machines; or remote, that is located in the spot most convenient for the operator. In many instances, it may be desirable to have a certain number of direct controls on the equipment, plus a separate remote panel having only the cycle control at the mixing head.

Controls and indicators should be selected to obtain the necessary product quality and for the convenience of the operator. The following might be included:

1) Main power switch and indicator light

2) Component temperature indicators and controls of heaters or chillers

3) Pump drive speed indicators, speed controls, on-off switches, and indicator lights

4) Mixing head drive speed indicator, speed control, on-off switch, and indicator light

5) Adjustable timer for automatic cut-off of dispensing cycle. Since the setting of a timer is a manual operation which requires a few seconds, several timers and a selector switch may be used to produce pours of different sizes consecutively

Figure III-9, small laboratory foam machine containing squeeze-bottle solvent flush. Courtesy Martin Sweets Co.

6) A selector switch to cut the timer out, for manual operation

7) Start and stop switches for dispensing cycle

8) An automatic counter may be desirable

9) Flowmeters for R-12, necessary for a frothing system, may be located on the control panel

10) Solvent flush control and indicator light

11) Automatic traverse switch

12) Conveyor speed indicator and speed control.

Solvent flush systems

Solvent flushing of the mixing chamber is necessary when shutting down, and, for many formulations, at the end of each pour before the next shot. Rather than risk a gradual material build-up on the mixing apparatus, it is safer to run through a shot of solvent while the mixing head is still running.

Several methods may be used, manual and automatic. The type of application and the budget will help to select the best one.

The manual or squeeze bottle method, which is used even on many elaborate installations, consists of a simple pint or quart size polyethylene bottle with a tube which runs into the solvent (Fig. III-9). When the bottle is squeezed, solvent is forced through the mixing head. The size of the bottle limits its capacity and it is advisable to have a number of squeeze bottles handy.

An automatic solvent flush may, on the push of a button, inject a pre-determined amount of solvent into the mixing head, follow this with a blast of air to clear lines and mixing chamber of solvent and vapors, then shut itself off. Solvent tanks may hold as much as 20 gallons. Timers are used to control the amounts of solvent and air.

All parts exposed to the solvent liquid and

its vapors must be resistant to corrosion to minimize maintenance.

6. CURING AND OTHER PROCESSING EQUIPMENT

Ovens

It may be desirable to use intermittent or continuous ovens for curing the product. Some applications may require total cure, while others may be partially cured only. For example, a continuous polyether flexible urethane slab operation may use chemicals which produce a bun which, at ambient temperature, takes at least 15 minutes to become tack-free. By subjecting the end product to a temperature of 250° F for four or five minutes, the tack-free time is reduced to a point where the slab may be sliced, even though total cure will take much longer. Cure temperatures and times vary with materials, and it is always best to get this information from the materials producers.

In slab operation, it is desirable to use materials which cure faster, so as not to hold up the production line. Longer cure times mean a longer installation. Normally, slabs are made to pass through a tunnel of infrared lamps appropriately positioned. The number of lamps, their proximity to the slab and the length of the tunnel depend on the formulation and the conveyor speed.

For on-off applications, time of cure and cure temperature are important in oven selection. For example, if 20 parts are produced per minute and a 30 to 35 minute cure is desirable, assuming parts must be ready every five minutes, the oven would have to accommodate 600 parts.

Viking Engineering Co. of England, represented in the U.S. by Viking-Chase Ltd., Pittsburgh, Pa., in cooperation with Elliott-Litton Ltd., British Motors Corp. and Shell Chemical Co., have developed a curing technique for flexible urethane foam based on the use of microwaves.

This technique has several advantages, such as a substantial reduction in the cost of molds, and a 60% reduction in the cycle time.

Metal cannot be used in the construction of molds for high-frequency curing: the epoxy molds cost about one-half as much as the conventional aluminum molds, and, in addition, because of the shorter cycle time, less molds are required.

Basically, the process is similar to the high-frequency process for the molding of expandable polystyrene beads, described in Section XIII, Part 3, chapter 6.

Viking has available a urethane foam curing unit, trade-named "Vitherm," for blocks 62 in. long x 24 in. wide and 8 in. high, operating on 230v current and consuming about 1.2 to 1.5 kw depending on application.

Ventilation-exhaust systems

Good ventilation is essential in rooms or areas where chemicals which produce toxic or harmful vapors or fumes are handled. Some chemicals, such as TDI (toluene diisocyanate) are highly irritating. Type of equipment, hood and exhaust duct design, depend upon the particular application.

Ventilation equipment should be designed by experienced personnel. In applications where toxic or irritating vapor producing chemicals are used:

1) Lids should be kept on all drums, tanks or vats in which chemicals are stored.

2) As much of the system as possible should be enclosed, particularly where higher operating temperatures are used.

3) The exhaust hood and manifold ducts should be located as close as possible to the source of escaping vapors.

4) The exhaust capacity of the ventilation system should be ample.

5) If the fumes are heavier than air (TDI fumes, for example, are about six times heavier than air), down-draft ventilation may be desirable.

6) If the size of the process machinery prohibits an exhaust hood, it is necessary to ventilate mechanically the entire room. Precautions should be taken to avoid pulling harmful vapors past the operators' faces.

Foaming conveyors

In continuous production lines, the liquid mix may be dispensed into a paper trough, which is backed or supported on a conveyor, which moves at a pre-determined speed. The conveyor must be integrated with the other equipment, since its speed is directly related to the speed of the traversing mechanism and the throughput of the mixing head. This must be controlled from the control panel.

The following is a list of features which should be included in the design of conveyors:

1) Variable speed—Conveyor speeds may range from 25 to over 100 ft per min. Speed may be varied by use of chains and sprockets

or timing belts and pulleys. A variable speed drive unit may be incorporated into the conveyor but this is costly.

2) Adjustable width—This is necessary when more than one width slab or bun is to be manufactured. For example for flexible urethane mattresses, it may be desirable to produce single bed and double bed widths, by providing the conveyor with adjustable sides.

3) Adjustable tilt angle—The angle of tilt of a conveyor will vary, depending upon throughout, formulation, and conveyor speed. This adjustment should be simple and quick.

4) Smooth and even riding—There must be positive tracking, even at high speeds and for long lengths, so the end product will have uniform appearance and physical characteristics. In foamed plastics, disturbances caused by uneven tracking may cause cell collapse, which, in turn, shows up as layer separation.

5) Heating of conveyors—If heating of the conveyor sides and bottom is required, there is a commercially-produced unit with this feature available. Attempting to do it in the plant may be likened to patent infringement.

7. PROBLEMS FREQUENTLY ENCOUNTERED IN THE USE OF FOAM MACHINERY

Each foam equipment manufacturer has his particular designs and methods. The objectives are essentially the same. This chapter deals with some of the problems most commonly encountered and, for each, it offers a solution. Many other methods of reaching the same end may exist.

Initial spot

Initial spot is the result of chemical component unbalance, in the very first part of a shot or pour (Fig. III-10). The product varies in appearance, depending upon which component is out of ratio, and the magnitude of the unbalance. Generally, it appears as a target pattern of rings inside of rings.

For continuous applications, equipment which produces foam, free of initial spot, may not be necessary, since the first part of the run can be disposed of. This is not the case with molded applications, where it is essential that each drop of liquid mix be homogeneous, properly proportioned, and thoroughly mixed.

In a two-component system where the components have the same viscosity and where other conditions, such as line pressures, are essentially the same, the initial spot problem

Figure III-10, example of "initial spot" in rigid foam, resulting from improper proportioning.

is minimum. The amount of time required to level off depends upon the temperature, the viscosity and the line pressure, and the rate of throughput.

In the case where there are three dissimilar components running at different ratios, the viscosity is somewhat different for each increment, and even though the time necessary to reach leveling off is very short, it cannot be neglected.

Viscosity differences alone may create a ratio unbalance, resulting in initial spot. Proper corrective measures must be taken. For example, a system may include a resin which contains Fluorocarbon-11, TDI, catalyst, and possibly a fourth and a fifth component. Because the resin must be maintained at a low temperature to retain the fluorocarbon, the mixture may be fairly viscous which results in high pressures. When the material is valved into the mixing chamber, which is under lower pressure, there may be a substantial surge. The isocyanate, because of its low viscosity, may flow into the mixing chamber, whereas the catalyst, being in small amount, may only trickle in. The objective is to compensate in some manner for the differences in viscosities, so that the very first drops of all components reach the mixing chamber simultaneously.

Another possibility which may result in initial spot, is the slippage of one or several drive units, where no positive type drives are incorporated in the metering system. This may cause a component ratio unbalance. Since slippage is not constant, there is no way of compensating or recalibrating for it. It is essential to investigate the positiveness of a drive unit to be sure that it meets the off-ratio tolerances of the formulation.

Clogging of metering tubes

Metering tubes, or ports, are sleeves or

bushings, used to increase velocity of material flow. They are removable and are located at the point where the valve block discharges into the mixing chamber. The diameter of the tubes must be consistent with material viscosity and rate of flow. To increase material velocity, a tube with a smaller inside diameter is used.

When using metering tubes with high viscosity materials, it is not uncommon to encounter clogging or cold-plugging of the passage. The material is being heated while it is recirculating, but the portion of the system from the valve to the discharge into the mixing chamber, where the metering ports are, is cool. Consequently, it leads to higher viscosity. When the valve is switched to mix position, a surge may be observed, particularly noticeable when there is a pressure gauge in the line, and the stream is retarded for a brief moment. The best way to correct this is to heat the area in which the material has tendency to cool, either by applying warm air or by installing some type of cartridge heater.

After-drip

Another minor problem with the metering tubes is the after-drip. Once a shot has been completed, the mixing head may appear to be leaking, while it actually is not. This after-drip is caused by material which was in the metering tubes at the instant the valve closed. Like a water faucet that has been cut off, it may tend to drain. The best method of avoiding this condition is to space shots or pours so that the metering tubes do not have time to drip; or, keep the tube as short as possible to minimize after-drip.

Metering tubes serve another purpose, which is actually where they get their name. During the metering process, it is necessary to catch the individual streams separately for weighing. This is made physically possible by providing spouts, or tubes, under which a cup or other metering container may be placed.

Metering tubes are available in various lengths, inside diameters, and overall design. This depends upon the function and type of mixing head, as well as the properties of the formula used. The metering tubes empty into the mixing chamber, and their length may be limited by the design of the impeller used.

Pressure balancing

Pressure balancing, which is used only for recirculating systems, may be defined as the compensation for differences in viscosities of the various components entering the mixing chamber at different velocities or at different times.

Fig. III-11 shows how pressure balancing works. The material is pumped by the pump (P) into the mixing head (H). Since this is a recirculating type head, the material may be either recirculated (R), or it may be discharged (M) into the mixing chamber, depending upon the position of the valving in the head. The pressure drop across the two possible paths of material flow, once the material passes through the valve, is rarely the same. Usually, because space is limited in the mixing head and because of the need for metering tubes of limited maximum inside diameter, the pressure drop across the mixing head discharge path will exceed that in the recirculating line. This being the case, by switching from "recirculate" to "mix" position, a considerable increase in pressure may be observed on the gage (G). The system cannot always properly adjust itself to such an instantaneous pressure differential; so, to compensate for the sudden pressure change, the lines, even reinforced ones, will expand, the pumps adjust themselves, the liquid may even be compressed to a certain degree. The result in the mixing chamber will be a delayed surge. The exact amount of delay depends upon the pressure difference between recirculate and mix, as well as the material's physical properties, design of equipment, passages, porting arrangement in mixing head, and metering tubes used. Since the pressure differential varies from component to component, there is no way of providing for equalized component surges.

By installing a needle valve in the recirculating line near the material tank, the above condition may be remedied. If, for example, the gage reads 300 psi in "mix" position and 150 psi in "recirculate" position, by adjusting the needle valve (N), the recirculating flow may be restricted until the gage registers also 300 psi. Thus by balancing the recirculating line pressure, the surge is virtually eliminated and the system is no longer subjected to sudden pressure changes.

Pressure developing

In systems which may call for the pumping of very low viscosity, watery-like liquids, such

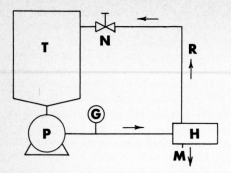

Figure III-11, method for obtaining pressure balancing.

Figure III-12, method for obtaining pressure developing.

as TDI and many of the catalysts, the materials may tend to trickle or flow irregularly into the mixing chamber. This is particularly true of the catalysts which must usually be metered at extremely low flow-rates.

One solution is to develop pressure in the feed line, which is the line from the pump to the mixing head, so that a steady flow is achieved. Referring to Fig. III-12, it is possible to install a variable restriction device, such as a needle valve, in such a manner, that the pressure on gage G_1 may be controlled. Normally, for a water-thin material, gage G_1 may barely register any pressure at all at low flow rates. By restricting the flow with a pressure developing device, D, a smooth flow is obtained. Gage G_2 is then the one to use in the pressure-balancing from "recirculate" to "mix", as described above. For example, to meter a water-thin catalyst at a rate of 20 g per min. there is no observable pressure on gage G_1 during recirculation. The pressure developing device, D, which, up to this point was open, is then closed gradually to obtain a readable pressure on G_1—for example, 80 psi. Now, switching the mixing head valve into the mix position, a pressure of 40 psi is observed on gage G_2. To balance the two streams, it is necessary to restrict the flow in the recirculating line by adjusting valve N, until gage G_2 registers a pressure of 40 psi, while the stream is recirculating.

Maintaining metering ratio

Testing the metering of each feed line of a foam machine can be done by weighing the quantity of material delivered, at the dispensing point, for a given time, usually a minimum of three seconds. The material is usually dispensed into disposable cardboard cups. The larger the sample, the higher the accuracy.

On occasions, consecutive samples taken over an identical period of time may vary; or the weight of the sample metered after four hours of running may be far from the weight of the initial sample metered.

This may be caused by several conditions:

● It may be due to power-line fluctuations. There is no simple way to correct this, but since the entire unit is affected by power fluctuations, each component is affected equally.

● It may be lack of temperature control. Some of the more viscous resins may experience exceptionally large viscosity changes with temperature differences of only a few degrees. Then, pressures throughout the system will be affected, and this ultimately affects the throughput.

● Lack of agitation may cause metering to be irregular. The material is agitated to maintain uniform temperature or viscosity, and unless this is properly done, erratic results may follow.

● A "clot" of foreign matter in one or several components of a foam system can cause a line pressure to build up and result in off-ratio metering. The clot may be forced free and locate itself in another part of the system, where it may cause more trouble.

Generally, if proper precautionary measures are taken, there is not much chance of foreign matter getting into a system. The clot can also be caused by a prepolymer skin or crust—TDI which has partially hardened, or some other pre-mix material which has partially reacted and solidified.

This situation may be corrected by inserting into the lines, some filters, preferably disposable. Some manufacturers locate the filters in the line before the material enters the mixing head; others may prefer to locate them in the recirculating line. Each location has its own merits. Usually, 10 to 25-mesh filters will best be used for straight TDI, and a typical triol (3000 M.W.) resin can be pumped at 70°F, at 20 lb per min without difficulty, through a 90x100 mesh filter. Catalysts should be filtered by all means. The finest mesh, commercially available, through which the catalyst can be pumped without building up pressure, is most desirable. This is usually around 10 microns.

● System leaks are one of the most obvious reasons for off-metering. In any pipe system through which liquid must flow, there must be a certain number of fittings and connections; the larger the system, the greater the possibilities of leaking pumps, loose fittings, gauled threads, etc.

In high flow-rate and/or high viscosity streams, a small leak is not too critical, and most of the time will not be noticed as off-ratio metering, as long as it remains constant.

However, in some of the streams metered at low flow rates, even a small leak may cause the ratio to be most irregular.

Tendency of materials to absorb moisture

This problem may be remedied by taking several precautionary measures. All tin catalysts, exposed to air, will gradually lose their activity. Prepolymer also reacts with water or humidity in the atmosphere to form a gelatin-type skin, which will harden in a few days. Therefore, all traces of moisture must be eliminated from the foam ingredients during storage.

All containers should be kept air-tight at all times. Once some prepolymer is poured out of a container, it is recommended to displace the air over the remaining portion with a blanket of nitrogen, and store the container in a dehumidified area at approximately 70°F.

Cavitation

Cavitation is the formation of cavities within a liquid-handling system, as a result of pressure reduction in a given area. It can waste a great deal of power and bring about many difficulties. It is one of the most frequent phenomena occurring in foam production and, surprisingly, one of the least discussed. Here are some examples of cavitation and means of overcoming the difficulty:

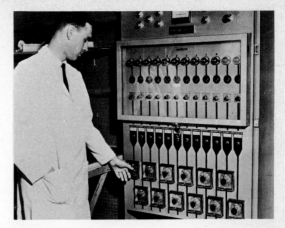

Figure III-13, preset amounts of 12 different chemicals are selected and weighed automatically to make flexible urethane foam. Courtesy Fairbanks, Morse & Co.

● Let us consider a feed tank filled with a prepolymer, closed *tightly* to keep out air and moisture. As material is pumped out of the tank, air cannot get in to displace the liquid. As a result, a vacuum is created, which may cause cavitation and a noticeable decrease in flow rate. The result will be progressively smaller shots in the same time interval. It may be necessary, in certain cases, to pressurize the feed tank with nitrogen to prevent a vacuum from forming. But, in most cases a small hole in the tank top may serve as an air vent.

● Usually a combination of several conditions will be present to effect cavitation. For example, these may be: pump speed too high, excessive viscosity of material, pump intake of too small diameter or too long, foreign material blocking suction side of pump. Cavitation at the pump is detected by some of the end effects which it produces: pressure gages in the feed lines will pulsate erratically; little or no material will be getting to the mixing head; or the metering may vary from shot to shot, for the same time interval.

Excessive pump speed may cause cavitation because the pump is trying to deliver more material than it can effectively deliver and also because heat is generated. When the materials contain a blowing agent, this heat may cause it to flash on the suction side of the pump, and this is another prelude to cavitation.

High viscosity materials, which cannot be heated because of the blowing agent they contain, may be handled by providing the shortest possible connection with the largest possible diameter between feed tank and pump. It might be advisable to put the feed tank under pressure, and to force-feed the pumps.

In addition to filters in the line, it may be wise to provide some screen at the outlet of the feed tank to catch any foreign matter which might accumulate and cause full-flow restrictions.

● One of the most complex aspects of cavitation in foam systems is that which occurs within the mixing chamber. There are so many variables and combinations of variables that might bring about cavitation, that one must be well-versed in fluid dynamics to be able to predict exactly what might happen in a well-defined situation. Among the many variables are: impeller rpm, rate of throughput, viscosity of components and its minimum to maximum differences, presence of volatile blowing compounds, mixing chamber design, diameter and length of porting, impeller-housing clearances, and type of seal used.

Several examples may illustrate the problems involved, and how closely each variable is related to combinations of other variables:

1) The amount of heat generated in mixing may be a function of heat of reaction, impeller-housing clearances, rate of throughput, and viscosity of components. Should the system contain a blowing compound, the heat generated may be such that the vapor phase would be affected. As vaporization takes place, a gas cavity is created, which may lead to cavitation.

2) Cavitation may also appear where a pressure reduction occurs in a constricted region. This happens sometimes when using cones at the point of discharge. Such a constriction, which also causes a high velocity region, may cause boiling of the blowing agent at normal temperature, because of sudden expansion. Overloading, such as may be caused by cones, may decrease mixer speed, and mixing chamber pressure may fall below the vapor pressure of the fluorocarbon. The most likely solution to such a problem might be to use a cone of larger discharge diameter, a different type of impeller, or a change in speed, all other conditions remaining constant.

The dynamics of mixing chambers is a complex and perplexing field, and although there are many schools of thought and various theories on the subject, much remains to be demonstrated.

PART II—THE DEVELOPMENT OF SPRAYED URETHANE

By Harold C. Fornwall

During the latter part of 1953 a study was undertaken to determine the problems encountered in spray application of plastic foam coatings with various catalysts. At this time the main interest was in the area of polyesters. After considerable research, it was decided that the technique would require a spray gun which would intermix the components and achieve the same results as obtained with a premixed formulation.

Two problems were paramount: a satisfactory degree of mixing and the necessity of accomplishing this mixing *outside* of the gun. Research had shown that satisfactory finishes or coatings when premixed had a very limited "pot-life," which is the allowed time between mixing and spraying. The premixed liquid would start to thicken, and go from liquid to semi-solid, or even to solid form, in about 20 minutes. Once in the solid form, solvents had little or no effect on it.

Research and field work led to the development of a first catalyst-type gun. In this gun, only the catalyst was injected into the center air chamber of the gun, with a venturi effect.

It is not generally known that the air which comes out of the center holes in the air cap develops most of the breakup, or atomization, while the air coming out of the horn holes in the air cap develops a fan-type spray pattern, necessary when the spray gun is used on the production line. (Fig. III-14)

As the trigger of the gun is pulled, the catalyst mixes with the center air stream internally and this produces the mechanical action necessary for intermixing with the fluid resin from center fluid tip outside the air cap. A complete trigger pull develops the necessary spray pattern. As the catalyst and the resin are mixed *outside* of the gun, the problem of pot-life is completely eliminated.

Early in 1954, rigid polyurethane foam appeared as a possible sprayed-in-place insulation medium. Early formulations involved the use of a castor-oil-modified polyester prepolymer with a water-amine catalyst. In gen-

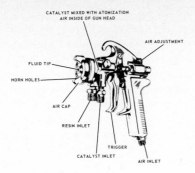

Figure III-14, original urethane spray gun. Courtesy DeVilbiss Co.

Fig. III-15, 1956 spray gun version. Courtesy DeVilbiss Co.

eral these formulations have a high viscosity, in the 10,000 cps range at room temperature. They are difficult to apply by spraying and to hold on a vertical surface. Initial coating thickness was rather low. Proper timing of the application of a second coat, to prevent collapse of the first coat, was a problem. As it was necessary to apply many successive coats to obtain the desired foam coating of one inch or more, the combined weight would at times pull the foam down from the surface (tank or building).

Progress in formulations was made. Late in 1955 the bottom of a condensate tank was spray-coated in 40 minutes, while a duplicate tank required 16 man-hours for the application of an equivalent amount of block-type insulation. This was probably one of the first urethane foam coatings spray-applied in the industry. The tank was at the Beloit, Wisconsin, plant of Wisconsin Power & Light Company. It was inspected recently and it appears to be at least 95% satisfactory; a few small areas on the surface indicate less than 100% insulation.

The next important step was taken in 1956 with the introduction of the quasi-prepolymer formulations, which, due to their nature, made use of catalyst of higher viscosity. This, in turn, developed a faster reacting foam and overcame some of the application problems mentioned. At the same time, the development of a new gun became a necessity: a new *twin-fluid-tip-gun* was developed. A solid column of one component emerging from the central tip was surrounded by a hollow cylinder of the second component, which was emitted from an auxiliary fluid tip. Then, air from a 16-hole circular air cap would, externally, mix together these two components, and produce the urethane foam to be spray-applied on a surface (Fig. III-15).

This program no sooner got underway when a major formulation change took place, involving the use of trichlorofluoromethane as a blowing agent, to produce an insulation with a much lower "K" factor than that of a CO_2-blown foam. At first the blowing agent mix had a very high viscosity, and a serious question was raised as to its sprayability.

About the middle of 1958 a medium viscosity (3800 centipoise at room temperature) polyether-trichlorofluoromethane-blown formulation was designed specially for spray application. Until this time, work had been carried out with modified formulations basically designed for mixing-head type of application. Today's formulations, when spray-applied, will foam and be ready for the next coat, in 60 to 90 seconds. Coatings over 8-inch thick have thus been applied on vertical areas without runs or sags.

At the present time several people in the field are working on the development and application of foam sprayed under controlled conditions. A satisfactory insulation was spray-applied on two tanks in 8 hours while a third tank of the same size requires 32 man-hours to insulate by conventional applications.

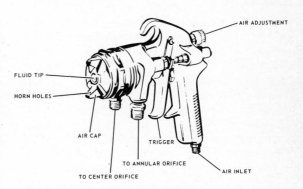

Fig. III-16, latest spray gun version, for dual-component catalyst. Courtesy DeVilbiss Co.

Spray-applied foam, however, is not the answer to all problems. It must be applied under carefully controlled conditions for best results. A much simpler approach and a greater field will be available as technology improves. The problems of obtaining lower viscosities with intermixing ratios, from 60-100 up to 100-100 cps is being consistently investigated. To date the average spray-applied polyether rigid foam formulation has a viscosity range from 300 to 1500 cps at about a 1:1 ratio. Formulations as low as 200 cps on both phases, with a 1:1 ratio, have been spray-applied.

All of this has led to the development of a fan-type spray gun with twin fluid tips which will now handle urethane, polyester and epoxy type coatings with the ease of normal spray-painting. (Fig. III-16)

The use of the two-phase-catalyzed formulation is still in its infancy. With basic leaders in the industry researching and developing dual-component products for building, home and industry, new, practical formulations are making their appearance on the market.

Latest development in the area of urethane foam application involves mounting of the spray gun on a machine which automatically insures uniform application on large surfaces, by constantly positioning the gun at the required distance from the surface. This is of particular importance when the surface is uneven, for example deeply-corrugated sheet metal.

PART III—EXPANDABLE POLYSTYRENE MACHINERY
By Stanley Szelwach

1. INTRODUCTION

Expandable polystyrene beads are produced by incorporating a volatile hydrocarbon blowing agent into granules of polystyrene, during or after polymerization. Subsequently, the expandable beads are heated, generally with steam, causing the polystyrene to soften and the blowing agent to expand with increasing pressure. The degree of bead expansion that results is governed by the temperature and the time of exposure. The bulk density of the raw, unexpanded polystyrene beads is approximately 40 lb per cu ft. They can be pre-expanded prior to molding to a bulk density of 1 lb per cu ft and even less.

Molding of expandable polystyrene can be accomplished by using simple contoured mold plates, which are hand-filled, clamped, immersed into hot water, cooled and subsequently emptied of the finished object. Such a procedure is laborious and time-consuming, and highly impractical for economical production. Molding presses and complex molds are used, which control automatically the filling of the mold and application of steam and pressure and assure quick and accurate reproduction of parts.

Various types of semi- and fully automatic machines are available. They range from the relatively simple hinged type, bench-mounted, steam-chest molds to the intricate, hydraulically-operated, large-platen-area press. In general, the more complex presses are capable of a wider range of applications and are suited for the sustained operation required for high production runs. No single equipment is suitable for all types of molding.

The choice of a particular machine, or combination of machinery, must be governed by an evaluation of the demands of the particular type of operation to which such machinery will be applied.

The relative merits of the different types of equipment available today are a controversial subject, and final evaluation must be left with the user. All the equipment described here will produce satisfactory results if used in the right way and handled by competent operators. In the final analysis, the most efficient combination of equipment is that which turns out a good finished product in the most economical fashion. It is essential, in that connection, that consideration be given to initial cost, amortization, complexity of auxiliary equipment required, latitude in mold design, and time required to get into production.

Training and skill of the operators are also factors of importance. Last but not least, the degree of quality of the final product must be established.

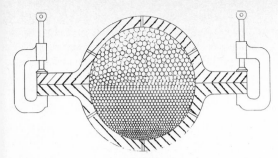

Figure III-17, what happens when raw, non-pre-expanded beads are heated.

2. PREFOAMING EQUIPMENT

In 1950, when expandable polystyrene made its debut, attempts at putting it to practical use were crude. The intermediate stage of pre-expansion, which is now current, was not used. Many efforts were made to charge the raw, virgin beads directly into a mold cavity and expand them into a finished object in a single operation. The best known example of the difficulties encountered is illustrated in Fig III-17. The density gradient in the finished sphere was extremely poor: the lower hemisphere would have a density of 3 to 4 lb per cu ft, against 1.5 to 2 lb per cu ft for the upper part. During early efforts at marketing these balls, they acquired the term of "goof balls," as they rolled on the ground or moved in the air in the most erratic fashion.

It was soon realized that an intermediate pre-expansion stage was necessary in order to control accurately the density of the finished molded product. Initial efforts, in the U.S.A., consisted in the use of a belt conveyor heated by infrared lamps. Density was a function of residence time under the lamps, which was controlled by a variable-speed drive. A vibrator was used to lay down a single layer of beads on the continuously moving belt. Various shortcomings put a stop to further development of that particular method. Lowest density obtainable was approximately 2 lb per cu ft, a definite fire hazard existed, operating cost was high, and products were not uniform.

Meanwhile foreign processors of polystyrene were developing other solutions. In Europe, in the early 1950's, a hot water pre-expander was developed, resulting in a continuous process: raw beads were poured into a hot water tank (200°F). As the beads absorbed heat, causing the blowing agent to expand, they rose to the surface and were raked off. Further processing involved centrifuging, to remove excess moisture, and finally hot-air drying and pneumatic conveying to storage bins.

Continued efforts toward simpler and more economical methods of pre-expanding resulted in the development of a variety of equipment. Steam was used in most cases instead of hot water. Batch-type expanders were often preferred, since they permitted maintaining closer density control. Slow and cumbersome, that method of pre-expansion was of little value in satisfying the high production requirements of a rapidly expanding field of plastics molding. Typical batch system of 1958 consisted of a rotating wheel with pockets containing measured quantities of raw beads. This wheel brought these pockets in contact with steam for a given time. Close density control was achieved, but high equipment cost and low output were deterrents to this process. Several of these units were built, installed, and some are still being used in areas requiring a well-controlled, low-density product.

The mid 1950's witnessed the appearance of the present day steam pre-expanders. The system involves the aspiration of the beads into a vertical tank equipped with an agitator. As the beads expand under the action of steam, they rise in the tank until they reach the level of a discharge chute and leave the tank. This arrangement permits continuous operation and good density control. Feed rates up to 600 lb per hour of 1 lb per cu ft density beads are readily achieved in the larger units currently available. Figure III-18 illustrates a

Figure III-18, a modern, continuous-type pre-expander, steam operated.

Figure III-19, bench mold and several molded objects of polystyrene foam.

Attempts are being made at using other means of pre-expanding the raw beads. One promising method uses hot air heating, and several companies have developed hot air pre-expanders. It seems, however, that there is a serious fire hazard, and that it is difficult to maintain uniform density, especially at low levels.

3. MOLDING MACHINES AND MOLDS

Production molding of expandable polystyrene began in a very limited manner with the use of the mold plates and the autoclave. The molds were hand-filled with beads, suitably clamped and inserted into the autoclave. After the molds had been sufficiently exposed to steaming, they were removed from the autoclave, plunged into a tank of water to cool, opened, emptied of the finished object and refilled (Fig III-19).

That method of molding, slow and costly, is used today to mold samples of parts, before placing them into production. That procedure allows prospective clients to see and study a design before committing themselves to a more substantial expenditure for production molds.

Autoclaves come in a variety of sizes and shapes, built to withstand pressures of from 5 to 30 psi, a pressure seldom, if ever, exceeded with this type of molding.

The use of the autoclave served as a springboard to develop further molds and machinery in this field of plastics processing. Actually, autoclaves, varying in size from very small units up to those which can accommodate an entire boat hull, are being used extensively.

Bench molds—During the mid-50's, considerable progress had already been made in Europe toward the improvement of molding techniques. It was only natural for the U.S. molders to carry forward along the same lines in their early stages of mold design. Thus, simple autoclave mold plates were surrounded with steam chests and placed in position on a bench. Suitable piping and valving for water, steam and air was attached and production was tremendously increased. The molds are generally hinged; clamping is accomplished by toggles or various cam devices allowing for quick opening and closing. Mold plates are perforated with tiny holes in areas of heavy cross sections, to permit rapid penetration of steam required for good "fusion" of the beads. It is not unusual to provide a pressure gage on each half of the mold for closer control of cycle.

typical modern pre-expander. In normal operation, raw beads are loaded into the hopper and allowed to flow through the funnel. Beneath the funnel is a steam-operated Venturi nozzle. Suction draws beads from funnel into the bottom of expander tank. Rate of flow is controlled by a valve. The longer the beads remain in the tank, the lower their density. Upon discharge from the tank, through the chute, the slightly damp beads are conveyed by air to a suitable storage bin to await further processing. To date, this method is the safest, most reliable and economical.

Several companies manufacture this type of equipment in various sizes ranging from 30 to 600 lb of beads per hour. It is recommended that the pre-expanded beads remain in storage at least six hours before being introduced into the molds, to establish equilibrium between inner gas and outside air. However, recent developments in molding equipment point the way to more integrated processes.

General procedure with bench molds is as follows: the open mold is cleaned with an air blast to remove loose beads and excess moisture that would affect the surface finish of the molded objects. Mold is closed to a "cracked" position and clamps are applied: there are shims to provide the proper crack spacing, although some molds have spring jacks which depress after the mold is filled and full clamp pressure is applied. Then, steam is allowed to enter upper and lower chests to preheat mold surface to about 180°F or 200°F. The pre-expanded beads are then introduced into the mold cavity with the help of an air Venturi, the air being evacuated through the "crack." In some molds there is no "crack" position and the air is allowed to be vented through the steam chests. When filling is completed, fill port is plugged, mold is fully clamped, and steam enters the steam chests, at the required pressure and for the required length of time. When "fusion" of the beads is completed, cooling water is admitted into both halves of mold for rapid chilling, and to stop any further expansion of the beads. After a sufficiently long period of cooling, the mold is opened, the finished object removed, and the process is repeated.

In this type of operation, it is usual to have several molds worked by one operator, the cycles being arranged slightly out of phase to permit progression from one mold to the next, with a minimum of lost time. Bench molding does not lend itself to the high production requirements of certain fields, for example packaging. Molds used in bench operation are generally less expensive than molds for larger, more automated machines. Bench molding is restricted to a narrow segment of the expandable polystyrene molding field. One notable exception, where such type of molding is economical and satisfactory, is for flotation parts. Large and heavy cross-sections can best be produced in this manner. Cycle time may reach as much as thirty minutes.

4. VERTICAL MOLDING PRESSES

Early in 1959, the first molding press specifically designed for expandable polystyrene was introduced. It was vertical and semiautomatic. A considerable number of units were put into service in a short time. Prior to the advent of this vertical press, molders had modified certain types of existing equipment, in attempts to develop faster molding techniques. These early do-it-yourself efforts

Figure III-20, one of the early vertical molding presses. Courtesy Miller & Van Winkle Co.

played a significant part in the evolution of the present day molding press. Old drill presses, outdated rubber molding presses were put into service, applying valves, piping and timers to achieve some sort of control on the air, the steam and the water required for molding polystyrene beads.

During this phase, objects made of the new material helped in collecting a great deal of information, as extensive laboratory and field testing went on. Data relative to molding temperature, steam pressures, expansion time and pressures and curing time were collected and helped the further development of molding techniques and equipment.

Fig III-20 depicts an early vertical press, with solid platens measuring 36 x 42 in. It was equipped with a 5-in. air cylinder to open and close the platens, and auxiliary mechanical locking clamps were necessary to keep the molds closed during the molding cycle. Air-piloted valves for water, steam and drainage are shown mounted on the right side of the frame. A control panel and sequencing timer allowed for timing of each successive phase of the molding cycle: it is mounted on the left, above pressure regulator for the compressed air.

Many improvements have taken place since this machine was first introduced: automatic fillers, mechanical pin ejector plates and air-assist to provide a positive break-away of the molded object from the mold surfaces, and removal of condensate during preheat period.

One of the latest developments in vertical presses for the molding of expanded polystyrene is the cup press. The version illus-

Figure III-21, a modern version of completely automatic vertical press, for disposable cup molding. Capacity is 1000 cups per hr. Courtesy Miller and Van Winkle Co.

trated on Fig III-21 produces over 1000 cups per hour, in 6, 8, 10 or 12 ounce capacities by interchanging molds. It has a 7 cu ft bead hopper, controls water temperature and pressure automatically.

5. HORIZONTAL MOLDING PRESSES

The need for higher clamping pressures, better ejection methods and greater automation was largely responsible for the development of the horizontal molding presses, which are the most widely used for expandable polystyrene in the U.S. today.

In this arrangement, a *fixed* platen, or grid, is mounted vertically, facing a *moving* vertical platen, or grid. Molds are held between the platens, and the press opens and closes horizontally—hence the name. In many aspects these machines are similar to die-casting and injection-molding presses, except for the large platen areas used for polystrene foam molding.

To evaluate the presses currently available in this field, a short excursion into the basic technology of the process may be in order.

Actually, the cycle consists of the same successive phases applying to bench molding. Five problems must be solved in the design of a satisfactory installation. First, the platen size must be determined; this, in turn, determines the size and bulk of the entire press. Secondly, the motive power and the clamping force must be selected for the job. Third, the controls and the degree of automation desired must be decided upon. Fourth, the correct type of mold must be selected. Finally, the valves, manifolds and piping are chosen. Correct evaluation of these factors determine, to a large extent, how economical and satisfactory the operation will be.

1) *Platen*—To determine the size of the platen, it is important to understand fully the nature of the product that is going to be molded. A product molded out of expandable polystyrene beads of 1.5 lb per cu ft density consists of 3.25% of polystyrene and 96.75% of air, by volume. Since the customer does not pay for air, the total weight of molded polystyrene processed per cycle on a press is the prime factor in deciding platen size. Larger platens, however, require greater clamping force, and the moving of a greater weight of platen and molds is costlier.

Conversely, a smaller platen press can cycle faster, be set up quicker and costs a good deal less. But smaller size platens limit the size of the parts that can be molded. Large platens also allow the mounting of multiple molds. The platen size finally determines the type of product that can be molded most economically: a custom molder would probably prefer a smaller size platen, while most captive molding operations would favor a larger platen.

2) *Motive power and clamping force* required to activate a press are usually selected after determining the pressure that must be maintained on the platen during the molding cycle. In addition to maintaining the required pressure, the power is also called upon to rapidly close and open the press. During the opening phase of the molding cycle, enough power must be available to easily open the mold containing the finished object. To satisfy all these requirements, various combinations of mechanical, pneumatic and hydraulic actuators are used. To achieve high clamp pressures, high compression forces are applied to a small volume of air or oil; conversely to get fast open-and-close action, large volumes of oil or air must be moved from one part of the system to another. A compromise must be reached between these factors.

Several systems have proven themselves acceptable in service:

a) *Straight air*—This method is generally employed on small platen presses of one to two sq ft of molding area. In this simple arrangement, compressed air at 100 to 125 psi moves the platen into molding position, maintains clamp pressure during the molding cycle and

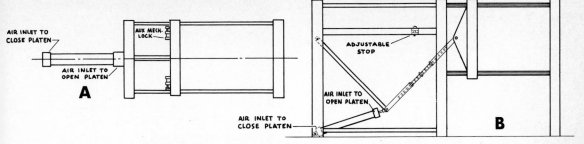

Figure III-22, in-line and offset air cylinders exercise their pressure differently; adjustment varies with type.

is then applied to the opposite end of the cylinder to open platen and mold.

Compressed air provides a very rapid close-and-open action. However, the cylinder forces that are developed are limited. For example, an 8 in. dia. cylinder with 100 psi air develops only 5000 lb of pressure. When applied to a 15 x 15 in. platen, this pressure means 22 psi, a minimum clamping force. Fortunately, the entire platen area is seldom used, as space is needed to mount the molds. But the limiting factor of a straight compressed air system for large presses is evident.

b) *Air and mechanical*—This combination is used with some degree of success. Compressed air is used to close and open the platen while mechanical locks, or clamps, are applied to develop a higher clamping, or holding force. In Fig. III-22a, the in-line arrangement of the air cyclinder permits the use of an adjustable stroke, but the force available for opening the platen is limited. The mechanical locks require some adjustment to match the shut-height of the various molds that may be mounted on the platens. This problem may be troublesome and may well override the advantages offered by the system. In Fig III-22b, the offset cylinder arrangement permits the development of high clamping pressures along with satisfactory opening forces. However the adjustable stroke feature must be sacrificed. A large block-molding machine is shown in Fig III-23.

c) *Air and oil*—This combination has been widely used on medium size presses due to its reliability and simplicity. High clamps pressures are obtained and sufficient break-away, or opening, forces are generated. Fig III-24 illustrates one of the commonly used versions of this combination. Compressed air at line pressure, 100 to 125 psi, is applied to the top of a reservoir of hydraulic oil. The oil flows

through large piping into the main cylinder, closing the press to the stand-off, crack, position. By closing a valve, oil is made to pass through smaller piping to a ratio pump. Air at 20 to 40 psi drives that pump and compresses the oil in the main cylinder to the desired clamping pressure. Upon completion of the molding phase, line pressure air at 100 to 125 psi is applied to the front of the main cylinder, a valve opens, permitting the oil to flow through the large piping back into the reservoir, and the press opens. This action is fast, simple and allows a high degree of reliability.

d) *Fully hydraulic*—This method of operating a molding press is generally reserved for very large machines having platens up to 24 sq ft of area. Hydraulic units employ low pressure to close and open the platens, and high pressure for clamping. This sort of press has been used for a long time for injection and die cast molding machines. Adapting these

Figure III-23, air-operated mold for large blocks. Courtesy Moldex Corp.

Figure III-24, an air-and-oil molding press for moderate size platen. Courtesy Crown Machine & Tool Co.

Figure III-25, automatic molding press for large objects. Courtesy Miller & Van Winkle Co.

proven methods to expandable polystyrene molding necessitated some changes, because of the handling of the greater mass of large moving platens, weighing up to a ton. A good system must rapidly move a heavy platen over a distance of 40 to 50 in., slow it down as it approaches its predetermined position, remain fixed in that position at a constant pressure for a given time, while full or intermediate clamping pressure is applied and held, and finally must open with a high break-away force. All this must be accomplished with smooth, vibration-free action at fast speed— five to six seconds to close and open over a 40 in. stroke. A good hydraulic system must repeat that action hour after hour, day after day, for long periods of time with little maintenance and no down-time.

One, two and three-cylinder systems have been used on expandable polystyrene presses, in order to achieve the desired results of minimum platen deflection, quick close and open action, fast clamping and uniform pressure. Fig III-25 shows a recent three-cylinder system applied to a heavy-duty molding press. Specifications are a high and uniform clamping pressure of 66 psi over the full platen area, on a dry cycle time of 12 to 13 seconds. (Dry cycle time is the time from fully open to fully open again.) Hydraulic and solenoid-operated valves are employed to shunt the oil through pipes and orifices of various diameters, so as to obtain the necessary flow rates and pressures. A fully hydraulic system for a large press is usually driven by a 7.5 to 15 hp electric motor coupled to a dual oil pump providing the desired volumes of oil at the required pressures.

3) *Controls and automation*—Once the sizes

and the movements of a press have been selected, it is necessary to provide the elements that will control and properly sequence the forces that are applied. At this stage, the mechanical and/or hydraulic actions of a press are married to the functional requirements of a mold. From the small, simple and manually actuated press to the large automated hydraulic press, controls are applied with solenoids, timers and relays. Solenoids open and close valves on the hydraulic system, also control the valves that supply air, steam and water to the molds. Timers are used to set the required intervals needed to perform a function and also to cause one function to overlap another. Relays shunt the power which actuates the solenoids and timers. Switches, lights, safety devices and various triggering circuits are also used.

The control cabinet for a medium-size semi-automatic press generally contains a minimum of three timers, three solenoids to control water, steam and drain, and several relays to sequence that part of the molding cycle that is automatic. These basic components permit operation of the following cycle:

a) *Preheat and close*—Steam lines are opened to preheat the faces of the mold and clear the condensate. One timer controls the duration of this portion of the cycle.

b) *Filling*—While in closed or cracked position, manual or automatic filling is done (Fig III-26); air that sucks in the beads by Venturi action leaves the molds through cracks.

c) *Fusing*—A second timer controls the application of steam to the mold to effect a fusion of the beads. Pressure for clamping the molds is usually applied at the same time.

d) *Cooling*—A third timer is used to control

the application of cooling water. This stops any further expansion of the beads, cools the molds and helps the easy removal of the finished parts.

e) *Open*—This is often accomplished by manual shunting of air or oil to the proper place in the system. The finished parts are ejected or picked off.

f) *Purge*—In certain cases, compressed air is admitted to drive off any residual cooling water from the molds.

This simple sequencing is suitable for molding parts of uniform cross section and shallow draw. Much of the present output of expandable polystyrene is molded on such presses, with this cycle. As the size and the complexity of parts increase, mold designs and construction features must be improved. Automatic presses with larger control cabinets, and more timers, solenoids and relays, must supply these additional features.

4) *Molds*—Selection of an adequate mold to produce a foamed polystyrene object at a definite cycle speed is an important and often controversial matter. A serviceable single cavity aluminum mold of one sq ft in area can be obtained for $300 to $500 when a standard steam chest is available, and when a cycle time of 2 to 2½ minutes is acceptable, for an object having a 1 in. cross section. When it is desired, for faster production, to cut down cycle time to as low as one minute, a bronze mold with thin sections, hand-finished and chromium-plated, can be obtained at a cost four to five times higher. Whether such an additional expenditure is justified depends strictly on the type of operation, the size and design of the object to be molded, the quantity to be manufactured, and the uniformity of the beads available. These variables also determine the selection of the number of cavities in the mold, the use of "slide runners" to clear the gates automatically between cycles, and the degree of automation built into the cycle. It is unwise, according to many experienced operators, to figure on continuous operation on the basis of a "60-minute hour" day in and day out, but much wiser to estimate the hour of actual molding on a 50-minute basis.

5) *Valves, manifolds and piping*—Having decided on the size, motive power and controls of a press, one factor remains to be determined, generally referred to as the "plumbing." Steam, water, compressed air and electricity must be brought to the molding press. The electrical power equipment is

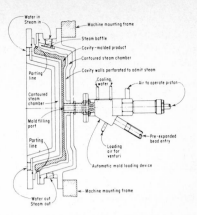

Figure III-26, automatic mold-filler for pre-expanded beads. Beads cannot be introduced into cavity under pressure, as they tend to clog passages. They are aspirated by an air-operated Venturi nozzle and delivered into mold while air leaves through crack.

usually taken care of adequately when the press is installed: electric power is needed to operate the hydraulic system motors, the various components in the control cabinet, and the solenoid valves at different points on the press.

Steam, water and air lines require much greater supervision, during their installation, if satisfactory economy is expected. In a medium size press, dry steam is delivered at 125 psi, through a 1 in. pipe. In cases where large molds are used and where the amount of beads molded per cycle exceeds 3 lb, a larger steam supply is necessary. The cost of steam varies, of course, with the type of installations: boiler, fuel used, insulation, etc. . . . . An average figure of 2¢ per lb of polystyrene molded is realistic.

Air is required to transport beads into the mold cavities, to operate certain types of presses, to eject the molded parts, to purge and cool the steam chests. For medium size presses in the six to ten sq ft of molding area, an air line of a minimum of ½ in. diameter is needed, capable of delivering air at 125 psi for any length of time. A larger line may be required for large molds which demand more air for ejecting, purging and cooling.

Water is used as a coolant. On fully hydraulic presses, it is also used to cool the oil in a heat exchanger. A 1 in. feeder line carrying water at 40 psi is considered satisfactory for medium presses. Since modern molds do not require much cooling, bigger presses do not use substantially more water.

Control of water and steam from the feeder lines into the molds is accomplished with diaphragm or sliding-gate valves, air or solenoid-operated. Drain valves are needed to dispose of the water from the mold during and after cooling. Drain valves supplied with presses must be much larger than the incoming water lines, for fast drainage of molds by gravity.

Keeping a molding press installation free from leakages and in a reasonably tidy condition is not a simple process, judging from the usual aspect of molding plants.

6. HIGH-FREQUENCY MOLDING

In order to improve both the aspect and the economy of molding polystyrene foam, attempts were made recently to heat the beads with high-frequency electric current, after incorporating into the mass of beads an additive which changes their dielectric properties. Instead of metal molds, which cannot be used for high-frequency heating because metal reflects high-frequency radiations, the molds are made of a non-conductor with a low electric loss factor such as polypropylene,

polyesters or epoxies. With high-frequency heating, the molding cycle is quite different from the steam molding cycle. Heating takes place in from 3 to 15 seconds depending on the size of the objects, then an expansion period follows, but the mold need not remain in place during that phase, nor during the subsequent cooling phase, as there are no air, water or steam connections.

Some of the advantages claimed for high-frequency electric molding are: elimination of steam and water, use of air restricted to filling the molds and, in certain cases, ejecting the finished object, much cheaper molds, less costly press, faster cycle, dry, cool finished product, and possibility of impregnating the beads with colors at the same time the molding additive is introduced.

Several manufacturers have been—and still are—evaluating the application of high-frequency molding of polystyrene foam in their operation—some for the production of laminates. A few operating details and economic objections which may soon be overcome have, so far, kept this process from becoming commercial.

PART IV—FABRICATING EQUIPMENT
By Herbert Brabandt Jr.

1. CUTTING AND FINISHING EQUIPMENT FOR FLEXIBLE FOAMS

A particular piece of equipment may be listed in this Part under either a "flexible" or "rigid" category. The manufacturers of this equipment are aware of the need for versatile machines and are sucessfully using many of them on both flexible and rigid foams. In some cases, to change from one type of foam to another, it may be simply necessary to make a few minor changes or adjustments on the machine, taking an hour or so of work.

Automatic cut-off saws

As the slab stock, which may measure up to 42 in. thick by 80 in. wide, moves down the conveyor, it must first be cut into workable lengths, depending upon the end product. First-cutting is accomplished with an automatic cut-off saw, which measures electronically the length of foam passing under its blade (Fig. III-27). When the precise length is measured, the saw blade travels vertically through the

block, while the entire saw unit travels at a speed synchronized with that of the foam conveyor. At the completion of the cut, the saw blade rises and returns to its starting position.

Skin removers, bottom slabbers and vertical side trimmers

A raw foam slab has a top surface which is not uniform, and both the sides and the bottom of the bun have a fairly heavy skin which, in most applications, must be removed.

Bottom slabber units—As long blocks of foam move through an automated fabrication line (Fig. III-28), they pass first through a bottom slabber unit which automatically removes the bottom skin without the need for turning the bun over. The bottom skin is conveyed to a wind-up station.

Vertical side trimmers—The next step in the fabrication line is the removal of the side skins, accomplished by passing the bun between vertical side trimmers. These are basically band-saws, each mounted on its own

Figure III-27, automatic cut-off saw to cut bun into desired sizes, with two separate motor controls for bun advance and saw motion. Courtesy Falls Engineering & Manufacturing.

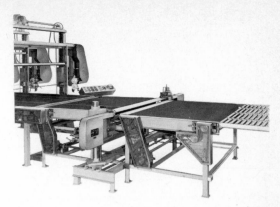

Figure III-28, bottom slabber to remove bottom skin of a bun, with automatic turn-over. Courtesy Falls Engineering & Manufacturing.

carriage on a common track so that it can travel in and out of the cutting position.

Deep-throat vertical saws

If the end products happen to be rectangular blocks that are, for example, used for furniture cushions, the foam must be cut to a width which is a multiple of that of the cushion. Deep-throat vertical saws on the fabrication line slit the blocks to proper widths at the same time as side trimming is being performed.

Leveling and splitting machine or gang slabber

Depending upon the type of fabrication and the volume of production required, the foam bun may travel through a single-head, conveyorized leveling and splitting machine, or gang slabber, equipped with as many as six splitting heads (Fig. III-29). The top crust is removed. If a single head machine is used, the conveyor must be reversed and the foamed bun returned to its starting position for each cut until it is split into the desired number of pieces. With a gang slabber, the top crust can be removed and the bun cut into sheets or slabs of required thickness in one or two passes.

Table-type leveling and splitting machines are available for splitting blocks of foam to various thicknesses. One machine has a horizontally moving table, 80 in. wide by 125 in. long, which is manually or automatically rolled back and forth under the horizontal splitting head. Equipment of this type may be purchased as a manually-operated unit, then converted to automatic as production requirements increase.

Vertical band saws

A number of vertical band saws are on the market. The better engineered saws have blades that cut in both directions. They have a horizontal rolling table which carries foam through the blade. An adjustable stop, which projects above the table at right angles, measures the amount of material to be trimmed off. Such saws can process material up to 36 in. thick and slabs as wide as 80 in., 10 feet long.

If angular cuts are required, jigs can be built to hold the block in a tilted position as it is pushed through the saw. If a great variety of angle cuts are required in small quantities, a saw with a tilting blade would be most appropriate.

Paring and roll-stock splitting machines

Use of foam as an interlining in clothing has created the need for equipment which can produce foam in wafer-thin, continuous sheets. Two types of equipment—circumferential par-

Figure III-29, four-head gang slabber. Each head can be set at a different height, to cut a bun into four sizes simultaneously. Courtesy Falls Engineering & Manufacturing Co.

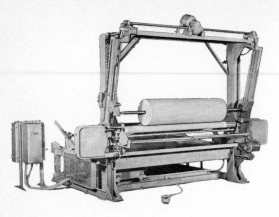

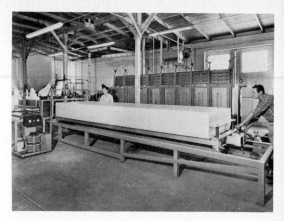

Figure III-30, circumferential paring machine. Courtesy Falls Engineering & Manufacturing Co.

Figure III-31, hot-wire cutting machine for large blocks (16 ft × 4 ft × 17 in.). Courtesy Dura-Tech. Corp.

ing and roll-stock splitting—have been developed for such purposes. Paring machines will pare a log of foam into a continuous sheet 1/16th inch thick and will hold extremely close tolerances (Fig. III-30). They are equipped with a device which winds the pared stock onto a paper core, and a splicing unit that joins sheets of foam stock together, so that pared stock from two or more logs can be packaged into one large roll. Rollstock splitters will, likewise, split material from slab stock into sheets as thin as 1/16th inch.

Die cutting machines

Foam parts can be die cut to odd-shaped items such as gaskets, cushions—up to three inches thick—insulation pads, automobile topper pads, and other similar products. There are numerous ways of applying the cutting pressure to the steel rule dies in order to get the desired cut. One of the most efficient methods involves the use of the roller die cutter. This method produces a clean cut with a true vertical edge. This is accomplished by compressing flexible foam to approximately 75% of its original thickness; then the steel roll of the die cutter passes over the back of the dies, and forces the cutting edges through the foam.

Other devices used for low volume die cutting include clicker machines, beam presses, and punch presses which may use standard or special stamping dies and can handle material in either roll or sheet form.

Buffing machines

Although foam can be molded into crowned

cushions using the one-shot method, it may be desirable to produce shaped cushions from slab stock. Buffing is used, although it may produce only two or three cushions per minute. There are drawbacks to this mechanical method of contouring: one is the dust produced, another is the problem of holding the cushion securely as it passes through the buffing chamber. Foams, being flexible, tend to "grab" and be thrown out of the machine. Buffing is a very slow method when much material must be removed.

2. CUTTING AND FINISHING EQUIPMENT FOR RIGID FOAMS

Flexible foam fabricating equipment has, in many cases, been successfully applied to rigid foams. One leading equipment manufacturer has designed its table-type splitting and leveling machines and vertical saws in such a way that they may be used for either rigid or flexible foams.

For large-volume work, rigid horizontal saws are now available which will automatically cut stock into the desired slab thickness. The saws are equipped with a 52-in.-wide table made to length for any particular application. The splitting head of such a saw is raised and lowered by an indexing mechanism. It will handle blocks up to 42 in. thick and will cut gauges from $\frac{1}{8}$ in. to 12 in. In rigid foams, the thickness usually ranges from one to four inches. Actual cutting is done by a band saw blade.

Various types of rigid foams require different gauge blades and tooth designs. The speed at which the blade travels is quite critical and a variable drive on the cutting blade is highly desirable. Various densities of foam not only require different blade speeds, but also different rates of feed. For example, polystyrene foam has been cut on a rigid saw at a feed rate of 30 feet per min with a blade speed of 10,000 feet per min, whereas a typical two-pound density urethane foam may be cut with a feed rate of 90 feet per min and a blade speed of 9,000 feet per min. Flexibility of blade speed and feed rate is a must in the fabrication of rigids.

Hot wire cutting

Hot wire cutting may be used in rigid foam for flat sheets and gentle contours. In Fig. III-31, a huge block of polystyrene foam is being cut into sheet or board stock. As the block is fed at a constant rate of speed into the bank of nichrome wires, which are brought to red-hot temperature by a variable voltage transformer, the wires burn through it, producing many thinner layers in a single pass. Different densities will require different cutting speeds, and accurate control of the voltage is critical, since line-voltage fluctuations may cause scorching. The material may be cut to width and trimmed for length in the same manner. The intense heat causes the wire to expand and each wire must have its own tension spring to take up the slack and make sure that the wire remains taunt.

Another use of the hot wire method is for profile cutting. Various cross-sectional configurations may be produced in this manner. The foam is forced through an aperture which is formed by hot wire and the part turns out in the profile of the hot wire. Standard machines with automatic feed are available for this type of operation. The hot wire does not destroy the cellular structure of the foam and it is practically impossible to distinguish the surfaces which are cut by hot wires from sawed surfaces, when the hot wire equipment is properly operated.

Shredders and choppers

Waste from die-cuts or hot-wire-profile-cuts can be ground up in a standard chopper to produce bits of foam varying in size from that of a pencil eraser to that of a walnut. This type of machine, which consists of sharp cutting blades spun by a high-powered motor, is dangerous, when not carefully operated; but it can be a very important aid to fabrication facilities. These cuttings have resale value, can be used to fill pads, cushions, pillows, and other similar items, and may well brighten the profit side of the balance sheet in a competitive operation.

Section IV—TESTING OF FOAM PLASTICS
By R. E. Jones, Guy Patten, and Samuel Steingiser

1. INTRODUCTION

Cellular Plastics, like other materials, must be characterized in some quantitative manner for a number of reasons: to allow the producer to check the quality of the product he makes, to compare specific properties of products from various sources, and to indicate relationship between performance and useful life of a product.

Methods developed must allow tests to be performed reasonably swiftly, and give answers reproducible both within a single laboratory and among several laboratories. After the testing methods are established by agreement and usage, quantitative property values must be determined to represent quality factors for a product, which are the bases for its specification. Minimum test values are specified, which define the product as fully as known methods allow.

Hopefully, some or all of the specified properties are indicative of the actual service performance of the product. However this is not always the case. There is no substitute for actual service conditions. Most methods try to accelerate the time factor so as to make a short-time test practical. But in doing so, an unknown factor is introduced, since acceleration results in an increase in a stress or a temperature or some other factor. In many cases also the specimen used in the test is not the entire object; or it may differ in shape from the actual product used by the consumer. Therefore, one can only attempt to approximate actual use test and infer from the results what relationship, if any, exists.

Development of test methods for cellular plastics is made by workers in groups such as the Cellular Plastics Division of the Society of the Plastics Industry, Inc. (SPI); the Sub-committee XX on Cellular Plastics of D-20 Plastics, and Sub-committee XXII on Cellular Rubber of D-11 Rubber of the American Society for Testing and Materials (ASTM); and Sub-committee IV-N of SAE-ASTM Technical Committee on Automotive Rubber. An attempt is made in each case to try to relate test method with end use. Some tests were accepted simply because history made them so; a case in point

is the test for compression set for flexible foam which was carried over from rubber practice with no relationship with actual field performance. There was a feeling that such a test was necessary, but how meaningful it was was never clearly understood.

In this Section, no attempt will be made to describe the standard test methods: reference to the appropriate ASTM and commercial Standards will be made. In some cases, no established standard method may be available; then an attempt will be made to describe tests used by various laboratories. It is hoped that these will serve as guides for the development of future standards.

2. GENERAL BACKGROUND AND ASTM REFERENCE LIST

Prior to 1954, the principal cellular materials available were the latex foam rubbers and sponge rubbers; for these materials there existed ASTM testing methods and specifications D-1055 and D-1056 (also adopted by SAE and as Federal Spec. Test LP-406 b).

In 1954, the Cellular Plastics Division of the Society of the Plastics Industry, Inc. was formed; its first task was the development of test methods and specifications for flexible and rigid urethanes, flexible vinyl, and rigid polystyrene. In the years that followed, a number of these tests were turned over to the appropriate subcommittee of the ASTM for promulgation as standards. The SPI group felt that this procedure, resulting in a single group of standards was more desirable than standards developed by several organizations. The SPI group also developed "Buyers' Guides and Commercial Standards" which serve another purpose but which are all based on standard ASTM tests.

Much of the ASTM development work has been to try to adapt to cellular plastics a method already standard in the plastics industry for non-cellular material.

Some tests were developed, however, which are unique for foams, such as the porosity test (D-1940-62T). Here there was a definite need for such a test.

As a result of these activities, the following list of ASTM methods and specifications, which have been *specifically approved for cellular plastics,* are available for use in the industry:

ASTM Designation	ASTM Committee	Title
		Test Methods for Rigid Cellular Plastics
C-177-45	C-16	Method of Test for Thermal Conductivity of Materials by Means of the Guarded Hot Plate
C-273-61	C-19	Method of Shear Test in Flatwise Plane of Flat Sandwich Constructions or Sandwich Cores
C-355-63T	C-16	Tentative Methods of Test for Water Vapor Transmission of Materials Used in Building Construction
C-393-62	C-19	Tentative Method of Flexure Test of Flat Sandwich Constructions
C-518-63T	C-16	Tentative Method of Test for Thermal Conductivity of Materials by Means of a Heat Flow Meter
D-790-61 (Proced. A)	D-20	Method of Test for Flexural Properties of Plastics
D-1621-64	D-20	Tentative Method of Test for Compressive Strength of Rigid Cellular Plastics
D-1622-63	D-20	Tentative Method of Test for Apparent Density of Rigid Cellular Plastics
D-1623-64	D-20	Tentative Method of Test for Tensile Properties of Rigid Cellular Plastics
D-1673-61	D-9	Method of Test for Dielectric Constant and Dissipation Factor of Expanded Cellular Plastics Used for Electrical Insulation
D-1692-59T	D-20	Tentative Method of Test for Flammability of Plastics Foams and Sheeting
D-1940-62T	D-20	Tentative Method of Test for Porosity of Rigid Cellular Plastics
D-2126-62T	D-20	Tentative Method of Test for Resistance of Rigid Cellular Plastics to Simulated Service Conditions
D-2127-62T	D-20	Tentative Method of Test for Water Absorption of Rigid Cellular Plastics
*	D-20	Proposed Tentative Method of Test for Thermal Conductivity of Cellular Materials by Means of a Line Heat Source

Work in progress in ASTM Committee as evidenced by at least a letter ballot in progress at either subcommittee or committee level.

ASTM Designation	ASTM Committee	Title
*	D-20	Proposed Tentative Method of Test for Porosity of Rigid Cellular Plastics by Means of the Air Pycnometer
		Specifications for Rigid Cellular Plastics
D-2125-62T	D-20	Tentative Specification for Cellular Polystyrene
*	D-20	Proposed Tentative Specification for Rigid Urethane Foam
*	C-16	Proposed Tentative Specification for Rigid Cellular Urethane Thermal Insulation
*	C-16	Proposed Tentative Specifications for Preformed Block-Type Thermal Insulation, Polystyrene, Cellular, Molded Type
		Methods and Specifications for Flexible Cellular Plastics
D-1564-64T	D-11	Tentative Specifications and Methods of Test for Flexible Urethane Foam
D-1565-60T	D-11	Tentative Specifications and Methods of Test for Flexible Foam from Polymers or Copolymers of Vinyl Chloride
D-1596-59T	D-10	Tentative Method of Test for Dynamic Properties of Package Cushioning Materials
D-1667-64	D-11	Tentative Specifications and Methods of Test for Sponge Made from Closed Cell Poly (Vinyl Chloride), or Copolymers Thereof
D-2221-63T	D-10	Tentative Method of Test for Creep Properties of Package Cushioning Materials
		Test Methods for Processibility of Cellular Plastics
D-2237-64T	D-20	Tentative Method of Test for Rate of Rise Properties of Urethane Foam
*	D-20	Proposed Tentative Method of Test for Total Volatile Content of Expandable Polystyrene Materials
		Test Methods and Specifications for Raw Materials of Cellular Plastics
D-1638-61T	D-20	Tentative Methods of Chemical Analysis of Urethane Foam Raw Materials
D-1715-60T	D-20	Tentative Method of Test for Gas Evolved from Chemical Blowing Agents for Cellular Plastics
D-1786-60T	D-20	Tentative Specifications for Toluene - diisocyanate and Poly (Oxypropylene Glycol)

ASTM Designation	ASTM Committee	Title

Through the use of various polymers we can effect gross changes in properties from Rigid to Flexible foams. "Rigid" foams may be characterized mechanically by their low extension in tension (perhaps less than 10%) and poor recovery after 75% deflection in compression (greater than 10% loss in height). Conversely, "flexible" foams are characterized mechanically by their high elongation in tension (greater than 100%) and excellent recovery after 75% deflection (less than 1% height loss). While "rigid" foams are generally stiffer than "flexible" ones, this is not necessarily true. There are other bases for defining "rigid" and "flexible" foams, but all definitions are complicated by the spectrum of properties for the different types of foams that span from "rigid" through "semi-rigid" and "semi-flexible" to "flexible". Because most test methods have been developed for foams characterized as either "rigid" or "flexible", this definition has been used as a basis for dividing the treatment of many of the foam properties in this chapter.

Many of the physical tests are influenced by the gases in the cell. Both the types of gases and their pressure-temperature relations become important considerations, especially for low density foams. For predominantly closed-celled foams, K-factor, dimensional stability, water vapor transmission and water absorption are examples of properties that may be of interest because of their unicellularity. For predominantly open-celled, low-density flexible foams, the dynamic resilience (liveliness) can be influenced by the ease of air flow through the cell structure.

Both direction of test and specimen location within a section of foam may influence physical property values. Cellular plastics may exhibit an anisotropy due to elongation of the cells, often in the direction of foam rise. For this reason it is common to designate test direction with respect to foam rise. Property variation from one location to another can result from differences in cell structure as well as polymer structure. The magnitude of these effects vary due to the type of polymer and the manner of foam formation. The possibility of property gradients, anisotropy, or both, make it very important in reporting test values to specify the method of sampling and the direction of test.

3. RIGID FOAM TEST METHODS

Density

Many of the important physical properties of a foam such as thermal conductivity, mechanical strength, heat capacity, etc., are specifically related to its density. In addition, density is commonly used to identify, in general terms, the over-all characteristics of the foam. Hence, a density measurement is usually a routine part of any foam characterization. The methods listed below are simple, yet yield the desired degree of accuracy for most purposes.

ASTM D1622-63 *"Apparent density of rigid cellular plastics"*—This method specifies the careful measurement of the linear dimensions of a foam specimen (to ± 1%) after proper conditioning. The specimen is then weighed (to ± 1%) and the density calculated in lb per cu ft.

The density of a foam can vary significantly from point to point within an object. This effect is especially noticeable when a surface skin is present. The exact location and nature of the density specimen should be noted. ASTM C303-56 "Density of preformed block-type thermal insulation" is similar to D-1622 and is being considered by ASTM C-16 for foamed plastic insulation.

Cell size

A number of non-standardized techniques are available for measuring cell size. These range from the use of a graduated eyepiece to the use of microscopic techniques. One particular method found to be convenient consists of taking thin slices (about 0.01 in.) from the cross-section under study by means of a microtome. The cell structure is then projected on a screen by means of a shadow projector. A reference grid on the screen facilitates the reading of cell diameters from a representative number of cells, and calculating the average cell diameter in millimeters.

Open cell content

All "closed cell" or "unicellular" foams contain an unavoidable percentage of interconnected or open cells. As the percentage increases, a loss in thermal conductivity and vapor barrier properties results. The measuring technique described below is complex but serves as a means of evaluating open cell structure:

ASTM D1940-62T *"Tentative method of test for porosity of rigid cellular plastics"*—The method is based on Boyle's law, which states that at a constant temperature, an increase in volume of a confined gas results in a proportionate decrease in pressure. If a chamber size is increased equally with and without a material present in the specimen chamber, the

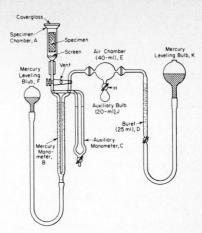

Figure IV-1, apparatus for open cell test ASTM D1940-62T.

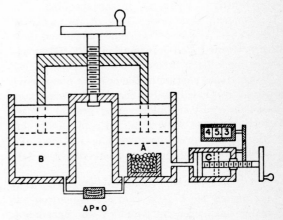

Figure IV-1a, air comparison pycnometer. A= sample chamber, B=comparison chamber, and C=equalizing chamber.

pressure drop will be less for the empty chamber. The extent of this difference and the actual volume of the material is a measure of percentage of closed cells (Fig IV-1).

Air comparison pycnometer—A convenient apparatus for measuring open cell content (available from Beckman Instruments, Inc. of Fullerton, California) consists of two equally sized chambers connected by a differential pressure gage (Fig. IV-1a). The volume of each chamber is decreased an equal amount by the movement of two pistons. Because one chamber contains the specimen, the volume of air is less, and the resulting pressure build-up is greater (From Boyle's Law: $P_1V_1 = P_2V_2$). A calibrated auxiliary chamber, connected to the test chamber, is adjusted until the pressure is equal to that of the empty chamber. The volume required is exactly that of the true volume of the specimen. The ratio of true volume to measured volume (from linear dimensions) is an indication of open cell content. The *percentage of closed cells value* is determined by making successive measurements and calculations.

Compressive properties

ASTM D1621-64 "Compressive strength of rigid cellular plastics"—Compressive strength and *modulus* are measured by compressing specimens in a testing machine with a crosshead speed of 0.1 in. per minute per in. of specimen thickness. Specimens may be of square or circular cross-section with an area of from 4 to 36 sq in. The minimum height is 1 in. and maximum height is no greater than the width or diameter of the specimen. The specimen is compressed 10% of its measured thickness. A stress-strain curve is plotted from the recorded load-deformation data. Compressive modulus is taken from the slope of the proportional portion of the curve. Compressive strength is calculated at the point of maximum load or at 10%, whichever is greater. *Note:* Certain foams show localized compressive effects. The over-all compression thus may not be linearly distributed throughout the test thickness.

ASTM C165-54 "Compressive strength of preformed block type thermal insulation" is being considered by ASTM C-16. Specimens, preferably 6 in. but not less than 5 in. square and of 1½ in. thickness are compressed in a

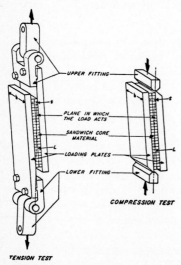

Figure IV-2, shear test apparatus for ASTM C273-61.

standard testing machine at a crosshead speed of not more than 0.05 in. per min. Specimens are compressed 5% of original thickness unless definite failure occurs before this point. Compressive strength in psi is reported at 5% deformation (or at failure). In addition, stresses in psi are reported at deformations of 1, 2, 3 and 4%.

Tensile properties

ASTM D1623-64 "Tensile properties of rigid cellular plastics"—Tensile strength, *elongation* and *modulus* are determined by testing circular "dog bone-shaped" specimens which measure 4¼ in. in overall length and have a 1 in. gauge length and 1.13 in. diameter (1 sq. in. cross-section). The flared ends are gripped by special jaws for pulling in a tensile machine at 0.05 in. per minute. It is desirable to use an *extensometer* so that a complete stress-strain curve may be obtained. Breaking load and elongation at moment of rupture are noted. From the above data, tensile strength, percent elongation and tensile modulus can be calculated.

Shear properties

ASTM C273-61 "Shear test in flatwise plane of flat sandwich construction or sandwich cores"—The test device pictured in Fig IV-2 facilitates shear testing of complete sandwich panels as well as of core materials alone. The test panels are loaded in shear parallel to the plane of the facings. From a complete load-deformation curve, it is possible to calculate the shear stress of the sandwich or core at any load (such as at proportional limit or at maximum load). From the slope of the stress-strain curve, it is possible to compute an effective shear modulus of the sandwich as a unit or of the core alone. The shear modulus obtained is that associated with the strains in a plane perpendicular to the facings and parallel to the direction of the applied forces.

Test specimens may vary in size, as long as the following proportions are observed: the specimen thickness is that of the sandwich, width is not less than twice the thickness, length is not less than 12 times the thickness.

Flexural properties

ASTM D790-61 "Flexural properties of plastics (Procedure A)—Various specimen sizes may be used providing the span is 16 times beam depth, and width does not exceed one fourth of the span. The beam is supported at both ends and center-loaded in flexure at the crosshead speed recommended in the method. For example, for a one-inch thick specimen, the method specifies a specimen of 1 in. width, 16 in. span and a crosshead speed of 0.43 in. per minute.

From the recorded load-deformation data, the following properties are determined:

a) Maximum fiber stress—which occurs at mid span, at outermost fiber, and may be calculated for any point on load deflection curve.

b) Flexural strength (Modulus of rupture) —which is the maximum outer fiber stress at break.

c) Flexural yield strength—the maximum outer fiber stress, if specimen does not break.

d) Modulus of elasticity—which is defined as the ratio of stress to strain within the elastic limit. The slope of the initial straight line portion of the load-deformation curve, expressed in psi, defines the modulus of elasticity.

ASTM C203-58 "Breaking load and calculated flexural strength of preformed block type thermal insulation" is being considered in ASTM Committee C-16 for foam plastic insulation. Preferred specimen size is 6 in. width x 12 in. length x 1½ in. thickness. The beam is center-loaded in flexure at 0.5 in. per minute. The breaking load in pounds is recorded, and the maximum fiber stress calculated and reported as "flexural strength". By recording load-deformation data, modulus and other properties can also be calculated. *Caution:* A length-to-depth ratio of as low as 8 to 1 is allowed (D790 specifies 16 to 1). This ratio may not be valid for certain foams.

Acoustical properties

Unicellular plastic foams, because of their small, non-interconnecting cell structure along with low density, are not highly efficient sound-absorbing materials. They are equal to wood, plastic and brick in sound absorption at lower frequencies and are somewhat better at higher frequencies. They are not as good, however, as commercial acoustical materials. The two methods listed below are commonly used to evaluate acoustical properties:

ASTM C384-58 "Impedance and absorption of acoustical materials by the tube method"— The apparatus consists of a tube of uniform cross-section and fixed length which is excited by a single tone of selectable frequency. The standing wave pattern in front of the speci-

men, upon which plane waves impinge at normal incidence, is explored by a moving probe tube or microphone. The method provides absolute measurement of the normal incidence sound absorption coefficient and the specific normal acoustic impedance of a material. In actual practice, however, waves impinge at random incidence; hence, a method is given to estimate random incidence values from the measured normal incidence test data.

ASTM C423-60T "Sound absorption of acoustical materials in reverberation rooms"— A reverberation room is a highly sound-reflective room in which special care has been taken to make the sound field as diffuse as possible. This method describes how a reverberation room is used to measure the sound absorption coefficients of acoustical materials. Because the samples are relatively large, and the sound is incident at random angles, the measurement is made under conditions approximating those of an actual installation.

Dimensional stability

Foams differ significantly in dimensional stability under various conditions of temperature and humidity. It is necessary to know to what degree a foam will expand, distort, or retract under service conditions. Many insulation applications demand a high degree of stability for an extended period of time. The tests below provide a maximum use temperature value as well as stability data at specified temperature and humidity conditions.

ASTM D2126-62T "Resistance of cellular plastics to simulated service conditions"— Specimens measuring 4 in. x 4 in. x 1 in. are exposed for 28 days to various combinations of temperature and humidity listed below. Weight and dimensional changes are noted, and other properties of interest are determined.

Dimensional stability tests

Condition	Temperature, °F	Relative humidity, %
A	73.4	50
B	−20	50
C	99.4	90-100
D	140	90-100
E	158	50
F	158	90-100
G	212	50

Maximum use temperature—This value is conveniently determined by exposing 6 in. x 2 in. x ½ in. foam specimens in a circulating hot air oven for a period of 24 hours or longer. Successively higher temperature levels are used with fresh specimens until an unacceptable dimensional change is measured. The highest acceptable temperature is the "Maximum use temperature under no load."

Water absorption

In certain applications such as buoyancy and perimeter insulations, it is necessary to know to what degree water can penetrate a given foam when submerged. Three of the many test methods in use are listed below. Correlation between methods and reproducibility within a given method are poor. Numerous variations exist such as the use of wetting agents, air stream removal of surface water, blotting of surface water, dipping in alcohol, which make comparison and interpretation of results difficult. When two foams are compared, care should be taken that identical test procedures are employed.

ASTM D2127-62T—"*Tentative method of test for water absorption of rigid cellular plastics*"—Test specimens measuring 4 in. x 4 in. x 1 in. are weighed, immersed under a 2-inch head of water for 24 hours, then reweighed. The difference in weights represents water absorbed into the foam (preweighing takes into account the water in cut surface cells). Results may be reported either in grams of water per 1000 sq cm of foam surface, or per 1000 cc of foam volume.

Military specifications MIL-P-16591 D and MIL-P-40619—Test specimens measuring 4 in. x 4 in. x 1 in. are weighed and submerged under a 10-foot head of water for 48 hours at room temperature. Specimens are then placed in a stream of air to remove surface water and reweighed. Water absorption is reported as lb of water gained per sq ft of surface area.

ASTM C272-53—"*Water absorption of core materials for structural sandwich constructions*"—Specimens measuring 3 in. x 3 in. x the material's actual thickness are preweighed, then immersed in water for 24 hours. After removal, they are dipped in alcohol and briefly dried in warm air to remove water in surface cells, then reweighed. Water absorption is reported as grams of water gained per cc of specimen tested. Percentage weight gain is also reported.

In an attempt to improve on the above methods, the two alternate techniques described below are being investigated. To date, however, no single method has been found satisfactory for all types of plastic foam. Considerable additional work and interpretation is

expected before a universal method is accepted.

Buoyancy technique—A foam specimen is immersed in water and the initial buoyant force measured. As water is absorbed, buoyancy decreases, and the equilibrium value is measured. The gain in water which causes the measured loss in buoyancy is calculated and reported. The main advantage is that surface water does not have to be removed or accounted for during testing. Major disadvantages are that in foams with gross defects, water penetrates so quickly that an initial buoyancy measurement cannot accurately be made, and secondly, foams which change dimension in water must be corrected for the effect this has on buoyancy.

Volumetric technique—A foam specimen is placed in a container from which extends a vertical capillary tube. The assembly is initially filled with water to a reference mark on the tube. The volume of water added over a period of time to maintain a constant level is thus a measure of volumetric water absorption. A major disadvantage is that certain foams expand in water, thereby causing the water to rise in the tube, in direct contrast to absorption behavior. The volume change in the sample can be measured and a correction made, but this is time-consuming.

Water vapor transmission

The rate at which water vapor passes through a foam at a given vapor pressure differential is of great importance in insulation applications. A high transmission rate often results in the accumulation of water and/or ice within the foam and at the interfaces, resulting in a loss of insulation effectiveness. The need for an additional vapor barrier sheet is determined by the barrier properties possessed by the foam itself. The two methods listed below are commonly quoted and correlate reasonably well:

ASTM C355-63T—"*Water vapor transmission of materials used in building construction*"—Because of confusion existing over terminology in this area, the following definitions are quoted directly from the C355 method:

a) Rate of water vapor transmission (WVT)—The rate of water vapor transmission of a body between two specified surfaces, or WVT, is the time rate of water vapor flow, under steady conditions, through unit area, under the conditions of test. An accepted unit of WVT is 1 grain per sq ft per hr. The test conditions

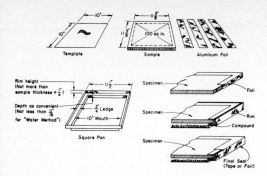

Figure IV-3, apparatus for water vapor transmission test ASTM C355-63T.

must be stated.

b) Water vapor permeance—The water vapor permeance of a body between two specified surfaces is the ratio of its WVT to the vapor pressure difference between the two surfaces. An accepted unit of permeance is a perm, or 1 grain per sq ft per hr per inch of mercury. Since the permeance of a specimen is generally a function of relative humidity and, to a lesser extent, temperature, the test conditions must be stated.

c) Water vapor permeability—The water vapor permeability of a homogeneous material is a property of the substance. This property may vary with conditions of exposure. The average permeability of a specimen is the product of its permeance and thickness. An accepted unit of permeability is a perm-inch, or 1 grain per sq ft per hr per inch of mercury per inch of thickness. Since the permeability of most materials is a function of relative humidity and, to a lesser extent, temperature, the test conditions must be stated.

Note: The definition does not imply that permeance is inversely proportional to thickness when the material is not fully homogeneous.

C355 provides for two alternate procedures, a *wet* test and a *dry* test. A specimen pan contains either desiccant or water, as desired, and is capped by the specimen which is not less than 6 in. in diameter or is not less than a 6 in. square (Fig IV-3). The assembly is placed in a controlled atmosphere and is weighed periodically. A plot of weight gain (or loss) as a function of time yields a curve whose slope indicates rate of vapor transmission. Proper calculation then provides the information in terms of WVT, Permeance, or Permeability.

Chemical resistance

The chemical resistance of a plastic foam is important. During installation many adhesives and mastics may contain solvents harmful to certain foams, and, during service life, various harmful solvents, oils, acids, etc., may come in contact with the foam. The resistance of a plastic foam to various chemicals is usually similar to that of the base polymer itself.

ASTM D543-60T "Resistance of plastics to chemical reagents"—This method provides a standardized procedure for evaluating the chemical resistance of plastics. Fifty-one standard reagents are listed for possible use. Alternate reagents may also be added if desired. The plastic materials to be tested are immersed in sheet form in the reagent for seven days or longer. Various test temperatures may be specified although it is common practice to use room temperature plus some elevated temperature such as 125° F.

After the immersion period, the specimens are removed and measured for weight and dimensional changes. Changes in general visual appearance are also noted. As required, mechanical property tests are then made and the percent change recorded.

Light stability

Many plastic foams are susceptible to rapid degradation by ultraviolet rays when exposed continuously to direct sunlight. For this reason, they must be covered during storage and suitably protected in exposed outdoor applications.

A number of accelerated tests are available, such as *fadeometer, weatherometer, sunlamp,* etc., but these are difficult to correlate with actual sunlight exposure. For this reason, tests are usually made by mounting the foam in outdoor racks and making periodic visual examinations. Failure is evidenced by excessive surface discoloration and/or degradation.

Fungus resistance

The resin portion of a plastic material is usually fungus resistant in that it does not serve as a carbon source for fungus growth. It is usually the other components, such as plasticizers, stabilizers, lubricants, and colorants that are susceptible. Many plastic foams contain a minimum of such additives and are, therefore, generally resistant to fungus growths.

ASTM D1924-61T "Determining resistance of plastics to fungi"—Fungus attack normally occurs under exposure conditions of 35-100°F and 60% to 100% relative humidity. Provision is made in this procedure to inoculate test specimens with six common fungus cultures. A subsequent incubation is then conducted for 21 days at 85°F and 85% relative humidity. The following observations and tests are then made:

1) Visual aspect: surface attack, discoloration, haze.

2) Loss of susceptible plasticizers, lubricants, etc., resulting in increased modulus, weight changes, dimensional changes and deterioration of electrical properties.

Thermal conductivity

One of the primary reasons for using plastic foams is their excellent thermal insulating quality. The coefficient of thermal conductivity, or "K" factor, is a measure of this property. A number of important variables affect "K" factor, i.e., moisture content, density, use temperature, and cell gas content (change with time).

ASTM C177-45 "Guarded hot plate"—This is the standard method for measuring thermal conductivity of insulating materials. Briefly, the technique consists of measuring the electrical energy required to maintain a central "hot plate" at a selected temperature. Test specimens cover each of the two hot plate surfaces and in turn are covered by "cold" plates which are maintained at a prescribed temperature. A guard ring around the four edges of the hot plate is controlled at hot plate temperature to prevent edge heat loss. All heat energy is thus transmitted from hot plate to cold plates through the specimens. The amount of heat transmitted is determined by the insulating effectiveness of the specimens and is measured by recording power input to the hot plate heaters. A low "K" factor thus indicates superior insulating ability and is determined by the following relationship:

$$\text{``K''} = \frac{q \, x}{A \Delta T}$$

Where: "K" = coefficient of thermal conductivity Btu-in./hr °F sq ft

q = rate of heat flow, Btu/hr

x = specimen thickness, in.

A = specimen area, sq ft

ΔT = temp. drop through specimen, °F.

ASTM C518-63T Heat flow meter—The heat flow meter apparatus is extremely valuable as a developmental and control tool. "K" factor values of reasonable accuracy can be obtained quickly and at low cost. The apparatus itself is economical to construct and easy to maintain.

The basic principle involves the use of a heat flow meter (thermopile) which is placed in series with the test specimen between a hot and a cold plate. The total temperature drop between the plates is divided between meter and specimen—the ratio depending upon the thermal effectiveness of the specimen. The resulting temperature drop across the thermopile develops an electromotive force which is measured and correlated to a rate of heat flow by means of a calibration constant. "K" factor is then calculated by use of the relationship given in the preceding test.

The meter may be calibrated either by use of standards available from The National Bureau of Standards or by direct calibration against a guarded hot plate. The meter must be rechecked periodically—usually at the beginning of each test day—by the use of a calibration standard.

Line heat source ("Probe")—This method has been approved by ASTM D20 for adoption as a standard method of test. A thermal conductivity "probe" contains a heating element along its entire length (hence the term "line heat source"). In addition, a thermocouple is located within the probe to sense temperature changes. When heat is supplied at a constant rate along the line source, the temperature rise is proportional to the logarithm of time and inversely proportional to the thermal conductivity of the surrounding medium. By properly installing the probe in foam test specimens, thermal conductivity values can be precisely measured.

Thermal expansion

The coefficient of linear thermal expansion (α) indicates the amount of dimensional change caused by a given change in temperature. The relationship is:

$$\alpha = \frac{\Delta l}{l \Delta T}$$

Where: α = linear coefficient of thermal expansion, in./in. °F

Δl = change in length, in.

l = original length, in.

ΔT = change in temperature, °F

Simple thermal expansion (and contraction) has no permanent effect on the material. If a

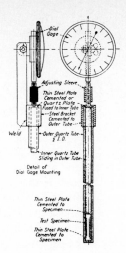

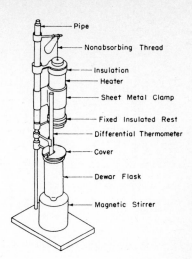

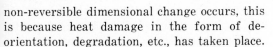

Figure IV-4, quartz tube dilatometer for measure of thermal expansion by ASTM method D696-44.

Figure IV-5, specific heat calorimeter for method ASTM C351-61.

non-reversible dimensional change occurs, this is because heat damage in the form of de-orientation, degradation, etc., has taken place.

In many instances the coefficient value for a foam is the same as for the base polymer. Directional effects in foams are quite common, and different thermal expansion behaviors may be observed along the various axes.

The coefficient changes abruptly at transition points. It is therefore wise to determine values at increments over the entire temperature range of interest. In this manner, appropriate values can be determined for temperature ranges above and below transitions.

A simple test method of reasonable accuracy consists of mounting a rigid foam specimen approximately 1 in. x 1 in. x 12 in. on a rigid frame. The specimen is fastened to the frame at one end and at the other end a dial micrometer, fastened to the same frame, records movement of the foam. Readings are taken at two or more temperature levels, a correction is made for expansion of the frame, and a coefficient value is calculated from the relationship given earlier.

A modification of *ASTM D696-44 "Coefficient of linear thermal expansion of plastics"* has been found suitable for accurately measuring rigid foams. The specified quartz tube dilatometer (Fig IV-4) and specimen sizes are used; however, the dial micrometer (which is allowed to develop up to 10 psi on the specimen) has been found to exert an unacceptable compressive force on foam specimens. Con-

sequently, a linear variable differential transformer has been substituted to record specimen expansion. The transformer core weighs only 15 grams and thus exerts less than 0.3 psi on a specimen of 0.4 in. diameter. Readings are taken at various temperatures and the coefficients calculated in the usual manner.

Specific heat

Specific heat is an essential property of an insulating material in unsteady state applications. It is part of the thermal diffusivity relationship, which defines the ability of a material to change temperature. Specific heat is a basic thermodynamic property of all substances, the value of which depends upon chemical composition and temperature.

ASTM C351-61 "Mean specific heat of thermal insulation"—This method employs the classical method of mixtures which consists of adding a known mass of test material at high temperature to a known mass of liquid at low temperature and measuring the resulting equilibrium temperature. The heat absorbed by the water and containing vessel (Dewar flask) is equated to the heat given up by the test material (Fig IV-5). From this expression the specific heat is calculated.

Flammability

Two independent factors must be considered when evaluating the flammability characteristics of a plastic foam. First is its ease of ignition. The temperature at which a foam will

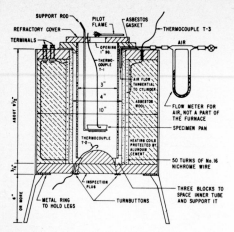

Figure IV-6, furnace for ignition test ASTM D1929-62T.

ignite is an index of its safety when in contact with various heat sources (steam lines, light bulbs, sparks, open flame, etc.). Secondly, the rate of burning once the foam becomes ignited. Since burning rate depends heavily upon the physical configuration of a material (i.e., large volume stacks, extended surface areas, small, individual items, etc.), it is necessary to use tests which closely simulate the conditions found in service.

Ignition temperature—A hot air ignition furnace technique was recently adopted by ASTM Committee D20, as *"D1929-62T" "Ignition properties of plastics"*. The method is based on the apparatus (Fig IV-6) described by N. P. Setchkin of the National Bureau of Standards in Research Paper RP 2052. A ceramic tube is raised to a chosen temperature by preheated air. The samples, weighing 2 to 3 grams, are suspended within the tube and ignition characteristics are noted. Air velocity is varied to achieve optimum ignition conditions, and the lowest air temperature causing ignition of the sample is recorded. Tests are conducted with a small external pilot flame in the discharge stream to determine "Flash ignition temperature." Tests conducted in the absence of the external flame determine "Self-ignition temperature."

Burning rate

Large scale tests—Surface flame spread is of concern when the material is used in building construction. A foam may be exposed, as in ceiling tile, or covered, as in plaster base. In any event, fire protection officials require flame spread data to properly assess fire hazard. The standard test is the ASTM E84-61 "Tunnel furnace" (Fig IV-7). Developed by the Underwriters' Laboratories, the furnace consists of a 25-foot-long tunnel of 21 in. x 21 in. cross section. The specimen, measuring 21" x 25' constitutes the roof of the tunnel. The apparatus is fired from one end by gas burners and flame is encouraged by controlled draft to spread along the underside of the specimen. The time-rate of flame travel determines the "flame spread rating." Red oak flooring is arbitrarily rated as 100 and cement asbestos board as 0. All other materials are rated by comparison. "Smoke density" and "fuel contributed" are also measured in the apparatus.

Small scale tests—"Bench" tests are useful for screening and developmental work preliminary to large scale testing. In special cases, where the amount of foam in the application is limited, small scale tests are indicative of "in use" behavior.

Intermediate scale tests—These provide a measure of surface flame spread and are used as developmental tests to predict large scale behavior. Results are not accepted, however, by Fire protection officials in lieu of large scale "tunnel" ratings.

ASTM D1692-59T "Flammability of plastics foam and sheeting"—Specimens measuring 6 in. x 2 in. x ½ in. are supported horizontally on ¼ in. wire mesh and ignited at one end by a Bunsen burner with wing top (Fig IV-8).

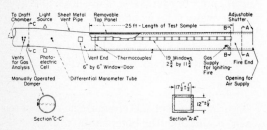

Figure IV-7, tunnel furnace for test ASTM E84-61 (UL 723).

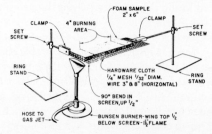

Figure IV-8, setup for flammability test ASTM D1692-59T.

Gage marks are drawn 1 in. and 5 in. from the ignition end for use in judging behavior. If no evidence of ignition is observed after 1 minute of flame application, the sample is judged "non-burning by this test." If the sample ignites but does not burn past the second gage mark it is judged "self-extinguishing by this test." If the sample burns beyond the second gage mark, the rate of burning is calculated and reported in inches per minute.

ASTM E162-62T "Radiant panel"—Developed at the National Bureau of Standards, this test utilizes a radiant burner operating at 1238°F to preheat the surface of a 6 in. x 18 in. specimen to encourage flame travel. The specimen is mounted at a 45° angle and is ignited at the top. The rate of flame travel down the heated face, plus the heat evolved, enter into a "flame spread index." Red oak is rated at 100 and cement asbestos board at 0. Other materials are rated by comparison. Smoke density is measured by observing the exhaust stack.

Forest products lab. 8-foot tunnel—This scaled-down version of the 25-foot tunnel measures flame spread in much the same manner as the larger test. A number of modifications include inclination of the specimen, natural convective draft, etc.

Dielectric constant and dissipation factor

ASTM D1673-61 "Dielectric constant and dissipation factor of expanded cellular plastics used in electrical insulation"—This method was designed specifically for the testing of plastic foams. Conventional methods are difficult, if not impossible, to use because of the thickness of foamed plastic specimens, plus the fact that the rough surface texture does not lend itself to the attachment of conventional electrodes. The basic apparatus consists of a bridge and resonant circuit having characteristics as prescribed in ASTM D150 (see below). Provision is made for the measurement of dissipation factor and dielectric constant tests at any desired frequency in the range between 60 cycles and 100 Mc per sec.

Because foamed plastics do not have surfaces suitable for attachment of conventional electrodes, prefabricated rigid metal plate electrodes must usually be employed. These may be of either the direct contact type or the non-contacting type as described in the method. Test specimens may be tested up to two inches in thickness in the form of either disks or squares. The diameter of a disk specimen, or the side of a square specimen, must be not less than four times the thickness and should preferably be eight times the thickness.

Other electrical properties

In addition to the above method for dielectric constant of foamed plastics, the methods listed below describe tests for various other electrical properties. Modifications would be needed to make them applicable to foamed specimens and they are simply listed for necessary background reference information and definitions.

ASTM D149-59 "Dielectric breakdown voltage and dielectric strength of electrical insulating materials at commercial power frequencies."

ASTM D257-58 "Electrical resistance of insulating materials" (covers procedures for the determination of insulation resistance, volume resistance, surface resistance, volume resistivity and surface resistivity).

ASTM D150-59T "AC Capacitance, dielectric constant, and loss characteristics of electrical insulating materials" (covers procedures for the determination of capacitance, dielectric constant, dissipation factor, loss factor, power factor, phase angle and loss angle).

ASTM general specifications

A general specification has been written for rigid styrene foam, ASTM D-2125-62T, and an ASTM specification for rigid urethane foams is nearing completion. In addition to providing a basis for specifying the basic properties of these materials, they also provide a reference list for the various ASTM test methods approved for that material. This is particularly important for rigid foams because separately designated test methods are used for the individual properties.

Also in process in ASTM are specifications for Rigid Cellular Urethane and Preformed Cellular Polystyrene for thermal insulation.

4. FLEXIBLE FOAM TEST METHODS

The current ASTM methods for Flexible Cellular Plastics (D-1564-64T, D-1565-60T, D-1667-64) all include tests and specifications for the basic properties. These basic specifications have been included in Commercial Standard TS-5577, Flexible Slab Urethane Foam for Bedding and Seat Cushioning, proposed to the U. S. Dept. of Commerce by the Urethane

Institute of the S.P.I., and awaiting final approval.

The pattern of presenting specifications and test methods for flexible foams has been quite different from that followed for rigid foams. For rigid foams, separate test methods were written for specific properties. For flexible foams, many tests apply to a particular type of material. Currently there are three such collections of tests listed under ASTM designations:

ASTM 1564-64T, Tentative Methods of Test for Flexible Urethane Foam—The latest revision of this tentative method published by ASTM is D1564-64T.

ASTM D1565-60T, Tentative specifications and methods of test for flexible foams made from polymers or copolymers of vinyl chloride.

ASTM D1667-64, Tentative specifications and methods of test for sponge made from closed cell poly (vinyl chloride), or copolymers thereof.

Each of these methods lists a series of "basic" and "suffix" tests. Detailed methods are described for all the basic tests and some of the suffix tests.

D-1564 (Flexible Urethane Foam) and *D-1565* (Flexible Vinyl Foam) are similar in that they concern open cell flexible foams. In the basic requirements, they have similar test methods for indentation load deflection. The other basic requirements that differ appreciably are steam autoclave exposure, dry heat exposure and static fatigue. *D-1565* also lists a compression deflection test for high load-bearing foams.

The methods of test for *D-1667* (Flexible Vinyl) apply to a closed-cell flexible foam. The one basic test is compression-deflection, similar to that in *D-1565*. A water absorption suffix test is included and is of importance due to the closed cell nature of the foam.

Density

ASTM D-1564 (Suffix W), D-1565 (Suffix W), D-1667 (Suffix W)—The density test consists of dividing the weight by the volume of a given section of foam and obtaining a density in lb per cu ft or gm per cc. The test is useful in quality control as a measure of the reproducibility of a process. Density is not necessarily an indicator or guarantee of other specific physical properties.

The test methods specify that the size shall be no less than 1 cu in. and the weight shall be

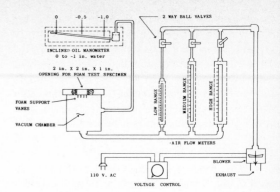

Figure IV-9, air flow apparatus (no ASTM standard).

measured within ± 1%. The accuracy of the dimension measurement is specified: *D-1564* calls for ± 1% of the dimensions to be measured. *D-1565* and *D-1667* specify the scale or gauge graduations.

Cell size

There are no ASTM methods for measuring cell size for flexible urethane foams although it is an important structural property and is currently referred to. One method uses a glass with 6 to 8 x magnification to count the number of cells touching a half-inch line. The count is doubled to obtain the number of cells per inch. Cell count is one of several characteristics that can be used to describe the appearance of the foam. Because of the personal element in determining which cells are to be counted along a line, the accuracy of the test is limited. For a foam having a cell count in the range of 50 cells per inch, the uncertainty of the method is at least ± 2 cells per inch, or ± 4%. If the cell structure is random (various diameters clustered together), obtaining high precision is even more difficult.

Open cell and air flow

The amount of open cell in flexible foams can be determined by ASTM *D1940-62T*, or by the air pycnometer test, already described. Flexible foams that have a predominance of open cells (as measured by *D1940*) can exhibit a wide range of resistance to air flow. Air flow measurements are obtained by measuring the amount of air in cubic feet per minute that will pass through a given cross-section with a specified pressure drop.

Although there is no standard test method, several testing apparatus, such as shown in Fig IV-9, are in existence. Work on standardization may be starting in the near future. It is recommended that the test specimen size be 2 in. x 2 in. x 1 in. thick, and that the pressure drop across the test specimen be 0.50 in. of water. The accuracy of the method is dependent to a large extent on the calibration of the rotameters and manometer. If the rotameters are factory calibrated to ± 1%, the accuracy of the airflow values is estimated at ± 2%. Since there can be considerable variation in air flow values within a large section of foam, the location from which a sample was taken should be noted.

Air flow values are proportional to porosity, and values ranging from 0.02 to 20 cfm can be obtained in foam. Flexible foams having low air flow values (less than 1 cfm) are often called pneumatic and sometimes mistakenly termed "closed cell" foams. Flexible foams having high air flow values in the range of 10 cfm have been used as air filters.

Load deflection

The stiffness or resistance to deflection of flexible foams can be measured by three different standard techniques. They all involve placing a foam specimen between two platens in a testing machine and recording load in pounds and deflection in inches as the platens are brought closer together. Each standard technique has a specific sequence of deflections and rest periods that must be followed in order to obtain reproducible results.

Indentation load deflection (ILD)

ASTM D-1564 (Method A), D-1565—the ILD test uses a 50 sq in. flat circular loading platen which deflects a specimen with a minimum area of 15 in. x 15 in. (D-1564) or 12 in. x 12 in. (D-1565) as shown in Fig IV-10. The ILD test simulates a person sitting on a seat cushion and is used widely in the comfort cushioning and bedding industry. Since the ILD test may be used on the complete part, the actual area and thickness vary. Following a preworking, when necessary, the specimen is deflected 25% of its original thickness and the load in pounds after a 1-minute rest is noted as the 25% ILD value. ILD values at other deflections may also be obtained and a ratio of these values to the 25% deflection value is reported. (A 65% ILD value is normally taken for D-1564.) An additional point may be taken at 25% deflection as the sample is unloaded, as allowed in D-1564. Higher ILD values indicate a stiffer foam.

Figure IV-10, indentation load deflection test.

The accuracy of the test for a given laboratory is about ± 2%. Due to the peripheral effects of the indentor foot, the ILD values are dependent on the thickness and area of the test specimen.

Indentation residual gage load (IRGL)

D-1564 (Method B)—The IRGL test uses a 50 sq in. flat circular loading platen similar to the ILD test. It differs in that the specimen is deflected to a constant load for IRGL rather than a constant thickness. Following a preworking, the specimen is loaded with 25 lb and the thickness after a 1 minute rest noted as the 25 lb IRGL value. IRGL values at other loads may be obtained. A 50 lb IRGL value and a 25 lb IRGL return value are generally considered. A higher IRGL value indicates a stiffer foam.

The accuracy of the IRGL test is about ± 2% for a given laboratory. IRGL values are dependent on specimen thickness and area due to the peripheral effects of the indentor foot.

Compression load deflection (CLD)

D-1564 (suffix D), D-1565, D-1667 — The CLD differs from the ILD in that the loading platen is larger than the test specimen. The specimen area is usually small, being 4 sq in. min. for D-1564 and 1.129 in diameter for D-1565 and D-1667. Following a preworking, when needed, the specimen is deflected 25% of its thickness and the load after 1 minute noted. This load in pounds divided by the specimen area in square inches is the 25% CLD in lb per sq in. A higher CLD value indicates a stiffer foam. The precision of the 25% CLD is about ± 2% for a given laboratory. One might

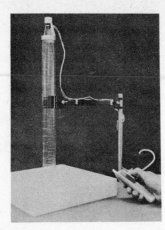

Figure IV-11, ball rebound resilience test.

expect the 25% CLD to be independent of the specimen area and thickness, but this may not always be the case and specimen dimensions should be reported.

Resilience (ball rebound)

D-1564 (Suffix R)—The resilience of a flexible foam is a measure of its liveliness or speed of recovery after deflection. The resilience of a flexible foam may be defined as follows:

$$\text{Resilience} = \frac{\text{Energy returned}}{\text{Energy applied}} \times 100$$

The actual value obtained depends on the type of test equipment used. Rate at which energy is applied and configuration of loading head and test specimen influence the value. The standard test for flexible foam resilience *(D-1564 suffix R)* is the ball rebound test shown in Fig IV-11. The test consists of dropping a steel ball from a height of 18 in. and noting the height of rebound.

$$\text{Resilience} = \frac{\text{Rebound height, in.}}{18 \text{ in.}} \times 100\%$$

A number of other methods may be modified to give a resilience value for flexible foam. These include the method of test for impact resilience and penetration of rubber by the rebound pendulum (ASTM Designation: D-1054) and the methods of test for mechanical properties of elastomeric vulcanizates under compressive or shear strains by the mechanical oscillograph (ASTM Designation: D-945).

The higher the value of resilience the more "lively" the foam. A ball rebound of 45% or higher indicates a high resilience.

Tension test D-1564 (Suffix T)

This test determines the effect of the application of a tensile load to a foam specimen. Values for tensile stress, tensile strength and ultimate elongation may be obtained.

A ½ in. thick specimen is stamped out with a die as shown in Fig IV-12, and bench marks placed on it. The specimen is mounted in the jaws of a tensile tester as described in *D-1564*. The jaws are separated at 20 ± 1 in. per min. and the load and elongation are noted until the specimen ruptures. The load at rupture divided by the original cross-sectional area of the specimen in sq in. is the tensile strength. The ultimate elongation is obtained from:

$$\text{Ultimate elongation} = \frac{d_f - d_o}{d_o} \times 100$$

where: $d_o =$ original distance between bench marks, in.

$d_f =$ distance between bench marks at the break point, in.

The tensile stress is obtained by dividing the load in lb at a predetermined elongation by the original cross-sectional area of the specimen. It is not usually reported.

The accuracy of the tensile test values is $\pm 10\%$.

Tear resistance test

D-1564 (Suffix G), often called the "block method," uses the test specimen shown in Fig IV-13. The specimen is mounted in a tensile tester as specified in D-1564 and the jaws separated at 2 in. per min. The accuracy of the test is estimated at $\pm 5\%$.

Compression set test

D-1564 (Method B), D-1565—The compression set test consists of clamping the foam specimen to a specified thickness, using flat plates and spacer bars, and maintaining this condition for 22 hr at 158° F. Following this exposure, the specimen is released and after a specified conditioning period the recovered thickness measured. The amount of deflection at which the specimen is clamped may be specified at 50% or 90% in *D-1564* and 50% in *D-1565*.

The compression set may be calculated in two ways:

1) Expressed as a *percentage of original thickness*

$$c_t = \frac{t_o - t_f}{t_o} \times 100$$

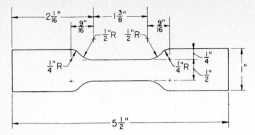

Figure IV-12, die for stamping tension test specimens.

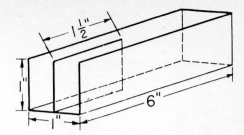

Figure IV-13, tear resistance test specimens.

2) Expressed as a *percentage of original deflection*

$$c_d = \frac{t_o - t_f}{t_c - t_s} \times 100$$

where c_t = compression set expressed as a percentage of original thickness

c_d = compression set expressed as a percentage of original deflection

t_o = original thickness

t_f = final thickness after specified recovery period and conditioning

t_s = spacer bar thickness

Since different values are obtained by the two methods, the basis of the calculation must always be specified.

Autoclave exposure test (D-1564)

The autoclave exposure test consists of treating a flexible urethane foam specimen 2 in. x 2 in. x 1 in. in a low-pressure steam autoclave and observing the effect on physical properties of the foam. The test consists of two sets of conditions:

1) Three hours at 104.4°C (220F°) (nominal) for polyester urethane foam, which shall be known as Condition "A."

2) Five hours at 121.1°C (250°F) (nominal) for polyether urethane foam, which shall be known as Condition "B."

Following a specified pre-conditioning, the specimens are exposed to Condition A or B and then given a specified post-conditioning. The compression-load-deflection (CLD) is obtained before and after exposure and the percent change from the original CLD is reported. A compression set test is also run on each specimen.

Dry heat test (D-1564) and air oven exposure (D-1565)

This test consists of exposing foam specimens at elevated temperatures in air circulating ovens and observing the effect on physical properties of the foam.

The method for urethane foam *(D-1564)* consists of exposing tensile specimens in an oven at 284°F for 22 hours. The tensile strength of the exposed specimens is obtained and compared with that of a matched set of unexposed specimens. The change in tensile strength is calculated from:

$$C = \frac{S_o - S_f}{S_o} \times 100$$

where S_o = mean tensile strength of unexposed specimens

S_f = mean tensile strength of exposed specimens

The method for vinyl foam *(D-1565)* consists of exposing an ILD or CLD specimen as specified for various grades in an oven at 212°F for 22 hours. Following a post-conditioning period, the Load Deflection is run and compared with the value obtained on the specimen before exposure. The change in load deflection is calculated from

$$C = \frac{D_o - D_f}{D_o} \times 100$$

where C = percent change in ILD or CLD

D_f = final value of ILD or CLD after oven exposure

D_o = original value of ILD or CLD before oven exposure

Fatigue tests

D-1564 (suffix H), D-1565 (basic and suffix H)—The ability to withstand repeated flexing without excessive loss in thickness or load deflection is an important characteristic of flexible foams. There are numerous types of tests which have been designed to measure this property. They vary from various dynamic treatments to tests at static constant load. *D-1564* lists six separate procedures as follows:

Figure IV-14, rotary shear tester.

1) *Procedure A:* Static, constant deflection.

In this procedure a 15 in. x 15 in. x specimen thickness is deflected 75% of its thickness between parallel plates for 17 hours. Thirty minutes after release of the specimen the thickness and ILD are measured.

2) *Procedure B*—Static, constant load.

A constant load of 1 psi is allowed to rest on a foam specimen 15 in. x 15 in. x thickness for 17 hours. Thirty minutes after release of the specimen the thickness and ILD are measured.

3) *Procedure C*—Dynamic, vertical deflection-constant deflection.

The foam specimen is flexed 75% of its thickness 250,000 times at a rate of 1 cycle per second. Thirty minutes after completion of the cycling the thickness and load deflection are measured.

4) *Procedure D*—Dynamic, linear shear—constant deflection.

A roller 18 in. long and 3 in. in diameter is mounted in an offset position (15°) with suitable means for obtaining 65% deflection of the test specimen. The specimen size is 15 in. x 15 in. x thickness. The sample is flexed for 20,000 cycles (40,000 flexes). Thirty minutes after completion of the test the thickness and ILD are measured.

5) *Procedure E*—Dynamic, linear shear—constant load.

The apparatus is similar to Procedure D, except that the rollers are loaded to obtain an original 65% deflection.

6) *Procedure F*—Dynamic, rotary shear—constant load.

The apparatus consists of a 12 in. diameter rotating plate driven by a constant speed motor, on which a ¼ in. thick foam sheet covered with canvas is placed, as shown in Fig IV-14. Rollers canted across the radial axes are constantly loaded so that the foam is compressed approximately 80-90% of its thickness. The foam sample is then alternately compressed and relaxed with shear action due to the constant load applied. The plate turns at the rate of 37 rpm for 50,000 revolutions. The rollers are set at an angle of 15° to the radius so as to produce this equivalent of shear. The weight applied to both rollers is 15 lb. The rollers are 1¼ in. in diameter by 3 in. long. Thirty minutes after completion of the cycling the thickness and ILD (using 1 sq in. circular indentor foot) are measured in the same areas as tested before cycling.

The following calculations are made for all *D-1564-T* fatigue test procedures:

1) Loss of thickness:

$$F_t = \frac{t_o - t_f}{t_o} \times 100$$

where F_t = per cent loss in thickness

t_o = original specimen thickness

t_f = final specimen thickness

2) Loss of load deflection:

$$F_L = \frac{L_o - L_f}{L_o} \times 100$$

where F_L = per cent loss of load deflection

L_o = original load deflection value

L_f = final load deflection value

In *D-1565* there are two types of fatigue tests. The static fatigue test consists of bending a 10 in. x 2 in. wide (1 in. maximum thickness) strip of vinyl foam 180° and placing it in an oven at 158° F for 22 hours. At the conclusion of the test the specimen shall show no cracks.

The dynamic flexing test in *D-1565* is similar to Method C in *D-1564*. It differs in that the amount of deflection is 50% or 25% (depending on the CLD as specified) rather than 75% deflection.

Creep and permanent set

D-2221-63T, Tentative Method of test for "Creep properties of package cushioning materials"—This test determines the extent and nature of foam cushion thickness change under a given static load. Specimens measuring 2 in. x 2 in. x 1 in. are loaded with the desired weight at the desired temperature. Periodic measurements of compression are taken over a one-week period. The load is then removed and the rate and amount of recovery over a one-day period is recorded. The permanent set, in per cent, based on the original thickness, is calculated. A plot is then made of per cent creep versus log time.

The rate and degree of creep and permanent set of a foam is an important factor in any load bearing application such as package cushioning.

The creep is calculated and reported in percent, based on the initial loaded thickness and the loaded thickness at any chosen time.

Dynamic properties of package cushioning materials

ASTM D-1596-59T—This test consists essentially of dropping a series of known weights through known distances onto a 4 in. x 4 in. x 1 in. pad of cushioning material. An *accelerometer* attached to the dropping weight detects the amount of shock developed upon impact and transmits this information by means of an electrical impulse to an oscilloscope, which in turn focuses the shock wave on its screen for visual or photographic observation. By proper calibration of the screen, the deceleration of the dropping weight can be read directly in "G" forces.

A series of data plots of peak deceleration versus static stress (dropping weight) for various foam thicknesses at various dropping heights yields information on optimum foam configuration for a given packaging condition. (Also see Section VI—Packaging).

5. RAW MATERIAL TESTS

Urethane foam

a) Toluene diisocyanate and polyol: Chemical analyses for the two main ingredients in urethane foams, toluene diioscyanate and polyol, are described in *ASTM D1638-61T, Tentative Methods of Testing Urethane Raw Materials*. The toluene diisocyanate is most often checked by foam producers for assay and acidity. The polyol is most often checked for hydroxyl number and water content. Specifications for three types of isocyanates and one type of polyol are given in ASTM D-1786-60T, *Tentative Specification for Toluene diisocyanate and Poly (Oxypropylene Glycol)*. Work is currently in progress in an SPI committee on test methods for modified toluene diisocyanates.

b) Other ingredients: Other ingredients are frequently added such as various catalysts, surface-active agents, fillers, plasticizers and colors. Control tests for these materials can usually be obtained from their suppliers. Foaming tests can be used as a quality control test to check either the minor or major ingre-

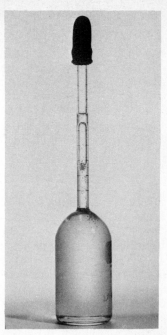

Figure IV-15, air bubbles in viscous prepolymer solutions (fluorocarbon-11).

dients. (See processibility chapter for Rate of Rise Test)

c) Fluorocarbon-11 content: Polyol and prepolymer masterbatches may be used containing fluorocarbon-11 as an auxiliary blowing agent. The fluorocarbon-11 content can be determined by several methods:

1) Specific gravity with hydrometer ($\pm$ 0.3% accuracy)

2) Density in "Babcock" bottle ($\pm$ 0.2% accuracy)

3) Refractive index ($\pm$ 0.5% accuracy)

The specific gravity and density methods take longer than the refractive index measurement, but give accurate results with a small investment in equipment.

With high viscosity solutions, the escape of air bubbles trapped during pouring is slow (See Figure IV-15). This time delay reduces the usefulness of the hydrometer with prepolymers because of the time delay and because moisture in the air may react with the isocyanate component. With low viscosity materials, a hydrometer can ordinarily be used.

The density of highly viscous prepolymer solutions can be measured in a moisture-free environment in Babcock bottles. Conventional pycnometers are satisfactory if they can be capped until the solution is free of air bubbles. The sample is sealed under a dry, inert gas in the Babcock bottle and allowed to stand in this

Figure IV-16, rate of rise height measurement apparatus.

dry environment until free of air. Although the liquid level in the Babcock bottle will drop as air escapes, the neck of the bottle is calibrated to permit measurement of the liquid volume.

Nearly all solutions may be analyzed by the refractive index method. Viscous solutions must be handled by techniques somewhat different from those used for less viscous liquids, but good precision can be obtained if air bubbles are permitted to escape from the liquid before it is placed on the refractometer prism. Only clear solutions should be used in the refractometer. Pigments, fillers, and certain silicone surface-active agents produce cloudiness or opacity, and the refractive indices of samples containing these products are difficult to measure.

Viscosity is generally measured with a Brookfield Synchro-lectric Viscometer (Model LVF). The use of this instrument is covered in ASTM D-1638-61T. As a process control the viscosity should be determined on the actual masterbatch that is being used, preferably at the operating temperature. However, as a control test it can be run at any convenient temperature.

Polystyrene foam

Expandable polystyrene beads may be checked as raw materials for total volatile content and water content. (See Processibility chapter for Expandability test.) Since the total volatile content consists mainly of expanding agent, with a minor amount of water, it offers a relatively quick reading of a vital material property and is helpful in establishing lot to lot uniformity. Work on establishing an ASTM method for total volatile content is nearing completion. In the test, specimens

weighing approximately 5 or 25 grams are placed in a container and weighed. The container is placed in an oven at 150° C for ½ hour, after which it is cooled and weighed. The total volatile content is calculated by dividing the weight difference by the original weight.

Work on standardizing a method for water content is to begin shortly in ASTM.

Vinyl foam

Work in ASTM D-20 was in progress during 1958 on a series of five tests for vinyl raw materials. Of these tests, only ASTM D1715-60T, "Tentative Method of Test for Gas Evolved from Chemical Blowing Agents for Cellular Plastics," was completed. Further work on these tests was discontinued until such time as the vinyl foam reaches greater commercial acceptance.

6. PROCESSIBILITY TESTS

Processibility tests concern properties that relate to the manner of foam formation. The values obtained from this type of test provide information of value in establishing process conditions and in checking raw material and process uniformity.

Urethane

Examples of processibility tests for rigid and flexible urethane foams that have received some attention by the industry are Rate of Rise (volume expansion), Rate of Temperature Change, Cure Rate (mold cycle time), and Determination of Mold Charge (packing). To date only the rate of rise test has been standardized. ASTM D-2237-64T, *Tentative Method of Test for Rate of Rise (Volume Increase) Properties of Urethane Foaming Systems,* was developed for *rigid* urethane foam, but may also be used for *flexible* urethane foam. The test is made in a cylindrical container with a float connected to a height measuring device, as shown in Fig IV-16. Using this device, a plot of height vs. time is obtained and plotted on semi-logarithmic graph paper. From this plot, the Extrapolated Initiation Time and the Extrapolated Rise Time are obtained.

Polystyrene foam

Standardization of a method of test for expandability of polystyrene materials is planned by ASTM D-20. A draft of the method is not yet available.

Section V—FOAM PLASTICS IN CONSTRUCTION

By George Murray

1. INTRODUCTION AND HISTORY

In less than two decades foamed plastics have matured from speculative laboratory curiosities to a firmly established family of construction materials. At first, foamed plastics were considered only as a direct replacement for conventional construction materials, but these multi-functional products soon gained recognition by contributing new concepts and new techniques to the construction industry. They have solved many long existent building problems through improved performance and ease of installation. Plastic foams have passed the crucial test of time and performance under a wide variety of rigorous environments.

The applications have varied from thin shell form liners (Fig. V-1) to low density core for panel construction and into the largest volume field of temperature insulation (Fig. V-2).

One of three conditions must be present to justify the use of plastic foam: (1) It must be able to perform a given function better than competitive materials at competitive cost; (2) it must be able to perform with equal efficiency at a lower cost; (3) it must be able to perform where other materials cannot serve.

Plastic foams have had the greatest successes in combination with more conventional building materials.

Specific application recommendations are constantly revised by material suppliers, because of refinements in foam technology and a continuing search by the chemical and building industries for improved installation techniques. It is suggested that current product specifications and application recommendations be consulted at the time of selection.

There are many factors affecting their use, such as public education, regulatory agencies, performance history and a changing architectural form. Their success is expected to continue as the chemical industry places even greater emphasis on refined engineering principles and technology for advanced applications and material development.

The first commercial production of plastic foam during World War II was for military applications. It was used principally as a flotation medium for life rafts on military transport ships. It was found that the same closed-

Figure V-1, polystyrene foam boards 3" thick combined with a system of "off-set" high tensile wires were used as a temporary structural form for concrete hyperbolic parabo- *loids. The foam remains in place and serves as thermal insulation, vapor barrier and plaster base. Courtesy of Purdue University, Civil Engineering Dept.*

Figure V-2, expanded polystyrene foam boards are being applied to a masonry wall with asphalt to provide thermal insulation in a low temperature freezer. Courtesy of The Dow Chemical Co.

Figure V-3, an inflated plastic coated fabric received a 6″ interior coating of sprayed polyurethane foam. The foam stiffened the fabric to make a complete self-supporting structure 20 ft wide, 51 ft 4 in. long, 10 ft high. Courtesy of Raven Industries Inc.

Figure V-4, interior view of the foam-fabric structure in Fig. V-3. An additional thickness of foam was sprayed at seven points in the cylindrical part of the building to serve as stiffening arches. Courtesy of Raven Industries Inc.

cell structure that insured flotation also provided thermal insulation. When released for public consumption it was first used as a moisture resistant insulating material for low-temperature storage buildings.

A great deal of emphasis was placed on prefabrication by the construction industry in the early 1950's. Large building components could be produced under closely controlled environment during inclement weather, allowing the assembly of buildings almost any time of the year. Handling and shipping these large components was a problem. Light-weight foamed plastic cores were combined with heavier wood, metal or concrete faces to produce easier-to-handle sandwich panels. These combinations yielded building components with weatherable surfaces and very low density, and with a high strength-to-weight ratio core.

Still another construction procedure was developed. A great contribution to the building industry was the "on site" erection of better quality or lower cost buildings, with new materials and new techniques.

Foamed plastics have contributed significantly to panel construction and to the development of new construction methods. As a result, the cost of finished buildings over the past decade increased at a lesser rate than the increases in either labor or materials.

Because of the chemical composition and nature of plastic foams, they can be "tailor-made" to obtain the best combination of properties for any particular end use.

The wide diversity of forms in plastic foams make possible many new and exciting construction techniques. Panels may be assembled from boards of foam (Fig. V-2), molded foam (Fig. V-10 and V-11) or foam-in-place liquid components (Fig. V-7) with wood, metal or plastic skins. Boards of foam may be used as a base for precasting building elements to be tilted into position for precasting large units to be lifted in final position or as a temporary structural form for curved shapes (Fig. V-1).

Liquid foam components may be molded into irregular shaped units for later assembly (Fig. V-6). There are unlimited possibilities for sprayed foams on wire or cloth lattices or on irregular inflated structures (Fig. V-3 and V-4).

Each of these construction techniques takes advantage of the high strength-to-weight ratio of plastic foams. While all of these techniques and methods have been proved physically practical, many require further study before they make broad commercial market penetrations.

The 1963 consumption of *rigid* foamed plastics by the construction industry is estimated to be over 400-million board-feet in the U.S. It is estimated that this rate of consumption will double in the next few years. This increase will be the result of advanced foam technology, expanding markets for present materials and development of new foams. These consumption volumes do not include the many millions of board-feet of *flexible* plastic foams going into auxiliary building applications in industry and home, in the form of upholstery cushioning, bedding, carpet backing, etc.

In contrast to other basic building material families, plastic foams are relatively new. Their growth rate increases rapidly and a very optimistic future can be expected with correct selection of well-engineered products for the expanding construction industry.

The construction industry is the largest industry in the U.S. It is composed of a great number of diverse groups. Considerable time will be required to educate these groups to the correct use of plastics. The chemical industry and the building industry are making conscientious endeavors toward the right education. There is encouraging evidence, in the field, of their progress. For example, two decades ago only one or two properties of a plastic foam were used in any application; today as many as six different properties, such as thermal insulation, moisture barrier, plaster base, structural strength, low density and ease of fabrication, contribute to a single application.

There are eleven plastic foams deserving of consideration for construction end uses at the present time. As the chemical industry continues in its search for new and improved materials, the list will become more complex. Two plastic foams, polystyrene and polyurethane, account for nearly all of the plastic foams used in the construction market today. Seven other basic foams, cellulose acetate, epoxy, phenolics, polyethylene, silicones, urea formaldehyde and vinyl, plus two copolymer plastic foams represent a small segment of the market. Each foam possesses unique properties or forms which give it commercial value.

Regulatory agencies

Many regulatory agencies have jurisdic-

Figure V-5, light-weight foam plastics may be easily fabricated with conventional wood working tools. Courtesy of The Dow Chemical Co.

tional control over construction materials and techniques. Federal agencies establish standards for federal buildings and many federally-financed buildings. Regional building organizations (state and municipal) establish standards or model codes governing construction in their area. Insurance and finance groups create standards for buildings and building materials.

Because of these complex regulatory agencies, it is difficult to make blanket statements concerning the acceptance or rejection of plastic foams. Instances can be cited where many plastic foams were officially accepted, approved or released by agencies as suitable for use in many applications within their jurisdiction. There is a reluctance to accept all products for all applications without sufficient assurance of satisfactory performance to protect the health and safety of occupants.

Representatives from the chemical industry and major foam manufacturers and suppliers are working closely with representatives of the regulatory agencies to define clearly their common problems. Only with mutual exchange of information and understanding can significant progress be made on an industry-wide basis.

2. TECHNICAL DISCUSSION

Classifications

Expanded plastics, cellular plastics and foamed plastics have become interchangeable terminology for the same family of materials. They are easily differentiated from other plastic polymers and resins by their low density,

Figure V-6, polyurethane foam panels, 3½" thick, 6 lb per cu ft density, are joined with foam-in-place urethane to form a 26½ ft diameter radome. The foam is transparent to electromagnetic waves. Courtesy of National Research Council of Canada.

Figure V-7, polyurethane liquid components are being sprayed onto an irregular tank surface for thermal insulation. Courtesy of Wyandotte Chemical Corp.

even though the density may vary greatly.

Plastics and foams may be classified in several ways to understand their behavior patterns, advantages and limitations.

A plastic polymer may be defined as either thermoplastic or thermosetting. There are a few exceptions to this rule: some plastic polymers may take either form depending upon their formulation. However, in fabricated foam form, these definitions are valid. A thermoplastic material may be compared to butter which can be heated, molded and cooled many times to change its shape. A thermosetting resin may be formed only once; it is similar in this respect to an egg which may be fried or boiled once but cannot again become a fluid egg.

Secondly, a foam may be classified according to its cell structure: closed noninterconnected cells, open connected cells or some combination of the two. The degree of open or closed cells influences its susceptibility to water and moisture permeation and absorption. The size of individual cells usually affects its physical properties, thermal conductivity or insulating effectiveness.

Plastic foams may be grouped according to stiffness (rigid or flexible) which is a function of the cell structure and the density.

Foams may also be classified according to their preparation. They may be extruded foam, molded foam, foamed-in-place, sprayed, or frothed. The manner in which a foam is produced can influence the density, physical properties, moisture susceptibility, thermal conductivity and cost.

Common properties of plastic foams

It is useful to compare plastic foams with other conventional building materials such as wood, glass, metal and concrete. For example, plastic foams are light-weight compared with other materials; they may vary from less than one lb per cu ft to 70 lb per cu ft. All rigid foamed plastics have a relatively high strength-to-weight ratio. The lower density closed-cell plastic foams are buoyant and provide varying degrees of thermal insulation and moisture resistance. Plastics are easily fabricated, generally on conventional woodworking equipment such as band saws, table saws and planers (Fig. V-5). Because they are inert, plastic foams resist rot, decay and attack by bacteria and fungus.

A significant common property of most plastic foams is transparency to electromagnetic radiation. This has made them particularly well suited for the construction of shelters over radar equipment, as radar waves may thus be transmitted or received without interference (Fig. V-6).

The predominant factors governing the selection of foamed plastics in construction are strength, thermal and moisture properties, all on the basis of cost. The strength and stiffness are a function of the physical properties of the foam and are influenced by the density, cell structure, rigidity and by the nature of the base polymer. Thermal properties are affected mostly by the density, cell size and base polymer. Water susceptibility or moisture resistance is a function of the plastic polymer, the cell structure, and the number of open and closed cells.

Forms of plastic foams

Plastic foams must be compatible with conventional building materials and easy to assemble. Plastic foams are available in many forms to make them adaptable to a wide range of installation techniques. This broad selection of forms permits greater versatility and adaptability in construction applications and influences the economy of a project.

Plastic foams are available in rigid closed-cell material, rigid open-cell material, flexible open-cell material, flexible closed-cell material, and combinations of these, in boards and special shapes.

Some foams are available as liquid component systems to be sprayed (Fig. V-7), foamed-in-place and frothed. Most liquid component foams also serve as an adhesive causing the chemically reacting foam to adhere to almost any material it touches. These foams are generally of a slightly higher density and slightly more expensive. But they can often be used on surfaces which are not readily accessible and avoid extensive cutting and fitting of board foams.

Cost

The cost of plastic foams will vary widely depending upon plastic polymer, formulation, density, form and availability. Plastic foams are most easily compared on a cubic foot basis considering the densities commercially available. For example, consider the effect of one variable, density, and one foam, rigid polyurethane; a cubic foot of 2 lb per cu ft density may cost as little as $1.50 while a similar cubic foot of 70 lb per cu ft density may cost as much as $50. The range of costs of commercially available forms of common low-density plastic foams is shown in Fig. V-8. It does not include all foam variables, but may be used as a relative guide.

Limitations

Foamed plastics cannot be used casually as

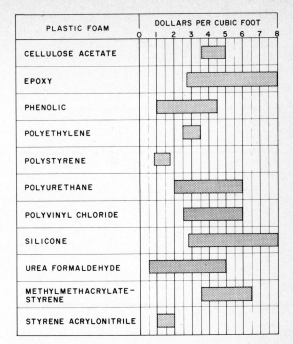

Figure V-8, cost comparison of plastic foams.

a cure-all for all building problems. The successful performance of any product in a construction application depends upon the appropriateness of selection for the functions which it must serve. The recommendations of foam manufacturers or suppliers for correct applications and methods of installation should always be followed.

A few general rules should be followed whenever plastic foams are used. Just as steel is protected from rusting, wood is protected against moisture and glass is protected from breakage, plastic foams should be protected from prolonged exposure to direct sunlight and high concentration of ultraviolet rays. Exposure to ultraviolet radiation for long periods tends to cause oxidation of the plastic polymer, reducing its efficiency. In most instances, protection is as simple as a coat of paint opaque to ultraviolet radiation.

Most of the plastic foams are available in flame retardant or self-extinguishing formulations. These should be used wherever possible in construction applications. But frequently plastic foams are completely encased in masonry, plaster or mortar which provide adequate flame protection.

Most foamed plastics have ignition—both flash-ignition and self-ignition—temperatures substantially higher than other common combustible materials. This means that they have less tendency to catch fire when in contact with heat sources, such as steam lines, light bulbs, hot wires, molten tar, etc. A much higher heat source, such as a flame, is generally required to cause a plastic foam to ignite. Ignition temperatures are given in Table V-1.

Table V-1—Ignition Temperatures of Foamed Plastics

Material	Flash ignition, °F	Self-ignition, °F
Polyethylene	645	660
Polystyrene		
granules	680	925
extruded foam (flame-retardant)	690	735
molded beadboard	655	915
Urethane foam,		
polyether (regular)	580	780
polyester (regular)	770	880
White pine shavings	500	500
Paper newsprint	450	450
Cotton sheeting	590	590

*Determined by ASTM D-1929-62T.

Some plastic foams are susceptible to moisture penetration and retention. This may be a deterrent in some applications.

3. APPLICATIONS

End uses

For brevity and simplicity, significant building uses are grouped into 14 major categories.

1. Cooler and freezer low-temperature insulation: This is presently one of the largest volume use for plastic foams. It requires good thermal insulation and moisture resistance with other properties depending upon installation techniques. Extruded and molded foam plastic boards are mostly used, especially polystyrene and polyurethane. Spray, foam-in-place and froth liquid component systems have been used, especially for polyurethane and epoxy (See also Section VIII).

2. Floating structures and docks: The primary requisites for flotation uses are low density, low cost and moisture resistance. Polystyrene and styrene copolymer foams, extruded or molded into boards and special shapes, are most often used (Fig. V-9 and V-10).

3. Foundation and slab perimeter insulation: Plastic foams with good moisture resistance, thermal insulation, and strength are required. Boards of extruded or molded polystyrene foams are generally used.

4. Joint and void fillers and gaskets: Resilience, moisture resistance and low density are prime considerations depending upon the specific use. Boards, special molded and extruded shapes or liquid component systems of polyethylene, phenolics, polystyrene, polyurethane, polyvinyl chloride and urea formaldehyde are used.

5. Masonry cavity wall insulation: Thermal insulation and moisture resistance are considerations here. Polystyrene boards were most often used until recent developments in polyurethane liquid systems.

6. Masonry wall insulation: Thermal insulation, moisture resistance and ease of installation are important. Boards of polystyrene and polyurethane are most often used; sprayed systems of polyurethane and epoxy in some cases. Techniques are available which include surfacing materials.

7. Panel core insulation: Thermal insulation, moisture resistance, structural strength, and ease of fabrication are the primary requisites. Molded, moldable, and liquid component systems all lend themselves to this use. Cellulose acetate, epoxy, phenolics, polystyrene, polyurethane and methyl methacrylate copolymer foams have been used, but polystyrene and polyurethane are most common. A wide range of skins include metals, woods, glass, plastic, tile and cement-like materials (Fig. V-6; V-9; V-11; V-12).

8. Pipe insulation: Thermal insulation, acceptance of temperature and ease of installation are important. Polystyrene and polyurethane foams are used in fabricated, molded and foam-in-place forms.

9. Plaster base insulation: Thermal insulation, moisture resistance, ease of installation and bond strength to cement-like materials are considerations. Molded and extruded polystyrene boards are generally used as are polyurethane and liquid systems in smaller quantities.

10. Roof expansion joints: Thermal insulation, flexibility and moisture resistance are prime requisites. Closed-cell semi-flexible polyethylene foam is popular.

11. Roof insulation: Thermal insulation, structural strength, and moisture resistance are important. Polystyrene and polyurethane boards and fabricated products are used.

12. Sound absorption and isolation: Cell structure and density are essential factors. Since all plastic foams are of a fairly low density, they lack the necessary mass to

Figure V-9, expandable polystyrene foam board, 1-in. thick, is encased in a blanket of reinforcing wire to serve as insulating core with concrete faces. Through-clips join interior and exterior faces. Courtesy of Koppers Co. Inc.

Figure V-10, low-density, closed-cell water and chemical resistant plastic foams are ideally suited for buoying floating docks and structures. They are especially useful in areas of changing water level. Courtesy of The Dow Chemical Co.

absorb sound energy. Open interconnected cell structures of such plastic foams as vinyl and urethane can slightly reduce sound reverberation. Low density foams such as polystyrene, placed as separators between two solid masses such as a structural floor and a wearing floor, isolate the direct transmission of impact sounds.

13. Tank, vessel and equipment insulation: Adaptability to temperature, thermal insulation and ease of installation are prime requisites. Boards and fabricated shapes of polystyrene and polyurethane and liquid systems of epoxy, polyurethane, and silicones are used. (Fig. V-7, V-13).

14. Thin shell form liner: Thermal insulation, moisture resistance, structural strength and bond strength to cementitious materials are basic requirements. Polystyrene boards are used (Fig. V-1).

4. PROPERTY SELECTOR TABLE

The plastic foam selector table (pages 10-11) provides a quick reference to common properties of commercially available plastic foams. It should be used only as a comparative guide for selecting appropriate foams for special applications as the properties vary slightly depending upon formulation and form.

The table can be most effective if the range of required properties are listed on a separate piece of paper in the same sequence as in the table. Then the paper is moved from top to bottom on the table comparing each set of prop-

Figure V-11, moldable polystyrene is expanded between plywood skins with perimeter ribs installed on wood beams as insulating structural roof panels. Courtesy of Koppers Co. Inc.

erties with those of potentially likely foams. A more detailed study of commercially available products in the acceptable groups should then be made before final selection.

5. WHAT IS EACH PLASTIC FOAM GOOD FOR?

Cellulose acetate foam

Cellular cellulose acetate is a thermoplastic polymer which may be extruded into rigid closed-cell foam shapes exhibiting excellent strength characteristics, a very good solvent resistance, and resistance to relatively high temperatures (up to 350°F). Cellulose acetate foam is fairly high in cost compared with

Figure V-12, insulated daylight is achieved with 1-in. thick, large-cell methyl methacrylate copolymer foam as a core between clear acrylic plastic skins for a roof skylight. Courtesy of The Dow Chemical Co.

Figure V-13, exoxy foam is sprayed on a 67-ft diameter sphere for storage of liquid ammonia (+20°F) as thermal insulation. Thickness: 1½ in. Courtesy of Shell Chemical Co.

Figure V-14, polystyrene foam is easily fabricated into standard shapes for application as pipe insulation. Courtesy of The Dow Chemical Co.

other plastic foams due mainly to its relatively high density of 6 to 7 lb per cu ft. The board or rod stock is easily fabricated. It is slow burning, has good resistance to water absorption and is a good thermal insulation having a "k" factor of 0.31 Btu/hr/°F/in.

The relatively high cost of cellulose acetate foam has retarded its use in building applications. Limited construction uses have been mainly for minor structural framing systems, ribs and panel construction to take advantage of its outstanding strength. Refer to Section XX for detailed information on Cellulose Acetate Foam.

Epoxy foam

Epoxy foam is a closed-cell thermosetting plastic insulation with high heat resistance available in a variety of forms. It has good chemical and moisture resistance and a very high strength-to-weight ratio. It has been used in some construction applications for some time, but broader use has been prevented by its high cost.

Epoxy foam densities of 4 to 10 lb per cu ft are common. Some formulations and foam systems permit densities as low as 2 to 3 lb per cu ft. Lower density foams could result in broader use of epoxy in construction.

Epoxy foams have a high heat resistance, up to 250°F, and the low density foams have very good thermal insulating qualities, k=0.11 to 0.18 Btu/hr/sq ft/°F/in. Formulations are available which incorporate flame retardency.

Epoxy foam is practical because it is available in rigid board form or liquid component systems, suitable for foaming-in-place and spraying. The liquid component systems also serve as adhesives (Fig. V-13).

Construction applications have been limited mainly to foam-in-place low density panel core systems and sprayed thermal insulation for tanks, vessels and walls. If its price comes down, it could be available in low-density board stock suitable for a wide variety of building applications.

Refer to Section XVII for detailed information on Epoxy Foam.

Phenolic foam

Thermosetting phenolic foam offers a great potential in the building industry because the resin is low in cost. It could be made available as a foam-in-place resin or as boardstock, but it must overcome some of its present shortcomings before reaching a substantial position in the building market. Phenolic foamed in place will act as adhesive with panel faces.

It can be foamed in a density range from about ⅓ lb per cu ft to 25 lb per cu ft with good dimensional stability. However, it lacks moisture and mechanical resistance and becomes dusty or friable at very low densities.

Phenolic foam has not made significant penetration into this market. It holds good promise for filling spaces in cavity wall construction, foaming-in-place or low density boardstock in sandwich panel construction. When it is used as foam-in-place wall insulation, a moisture vapor barrier is necessary.

Phenolic cellular mortar

Phenolic spheres can be combined with a resinous binder to produce a low density (10 to 40 lb per cu ft) mortar-like foam with a high strength-to-weight ratio. In combination with other materials this modified phenolic foam offers possibilites as a low density core material for structural panels.

Refer to Section XVI for detailed information on Phenolic foams.

Polyethylene foam

Semi-rigid foamed polyethylene is a closed cell thermoplastic material with excellent low temperature flexibility, good moisture vapor barrier characteristics and fairly good thermal insulating properties.

Extruded polyethylene foam is available in a variety of standard shapes including tubing, rod, and flat boardstock. Low density polyethylene foam retains many of the properties associated with polyethylene resin such as chemical resistance, moisture resistance, toughness, and flexibility; with a density of 2 lb per cu ft it weighs only about 1/30th as much as the non-foamed polymer.

The thermal conductivity or "k" factor of low density polyethylene foam is about 0.35 to 0.40 Btu/hr/sq ft/°F/in. It remains flexible at temperature as low as −60°F.

Both low and high density polyethylene resins can be foamed to densities of 20 to 40 lb per cu ft, that is one-half or one-third the natural resin density, for use as construction wire and cable insulation. The significant properties for this application are moisture resistance, toughness, abrasion resistance, chemical resistance, and flexibility.

The present end uses for both high and low density polyethylene foam include electrical wire and cable insulation; industrial pipe insulation; roof expansion joint insulation; joint filler strips and storage tank insulation.

Refer to Section XIV for detailed information on Polyethylene foam.

Polystyrene foam

More polystyrene foam is used in the construction industry today than any other rigid plastic foam material. It is a low density closed-cell thermoplastic foam. Available in a wide variety of sizes and shapes, in two forms, it is easily fabricated and installed, exhibits good insulation and vapor barrier characteristics and costs from $0.80 to $1.50 per cu ft depending on form and density.

The two basic forms of rigid polystyrene foam are extruded and molded. It may be extruded into boards, logs and planks or it may be molded into standard or irregular shapes. Polystyrene foam can be manufactured in densities from 1 to 30 lb per cu ft but most commercially available foam is in the density range of 1 to 5 lb per cu ft. The closed cell structure makes it a good thermal insulator, resistant to water absorption. The thermal conductivity is in the range of 0.23 to 0.30 Btu/sq ft/hr/°F/in., which makes it well suited for low temperature insulation. As a rigid foam, it has a high strength-to-weight ratio and is often used in structural or semi-structural applications. Foamed polystyrene is available in flame retardant or self-extinguishing formulations for the building industry.

A wide variety of adhesives is available for bonding the foam to itself or other common building materials.

Expandable or molded polystyrene can be foamed-in-place into irregular shapes. A cavity filled with small beads, or partially expanded pellets of polystyrene containing a gaseous material, is subjected to heat. The additional heat causes the beads to expand, fill the mold, and fuse one to another, to produce a uniformly knit material. Moldable polystyrene can be foamed into a wider range of densities particularly in the lower density range with a corresponding change in physical properties.

The principal uses of polystyrene foam in construction include boards of polystyrene foam attached to conventional building frames for low temperature insulation (Fig. V-2);

Figure V-15, urethane foam is being sprayed into the cavity of a stud wall as thermal insulation in an electrically heated home. Courtesy of E. I. du Pont de Nemours & Co.

foam boards placed between masonry wythes as cavity wall insulation; boards placed under concrete slabs or between a structural slab and a wearing slab for thermal insulation and sound isolation; boards placed around the exterior of slabs or foundation walls as perimeter insulation; expanded or expandable polystyrene foam placed between rigid facings as a low density insulating core (Fig. V-9 and V-11); boards of foam placed over structural roof decks for roof insulation; fabricated and molded pipe insulation (Fig. V-14); semistructural form and form liners for thin shell construction; logs and billets as buoyancy media under floating structures; boards bonded to masonry walls as an insulating base for plaster, wall board or paneling; railcar, truck and house trailer body insulation; crawl space insulation; and insulated backer board for metal siding.

Refer to Sections XII and XIII for more detailed information on polystyrene foam.

Polyurethane foam

Polyurethane foam is the second largest in volume of the rigid plastic foams used in the construction industry. It is particularly important because of its unique properties and availability in a variety of forms. This thermosetting plastic is available in flexible or rigid board form and special shapes, or as chemical components for foam-in-place, froth, or spray applications. There are slight varia-

tions in properties depending upon the form All of the rigid forms may be characterized as low density, closed cell foams with good thermal insulation, heat and chemical resistance. The liquid systems will produce slightly higher density foams but they will also serve as an adhesive bonding to the surfaces with which they come in contact. Urethane foams may be formulated from a wide variety of chemicals to allow greater flexibility in tailoring foams for specific end uses.

Rigid urethanes may be foamed to densities from 1½ to 30 lb per cu ft with resulting wide variety of properties. They have good strength, stiffness and rigidity with a high strength-to-weight ratio.

Closed cell urethanes provide good thermal insulation, "k" = 0.14 to 0.17 Btu hr/sq ft/°F/in. Thermal conductivity tends to be lower shortly after manufacture and increase slightly with time to stabilize near the higher value. Formulations can be made self-extinguishing. Good heat resistance permits continuous use at temperatures up to 250°F.

The closed cell structure provides good water resistance. Urethane foams have good chemical resistance permitting a wide choice of adhesives for installation of boards and molded shapes.

Rigid urethane foam may be molded into boards and irregular shapes. It is well suited for low temperature insulation because its low thermal conductivity permits reduced thicknesses compared to most other foams. However, the cost per board foot is somewhat higher and balances the saving in thickness. In many applications, thickness is often an asset especially in structural uses. Reduced thickness has greater significance in the manufacture of appliances than it does in most building uses except possibly in the areas of low temperature insulation, transportation and mobile homes.

Sprayed polyurethane foam has only in recent years come into prominence in construction applications (Fig. V-15). It is especially well suited for the application of insulation on irregular surfaces such as large outdoor storage tanks and spheres, walls embellished with mechanical and electrical equipment and in inaccessible voids. The surface of sprayed urethane foam tends to be slightly irregular because of a 30:1 to 40:1 expansion ratio of liquid to foam.

Frothing produces a polyurethane foam very similar in composition and properties to foam-in-place liquid foam. The difference is observed at the dispensing point where spray compositions are released as a mixed liquid while froth emerges as a foam substance resembling whipping cream or aerosol-dispensed shaving soap (Fig. V-16a and b). For example, froth foam may expand only three to six times its dispensed volume while liquid components expand 30 to 40 times their dispensed volume. A variation in application thickness of 1/1000 of an inch in the sprayed chemicals would result in a foamed surface variation of about 1/16 inch while a similar variation in application thickness of froth foam will result in only about 5/1000 inch variation on the finished surface. The pressures created by high expansion must be considered when foam-in-place liquid systems are placed in closed containers.

The great latitude in formulating urethane foams makes it possible to vary the percentages of open and closed cell. As the amount of open cells increases the foam tends to become more flexible. The open cells provide some sound absorption, resilience, toughness, chemical resistance but allow free passage of liquids and gasses.

The primary end uses for all forms of rigid urethane foam include low temperature storage buildings, floor, wall, and roof insulation, insulating core for building panels, pipe insulation, tanks and vessel insulation (Fig. V-7), cavity wall insulation, void fillers, walk-in coolers and freezers, and backerboard for metal siding, mobile homes, trucks, trailers, and railroad cars.

Flexible, open cell urethane is used for joint fillers, gasketing, cushioning and sound absorption applications.

Refer to Sections IX and X for more detailed information on Urethane foams.

Polyvinyl chloride foams

Thermoplastic vinyl foams may be formulated in many ways to obtain different combinations of properties. They include flexible, open cell, partially open cell, semi-rigid, or rigid closed-cell board foams. The density of vinyl foams can vary 4 lb per cu ft to 75 lb per cu ft which is the density of solid vinyl resin. Vinyl foams are chemically inert, inherently self-extinguishing or flame retardant and exhibit good chemical resistance.

High density vinyl foam extruded in the range of 40 lb per cu ft or more, with a high

Figure V-16, a comparison of (left) foam-in-place liquids and (right) froth urethane foams.

modulus of elasticity, low compressibility and resilience, is particularly well suited for window glazing splines and gasketing. It is more economical than a solid vinyl extrusion.

Low density closed cell vinyl foam is extruded in a wide variety of cross sections. It is a tough, resilient gasketing material at densities down to 7 lb per cu ft.

Low density cellular vinyl has very good sound absorption characteristics, comparable to hair felt. When combined with more durable surfacing materials it can serve in building acoustical applications.

Open cell flexible vinyl foams are very soft and resilient, permitting free passage of gases and liquids. They are used mainly as electrical insulation, sound absorption and cushioning applications.

Rigid closed cell vinyl foams have good thermal insulation properties but have not been used extensively in this country. This is mainly because of the higher density and resulting higher costs, compared with other plastic foams with similar properties. Rigid vinyl foam boards are used for low temperature insulation in Europe; they could become popular here.

Although small in present volume compared with the major foams in construction, vinyl foams are used mainly for gasketing, joint filler strips, glazing strips, electrical insulation and acoustical insulation.

Refer to Section XV for more detailed information on Vinyl foams.

Silicone foams

Rigid, closed cell, thermosetting silicone foams exhibit exceptionally high heat resistance. They have not been widely used in construction applications because of their high cost. Technological advances could result in broader construction uses.

A continuous allowable operating temperature of 500°F for silicone foam is significantly higher than for most other plastic foams and provides an outstanding advantage in insulation of high temperature equipment. It is a rigid closed cell foam, generally in the medium density range of 3½ to 5 lb per cu ft, which provides a high strength-to-weight ratio. Silicone foam has a low thermal conductivity, "k" = 0.30 Btu/hr/sq ft/°F/in., providing good thermal insulation. It has good electrical insulation properties, good chemical resistance and low water absorption characteristics.

Although not commercially available in large volume, silicone foams can be made in rigid board form or as chemical component systems for foaming-in-place and spraying. The potential wide variety of forms and their outstanding properties could make them useful for future applications in the building industry.

Silicone rubber foams may be made with open or closed cells in densities of 5 to 30 lb per cu ft for high temperature thermal insulation and vibration control.

Construction applications of silicone foams have been limited thus far to high temperature insulation of pipes and equipment, and vibration control.

Refer to Section XVIII for more detailed information on Silicone foams.

Urea formaldehyde foams

Thermosetting urea formaldehyde plastic foam may be manufactured in board form or made available in liquid components for foaming-in-place. It is very low in cost and can be produced in very low densities of ½ to 10 lb per cu ft. It provides good sound insulation and thermal insulation, "k" = 0.20 Btu/sq ft/hr/°F/in.

These advantages, however, do not guarantee its use in the construction industry. It must first overcome such disadvantages as very low strength especially at lower densities, high moisture absorption resulting from the large percentage of open cells, narrow temperature resistance range (maximum continuous use temperature 120°F) and heat stability.

In spite of its shortcomings, urea formaldehyde foam is finding limited use in construction for low temperature insulation, foaming-in-place fill for large inaccessible void areas and acoustical insulation.

Refer to Section XX for more detailed information on Urea formaldehyde foam.

Methyl methacrylate-styrene copolymer

Extruded thermoplastic methyl methacrylate-styrene copolymer closed cell foam may be best characterized as a large cell, light-transmitting, decorative, insulating foam.

It is light weight, with a density below two lb per cu ft, and may be easily fabricated on conventional wood working equipment. The closed cell structure provides thermal insulation with a "k" of .50. It has excellent light stability. Its light transmission is up to 65% for a 1 inch thickness, and the multi-diaphram irregular cell structure diffuses the light well. It is available in cut boards 1 inch, 1½ or 2 inches thick, 16 inches wide and 8 feet long, or in uncut billets for shop fabrication.

Boards of methyl methacrylate-styrene copolymer foam provide a low density light-transmitting core material between colored, translucent or transparent sheets of glass or plastic, or bonded with suitable adhesives to form sandwich panels for use in exterior walls, door lights, roof skylights (V-12), room dividers and drop ceilings.

Styrene—acrylonitrile copolymer

Closed cell thermoplastic styrene-acrylonitrile copolymer plastic foam is molded from gas-containing plastic beads into a well fused billet. The properties of this copolymer foam most closely resemble those of polystyrene foam but with improved chemical resistance. It is a rigid, low density (2 lb per cu ft), water resistant, insulating foam.

The primary construction use of this foam is as a flotation medium for floating structures and docks where gas spillage, floating oils and other contaminants come in frequent contact with the foam. Each cubic foot of foam will buoy fifty to sixty pounds (Fig. V-10).

Section VI—FOAMED PLASTICS IN PACKAGING

By Robert G. Hanlon

1. INTRODUCTION

The packaging of industrial and consumer commodities and the protection of sensitive instrumentation by cushioning against the effects of shock and vibration have undergone considerable change during the past 20 years. Much has been learned since World War II in the field of packaging. Now scientific methods are being employed in package design and exciting new materials and processes continue to be developed to give the designer additional tools with which to work.

Lightweight plastic foams are being used in conjunction with and replacing many of the standard packaging materials because of their unique characteristics and properties, ability to be easily fabricated, and excellent economies when compared to the rising costs of wood and paper products (Fig-VI-1). The sales volume of all packaging materials in 1961 exceeded 21 billion dollars. Foamed plastics, because of their relative infancy in this market, accounted for a relatively small percentage of that figure but in 1962 between 15½ and 18 million pounds of foam plastics were used in

packaging. Increases in the last two years are lending additional evidence that foam plastics will continue to be one of the fastest growing material areas in packaging for several years to come. By 1967, market researchers predict that between 80 to 100 million pounds of foamed plastic materials will find their way into packaging applications.

Three functions of packaging

From the time they are produced through the ensuing marketing stages until they are finally sold or consumed, most commodities require some *protection* from the elements and against abuses encountered during shipping, handling, and storage. In addition to providing such protection, the package has been found to be a powerful merchandising tool. As a result, most consumer goods and many industrial goods are packaged for sale utilizing the ability of the package to present a sales message to the prospective buyer. A third function a package may be called on to perform is *convenience,* either to the ultimate purchaser or consumer, or for increased ease of assembly at the packaging line. Stacking bosses or other interlocking features, handles, and even integrally incorporated color code systems can make a package more convenient to ship, store, and handle.

The relative importance of these three functions depends upon a number of factors which the product manufacturer must evaluate: protection of the product and attractiveness may be of importance, but the materials going into the package and the methods by which they are assembled may vary greatly.

2. FOAMED MATERIALS FOR PACKAGING

Polyethylene foam

Expanded polyethylene is available commercially in the form of ovals, untrimmed planks (with a skin surface), trimmed planks, round rods, and thin sheet tubing. Polyethylene foam is manufactured at a density of

Figure VI-1, variety of packages made from foamed plastics.

approximately 2.0 lb per cu ft that is expanded about 30 times from the solid state of polyethylene. It is a cellular, lightweight material with each cell closed off from its neighbor. Polyethylene foam is a tough, resilient material coupled with good flexibility characteristics. It provides high energy absorbing characteristics for insert packaging applications (Fig-VI-2). Its spring-back rate is slow enough so that the energy absorbed during a sudden shock is not released with equal rapidity; rebound occurs at a relatively slow rate.

Polyethylene foam can be fabricated with conventional hand tools. Power tools such as band saws and routers may be used to shape the material. Due to its flexible nature, polyethylene foam is most easily fabricated by tools or equipment with blades or bits having a slicing type action. Polyethylene foams can also be fabricated by the use of electrically heated resistance wires. They may also be thermally shaped by the use of contoured molds equipped for both heating and cooling. For a more detailed description of foamed low-density polyethylene, see Section XIV.

Extruded expanded polystyrene

Expanded polystyrene is the oldest form of foamed polystyrene. Available in block or board form, it is a relatively coarse-celled rigid foam product of uniform and homogeneous composition. Its use as a packaging material has usually been limited to positioning and display of many products where its crystalline surface promotes cleanliness and sparkle to the packaged item (Fig-VI-3).

Expanded polystyrene's use is limited to applications requiring "one time" energy absorption since it crushes and does not recover after impact. Expanded polystyrene is attract-

Figure VI-3, the crystalline surface of extruded expanded polystyrene promotes cleanliness and sparkle to pharmaceutical trays and platforms fabricated by Foam Pak Inc.

ing considerable interest in the space and missile fields where its use as a "one time" energy absorbing material is often desirable. This material is being considered for landing instrumented space capsules on the moon and other planets where high energy absorption is required without undesirable rebound characteristics. Expanded polystyrene may be fabricated much in the same manner as expanded polyethylene with conventional machine tools or hot wire equipment. For additional information on extruded polystyrene, refer to Section XII.

Expandable polystyrene beads

Perhaps the most widely accepted foamed material used for packaging is expandable polystyrene. This unique material is manufactured in the form of small translucent beads or granules containing an expanding agent. The particles are free flowing and when expanded by the application of heat produce an opaque foam which has little or no odor, is non-toxic, and contains nothing of food value. Expandable polystyrene materials offer many properties desirable in a packaging material: light weight, high strength-to-weight ratio, attractive surface, low moisture absorption, high energy absorption, and good insulating properties. Expandable polystyrene materials are processed in a number of different ways for use in packaging.

A. *Steam chest molding*—This method of processing incorporates the use of steam and its inherent ability to transfer heat evenly and efficiently for the purpose of foaming expandable polystyrene particles in place within a mold. The beads or granules are normally "prefoamed" to the desired density prior to

Figure VI-2, delicate optical prisms are packaged with polyethylene foam fabricated by Tainor-Tek Inc.

molding, by application of heat or steam. The hydrocarbon foaming agent within the individual granules causes the softened material to expand into discrete multi-cellular foam spheres or pellets.

In practice, many of these "prefoamed" particles are confined in a retaining mold then subjected to additional steam and pressure causing them to expand further and knit together to form a uni-cellular homogeneous plastic foam article. The unlimited variety of shapes and sizes that can be molded and the low cost of processing are benefits of interest to the molder and ultimate consumer of packaging materials (Fig-VI-4). Steam chest molded expandable polystyrene has excellent impact or shock absorbing properties. For further information on the technical aspects of steam chest molding expandable polystyrene, refer to Section XIII.

B. *Radio frequency molding*—Recent developmental activity in the molding of expandable polystyrene includes the use of radio frequency or dielectric equipment to generate sufficient heat within a retaining mold to fuse the prefoamed particles into a foamed article. The use of radio frequency equipment requires that the expandable polystyrene be "activated" so that it can be heated by the radio frequency field. Polystyrene is normally "transparent" to radio frequency. In order to cause expandable polystyrene to heat under the action of high frequency vibrations, suitable additives must be incorporated. Conversely, materials used in molds must be transparent to radio frequency to prevent heating and absorption of the radio frequency field.

C. *Foam extrusion*—Flexible fine celled polystyrene foam sheet and film can be produced by extruding expandable polystyrene granules. The extrusion technique involves feeding the raw granules in conjunction with a suitable nucleating system into an extruder. As the material passes through the extruder, the granules are melted and fused. Pressure maintained within the system prevents the hydrocarbon agent from expanding too soon. With suitable control, the material leaves the die orifice as a homogenous gel, then the hydrocarbon expands forming a multi-cellular foamed material.

Recent developmental activity in this area includes the processing of *non*-expandable materials. This more direct techniques provides for the introduction of the foaming agent

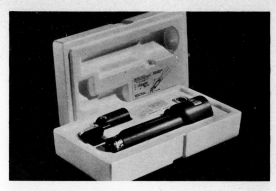

Figure VI-4, Electro-Voice microphone packaged in an encapsulating foam package molded of expandable polystyrene beads by Kalamazoo Plastics.

Figure VI-5, package thermoformed from extruded expandable polystyrene sheet.

separately at some point within the system, eliminating the need for the raw material containing the expanding agent.

When extruded into low density foam sheet the material may be formed into a wide variety of configurations for packaging applications (Fig-VI-5). Thermoforming techniques utilize conventional vacuum and pressure methods.

If extruded into sheet with a thickness of 10 mils or less, the material falls into the film category. The thin foamed material can be embossed and/or laminated to other materials. Its attractive surface texture and ability to be internally colored make it a useful material for many consumer packaging applications. For further information on the extrusion method of processing expandable polystyrene materials, refer to Section XIII, Part 2.

D. *Injection molding techniques*—By injection molding expandable polystyrene, a unique product results consisting of a foamed core surrounded by a relatively smooth surface skin. The texture and wood grain effect of the

Figure VI-6, cigar gift package for reuse as humidor or decorative canister produced from injection-molded expandable polystyrene by Madan Industries.

Figure VI-7, expandable polystyrene strands foamed to produce very low density loose fill packing material.

surface skin provide beauty to the fabricated package.

The molten plastic is maintained in a compressed state within the heating cylinder of the injection molding machine by the pressure of the hydraulic ram during the injection stroke. After it leaves the nozzle and enters the mold cavity, pressure is released and expansion takes place. The unusual surface texture obtainable by this technique offers significant design features for display and merchandise packaging (Fig-VI-6). Foam densities thus obtained are considerably higher than with other fabrication techniques and result in a very rigid foam product. Densities obtained are generally in the order of about 25 to 35 lb per cu ft.

E. *Foamed polystyrene strands*—Strands of

expandable polystyrene, similar in nature to their granular counterparts are being foamed into a low density dunnage material for loose-fill packaging applications. The material is foamed in continuous steam foaming equipment producing a highly shock-absorbent product with densities as low as 0.5 lb cu ft. Because the foamed strands tend to interlock, "settling" of packed items and loosening in the pack is minimal (Fig-VI-7).

Urethane foams

Urethane foam materials have attracted considerable interest for many industrial, military, and commercial packaging applications. Urethane materials have extremely versatile properties. Formulations can be varied from extremely rigid to very flexible within a wide range of densities. Urethane foams are of two basic types: polyester and polyether materials. Polyester-based urethanes were the first to be developed but due to their relative high cost are not being used to any extent for packaging. Polyether-based foams are made by reacting toluene diisocyanate with polyglycol materials.

The greatest technical advance made in recent years has been the development of what is known as the "one shot" system in which the blowing agent, the polyol, the catalyst, and the emulsifier are all pre-blended, and the isocyanate is added at the last minute. When this technique is coupled with a still more recent development in which the ingredients are "frothed" prior to dispensing, producers can get greater uniformity of foam densities, develop thinner skins, lower temperatures and pressures, better flow characteristics; thus less costly jigs and dies can be used.

Foaming urethane "in place" completely surrounds the product to be packaged. Urethanes may also be molded within a retaining mold to produce package inserts and package parts can be fabricated from flexible or rigid board stock (Fig-VI-8). Urethanes can be sprayed onto some products to encapsulate them completely in protective foam. Rigid urethane foams are one of the best thermal insulating materials available. Temperature-sensitive products requiring control of the thermal environment during shipping and storage can receive excellent protection by the use of rigid urethane foam materials. Sections IX, X, and XI describe urethane foam materials in detail.

Miscellaneous foams

The three aforementioned plastic foam materials comprise approximately 97% of the use of all plastic foam materials in packaging. Epoxy, urea-formaldehyde, latex and vinyl foams are enjoying little application in the packaging field at present. Vinyl foams are comparatively expensive and urea-formaldehyde and latex are still in development. Urea-formaldehyde could, however, become one of the least expensive plastic foam materials due to the low cost of its basic ingredients. Vinyl foams may find their way into specialized packaging applications where their relatively high cost is not a major factor. Epoxy foams are expensive and their characteristics are not particularly suited to most packaging applications.

3. PROTECTIVE PACKAGING

All materials and products are subject to certain hazards during the interim period between manufacture and use. The degree of protection afforded a product will vary according to specific factors such as storage conditions, length of time in storage, and shipping and handling.

Regardless of how a product is transported, it may be accidentally dropped, subjected to shocks and vibrations on the carrier, or shoved and loaded incorrectly by careless cargo handlers. In addition, many products are subject to drastic changes in temperature and other climatic conditions. Many products are stored for long periods before sale and use.

The product and the manner in which it is handled, shipped and stored dictate the package required and the materials used in its assembly. This concept must always be kept in mind when designing protective packaging.

Protection against deterioration

Certain materials deteriorate upon standing. While deterioration must be expected, proper package design can reduce the rate of deterioration to a minimum. In most cases, deterioration is a chemical change, but it can be physical as well. For example, the cold flow of, or deformation of rubber.

Deterioration annually causes many millions of dollars worth of damage to merchandise and equipment before it reaches the user, through loss of quality, strength or usefulness.

In considering deterioration, the materials

Figure VI-8, delicately adjusted precision optical instruments packed in flexible urethane foam by the American Optical Co. Photo courtesy of Mobay Chemical Co.

involved may be divided into two general headings: inorganic and organic.

Inorganic materials—The most common form of deterioration of inorganic materials is corrosion. Corrosion tends to destroy most metals; it results from exposure to rain, snow, heat, cold, salt water, corrosive fumes, perspiration, humidity, etc. There are three common causes of corrosion: oxidation, chemical attack and electrolytic action.

● About 70% of all corrosive damage to metals is caused by the reaction of metal with oxygen in air in the presence of moisture or water vapor. Packaging materials consisting of closed cell plastic foams are generally resistant to water absorption. They do not break down in the presence of moisture and do not allow water to come in contact with critical metal parts. A properly sealed container of closed cell plastic foam can actually be submerged under water. Foam containers are not considered perfect moisture vapor barriers; therefore, where protection is required over extended storage periods, adequate vapor barrier materials are used in combination with the plastic foam package, and provide excellent resistance to corrosion.

● Exposure of metals to chemicals such as acids, alkalis, or salts in the presence of water can cause severe pitting and etching of their surfaces. This may result from fingerprints, soldering and welding fluxes, factory marking inks, cutting and cooling compounds, even some inadequate packaging materials. Most plastic foamed materials maintain a neutral pH.

● Electrochemical deterioration can take place when two different metallic components are connected and exposed to water or another electrolyte. A battery will be formed and current will flow. If a sufficient potential difference exists, corrosion will occur with the more electronegative component being attacked.

The essential element for this action is an electrolyte. While high relative humidity in the air may be a sufficient electrolyte for corrosion, it is usually accelerated by the presence of water.

Organic materials—Other forms of deterioration take place in organic materials. For example, rubber is subject to oxidation, loss of plasticizer, continuing vulcanization (hardening), and attack by micro-organisms. It is also subject to deterioration from high temperature and static pressure. Temperature and humidity may stimulate fungus and bacteria growth on fabrics, paper, wax, leather, wood, and many other organic materials. Too little moisture may cause excessive drying in fabrics and wood products. Tapes may lose adhesiveness; papers may become brittle.

The deterioration of oils and greases through oxidation and the separation of fractions during long periods of storage may result in failure of a piece of delicate machinery which these materials were meant to lubricate.

Food packaging is a good example of everyday concern over organic deterioration. Some packages are merely convenient and attractive, but others must hold foods for weeks and months in low-temperature storage or modified atmospheric conditions, followed by extensive transportation.

Fruit deterioration, for example, may result from natural processes by decay organisms, or by physical damage. The natural deterioration of a fruit starts when it is picked. The most important function of the fruit package is to prevent damage, which not only hastens organic deterioration, but alters appearance and reduces quality. Fresh fruits are subject to a great variety of damaging vibrations and impacts.

Plastic foams can do much to protect fresh fruit and vegetable products against the effects of friction scarring, bumps and bruises during shipping, handling, and storing.

Protection against physical damage

Nearly all materials and products are subject to physical damage during the interim between production and use. The package designer must anticipate the hazards his product may normally encounter, and design against possible damage during that period.

Physical damage occurs primarily as a result of the improper package design, inferior workmanship, misapplication of materials and rough handling.

Unfortunately, even though every precaution and design consideration has been taken into account, rough handling is difficult to control. The demarcation between normal and rough handling is fine, and unless the package is being obviously mishandled, the burden of responsibility is often placed with the packaging engineer. A certain amount of damage can often be tolerated by a manufacturer as long is it is limited by correct protection. Of course, the cost must not outweigh the savings obtained by using sound engineering and proper materials in the package.

Cushioning—Where articles are likely to be subjected to impact, vibration, or abrasion, they require protection by special materials or devices that will absorb part of the impact force or vibration.

An extremely important and effective use of plastic foams is for shock protection of fragile articles. They must be protected against forces from any direction, since containers may be dropped on any corner, edge, or face.

Cushion Blocking— This is used primarily to restrain or limit the movement of an article within a package. Many packages require a material for blocking as well as shock cushioning, and foamed plastics, when properly applied, can meet both requirements. The use of molded foam to restrain small, irregularly shaped articles often saves time and money, even though cushioning is also required for shock protection purposes.

4. DESIGN CONSIDERATIONS

The term "load type" refers to the physical characteristics of the item inasmuch as they contribute to the support of or damage to the container. The same kind of container can be designed for adequate protection of several items by adjusting its constitutents. The design of any foamed plastics container is influenced by the load type.

Load type 1: easy load

Easy loads include: (a) articles of moderate density packed in an inside container that completely fills the outside container and that *supports all faces of the outer container,* (b) a single article of sufficient strength to withstand the forces encountered in transportation and handling, and provides uniform support to all faces of the shipping container. Loads of this type are relatively rugged, but may require protection against abrasion, marring, or denting. Examples of Type 1 loads are wood or metal chests, tool kits, etc.

Packages which meet the Type 1 load criteria generally demand less in physical properties than do either Type 2 or Type 3 loads due to the ability of the package contents to bear a greater portion of the load. Since the degree of protection is less critical, the main requirement of the package from a physical standpoint is simply to remain intact under normal conditions (Fig-VI-9).

Load type 2: average load

This load is composed of more than one item or interior container giving *some support* to all faces of the shipping container. Examples are goods in metal cans, bottles individually protected with inserts or boxes, and hardware items that have been individually boxed or protected.

Packages for Type 2 loads include multiple cavity containers that encapsulate their contents but are not overpacked in exterior shipping containers. Multiple cavity containers or inserts that do not completely encapsulate their contents must be overpacked in exterior shipping containers to meet the Type 2 load requirement. (Fig-VI-10).

Load type 3: difficult load

This type of load gives little or no support to the shipping container. The contents can be extremely heavy, very fragile, very irregular in shape, or bulk materials that are free to shift and flow, or a combination of all these factors. Items in this category furnish little or no support to the faces of the shipping container. Rather, in many instances they tend to apply concentrated forces on the containers' surfaces. Examples are dense articles such as rivets, bolts, and nuts, machine parts, and castings that are free to shift.

The use of plastic foamed materials in Type 3 loads is usually limited to inserts within an exterior container to cradle very irregularly shaped articles or to cushion delicate items against the effects of shock and vibration (Fig-VI-11). When designing containers to be molded of rigid or semi-rigid plastic foams for Type 3 (free flowing) loads, generous internal radii and minimum external radii on edges and corners will do much to strengthen

Figure VI-9, old and new Type 1 load package. New one is molded of expandable polystyrene.

Figure VI-10, old and new Type 2 load. New package and inserts molded of expandable polystyrene.

Figure VI-11, Type 3 load package made of blocks of polyethylene foam glued to corrugated cartons in various configurations to protect delicate electronic equipment. Photo courtesy of Dynapac Co.

the container. At the same time, the corners and edges act as "crush points" to absorb some of the forces of impact.

Cushion characteristics

A fragile item, when dropped, must upon impact be allowed to decelerate through a given distance and time to prevent breakage. If the item's fragility, or G factor, is known and the height of anticipated drop has been determined, adequate cushioning can be de-

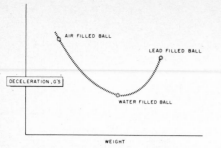

Figure VI-12, rough representation of the cushioning ability of a foam plastic.

Figure VI-13, equipment for drop tests to check cushioning ability of various materials.

signed to allow the dropped item to slow down sufficiently.

The ability of a given cushion to absorb shock can be visualized by imagining three ping pong balls, one of the regular air-filled variety, one filled with water to add weight, and the third filled with lead shot, dropped individually from a given height, say 30 inches, onto a two inch thick flexible urethane foam cushion. The air-filled ball would deflect the foam very little upon impact and thus experience a relatively high deceleration in G's; it would stop in a very short distance and time after impact. The water-filled ball would sink into the foam somewhat farther upon impact, perhaps an inch. This would allow it to decelerate through a greater distance and time resulting in a lower G level. The lead-filled ball would strike the cushion and sink deeply into it. In fact, it might sink so deeply that the cushion would absorb all the impact it is efficiently capable of absorbing. Any remaining energy must be absorbed by the cushion support. When this occurs in practice, the cushion is said to have "bottomed out". The cushion has first slowed down the ball, but the remaining momentum results in a rapid deceleration and a high G load upon bottoming. (Fig-

VI-12). Actual design curves are obtained with equipment such as precision dropping heads, accelerometers, bridge amplifiers, and oscillographs (Fig-VI-13).

Dynamic test data

A convenient method of expressing the cushioning characteristics of materials involves the use of curves obtained from dynamically testing the material under simulated conditions of drop. A different curve is required for each thickness of material and for each height of drop. The curves are a good indication of the type of protection to be expected from a given material.

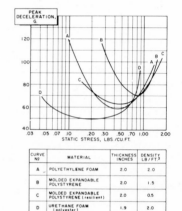

CURVE Nº	MATERIAL	THICKNESS INCHES	DENSITY LB/FT³
A	POLYETHYLENE FOAM	2.0	2.0
B	MOLDED EXPANDABLE POLYSTYRENE	2.0	1.5
C	MOLDED EXPANDABLE POLYSTYRENE (resilient)	2.0	0.5
D	URETHANE FOAM (polyester)	1.9	2.0

Figure VI-14, dynamic cushioning data for various foams.

Fig-VI-14 illustrates a series of dynamic test curves for various plastic foam materials at a drop height of 30 inches. These curves show typical test data for a foam thickness of two inches.

Let us illustrate in simplified form the practical use of the curves for designing a protective package for fragile items, when the degree of fragility is known, and assuming a maximum height from which the package might be expected to be dropped during shipping.

Degree of fragility

Fragility is normally expressed in terms of "G's", one "G" equaling the acceleration due to gravity (g = 32.2 feet per second). A given body in a static condition exerts one "G" upon its support regardless of its weight. If this body is raised and allowed to fall freely, it will accelerate in its fall due to the force of gravity until it collides with its support or the earth. The stop, or sudden deceleration, causes the body to experience a weighted condition several times its static weight. This multiple of weight can be expressed in terms of G's. If the body experiences a weighted condition upon impact of 20 times its static weight, it is said to have experienced 20 G's. A jet pilot experiences such a condition when he pulls out of dive. He must not exceed his "G limit." If the airplane is not designed and stressed to withstand high G loads during such maneuvers, the wings would likely come off.

The same thing is essentially true with fragile objects. The degree of fragility, or G factor of an object, is its ability to withstand deceleration. G factors can be determined by subjecting the object to destructive evaluation, on a specially designed shock machine.

Unfortunately, the degree of fragility for many fragile objects is not easily determined. The necessity for determining fragility factors for many parts of missile equipment has contributed significantly to the realization, by manufacturers, that such determination is important for properly designed packages.

A so-called "educated guess" of acceptable G factor for a certain object can be dangerous for two reasons. First, if the guess is too low, the package may be overdesigned, at higher cost than necessary. Secondly, if the G factor is guessed too high, high damage claims may result.

Table VI-1 is shown for *approximation* only. It is not a substitute for testing. The

Table VI-1—Approximate Allowable G-factors for Various Objects

Extremely fragile	
Missile guidance systems, precision-aligned test instruments	15-25 G's
Very delicate	
Mechanically shock-mounted instruments and electronic equipment (Shock mounts should be firmly secured prior to packaging. They are provided for in-service protection only.)	25-40 G's
Delicate	
Aircraft accessories, electric typewriters, cash registers, and other electrically operated office equipment.	40-60 G's
Moderately delicate	
Television receivers, certain aircraft accessories	60-85 G's
Moderately rugged	
Laundry equipment, refrigerators, appliances	85-115 G's
Rugged	
Machinery	115 G's and up

final test of any package design is the ability of the package to protect the product under expected handling conditions.

Anticipated height of drop

The anticipated height of drop considered in designing a package is determined by the type of handling the package is expected to receive from the time it is sealed until it reaches its destination. Here a line between normal handling and rough handling conditions should be drawn. For example, if a package is heavy and bulky and would never be lifted any higher than 12 to 18 inches by a lift truck, the item should be protected to withstand a possible accidental drop from that height. An accidental drop occurring within this range would be considered normal handling. If this same package were dropped off the back of a truck, from a height of perhaps 42 inches, this would be considered rough handling, an abnormal hazard for which design protection might not normally be provided. If a lightweight package is likely to be thrown by a postal clerk or a handler, a test height of 42 inches might be more realistic.

Table VI-2 can be used as a guide in estab-

Table VI-2—Height of Drop Estimates

Weight range Gross weight, lb	Type of handling	Drop height, in.
0-20	1 man throwing	42
21-50	1 man carrying	36
51-250	2 men carrying	30
251-500	Light equipment handling	24
501-1000	Light equipment handling	18
1001-up	Heavy equipment handling	12

lishing height of drop estimates.

Applying the dynamic curve data

A typical dynamic curve for various plastic foam materials tells a significant story. It gives the material's most efficient static loading range in lb per sq in. and at the same time tells approximately how much protection can be expected within this loading range for a given cushion thickness and height of drop.

The word "approximately" requires explanation. As described above, data are obtained by dropping a series of known weights onto a pad of the cushioning material under test. The cushioning material deflects and compresses upon impact, absorbing shock, but perhaps bulging a bit at the edge in doing so. In other words the test is conducted upon an essentially *unrestrained* cushion sample.

Many foam cushions are applied as inserts within a container. Upon impact, the container restrains the foam and prevents this bulging from occurring. When a package is designed to eliminate this, friction can still enter the picture. Most protective packages are designed to protect equally as well, whether dropped on one face of the container or another. Upon impact, the foam at that point within the container will compress and absorb shock. The foam positioned along the sidewalls will have to resist a frictional, or shear force, due to its intimate contact with the product and with the container. These factors, and certain others such as a possible pneumatic effect within the container, may alter substantially the apparent cushioning properties of a material. Designers must be cautioned against "splitting hairs". A 10% safety factor should always be added to the cushion thickness, to compensate for container interior effects.

To illustrate the use of the dynamic curve data, let us consider a hypothetical problem, with polyethylene foam.

Given: A fragile object in the shape of a 10 inch cube, which can withstand an impact deceleration of up to 60 G's perpendicular to any face. The object weighs 30 pounds and must be protected against a 30 inch drop height.

Problem: Find the minimum thickness, bearing area and resulting volume of polyethylene foam required to adequately protect the object.

Solution: Referring to the dynamic data on Fig. VI-15, it is observed that the optimum protective characteristics for two inches of polyethylene foam from a 30 inch drop height are about 58 G's at .45 psi. Two inches of polyethylene foam then will adequately protect the object. At the 60 G level, it can be seen that two inches of foam can be applied over a static stress range of from .35 to .60 psi. In order to reduce bearing area to a minimum and thus conserve cushioning material, the following formula can be applied:

$$A_{min} = \frac{W}{F_{max}}$$

where A_{min} = minimum bearing area of the object on the cushion
F_{max} = maximum static stress at which the foam will protect the object
W = weight of object

F_{max} in this problem is approximately 0.60 psi (from the curve). Therefore, A_{min} = 30 lb ÷ 0.60 psi = 50 sq in. In theory then, 2.2 inches of polyethylene foam (including 10% thickness safety factor) distributed over an area of 50 square inches on *each of the six faces* of the cube will adequately protect it from damaging shocks under the conditions imposed. This is equivalent to 660 cu in. of foam.

The concept of minimum bearing area for economic reasons does not always hold true for adequate protection. Thick materials tend to buckle when compressed on a small bearing area instead of compressing uniformly. According to an empirical formula developed by Kerstner in "General Principles of Package Design" a cushion will not buckle when the minimum bearing area on a surface is equal to or greater than: $(1.33 \times t)^2$ where t = thickness. This is expressed as $A_{min} = (1.33 \times t)^2$. In our example, A_{min} is 50 square inches and $(1.33 \times 2.2)^2 = 8.5$ sq in. Thus we are well within the requirement, and 50 square inches can be safely applied without fear of buckling during compression.

Vibration control

Nearly all forms of transportation produce vibrational forces, which must be considered when designing protective packaging. Many equipment parts contain components that may be damaged by steady vibrations at a particular frequency.

A product supported on a cushioning material has a natural vibration frequency. When vibrated at that frequency, it will vibrate many times harder than at a frequency just above or below. This movement can cause the product to swing violently; it may damage itself by hitting the container, or the vibrational force may break down the cushion until it no longer protects the product. Component parts of an object may have their own natural frequencies; these must be considered when providing for protection against vibrations.

Many studies have been made to determine the most common frequencies encountered on different carriers. With some exceptions, the following is applicable:

Railroads—From many tests conducted by both military and civilian agencies, forcing frequencies developed by a freight car moving at speeds ranging from 20 to 91 miles per hour are two to seven cycles per second.

Trucks—The actual forced vibrations from trucks are so varied that it is difficult to designate those most prevalent. If the truck route is over a dirt road or an extremely rough road, a frequency range of 20 to 70 cycles per second may be applicable. For normal highway travel, vibration range is from 70 to 200 cycles per second.

Aircraft—Different types of aircraft produce different forcing frequencies and accelerations during take off, flight, and landing.

For package design, the significant conditions are those on the floor of a reciprocating engine cargo aircraft in flight. Definite frequencies are developed by the engine propeller speed and propeller blade passage. The two most repetitive groups of frequencies found in this type of aircraft are approximately 20 cycles per second and 60 cycles per second.

Ships—The principal forces causing ship vibration are interference of the flow of water with the ship and its propellers and imbalance or misalignment of the propeller shaft system. Vibrations differ at different sections of the ship and may range from 11 cycles per second on deck to 100 cycles per second in bulkheads, below.

An equation has been developed to approximate the natural frequency of a package:

$$F = \frac{2\,G}{\sqrt{H}}$$

where F equals natural frequency, G equals G factor for which the package has been designed, and H equals estimated drop height in inches.

If the natural frequency of the package is near the forcing frequencies encountered during shipment, it may be necessary to subject the package to vibration tests to determine the effects on the package contents, and alter package design as needed.

Vibration technology for packaging is still limited in scope. Work is being carried out by several research laboratories to determine effects of vibration, methods of damping, and an analytical approach to package vibration control.

5. THERMAL INSULATION

Adequate thermal insulation is a major requirement for packaged items that must

Figure VI-15, frozen food shipping container made of plastic foam provides protection against the effects of temperature.

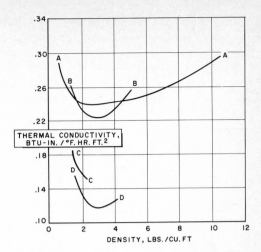

Figure VI-16, relation between thermal conductivity and density of foams.

have a controlled thermal environment. Temperature control is of vital concern for the packaging of frozen foods (Fig-VI-15), pharmaceuticals, and other perishables as well as for heat-sensitive, delicate missile controls or navigational systems. It may be desirable, for example, to ship a temperature-sensitive biological sample through the mails and protect it against extremes of temperature.

Proper utilization of thermal insulation material is required. Plastic foams contain literally thousands of tiny cell structures that provide a highly efficient thermal insulating material.

The effectiveness of a material as a thermal insulator is measured by its thermal conductivity (k-factor). A low thermal conductivity indicates superior insulating ability. Thermal conductivity of plastic foams depend upon density (Fig-VI-16).

Calculating insulation thickness

The following information is needed to design adequate thermal insulating of a packaged product:

A) The extremes of temperature environment to be encountered during shipment.

B) The duration of exposure to these temperatures.

C) The range of temperature within which the product must be maintained.

D) The temperature of the object as packaged.

E) The weight and specific heat of the object.

F) The conductivity characteristics of the

thermal insulation and other packaging components employed.

Where this information has been obtained, calculations can be made to determine the thickness of foam required and to establish the maximum exposure time of the insulated item to a temperature extreme. The following equations apply:

Duration of the desired protection:

$$T = \frac{Q}{9} \qquad (1)$$

Q is the amount of heat or energy absorbed by the object:

$$Q = cm\,(t_1 - t_2), \qquad (2)$$

q is the amount of heat transferred per hour when subjected to a given environment with a fixed temperature differential (or "driving force") across one or more materials:

$$q = \Delta t / R_t \qquad (3)$$

This equation is generally used where a refrigerant such as ice or dry ice is used in the package. These materials have the ability to maintain a constant temperature while at the same time absorbing energy and melting due to their "latent heats of fusion."

If no refrigerant cooling medium is placed in the package, a variable driving force exists whereby the packaged product gradually changes temperature over a given time. Where no cooling medium is incorporated, a temperature change within the product takes place,

$$q = \Delta t_{1n} / R_t \qquad (4)$$

Thermal resistance R_t is the sum of resistance to heat flow of the packaging materials plus air film resistance on the package outer surface. In many insulated packages, more than one material will be utilized in series (sandwich fashion). In this case, R is determined for each individual component material.

$R_t = R_{material\ 1} + R_{material\ 2} + R_{material\ 3}$ where where $R = x/kA.$ (5)

While thermal transmission of most homogeneous materials is expressed in terms of thermal conductivity k with units of Btu-in./hr-sq ft-°F, the thickness of many non-homogeneous materials such as corrugated boxboard is determined largely by flute height. Expression of thermal transmission in terms of thermal conductivity in such cases is awkward. In other words, increasing the insulation thickness must be done in multiples of the original

Table VI-3—Symbols Used for Thermal Insulation Formulas

A = inside surface area of component packaging materials*
T = time, hours
m = weight of product, pounds
c = specific heat of product, Btu/lb. °F
t_1 = original temperature of product or refrigerant (if used), °F
t_2 = final temperature of product, °F
t_a = ambient or external environment temperature, °F
x = thickness of insulation, inches
k = thermal conductivity of the insulation, Btu-in./hr-sq ft-°F
Δt = temperature differential, which is original temperature of product, t_1, minus ambient temperature, t_a, $(t_1 - t_a)$
C = thermal conductance, Btu/hr-sq ft-°F
t_{1n} = driving force, or log mean temperature change, which is

$$(4)\quad \frac{(t_1 - t_a) - (t_2 - t_a)}{\ln\left[\dfrac{(t_1 - t_a)}{(t_2 - t_a)}\right]}$$

R = thermal resistance = $\dfrac{1}{C}$

*The calculation of inside surface areas of component materials introduces a small element of error into the problem. The correct value would be a "mean" area falling between the outside and inside surfaces of a material. For most applications, however, and for ease of calculation, that error is considered negligible.

Table VI-4—Average Values of Thermal Conductivity near 68°F

Substances	Btu in./hr sq ft °F
Metals	
Silver	2930
Copper	2680
Gold	2030
Brass	750
Steel	320
Aluminum	1390
Non-metallic solids	
Wood (across grain)	0.9
Glass	4.0
Enamel	6.0
Porous and cellular materials	
Fiber blanket insulation	0.27
Glass or mineral wool	0.27
Sawdust	0.41
Corkboard	0.30
Molded expandable polystyrene (1.5-3.5 lb per cu ft density)	0.24
Expanded polystyrene (2.0 lb per cu ft density)	0.28
Expanded polyethylene (2.0 lb per cu ft density)	0.35
Rigid urethane (polyether) (3.0 lb per cu ft density)	0.15
Flexible urethane (polyether) (3.0 lb per cu ft density)	0.22

board thickness. A more practical and convenient procedure is to express the transmission results in terms of thermal conductance (C) of a single thickness of corrugated board with units of Btu/hr sq ft °F (Tables VI-4 and VI-5). Thermal resistance R for such materials is expressed as: $R = 1/C$.

Example 1 — A solid, temperature-sensitive product is to be shipped in a package molded of expandable polystyrene. Time in transit is expected to be no longer than ten hours. The product weighs three pounds and has a specific heat of 1.00 Btu/lb °F. The product fits snugly into the package, which has an interior surface area of 0.85 sq ft. As packaged, the product temperature is 35° F. It must not rise above 50°F in transit. The average ambient temperature is 75°F. What thickness (x) of 2 lb per cu ft density foam is required to adequately protect this product?

Given: $\quad A = .85$ sq ft $\qquad c = 1$ Btu/lb °F
$\qquad\qquad T = 10$ hr $\qquad t_1 = 35$°F
$\qquad\qquad m = 3$ lb $\qquad t_2 = 50$°F
$\qquad\qquad\qquad\qquad\qquad t_a = 75$°F
$\qquad\qquad k = .24$ Btu-in./hr-sq ft-°F

Substituting in equation (2):

$$Q = 3 \times 1 \; (35° - 50°)$$
$$Q = -45$$

In equation (1): $10 \; hr = \dfrac{-45}{q}$

$$q = -4.5$$

The amount of heat transferred will vary with the gradual change in product temperature. This necessitates calculation of the log mean temperature differential or driving force:

$$\triangle t_{In} = \frac{(35° - 75°) - (50° - 75°)}{\ln \left[\frac{(35° - 75°)}{(50° - 75°)} \right]}$$

$$= \frac{-15}{\ln 1.6} = \frac{-15}{.47} = -32°F$$

In equation (4) then: $-4.5 = \dfrac{-32}{R_t}$

$$R_t = 7.1$$

R_t, or 7.1 in this case, is the sum of the individual resistances of the foam and the air film coefficient.

From equation (5): $R_{foam} = \dfrac{x}{kA}$

and: R_{air} (exterior air film coefficient) $= 0.17$
Foam thickness (x) can now be determined by applying equation (5):

$$R_t = R_{foam} + R_{still \; air}$$

and simplifying:

$$\frac{x}{KA} = R_t - R_{still \; air}$$

$$x = KA \; (R_t - R_{still \; air})$$

$$x = .24 \times .85 \; (7.1 - 0.17)$$

Answer: $x = 1.41$ inches of foam required.

Example 2—A given package consists of a rectangular glass bottle with an inside surface area of 2.07 sq ft and a wall thickness of ⅛". This bottle contains a temperature sensitive liquid weighing eight pounds with a specific heat of .90 Btu/lb °F. The bottle is packaged in a 2" thick molded container of rigid polyether urethane having a density of 3 lb per cu ft and an inside surface area of 2.15 sq ft. This assembly is placed into a 200-lb test, B-flute, corrugated container with an inside surface area of 3.53 sq ft. Determine the length of time this package will protect its contents, if the liquid is packaged at 68°F and is allowed a temperature drop of 36° at an ambient external shipping temperature of 20°F.

First determine the combined resistance of the materials involved (R_t), using k and C values from Tables VI-4 and VI-5.
From equation (5):

$$R_t = R_{glass} + R_{foam} + R_{corrugated} + R_{air \; film \; resistance}$$

$$R_t = \frac{.125}{4.0 \times 2.07} + \frac{2.0}{.15 \times 2.15} + \frac{1}{2.9} + 0.17$$

$$R_t = .015 + 6.2 + .34 + 0.17$$

$$R_t = 6.73$$

Determine $\triangle t_{In}$:

$$\triangle t_{In} = \frac{(68° - 20°) - (32° - 20°)}{\ln \left[\frac{(68° - 20°)}{(32° - 20°)} \right]}$$

$$= \frac{36°}{\ln 4} = \frac{36°}{1.39} = 25.9°$$

From equation (4): $q = \dfrac{\triangle t_{In}}{R_t} = \dfrac{25.9°}{6.73} = 3.85$

From equation (2): $Q = cm \; (t_1 - t_2)$
$\qquad = .90 \times 8 \; (68° - 32°) = 259$

From equation (1): $T = \dfrac{Q}{q} = \dfrac{259}{3.58} = 67.3$

Answer: 67.3 hours

6. ADDITIONAL CONSIDERATIONS

Moisture resistance

The extent to which a material will function as a moisture barrier depends upon its rate of permeability to water vapor. The ability of a

Table VI-5—Thermal Conductance of Corrugated Boxboard C, near 68°F	
	Btu /hr sq ft °F
Corrugated A flute	1.8
Corrugated B flute	2.9
Corrugated C flute	2.3
Double wall BC or CB flutes	1.3
Double wall AB or BA flutes	1.1
Double wall AC or CA flutes	1.0
Double wall AA flutes	0.9

package fabricated from a given plastic foam to resist the penetration of moisture or to retain it, if necessary, is important for many packaging applications from the standpoint of product protection. For example, the exclusion of moisture may be highly desirable when packaging metal products subject to corrosion particularly for long term storage. On the other hand, certain foods may require the retention of moisture in order to maintain freshness. Many variables account for differences in moisture transmission characteristics of foam materials. Density, the degree of open or closed cell structures, and material composition affect moisture transmissibility. When this is important, the manufacturer of the foam should be consulted.

Chemical resistance

Chemical resistance of the packaging material may be of importance where there is possibility of chemical attack. Preservative oils and greases, lubricating fluids, and certain solvent vapors can attack and degrade plastic materials to an extent that renders them completely ineffective.

Occasionally an incompatibility between several plastic materials is noticed. Certain plasticizers used in vinyl plastics, for example, may be incompatible with parts molded from expandable polystyrene, resulting in a color change or other undesirable change in the vinyl parts. Usually a change of plasticizer will solve this difficulty.

Urethane foams are among the most chemically resistant foams available for packaging. Polyethylene foam is next in line; it is resistant to most solvents and chemicals at room temperature. Polyethylene foam shows no effect when brought into contact with fuel oil and heavier hydrocarbons, but will swell when submerged for any length of time in gasoline; it also is susceptible to chemical attack by various solvents at temperatures above 130°F. Polystyrene foams are not soluble in aqueous acids nor are they affected by aliphatic hydrocarbons or alcohols, but they are attacked by aromatic or chlorinated hydrocarbons, ketones and esters.

Where contact is likely to occur in a proposed packaging application, tests should be conducted with the foam considered, to determine the effect of the contact. Polystyrene foams are the least solvent-resistant of the three foams. Certain solvent-resistant copolymers are being developed for packaging

applications requiring this characteristic.

Dusting characteristics

Cushioning materials used in packaging should be non-dusting. This is very important when packaging sensitive electronic equipment or missile components, where dust might interfere with the operation or even render the equipment useless. Dust may scratch a highly polished metal surface. Some packaging operations are carried out with surgical cleanliness for safety's sake. For example, fuel transfer components for missile systems which will carry liquid oxygen must be microscopically cleansed of all organic contamination and packaged to maintain that degree of cleanliness.

Non-dusting materials should be used to maintain tidiness for a product which must be merchandised.

Foamed plastics for packaging can perform admirably in this respect. Properly formulated flexible urethanes, polyethylene foam, and parts produced from expandable polystyrene are essentially non-dusting. Fabricated foams or materials which have been mechanically formed and left with a rough surface can present a dusting hazard unless that surface is properly treated. Rigid materials such as rigid urethane and expanded polystyrene foams are somewhat subject to dusting when exposed to abrasion.

Useful temperature range

Where temperature conditions are likely to vary during shipment and storage, the temperature range of the packaging material should be known. The military is particularly concerned over the ability of a packaging material to stand up under extremes of temperature. Performance must be assured at the lowest temperatures encountered in arctic regions as well as under the extreme heat of desert areas. Military supplies and equipment may be stored for long periods, then shipped anywhere in the world at a moment's notice.

The physical properties of a plastic foam vary depending upon the thermal environment. At low temperatures, foams tend to become stiffer and at higher temperatures, more flexible. Of the three basic plastic foams considered, urethanes are the most heat resistant, with a useful upper limit of approximately 250°F and a lower limit of −100°F. Environmental temperature limits for polystyrene foams are approximately 185°F maximum and −80°F minimum. The limits for polyethylene foam should be kept within 165°F maximum and –65°F minimum.

Creep characteristics

The ability of a given cushioning material to resist thickness loss under static load is known as its resistance to "compressive creep." Most cushioning materials are subject to a certain amount of creep as a function of static load and time. Creep characteristics of cushioning materials are important where extended periods of product storage are anticipated. Some materials compress with time under load to the extent that the packed object becomes loose and free to shift within the package; this seriously reduces the effectiveness of protection.

Creep is generally expressed as per cent of thickness loss of the original thickness. Realistically, the time period should represent the period of expected storage, or actual "product-package" combination. An allowable loss (not exceeding 10%) should be considered when selecting cushioning materials for specific applications over known periods of "in-package" environment.

7. CLOSURES FOR FOAMED PLASTIC PACKAGES

A consideration in the design of any package is the method used to close it and keep it closed during the period of shipment, storage, and handling. Closures fall into two general categories, single use and reuse. Single use closures are those most commonly encountered in industrial and military usage, for shipping containers and for export. Once the container is opened a new closure must be incorporated to reship. An example of a single use closure is a tape closure. Reuse closures are most commonly found on interior containers for consumer or commercial use. An example of a reuse closure is a screw cap or a zipper.

Single use—Tape closures

Tape closures for fully encapsulating molded containers of expandable polystyrene are most common, particularly where the package is also the exterior shipping container. Paper, plastic, and filament-reinforced pressure-sensitive tapes which provide effective adhesion to expandable polystyrene are now available. These tapes are most effective when they completely encircle the package, overlapping at the ends so that the tape adheres to itself. Recessed strips in the foam can be incorporated in the package design to assist in the application of the tape.

The information given here is intended as a guide for the use of tapes for molded containers, but special conditions, tape types, and economics may alter the recommendations.

Table VI-6—Number of Tape Strips Which Should Cross Package Parting Line

Length of parting line	Number of tape strips
Up to 9″	1
9″ to 18″	2
18″ to 36″	3
36″ to 64″	4

Table VI-6 indicates the number of strips to be applied, depending upon the length of the package parting line. Table VI-7 indicates the

Table VI-7—Width of Tape Strips Which Cross Parting Line

Gross weight of product, lb	Number of tape strips as determined from Table VI-6			
	1	2	3	4
Up to 20	1/2″	1/2″	1/2″	1/2″
20 to 40	1″	3/4″	3/4″	1/2″
40 to 60	1-1/4″	1″	1″	3/4″
60 to 80	1-3/4″	1-1/2″	1-1/4″	1″
80 to 100	2″	1-3/4″	1-1/2″	1-1/4″

width of the tape required, depending upon the weight of the product and the number of strips used.

The type of tape used depends upon the requirements of the package. A good grade of pressure-sensitive paper tape may be sufficient for many applications while others may require a stronger, plastic tape or even a filament-reinforced tape. A rule of thumb for positioning tape strips is: where two or more strips are involved, the two strips closest to the edge are positioned 1/6 of the package dimension from the edge; any additional strips are equally spaced between the two edge strips; where only one strip is required, it is centered at equal distance from the edges of the package.

Example—A tape closure is desired for a product weighing 45 lb in a container molded of expandable polystyrene measuring 22″ x 17″ x 6″. How many strips are required and of what width? How should the tape be positioned?

According to Table VI-6, three strips of tape are required across the 22″ dimension of the package, and two strips across the 17″ dimension. Since the product weighs 45 lb, Table VI-7 indicates a tape width of 1″ for both length and width of the package. Across the 22″ dimension of the package, the outside strips are located 3-2/3″ from each end (1/6th of the length) while the third strip is centered between these two.

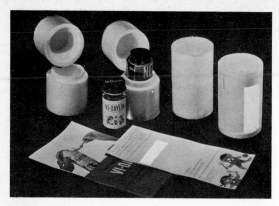

Figure VI-17, insulating package molded of expandable polystyrene using complete wrap-around label as closure for mailing. Courtesy Abbott Laboratories.

Across the 17″ dimension, each of the two tape strips is positioned approximately 2-5/6″ from the edge (1/6 of the width).

Single use—Labels

Many small plastic foam packages can be adequately closed and sealed with a shipping label. The label accomplishes its original purpose of identifying and/or addressing the product, while also serving as a closure (Fig-VI-17). The best labels for this purpose are the pressure-sensitive type, with adhesives specifically adapted to the plastic foam used. Whenever possible the label should completely wrap around the package so that it overlaps and adheres to itself. Care should be exercised, when designing the label, to see that when the package is opened the printed description is not destroyed. A closure label should be large enough to cover as much of the exposed parting line as possible. While labels are not basically intended as closures, this secondary function can be quite effective and inexpensive.

Figure VI-18, example of stapling of a plastic foam package.

Single use—Stapling

Stapling and metal stitching have long been used for sealing in the fiber box industry. Using wire staples for closing a vacuum-formed container of extruded polystyrene foam sheet, or wide staples to close a rigid or semi-rigid foam container, can be quite effective (Fig-VI-18). The staple is crimped by the external pivoting arms of a pneumatic stapling device: these arms puncture the material and crimp the staple at a predetermined depth within the foam. A number of such staples evenly positioned along the closure line makes a very effective and positive closure, providing the package is of the tongue and groove design to prevent lateral movement of one half of the package with relation to the other. This stapling technique can also be used to hold foam inserts within a container.

Single use—Heat shrinkable film

Specially oriented plastic film, such as polystyrene or polyethylene, may be used to effectively join two halves of a molded foam package or to hold the contents of a thermoformed polystyrene foam sheet tray snugly in position while displaying the natural color and texture of the product. The film is wrapped manually or automatically around the package or tray, which is then passed through a shrink tunnel where heat is applied to effect a tight and completely transparent closure. Labels can be laid on the package prior to overwrapping.

Single use—Adhesive

Adhesives are used where reuse of the container is not required. Adhesive for plastic foams are classified into two types; drying and setting. Adhesives that reach the bonded state by evaporation of a liquid are known as drying type adhesives. They include resins, rubber or asphalt emulsions, and solvent systems. In all instances the liquid must evaporate to effect a full strength bond. Many drying adhesives contain polystyrene solvents, and tests should be conducted to detect solvent attack before using an adhesive with polystyrene foam packages. Adhesives that reach full bond strength through a chemical reaction are called setting type adhesives. They include such materials as epoxies and resorcinols. Most setting adhesives contain little, if any, solvent. Setting adhesives generally do not have high initial tack, but the ultimate bond strength is high.

Some adhesives popular for bonding a

foamed plastic to itself or to other materials are the pressure sensitive types, many of which are available commercially. These are drying type adhesives.

Single use—Tear strips or wires

This method incorporates the use of a wire or tape as an opening device to cut through the foamed plastic. This patented technique is particularly well suited where foaming-in-place urethane is used. A wire of sufficient tensile strength is taped or otherwise fastened to the object to be foamed in place. The tear wire is then wrapped around the circumference of the object to facilitate opening. The free end of the wire is positioned so that it will appear as a loop outside the foam after the object has been foamed-in-place. The package is conveniently opened by pulling the wire around the package, cutting the foam neatly into two halves.

Reuse closures—Full or partial telescope and friction fit

Molded or fabricated foam containers can be designed so that one-half of the container telescopes fully into the other half. These may then be packed in quantities in an external shipping container without further individual closure devices. The use of a telescope pack makes it often possible to pack objects of different heights (Fig-V1-19).

A friction fit closure can be used with lightweight products which are to be overpacked for shipment. These containers generally incorporate tongue and groove devices molded to produce good friction contact. This friction plus a gasketing effect tend to hold the package together because of a slight differential air pressure created upon opening the container.

Reuse closures—Pillbox or drawer type

This type of closure uses a tray and sleeve concept. The "tray" may be a molded or fabricated plastic foam. Products are then recessed into the foam. The outer sleeve may consist of extruded and fabricated polystyrene foam sheet, transparent plastic sheet, or fiber board. To close, the tray is inserted into the sleeve and taped at each end, or, if desired, left as is (Fig-VI-20). This type of closure lends itself to various merchandising techniques. A number of packages are generally overpacked in a larger shipping container.

Figure VI-19, full or partial telescope package.

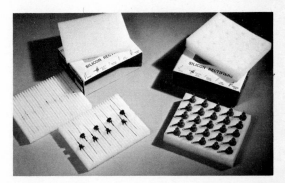

Figure VI-20, drawer type package—electronic items packed in polyethylene foam trays with printed chip board sleeves.

Reuse closures—Screw or snap caps

Screw or snap cap closures have not been widely used for foam packages due primarily to the necessity of providing special thread molding devices within the mold. As advances in molding technology are made and additional markets open up such closures may become popular.

Reuse closures—Special devices

A number of special devices for use as closures can be incorporated into foam packages during the molding or fabricating process or afterward. Special hinges and catches have been molded from polypropylene, and inserted into special positioning devices within a mold. The foam is then molded around these inserts to provide a finished hinged package. Clips, friction pins, and other devices can be incorporated into plastic foam packages to make special closures.

Hinged containers can be formed from extruded polystyrene foam sheet. The development of specialized closures is limited only by the ingenuity of the processor.

Figure VI-21, expanded polystyrene foam package for display.

Figure VI-22, fine-celled flexible urethane foam which has been fabricated, dyed and printed into a fabric-like material.

8. MERCHANDISING ASPECTS OF PACKAGING

The popularity of the supermarket and other self-service stores has resulted in the consumer package becoming a powerful merchandising tool. The package must speak for itself. It must stand out among the myriad of competing products and say "buy me" to each prospective customer (Fig-VI-21).

Because of a highly competitive situation, manufacturers are constantly searching for new and versatile materials and improved decorating techniques to provide the distinctive touch that will make their products' package a better salesman than the competition.

The versatility of foamed plastics and the various methods of fabrication provide an extremely wide latitude in creating attractive and functional package designs.

Design consideration

The ability to mold or fabricate plastic foams in a wide variety of shapes makes them truly effective merchandising tools. In addition to the purely functional aspect of protection, textures may be incorporated to simulate a variety of surface finishes. Intricate designs, raised or depressed lettering, etc., can easily be added into the mold. Moldable foams offer extreme design freedom.

Foam film or sheet extruded from expandable polystyrene may be embossed, formed, textured and even laminated to achieve a wide spectrum of decorative packaging possibilities.

Colored materials

Integrally colored foam materials offer a depth of color not achievable with ordinary flat surfaces of conventional materials. The ability to "build in" colors offers many advantages to the merchandiser. Expandable polystyrene is available in several internally colored formulations which may be mixed prior to molding. Polyethylene foam and urethanes may be formulated with colors. Thin, flexible urethane fabric-like foam is being dyed and printed (Fig-VI-22). It may be laminated to paper or plastic sheet of any number of materials for fabrication into gift or display packages. The use of color in foam packages is just beginning to be exploited for merchandising purposes.

Printing and decorating

Printed words, identification, directions, guide numbers, or design, are often desirable on packages made of plastic foams for decoration as well as information. Numerous methods are available for decorating these materials.

Printing methods—The type of printing job wanted and the equipment available are major factors in determining which process should be chosen. If two or three hundred packages only are to be printed, silk screen printing may be called for. For large volumes, the high speeds and drying properties of flexographic or lithographic processes may be more economical and better suited. Lithographic printing can be most effectively used on large volume multi-color jobs were good registry is required. Hot stamping and roller coating are other means of printing that should be considered in selecting the proper method for a particular application.

The number of colors required is a determining factor in the choice of a decorating method. When more than one color is required, the cost increases. Offset printing is the only technique which can handle as many as four colors at a single pass, although not all offset presses can print four colors at once. In hot stamping, more than one color calls for additional dies and equipment. Each extra color in screen process printing requires a separate pass with drying between passes. Additional screens and equipment for each color raises the cost substantially.

The costs of hot stamping and of screen process printing are about equal. Photographic screens are less expensive than hot stamping dies, but screen process printing requires drying after each pass, whereas hot stamping dries immediately. Roll leaf for hot stamping is more expensive than screening inks, and the size of the area to be decorated can become a major factor in deciding between the two processes.

Screen process printing—This process is in essence a stenciling technique which lays down a heavy film of ink in the form of a design. The process is simple compared to other printing techniques. It offers one of the most economical means of decorating plastic foam articles, on both flat and curved surfaces, and it is readily adaptable for multi-color decorating, by using a series of screens for each separate color.

Photographic stencils are commonly used and are best for intricate designs. Stencils of this type can be procured from companies specifically set up to do this type of work.

Typical production rates range from 250 to 500 parts per hour by hand, 400 to 1000 parts per hour with a mechanical unit. Automatic equipment is progressing and in some instances has reached 5000 parts per hour. The cost of screens, even for multi-color jobs, is comparatively small, but lack of speed, except for specialized items, has limited the use of the screen process to small volume jobs.

Roll leaf hot stamping—This process consists of transferring a coating from a flexible ribbon to the foam by pressure and heat. The flexible ribbon is called "roll leaf."

This method is suitable for flat, concave, or convex surfaces including round or tubular shapes. Production rates vary depending upon the particular application and the equipment used.

Temperatures, pressure, and dwell time are interrelated and their values depend upon the depth of impression required, the degree of clarity desired, the size and shape of the part, and the type and density of the foam to be stamped.

Roll leaf foils are manufactured to release pigments from the carrier ribbon at about 325-375°F. This temperature range was selected on the basis of desired properties: hardness, gloss, top rub, cleanliness, and resistance to solvents. The temperature used in hot stamping depends on the material to be printed, therefore the temperature at which the pigment is released from the ribbon varies also with the material. In ordering roll leaf, it is important to specify the type of foam to be imprinted.

Roll leaf hot stamping offers several advantages compared to roller coating. Imprinting and coloring are done rapidly and simultaneously. Two or more colors can be stamped at the same time using separate rolls for each color. Roll leaf stamping is estimated to cost only about one-third as much as roller coating in certain long-run application, but it is more expensive than silk screening for short runs.

Roller coating—This is a type of printing in the broad sense of the word. Small raised areas such as letters, figures, and designs may be decorated by roller coating. This method is sometimes used as an alternate for roll leaf hot stamping.

Hand rolls are commonly used for short runs and for areas that cannot be rolled by machine.

The paint must have good adhesion, since raised areas are often subjected to wear. Paints used in this type of application must have high viscosity and be formulated with solvent systems that do not attack the foam.

Automatic roller coating machines are available for handling large runs, but must be well-adapted to the particular job to be economical.

Flexographic printing—Flexography is a process whereby printing is accomplished with a fluid ink using rubber type or plates.

The standard flexographic press is of the rotary type, with one or more color stations.

Economy, versatility, quality, and relative simplicity are flexography's major points. Where required, this process can decorate foam articles with multi-color printing at extremely high speeds.

Most flexographic inks dry primarily by evaporation in 10 to 20 seconds, at room temperature. This drying may be speeded up through the use of hot air rapidly circulating on the printed foam surface after each color is printed.

The fast drying qualities, quick, easy

changeovers, and extreme versatility of the flexographic process combine to make it a real contender in the packaging business.

Choice of inks—No matter which type of printing is used, ink must be supplied in one form or another. The following information is useful in that connection:

1) The type of plastic foam must be known to the ink supplier, as certain ink solvent systems may attack the plastic.

2) The type of printing equipment available determines the type of ink.

3) The type of drying equipment available aids in determining the drying time of the ink.

4) Time and temperature are important factors for continuous drying.

5) The type of product being packaged may determine the type of ink to be used. Inks used in some applications must be approved by the Food & Drug Administration when it comes in contact with food.

Surface treatments

A coating may be desirable to limit surface damage and weathering, or to beautify and decorate. Some coatings or surface finishes may be applied on a molded foam article during the molding process, but usually, coatings are applied as a secondary step, after fabrication.

Surfacing added after molding—Paints and lacquers may be used for coating molded containers for decorative purposes. However, many paints and lacquers contain solvents harmful to polystyrene; a check should be made, to be sure that undesirable solvent at-

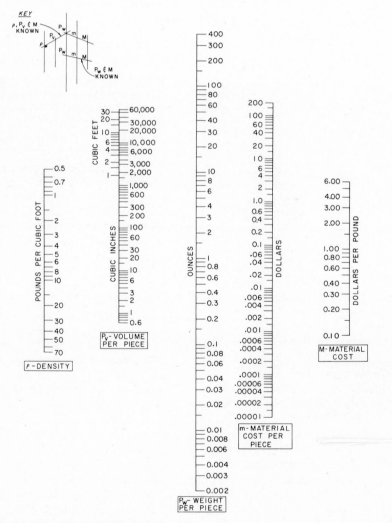

Figure VI-23, nomograph to determine the cost of material for certain packaging foams.

tack does not occur on the surface of the foam.

Flocking may be accomplished by using conventional flocking techniques with a suitable adhesive system.

Hard surface facings such as wood, metal, or plastics may be fastened to foam by direct lamination with compatible adhesives.

Surfacing added or formed during molding

A unique method for producing sandwich type construction is to expand foam materials between preshaped facings. The facing may be precoated with a rubber or resin solvent-based adhesive prior to foaming or, in the case of urethanes, accomplished without adhesive. A preshaped facing may be applied to one side of the foam only, such as the exterior surface of a package. Where complete encapsulation of the foam by a facing material is required, specialized molding techniques are used, several of which are covered by patents. Some typical facing materials are high impact polystyrene, high density polyethylene, metal, cured and reinforced polyester, and even wood.

Designing the part for decorating

Since decorating is usually the final stage of operation, it may receive little thought in the design of the package. The foam part should be designed to facilitate ease of decorating whenever possible. For example, a part that will be hot-stamped should be designed so that the entire design to be stamped appears on a flat surface. This will lower the cost of the dies required. Clearance with the stamping die and stamping tape should be provided near the area to be stamped.

9. COST OF PACKAGING

The cost of packaging with foamed plastics as compared with the multitude of other available packaging materials is a matter of extreme importance. Surprisingly, the cost of packaging a product, and the factors which enter into this cost are often overlooked by firms which are busily engaged in cutting manufacturing costs in other areas.

A nomograph (Fig-VI-23) can be used to relate the amount of plastic foam, its density, the unit cost of the raw material and the total raw material cost of a package.

Material costs, however, are just one aspect of the problem, when deciding between materials for packaging. Low cost materials do not necessarily mean the most economical pack-

ages. Often a larger expenditure for packaging materials results in considerable savings in other areas.

One important consideration which affects the overall package cost is its weight. The ability to ship an item with the least amount of weight means a savings in handling and shipping. The high cost of transportation makes many companies increasingly aware of the value of foamed plastics and their extreme lightness. Additional costs are those of warehousing and inventory of packaging materials, of fabrication and/or assembly labor.

Accurate records of the cost of damage experienced can be a useful tool in determining the overall efficiency of a given package. Some manufacturers, for example, consider a certain amount of damage tolerable, when it is limited by a correct amount of protection. This matter is carefully watched, to be sure that it does not drop below a minimum which may indicate that the products are overpackaged at an excessive cost. The cost of excessive protection should not outweigh a condition obtained by sound engineering principles and use of proper materials in package design. On the other hand, damage claim statistics may indicate areas where additional protection should be considered.

PACKAGING DEFINITIONS

Cushioning: (1) Interior packing used primarily for protecting the package contents against shock and vibrations. (2) In a narrower sense, a uniform material, as compared with a built up structure, used as a shock or vibration isolator.

Acceleration: The rate of change of velocity with respect to time.

Blocking: Material used primarily to position an article in a container.

Bottoming point: That point on the stress-strain curve of a cushioning material where further increase in stress produces no increase in strain. For practical purposes, it is often approximated.

Cycle: In a vibrating system the complete motion of the body from position of rest to maximum excursion on the one side, back through the position of rest, to maximum excursion on the other side, and back to the position of rest.

Deceleration: Acceleration in a negative direction.

Damping: Dissipation of energy by a cushioning material.

Density: Weight per unit of volume.

Elasticity: The tendency of a body or system to return to its original size and shape after having been deformed.

Energy: The capacity of a body or system for doing work.

Force: The action on a body which changes, or tends to change the state of motion of the body acted upon.

Frequency: The number of times a given phenomenon is repeated per unit of time.

Natural frequency: The frequency at which a body will vibrate if displaced and allowed to vibrate freely.

g: The acceleration of gravity, 32.2 feet per second per second.

G: The ratio between an acceleration and the acceleration of gravity.

G Factor: The ratio of the maximum acceleration that an object can withstand without incurring damage, to the acceleration of gravity.

Inertia: A measure of the reluctance of a body to change its velocity or its state of rest.

Shock or vibration isolator: Any material or structure which tends to diminish the effect of shock or vibration on an object.

Load: The force, in units of weight, applied to a body.

Mass: The quantity of matter in a body. Mass equals weight divided by the acceleration of gravity.

Momentum: A measure of the tendency of a body to continue in motion in the same direction at the same velocity.

Mount: A fabricated shock or vibration isolator, usually consisting of an elastic member and one or more relatively inelastic members, fastened between an object and its supporting container or structure.

Resilience: The potential energy stored in a deformed body.

Resonance: Additive effect produced in a vibration by another vibration of the same frequency; a harmonic frequency.

Resonant frequency: That frequency at which the magnification factor is at a maximum.

Set: A measure of the inability of a material to return to its original dimensions after removal of stress.

Packaging, consumer: The preparation of goods which by reason of construction or design cannot be shipped without further protective packaging, generally an outer shipping container. Example: cans, folding paper boxes, glass containers, paper bags, etc. These items often emphasize the merchandising aspect of packaging and require additional physical protection during shipment.

Packaging, industrial: A loose term referring to one aspect of packaging in which the goods are usually packaged for industrial buyers rather than for consumer buyers. It often includes the packaging of consumer durable goods like stoves, refrigerators, air conditioners, radio and television receivers, etc.

Packaging, military: The preparation of goods for shipment to the Armed Services in accordance with prescribed military packaging specifications or directives. Emphasis is on protection of the goods. Trade names or consumer appeal are unimportant, but identification and protection are paramount.

Packaging, protective: The functional aspect of packaging in contrast to its merchandising aspect. Protective packaging safeguards its contents from deterioration or loss, from the time the package is closed until the ultimate opening by the user. Varying degrees of protection may be incorporated depending on the need for protection from environment, hazards, and time for which the protection is required.

Permanent set: The amount of set measured after a definite time following removal of stress.

Shock: A suddenly applied force, or a sudden change in direction of a motion, or a sudden change in velocity of motion.

Strain: The change in unit dimension of a body when it is deformed under load or stress.

Stress: The load per unit of area applied to a body.

Velocity: The time rate of change of position or speed of a body.

Vibration: A motion which reverses itself periodically.

Free vibration: Vibration occurring without external forces being applied.

Forced vibration: Vibration of a body resulting from application of an external force during an explicit time.

Section VII—OTHER AREAS OF APPLICATION
PART I—ELECTRICAL APPLICATIONS OF FOAMED PLASTICS
By René J. Bender

1. FOAMED PLASTICS FOR CABLE INSULATION

Because of their high resistivity and their good physical properties over a range of temperatures acceptable for most commercial applications, solid plastics make good electrical insulation materials, and are being used increasingly, replacing paper for underground high-voltage cables.

Foamed plastics have the additional advantage of lower weight, thereby reducing substantially the cost of both material and installation.

For over ten years, *polyolefins* (polyethylene, polypropylene) have been used in steadily greater volume, and improvements have been worked into their qualities of low loss factor and low capacitance, making them an ideal insulating material for TV pair cable, antenna cable and co-axial cable.

Foamed FEP fluorocarbons can now be added to the list of foamed plastics used in this field (see Section XIV, Part II and Section XX, Part IV).

Table VII-1 gives a comparison of insulating properties of various foamed products and of solid low-density polyethylene. High-density foam from high-density polyethylene, with about 30% cells, is a substantial improvement over the standard polyethylene foam from the standpoints of abrasion resistance and tensile strength, although its loss factor is slightly higher. Foamed *polypropylene* which has an excellent dielectric constant and high mechanical strength does not resist low temperatures without becoming brittle and also has a high loss factor. Additional work is being carried out by several researchers on foamed polyethylene-polypropylene combinations.

High-density polyethylene foam can be extruded with a great variety of extruding machines, ranging from 1-in. to 3½-in. in barrel diameters, and with all types of screws, at speeds varying from 20 to as high as 2200 ft per min. Changes of density during the extrusion process can also be obtained over a wide range. This type of insulation can be made as thin as 0.005 in. Extrusion temperatures, varying from 290°F to about 380°F, must be somewhat higher with high-density polyethylene foam than with the standard low-density polyethylene for which it is generally held at 250°F for the rear zone and 300°F for the head. Preheat temperature of the extruded plastic is an important factor in controlling the strength of thin wall insulation, and must be maintained within narrow limits, about 250°F for standard low-density polyethylene, 300°F for high-density foam, still higher— 400°F—for cellular polypropylene.

Working with polyethylene, and also with a blend of polypropylene and about 10% of polyisobutylene, the Bell Telephone Laboratories recently developed a method for improving the dielectric properties of the foam. It consists in adding powdered azodicarbonamide to the resin pellets in the funnel above the extruder. Air or nitrogen is used as blowing agent, and is injected into the molten resin

Table VII-1—Comparison of Insulation Properties

Properties	Solid poly-ethylene	Standard cellular poly-ethylene	High-density cellular poly-ethylene	Cellular poly-propylene	Cellular vinyl
Density	0.92	0.50	0.65	0.65	0.84
Tensile strength, psi	2100	670	2800	3100	3500
Cold bend, at −60°F	OK	OK	OK	Fails	Fails
Scrape abrasion (cycle life at wear-through)	20-30	1-2	20-30	20-30	20-40
Power factor, 1 mc	0.0002	0.0004	0.0006	0.0021	0.012
Dielectric constant, 1 mc	2.28	1.5	1.7	1.6	1.8
Loss factor, %	0.456	0.060	0.102	0.336	2.16

Figure VII-1, extrusion of foamed plastic at Bell Laboratories.

shortly before it emerges from the extruder, at a low-pressure point located between two high-pressure zones. The organic powder acts as a nucleating agent. Upon decomposition, it creates "hot spots" in the foam and tends to multiply the cells while reducing their individual size, in the extruded foam (Fig VII-1 and VII-2).

2. FOAMED PLASTICS FOR ENCAPSULATION

Waxes and bituminous compounds have been used for encapsulation of electrical equipment for a long time. Their obvious limitation is their weak temperature resistance. The first plastic embedding was made in 1906 by Dr. Leo Baekeland with a phenolic resin. Great advances were made in the art of encapsulating and embedding during World War II. Generally, a distinction is made between electronic parts made by "casting," that is by molding with recovery of the mold, even though this mold may not be reusable, and by "potting," where the container in which the encapsulating material is poured becomes a part of the finished object.

General limitations of encapsulating with any material are:

- Difficulties of repair
- Thermal limitation of the material
- Heat dissipation requirements of the object
- Increased weight over the same object non-encapsulated
- Dielectric properties
- Variable internal stresses within the casting

Foamed plastics have, over the solid plastics used for encapsulation, the advantage of lighter weight, which makes them attractive in the fields of aircraft construction, space travel and missiles. Besides, they are generally the most inexpensive per cu ft of all materials available. They can be applied either by a conventional foaming-in-place method, or by placing the resin and a blowing agent into the mold, and curing under heat.

Urethanes are the most widely used for foaming-in-place. Their electrical properties can be made to vary when the density is varied (Fig VII-3, 4 and 5) and that density can

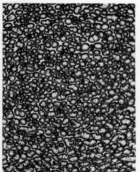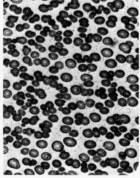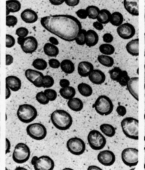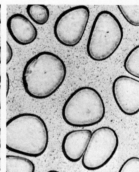

Figure VII-2, nucleation during extrusion causes hotspots which increase number of cells, reduces their size, improves electrical quality. Courtesy Bell Laboratories.

FOAMED PLASTICS

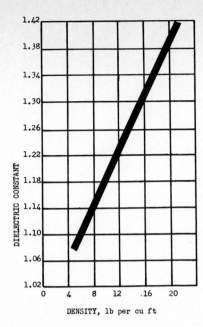

Figure VII-3, variation of dielectric constant with urethane foam density, at frequency of 1 Mc and temperature of 72°F.

indeed cover a wide range—from 2 to 20 lb per cu ft. Either polyester- or polyether-based urethane foam is used, but polyethers are generally considered preferable today. They have a smoother compression load resistance curve, with practically no "plateau" effect; they have better low-temperature flexibility (at a few degrees below zero) and a better resistance to humidity and to solvents. There is little to choose between one-shot or pre-polymer-processed urethanes when it comes to their electrical properties. Adhesion of urethane to most surfaces which they are encapsulating is very good. Limitation of urethane foam—which can be to a great extent overcome by correct designing—is a reduction of its good dielectric properties when exposed to extreme humidity for long periods of time.

Epoxy foams, at a density of 5 to 7 lb per cu ft, are among the toughest encapsulating agents available. Great strength can be imparted to the assembly by submitting it to a baking process for one to two hours at 165 to 212°F to obtain full cure, before slow cooling. Physical limitation is also a lessening of the electrical qualities, after long exposure to high humidity.

Phenolic foams are very light—from 0.3 to 1.5 lb per cu ft—and the most economical. They have good thermal insulation properties,

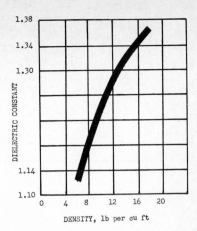

Figure VII-4, variation of dielectric constant with urethane foam density, at frequency of 500 kc and temperature of 72°F.

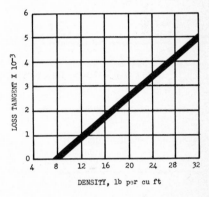

Figure VII-5, variation of loss tangent with urethane foam density, at a frequency of 9.375 kMc and temperature of 72°F.

which may be an advantage, but in many cases may also be an objectionable feature, when heat dissipation is necessary. They are also good soundproofers. They are used more readily as protective shipping material than for encapsulation, because the catalyst used for their cure tends to corrode the encapsulated parts.

Silicone foams are available in rigid or flexible form, and are particularly valuable for high-temperature applications—up to 700°F. The rigid silicone foams weigh 12 to 16 lb per cu ft, have a uniform multipore structure, spherical and unicellular, and do not burn. Their dielectric constant is 1.23 to 1.26 at 10^5 cycles, with a power factor of 0.00102 to 0.0004. Their thermal conductivity, K-factor, is 0.3 at room temperature. The flexible silicone foams are a little heavier—about 20 to

25 lb per cu ft—with a dielectric constant of 2.8 at 10^5 cycles, and a higher thermal conductivity of K = 0.6. These are interesting encapsulating foams for high power, high frequency applications at high temperatures, but they are quite expensive.

Foamed-in-place polystyrene, made from pre-expanded beads (Section XIII, Part I) have good uniform cell structure and good dielectric properties (Table VII-2) but they must be processed in special molding machines, using steam, water and air (Section III, Part III) which may be impractical for certain small scale applications. Generally, multi-cavity molds can be used to good advantage. They are thermoplastic materials, with a temperature limitation of 175°F. Combinations of epoxy resins and polystyrene beads have been prepared: the exothermic heat of the epoxy during its cure suffices to fuse the beads, and a strong material is obtained in a simpler manner.

Low-density compounds with low-density fillers are being used for encapsulation. The resins are polyesters or epoxies, and the fillers may be glass, silica or microballoons (Table VII-3). Mixing must be done very carefully to avoid spotty agglomerations of filler or buoying of filler to the top of the mixture during processing.

Table VII-2—Typical Electrical Properties of Foamed-in-place Polystyrene

Dielectric constant, at 60 cps	1.19 to 1.24
Dielectric constant at 1000 cps	1.05 to 1.07
Dielectric constant at 10^6 cps	1.02 to 1.05
Dissipation factor, regardless of frequency	under 0.0005
Loss factor, regardless of frequency	under 0.0006
Volume resistivity, megohm-in.	below 1.5×10^7
Volume resistivity, ohm-cm	below 3.8×10^{13}
Surface resistivity, megohms	below 9.8×10^6
Dielectric strength, volts/mil,	
Short time	48 to 50
Step-by-step	49
Arc resistance	None; melts at first spark

Table VII-3—Properties of Epoxy Compounds Using Various Low-density Fillers

Formulation	Shrink-age, %	Hardness after cure (Shore D)	Density, at 21°C	Tensile strength, psi	Thermal conductivity, Btu/(hr) (°F) (ft) (in.)	Linear thermal expansion, (in./in.) (°C) (25-100°C)	Dielectric constant at 25°C	Power factor at 25°C	Volume resistivity, ohm-cm	Dielectric strength, volts/mil
100 parts epoxy 10.5 parts curing agent	0.12	80-85	1.17	8,000	2.68	8.7×10^{-5}	1 kc—3.8 1 Mc—3.7	1 kc—0.0035 1 Mc—0.015	25°C 8.7×10^{14}	400-500
100 parts epoxy 100 parts 325-mesh silica 10.5 parts curing agent	0.08	80-85	1.59	5,500	6.38	8.6×10^{-5}	1 kc—3.4 1 Mc—3.4	1 kc—0.003 1 Mc—0.012	25°C 1.3×10^{14} 65°C 6.2×10^{13}	>330
100 parts epoxy 15 parts phenolic microballoons 10.5 parts curing agent	0.14	80-84	0.86	3,300	1.91	8.2×10^{-5}	1 kc—3.2 1 Mc—2.7	1 kc—0.003 1 Mc—0.014	25°C 1.0×10^{14} 65°C 5.3×10^{13}	>300
100 parts epoxy 34 parts clay spheres 10.5 parts curing agent	0.06	75-80	1.01	2,000	2.47	6.7×10^{-5}	—	—	—	—
100 parts epoxy 4 parts urea-formaldehyde spheres 10.5 parts curing agent	0.17	80-85	1.01	4,050	4.15	8.6×10^{-5}	—	—	—	—
100 parts epoxy 14 parts glass microballoons 10.5 parts curing agent	0.25	80-85	0.95	4,200	4.56	8.2×10^{-5}	—	—	—	—

A relatively new technique of foam encapsulating is based on the use of *syntactic foams,* that is, a powdered resin containing as much as 50% of glass or phenolic microballoons (Section XVI, Part II) and cured by exposure to heat—temperature of 250°F for 45 minutes. The phenolic microballoon product is generally flexible, the glass balloon material, rigid. The resin may be a polyethylene, an epoxy or a urethane. The polyethylene, which dissolves readily in hot aromatic or chlorinated hydrocarbons, can be removed by a conventional vapor-solvent degreasing cycle if any repair becomes necessary to the encapsulated parts.

The density of these materials is usually above 20 lb per cu ft (Table VII-3). Additional strength is given to these physically weak encapsulants by providing them with an "eggshell" coating of an unfilled epoxy, aminecured, not over 0.010-in. thick. These syntactic low-density foams are particularly advantageous for the encapsulation of electronic welded modules.

When embedded electronic packages are intended to be exposed to great extremes of environment, they must be tested for their behavior under the conditions which they must resist. These may be: very high or very low temperatures, thermal shock, high vacuum, high humidity, salt sprays, thermal aging, effect of fungus, mechanical shock, intense vibrations, and exposure to nuclear radiation.

Silicone resins are said to maintain their properties after exposure to doses of 1000 megarads of γ radiation. Silicone rubber becomes brittle after exposure to 100-500 megarads of γ radiation. (A megarad is a unit of absorbed dose: 1 rad = 100 ergs per gram.) Its usefulness therefore depends on how much flexibility is needed. Dielectric losses are generally greater during irradiation than before or after, but major properties are not significantly altered after exposure to 1000 megarads.

PART II—FOAMED PLASTICS IN SURGERY
By René J. Bender

1. INTRODUCTION

Plastic foams play a growing part in surgery, due to their physical properties which, in many applications, make them, to a degree, comparable to living tissues.

A distinction must be made between their use for external and for internal applications. To these two extremes must be added certain borderline applications where they remain in contact with internal parts of the body for a limited time only—for example when they are applied as protective coatings over wounds, or when they are introduced into the digestive system to make a flexible casting of its internal condition.

What plastic foams are suitable? For external applications, any flexible plastic foam which can be kept clean—if not sterile—has been used, the selection being made on the basis of resiliency, resistance to abrasion and to chemical attack, absorption—or lack of absorption—of moisture, degree of flammability and, to a lesser degree, cost (Fig VII-6). In this regard, flexible polyurethane, polystyrene and polyvinyl foams have been used, frequently replacing natural or synthetic foam rubber.

For internal applications, essential requirements are chemical inertness and acceptance by the surrounding body tissues. Certain foamed plastics possess such an inertness, and the character of the foam, its spongy structure, makes it much more acceptable to living environment, because it does not interfere with the movement and exchange of fluids that normally take place within the body. Among the plastic foams which have been used internally with success are several silicone elastomers and a polyvinyl alcohol sponge, best known under the name of "Ivalon." The silicone sponges are of two general types: a) heat-vulcanizing stocks which are produced at the plant by exposure to heat; and b) room temperature vulcanizing stocks, or RTV's. The latter are supplied as viscous base materials into which the user stirs a catalyst; this brings about foaming and vulcanization within minutes at room temperature.

2. PLASTIC FOAMS IN PLASTIC SURGERY

Plastic foams, from flexible urethane to silicones, are being used for plastic surgery. The difficulty, in many cases, is to fasten the implanted prosthesis properly and have it re-

Figure VII-6, various medical material of foamed Silicone. Courtesy Becton, Dickinson and Co.

tained, often without the help of bones which, from that standpoint, make orthopedic surgery easier.

Doctors J. Barrett Brown, Minot P. Fryer and David A. Ohlwiler, of the Department of Surgery of Washington University, in Saint Louis, hold the belief that "in plastic surgery with defects close to the surface and with but little covering tissue, there is a more difficult problem of getting a foreign body to be retained, and still more so if there is a movement of the prosthesis or the tissues around it. In the field of plastic surgery, the breast offers a fairly deep place for implantations, but still without the rigid fixation of a bone prosthesis, and with the more difficult objective of normal surface contour."

One of the solid silicone elastomers, "Silastic 372," has been used extensively to make prosthetic parts for plastic surgery: ear armatures, columellae and struts for noses. Sponges made of another Silastic stock are being used for building up cheeks and receding chins (Fig VII-7, 8, 9 and 10). Dr. Maury L. Parkes, of Beverly Hills, Calif., believes that correction of micrognathia (receding chin) is necessary in producing an aesthetically satisfying profile in many cases, even without the presence of nasal deformity. Due largely to the availability of silicone rubber, augmentation is now a very simple procedure, he says, requiring only 15 minutes under local anesthesia.

A silicone rubber which vulcanizes at room temperature has been injected into tissues and allowed to vulcanize *in situ*. It has served to build out depressed areas of the head, to rebuild women's breasts (mammary augmentation) (Fig VII-11 and 12) and for creating a raised area in the back of the throat for cases of velopharyngeal incompetencies. Most doctors prefer the coarse cell silicone rubber sponge for breast augmentation, and the fine cell sponge for more apparent facial implants.

Silicone sponge is also being used in thousands of operations for surgical correction of detached retinas (Fig VII-13). A silicone sponge scleral buckler was developed by Dr. Graham Clark of New York. This consists of a sponge sheet about 0.080" thick. Sponge rods of varied diameters are currently being developed as well for this procedure.

Very few materials will stick to silicone rubber: therefore it must be held in place by

Figure VII-7, typical example of reconstructive surgery, before.

Figure VII-8, the same subject, after surgery with plastic foam (eyes and chin). Courtesy Dr. J. B. Brown, St. Louis, Mo.

Figure VII-9, another example of plastic surgery (cheek and mouth).

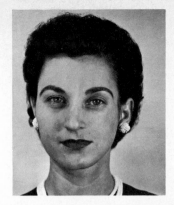

Figure VII-10, the same, after plastic reconstruction. Courtesy Dr. J. B. Brown, St. Louis, Mo.

sutures, or by attaching a "skirt" of "Dacron" cloth to it. The cloth acts as a stroma, which means that it allows tissue to grow in and hold the prosthesis in place. Dacron can be attached to the sponge by means of silicone adhesive (Dow Corning Medical Adhesive Silicone, Type A).

3. INTERNAL USES OF PLASTIC FOAMS IN SURGERY

Two types of foams, or sponges, are being used most consistently for internal surgery: polyvinyl alcohol and silicone foam.

The polyvinyl alcohol, a white sponge with rather large cells, was originally developed by the Simoniz Co. for industrial purposes, and given the registered tradename of "Ivalon." Today polyvinyl alcohol foam is made exclusively by Unipoint Laboratories, High Point, North Carolina. The basic molecule of Ivalon comes in long chains:

$$-CH_2-CH-CH_2-CH-CH_2-CH-CH_2$$
$$\qquad OH \qquad OH \qquad OH$$

It is rather hard and rigid when dry, soft and pliable when wet.

Its introduction into the surgical field was promoted by Clay-Adams Inc, New York, suppliers of surgical and medical equipment. In 1963, the name Ivalon was abandoned. Clay Adams continues to sell the product under the name of "Intramedic Surgical Sponge." It comes in blocks $8\frac{1}{2}$ x $5\frac{1}{2}$ x $2\frac{3}{4}$ in. and 13 x 9 x 3 in.

For burns therapy (see below), it is handled in sheets by Johnson and Johnson. Various applications of Ivalon in internal surgery have been reported in detail in the medical literature—going from repairs to the oesophagus to bone prosthesis, including cardiovascular surgery, and plastic surgery of the nose. One of the characteristics of Ivalon sponge is that living tissues will build up right into its cells, incorporating the foreign body into their structure instead of trying to evict it.

Slicones have a long surgical history. Their use in this field is singularly enhanced by the

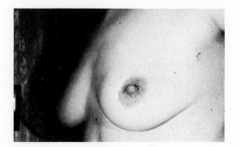

Figure VII-11, repair of post-partum breast atrophy with 3 in. silicone coarse.

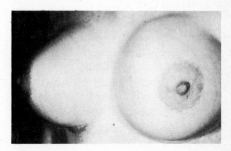

Figure VII-12, grade implant; before and after operation. Courtesy Dr. V. Demergian, Jackson Clinic, Madison, Wis.

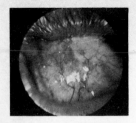
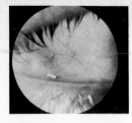

Figure VII-13, surgical correction of detached retina. Courtesy Dr. H. J. Breslin.

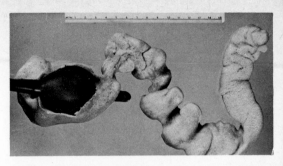

Figure VII-14, mold of inside of colon, obtained by plastic enema method, using room temperature vulcanizing silicone (RVT). Courtesy Dow Corning.

constant work carried out at Midland, Michigan, since 1959, by the Dow Corning Center for Aid to Medical Research.

4. SUPERFICIAL USE OF PLASTIC FOAMS

This refers specifically to the use of a synthetic sponge for the temporary closure of granulating burn wounds, a procedure developed originally by Dr. W. M. Chardack in Buffalo, N.Y., and Drs. Byron Boyer and Mary Martin in Cincinnati. The material is the open cell sponge synthetized by the formalinization of polyvinyl alcohol. Sometimes one side is heat compressed to make it less porous and reduce the loss of protein. But according to latest practice, the uncompressed application is better, and the protein drainage is not considered too important. The sponge can be sterilized by autoclaving or by treatment in ethylene oxide gas. It can be held in place by suture or simply by pressing over the wound. A thin bandage loosely wound around it may be useful in retaining moisture. The sponge must be well applied and good adherence to the wound is desirable lest infection appears. This treatment has been applied to cases where as much as 50% of the body surface was burned, particularly on children. After a period of from 20 to 30 days, it can be removed gradually, and skin grafts applied.

5. USE OF SILICONE FOAM TO EXAMINE THE COLON

One unique application of RVT (room temperature vulcanizing) silicone is the making of accurate molds of the interior of the human intestine to diagnose abnormalities such as lesions, diverticulae, polyps or obstructions which cannot be detected by X-rays. The process consists in giving the subject first a cleansing enema, then an enema of silicone and liquid mixtures, with a stannous octoate catalyst. An industrial sealant gun is used to introduce the mixture into the colon through a Foley bag catheter. The mold is expelled into a bedpan within about five minutes; this results in an accurate, permanent cast of the lower colon. Suspicious areas of the cast are washed with lactated Ringer's solution which is examined for cancer cells. The mold is then washed with detergent, dried and photographed. The method is safe and painless. A recent survey, described in the *American Journal Of Roentgenology* reports that 41 anomalies calling for treatment were found among 80 patients in the age range from 6 to 88 years, 18 over 70 (Fig VII-14).

6. HOW ARE PLASTIC FOAMS ACCEPTED IN SURGERY?

The use of foreign materials inside the human body is not recent; Egyptians and Chinese used artificial sutures thousands of years ago, and for centuries teeth were filled with cement-like materials. Yet until very recently, it was believed that the best replacement for any part of a body was a tissue taken from the same body, or at least an identical tissue taken from another body. This belief led to the creation of banks for bones, cartilages, corneas and vascular parts, in addition to the well-known blood banks. Today, that theory seems to have been disproved; the human body will tolerate and benefit from implantation of substantial amounts of foreign materials, providing these are of the right sort, and the implantation technique is sound.

But the chemistry of the body still raises unsolved problems, and repair or replacement of living parts must be approached with extreme caution. Any material used must answer to these requirements:

1) It must be chemically inert, chemically saturated.

2) It must be capable of standing the physical strains imposed upon it: stress, friction, flexure.

3) It must be and remain sterile.

4) It must not cause reactions in the body, such as heat, inflammation, formation of undesirable tissues or malignant tumors.

5) It must be capable of being easily fabricated in the forms desired.

The degree of inertness of a material introduced into the human body, its compatibility with body tissues and fluids, its tendency to generate antibodies (defensive substances which try to absorb it or reject it), fibrous tissues which try to isolate it, and reactions leading to malignant tumors are still controversial matters, as can be seen in the voluminous literature currently published.

Dr. Enid Oppenheimer, in the college of Physicians and Surgeons of Columbia University, New York City, carries on the work which she started with her late husband, Dr. B. S. Oppenheimer. From her extensive experience, these facts seem to emerge:

1) Malignant tumors are induced in rats and mice with all plastics imbedded in the form of a film or sheet, notwithstanding wide differences in chemical structure. Similarly, metal foils, glass coverslips, and miscellaneous materials such as vegetable parchment, flakes of mica, and discs of horn also cause tumors.

2) If the material is embedded in a different physical form, the tumor incidence is reduced. Perforated films show a reduction in tumor incidence of about 50% from that with solid films, *plastic sponges show a still greater reduction,* and with textiles, loose fibers, or powders, the tumor incidence is almost zero.

3) Induction of tumors by the solid films appears to be dependent on the formation of a dense inactive fibrous sheath or pocket, which occurs around the film only. It is among the cells lining this pocket wall that the carcinogenic change first occurs, and removal of the film after this stage does not preclude tumor growth.

4) Other forms of materials (sponges, powder, etc.) allow the passage of connective tissue elements such as cells, fibers, and blood vessels, which penetrate the interstices of the material and maintain an apparently normal activity, in contrast to the final inactive state of the fibrous pocket wall around the solid film.

5) The malignant tumor does not occur until between one and two years after insertion of the implant. If a comparison is valid between these results with rats and those which might be expected in man, then on a life span basis it would take between 25 and 30 years for a malignant tumor to develop in a human body under similar conditions.

6) These results seem to be confirmed by other researchers in the U.S., and by Dr. John T. Scales in Great Britain and Dr. H. Nothdurft in Germany.

Dr. Oppenheimer's conclusions: be very cautious in the use of any sort or prosthesis to be left permanently in the body; and if this is absolutely necessary, a porous textile or spongy plastic should always be selected in preference to a dense, impenetrable film. In older persons, the risk is very much reduced.

According to Dr. Ethel G. Mullison, staff associate of the Dow Corning Center, there has been no evidence of cancer forming because of implant of silicone in humans. This makes the material very valuable as an insulation for electrodes and electronic devices implanted in the body of astronauts to study the effects of space flight.

Infection is the worst complication that may occur with any implantation: the continuous sponges with connecting interstices afford a perfect culture medium, with serum and blood throughout all the channels, and body warmth for incubation, with no "live" blood circulating through the foam. But these infections usually cause very little cellulitis after drainage tracts are established. In fact, according to Drs. J. B. Brown, David A. Ohlwiler and M. P. Fryer, "the absence of cellulitis and the rapid clearing with removal of the implant, may even suggest the *use* of sponges in cryptic infections and chronic sinuses, as a collecting agent, and find out if a properly timed removal of the foam implant might help *clear* the infection."

Polyvinyl alcohol and other foams once infected may have to be removed and a fresh start made later.

Section VIII—PLASTIC FOAMS FOR REFRIGERATION AND ASSOCIATED INSULATION

By R. H. Harding, F. Hostettler and T. J. Mahoney

1. INTRODUCTION

Cellular plastics are helping to develop new economies in the fabrication, operation, and maintenance of refrigerated transport, structures, and appliances. The value of these materials is based primarily on excellent thermal insulation, combined with useful strength and vapor barrier properties, at low total weight. Those rigid foam systems which can be molded *in situ* by automated equipment are particularly attractive for complex installations, since they eliminate the costly fitting of conventional boards and bats. The monolithic character of such poured-in-place or sprayed-in-place foams contributes to operating efficiency by eliminating joints, and may permit cost-saving simplifications in product designs.

Many factors influence a foam's ability to act as insulation against wide temperature variations. Internal factors include foam density and cell size, proportion of open cells, amount and composition of gas entrapped in closed cells, and inherent properties of the polymer foamed. External factors include methods of application, adhesion to adjacent surfaces, physical integrity and durability, thickness, and imposed stresses. External factors independent of the foam include environmental moisture content, wind velocity, probable exposure to vibration and racking, nature of adjacent structural materials, and the cooling system's ability to remove heat from the insulated cavity.

2. FOAM SYSTEMS

Many polymeric materials have been converted into foams during the past several decades. As in the case of solid plastics, foams can be classified as thermoplastic or thermoset. The thermoplastic foams consist of expanded linear polymers exhibiting the relatively sharp melting range normally associated with the base polymers. In contrast, thermoset foams are based on crosslinked polymers which normally do not exhibit a sharp melting range, although they show plastic flow at elevated temperature. The softening range of a thermoset foamed plastic depends to a large extent upon the molecular structure of the base polymer. Within the same class of thermoset foams, one can vary the mechanical and physical behavior of the product widely by relatively small changes in molecular structure. In the case of urethanes, for example, one can tailor-make foamed plastics having an upper use temperature very near that of polystyrene foam. Conversely, by changing the molecular structure by means of high crosslink density, by introduction of more aromaticity, or both, it is possible to synthesize foamed plastics which decompose near 300°C without exhibiting a distinct softening range.

In the field of low-temperature insulation, urethane and polystyrene foams are gradually gaining substantial acceptance in competing against fiber glass, foamed glass, and other materials. Other foamed polymers have found only limited use in the insulation field, due partly to economics and partly to difficulty of application.

Polystyrene

Polystyrene was the first plastic foam to replace some of the older traditional insulating materials. The extrusion of foamed polystyrene, based on Swedish developments of the mid-1930's, became commercial in the United States in 1944. Expandable polystyrene beads were first developed in Germany about 1952 and introduced in the United States in early 1954.

Polystyrene is an inexpensive material commercially available in large quantities. It is easy to process at low temperatures and pressures to produce cellular materials.

The resulting foam is light, rigid, has relatively good thermal conductivity, is predominantly closed-cell, and is water-resistant. It can be made "self-extinguishing" by addition of inorganic flame-retarding agents. Polystyrene foam will soften and melt at 85-90°C, and any portion of the foam which has been exposed to this temperature range will collapse.

Because it combines useful properties with low cost, polystyrene foam is widely used for refrigeration largely in commercial applications, and seldom in appliances.

Urethanes

Urethane foams are available in a number of formulations, some producing essentially open-celled flexible foams, and others producing rigid foams that are essentially closed-cell. The flexible foams have found wide-spread use in the furniture, automotive, packaging, and many other industries. The rigid foams have found selected use in the refrigerator appliance industry, as low temperature insulation, and in the construction industry. The fact that urethanes can be manufactured as rigid or flexible boards and sheets and that they are available in formulations for pour-in-place, froth-in-place, or spray-in-place, emphasizes their versatility (see Sections IX and X).

3. REFRIGERATION APPLICATIONS

Important markets for foamed plastic insulation exist in refrigerated trucks, trailers, and railroad cars. Other areas include ships and barges, industrial tanks and pipelines, cold-storage warehouses, walk-in coolers, retail display cases, household refrigerators and freezers, air conditioners, water and beverage coolers, and picnic jugs. The most significant penetration of these markets has been achieved to date by polystyrene and urethane foams. Refrigeration-type applications consumed

Figure VIII-1, urethane foam is being spray-applied on a propane storage tank in Florida. Courtesy Cook Paint & Varnish Co.

Figure VIII-2, urethane-insulated propane storage tank in Venezuela. Courtesy Cook Paint & Varnish Co.

Figure VIII-4, cold storage peanuts warehouse in Georgia is the central white portion of building. Over the 6 in. thick polystyrene foam panels, there is a facing of ¼ in. treated plywood overlaid with white acrylic coated aluminum. Courtesy Koppers Co., Inc.

Figure VIII-3, application of urethane in truck bodies for refrigerated transportation service. Courtesy Binks Manufacturing Co.

Figure VIII-5, interior of refrigerated trailer, urethane coated. Courtesy Great Dane Trailers, Inc.

Figure VIII-6, spraying equipment, with automatic control board, to apply urethane foam to refrigerated trailers. Courtesy Great Dane Trailers, Inc.

about 6 and 25-million lb of these materials, respectively, in 1963. Various applications are shown in Fig. VIII-1 to VIII-6.

The stimulus to improve overall economy by incorporating new materials in product designs is greatest for highly competitive industries. Accordingly, refrigeration applications are expected to consume about 9 and 127-million lb of polystyrene and urethane foams, respectively, in 1968. These figures anticipate average annual growth rates near 10% for polystyrene and 40% for the urethanes.

Polystyrene foam has found its utility in freezer and cooler rooms, refrigerated appliances and transportation equipment, and many smaller items. At 9 to 11 cents per board-foot it provides about the same level of insulation as dry glass fiber, which may cost as little as 2 cents per board-foot. Successful competition hinges on the value of such foam characteristics as strength, moisture resistance, and moldability.

Urethane foams are superior insulants but must compete from a still higher price level, currently about 15 to 20 cents per board-foot. Precut boards are used in much the same way as expanded polystyrene, but resist more solvents and higher temperatures. Foaming rates and properties can be adjusted by appropriate formulation and manufacturing changes.

The advantages of reactive "self-foaming" systems are evident. Ingredients are shipped and stored conveniently as liquids, which can be mixed and deposited where needed by precision equipment requiring little operating labor. Mix volume increases 30- to 40-fold in a few seconds, and foams can usually be handled in minutes. The adhesive nature of expanding urethanes can be utilized to seal them in place. Combined with the lightweight foams' inherent strength, this characteristic may permit cost-saving modification of a product's structural components (*e.g.*, thinner skins and fewer bolts). Because an inch of fluorocarbon-blown foam is equivalent to 2 or 3 inches of other insulants, a refrigerated chamber's payload can be increased with no change in specified exterior dimensions. Alternately, the cooling system's heat removal capacity can be reduced at constant insulation thickness.

The following comments relate this discussion more specifically to end-use areas. As might be expected, innovations are normally based on foamed-in-place urethanes.

Transportation

Food transportation may represent the fastest-growing market for rigid urethane foam. Fresh items (fruits, vegetables, meats, dairy products) must be shipped at temperatures ranging from 28°F for figs to 65°F for tomatoes. Frozen items range from ice cream at —20°F to packaged foods at 0°F.

A code recently introduced by the Association of Food and Drug Officials of the United States requires that 0°F be observed as a maximum for frozen foods in transit, and forbids the refreezing of accidentally thawed products. This requirement has given impetus to the study of more efficient refrigeration and insulation systems.

A typical 40-foot truck trailer contains about 1000 lb of foam, distributed as a non-settling shell about 3 inches thick. Because 6 inches of glass fiber are required to provide the same nominal insulation, the foamed reefer has 200 cubic feet of extra cargo space and a significantly lower overall weight. By sealing body joints against air leakage, foam reduces heat input to the point where total cooling loads are actually 30% less than with dry glass.

The integral structure of poured-in-place or properly installed board foams also helps eliminate the moisture pick-up which is common in conventional reefers (drain valves must be provided with glass fiber). Water eventually overloads cooling systems by short-circuiting the insulation. Water accumulation reduces payloads and increases operating overhead: a week or more may be needed to recondition some waterlogged insulants by evaporating as much as 1500 lb of condensate.

Since road vehicles frequently sustain minor damage, economical repair is a definite asset. Damaged areas can be refoamed easily when urethanes are used, preferably by letting fresh mix expand to bond intimately with the original material as it fills the void.

High performance and operating economy are not the only advantages of urethane in the transportation industry. A pilot project of Union Tank Car Company demonstrated that insulating a railroad tank car by foaming a urethane in place reduced overall labor and material costs 50% below the corresponding figure for a block-type installation.

Foams are being increasingly accepted for transportation: Lloyd's Register of Shipping approves the use of rigid urethane foam for low-temperature marine and land insulation, so urethanes will find increasing uses in foreign-built ships. Acceptance by domestic shipyards is already confirmed; interest currently centers on tankage for liquefied petroleum gases.

Appliances

Insulation for household appliances represents a potential yearly application of 50 to 60-million lb for rigid urethane foam. Most manufacturers now offer a foam-containing refrigerator or freezer, usually a top-of-the-line model. The performance of these limited-production units will presumably lead to optimized designs suitable for broader application in future production.

Few service data have been made public. Advertising emphasizes thin-wall construction which, combined with other design modifica-

tions, provides up to 40% more storage space in fixed exterior dimensions. The foam-in-place technique reportedly permits replacement of 16- to 18-gauge sheet metal by 22- to 24-gauge skins. These developments are clearly based on the superior K-factors and good mechanical properties of urethane foams.

In general, the technical advantages of foam in transportation carry over to appliances. Because they are stationary the latter experience less difficulty with air infusion. They also operate in milder environments and are less subject to physical damage.

Industrial

Storage tanks for anhydrous ammonia, liquified petroleum gases, and similar bulk products are being insulated with polystyrene and urethane foams. The latter are often sprayed-in-place to minimize installation cost. Exposed foam surfaces are coated to improve weathering, help maintain the lowest possible K-factor, and reduce hazard in case of accidental fire.

Pipe valves are insulated by foaming-in-place to eliminate the tedious fitting, wiring, and caulking associated with board and block insulants. The same technique may be applied to tees, elbows, and short lengths of pipe located where access is difficult. Straight lines are insulated using conventional half-round sections which have been precut or molded in appropriate sizes. It is interesting to note that flexible urethane foams demonstrate some utility in this area: an annulus slit down one side becomes a snap-on pipe cover.

Despite its technical assets, foam must be applied to industrial piping with caution. Since any organic material can burn, insulated lines running through a plant might help spread accidental fires. Low-temperature insulation on such pipes is normally protected by heat-resistant coverings which minimize contact between air, or combustion gases, in case of fire, and relatively heat-resistant grades of rigid foam.

Miscellaneous

Design trends are difficult to anticipate for many refrigerated products. Some observers feel that virtually all cold-storage warehouses will ultimately be built by fastening urethane-cored curtain-wall panels to structural frames. Perhaps such predictions stem from reports that lightweight, metal-skinned panels have been foamed-in-place with one-sixth the labor required to fabricate similar panels using rigid board.

Polystyrene and urethane foams effectively insulate walk-in coolers. Since most installations are custom-fitted within variable space limitations, modular panel construction is seldom appropriate. Because only moderate volumes of foam are required by each unit, set-up costs for pour-in-place or spray-in-place equipment may become significant. Cut board will therefore probably continue as a preferred medium for this area.

The display cases in retail stores resemble large domestic refrigerators and freezers, but cooling loads are much heavier and far less uniform. There exist strong financial incentives for effective utilization of commercial floor space. High-performance foams contribute to the solution of both problems.

4. TESTING THE FOAMS FOR REFRIGERATION

The chemical and physical properties of polymers and blowing agents decide the potential utility of resulting foams. For a system chosen within satisfactory limits to produce serviceable foam it must be processed under manufacturing conditions directed toward specific end uses. Analysis of foam ingredients is therefore not sufficient to guarantee performance: the foams themselves must be studied.

Because of its technical and economic significance, foam density is one of the important characteristics. For fundamental investigations and quality control purposes, small specimens are usually cut and tested as detailed by ASTM D1622. For foam-containing products, effective density is logically based on the total weight of material charged to occupy a given volume. Measured "overall" densities generally exceed cut "core" densities because of the natural occurrence of continuous polymer skins on the foam surfaces. Differences between the two densities tend to increase with the magnitudes of thermal gradients across expanding foams and with the surface-to-volume ratios of the cavities filled.

Basic tests

The entire manufacturing process influences cell *structure,* a distinctive feature which often affects foam performance as much as any other variables. Correlations among foam properties, production techniques, or formulations must also consider structural effects to have much fundamental significance.

Physical structure can be defined as the amount and geometric arrangement of polymer in a foam. The first factor relates directly to density, while the second includes closed cell content, cell size, cell shape, polymer distribution within cell walls, and normal variations in each of these items. Density can be measured accurately with ease, but techniques defining all other structural details are not available yet.

Microscopic inspection can provide estimates of cell size and shape. It can indicate qualitatively how solids are distributed and whether cells are mainly open or closed. The approach incorporates several practical disadvantages, however. It is time-consuming, requires skilled interpretation of observations, and commonly employs too small a sample to be representative.

One apparatus yields some information about open cell content, and its use has since been standardized in ASTM D1940. Essentially, the method compares the apparent volume of a test specimen with the volume of air it displaces. The difference between these figures is the volume of open cells in that specimen.

Screening tests

Foam properties are commonly determined on a small scale according to procedures listed in Section IV. The pertinence of such data to refrigeration varies considerably. Overall density and K-factor are always important through their direct effects on cost-performance relationships. Core density and porosity help explain whether an optimum K-factor has been approached. Mechanical properties are of interest when product designs call on the foamed insulation to bear some externally imposed load. Since physical durability is obviously important, procedures have been devised to measure a foam's stability under various types of exposure. Product safety presumes some adequate level of fire resistance. Electrical properties are seldom critical because foams generally insulate electrically as well as thermally.

It should be noted that cellular plastics are commonly anisotropic: their cells tend to elongate in the direction in which they move during foaming. As a result, strengths and transfer rates tend to be higher when measured parallel to the rise than when measured

Table VIII-1—Comparison of Some Commercial Low-temperature Insulants

Material	Physical state	Density, lb per cu ft	K-factor* @ 74°F
Dry cellular gypsum	Stiff fibrous sheet	8-30	0.35-1.0
Dry gypsum	Loose powder	26-34	0.50-0.60
Glass foam	Rigid block	9-10	0.38-0.55
Dry hair felt	Flexible sheet	6-13	0.25-0.37
Dry mineral wool	Loose fiber	6-18	0.26-0.32
Dry corkboard	Semirigid	7-11	0.27-0.30
Dry glass fiber	Batting, stiff board	0.5-12	0.22-0.29
Expanded polystyrene,			
Extruded	Rigid board	1.5-2.5	0.26-0.32
Bead	Board, molding	1-2	0.23-0.28
Urethane foam,			
CO_2-blown	Board, molding	1.5-3	0.16-0.24
Fluorocarbon	Board, molding, coating	1.5-3	0.10-0.20

*Effective thermal conductivity, Btu /(hr) (sq ft) (°F /in.)

in the perpendicular direction. Test results must therefore be accompanied by a complete description of specimen geometry, and of the foam sample from which the specimen was taken, if they are to have maximum utility.

The significance of data from these tests is further limited by the fact that they are applied to cut-foam specimens, while it is actually the foam-containing product whose performance must be satisfactory. Since the properties of a composite structure can be quite different from those of its components, data obtained from small specimens technically provide a basis only for preliminary design decisions and quality control specifications.

Application tests

Interpreting data from screening tests is complicated by the fact that their significance in end-uses is usually not known with any precision. Since overall performance depends on the design of each foam-containing item, promising products must be fabricated and studied in actual service. Where possible, prototypes are submitted to realistic application tests.

For example, the U.S. Department of Agriculture, the National Bureau of Standards, and the Truck Trailer Manufacturers Association studied factors influencing heat transmission through insulated trailer bodies. A standard test was evolved and accepted by the industry. The procedure involves measurement of the cooling load required (power consumed) to maintain a trailer's interior at 0°F while 100°F, 50% relative humidity air circulates across its exterior.

The performance of home refrigerators and freezers is studied by similar techniques, although emphasis is usually placed on the stability of "heat leak" factors with time rather than in forced air drafts. Safety hazards associated with appliance door and wall panel designs are commonly assessed in a 25-foot tunnel having gas burners at one end (ASTM E84). The material or assembly tested becomes the 18-inch wide tunnel ceiling. Observations are related to the performance of cement-asbestos board and red oak, whose surface flame-spread rate and smoke density are assigned values of 0 and 100 respectively. Results help determine whether the appliance will receive Underwriters' Laboratories approval.

The components of warehouses and other refrigerated structures may be subjected to still larger fire tests. In ASTM E119, for example, walls or other building members are loaded realistically and then heated on one side by air at temperatures following a temperature-time curve: from 1000°F to 1700°F in one hour, then, up to 2300°F in four hours and longer. Exact procedures and acceptance requirements are specified for various types of building components and occupancies.

Many other realistic tests have been designed to evaluate product performance and safety in service, but have not been formally standardized for industry-wide acceptance.

5. FOAM PROPERTIES

Appropriately selected and effectively applied foamed materials can reduce installed costs below levels associated with conventional insulants of long standing. This fact alone is not, however, sufficient to gain broad acceptance. Equivalent or superior performance must be obtained in service. This condition is met by most cellular plastics.

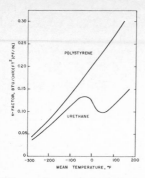

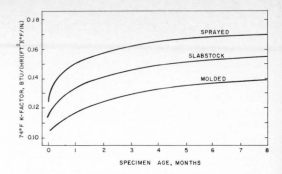

Figure VIII-7, effect of test temperature on K-factors of rigid 2 lb per cu ft foams (inch-thick specimens cut from unicellular moldings).

Figure VIII-8, K-factors of rigid 2 lb per cu ft fluorocarbon-blown urethane foam (inch-thick specimens cut from unicellular products and aged at 80°F).

As refrigeration insulants, lightweight unicellular rigid foams are comparable or superior to many conventional products (Table VIII-1). They supplement this major requirement with other properties in combinations which enhance their overall value. The following review, restricted to expanded polystyrene and urethane polymers, comments on the relation of cell structure and gas content with properties of importance in this field.

Heat transfer

K-factor—Most insulants serve to minimize heat radiation across and convection within the essentially air-filled gaps they occupy. Plastic foams can be unusually effective barriers against these heat transfer mechanisms. Their cells can enclose vapors with thermal conductivities lower than air (K=0.18 @ 74°F), a condition realized when urethanes are blown with fluorocarbon (K=0.06 @ 74°F).

Conductivities of solids and gases rise with temperature but are nearly independent of pressure. Conductivities of gas mixtures depend on their composition. Because fluorocarbons are low-boiling liquids, they begin to condense within a foam at a temperature normally below ambient. Traces of air are always present, and as temperature is further reduced, more of the better insulants become ineffective. Gas-phase conductivities therefore undergo a sort of "reversion" not experienced in air-filled foams. Figure VIII-7 illustrates this phenomenon for a freshly-prepared urethane foamed with trichloromonofluoromethane as blowing agent.

Although rates may be very slow, gases will theoretically diffuse through solids under the influence of partial pressure differences. This

mechanism "dilutes" insulation efficiency when air is allowed to permeate materials containing vapors. Molded, slab, and sprayed specimens are approaching "equilibrium" K-factors near 0.15, 0.16, and 0.18 respectively on Figure VIII-8.

Slabstock is nearly isotropic while other foaming processes cause cells to elongate in the direction they move during expansion. Heat and gases transfer through sprayed and molded foams parallel and perpendicular to their respective rise directions (the exception: specimens cut from thin moldings expanded skin-to-skin develop K-factors intermediate between slab and sprayed foams). This geometry places successively more cell "layers" in every inch of sprayed, slab, and molded foams of constant cell volume, thereby progressively increasing their resistance to air penetration and reducing their K-factor drift rates. This "cascade" effect is magnified on Fig. VIII-9 where specimens cut from a single material to various thicknesses have aged.

Gases diffuse more rapidly through a given solid as temperature rises. Some relationships between aging temperature and effective "cell layers per specimen" can be seen by comparing Figures VIII-10 and VIII-11.

Because solids and liquids have much higher thermal conductivities than gases and vapors, low density is generally associated with quality insulation. However, no solid can bar radiation or convection at zero concentration and an optimum density always exists. Cell wall thickness and temperature have similar but inverse effects on air penetration, so K-factor drift rates increase when foam density is reduced with other factors constant. In practice, cells

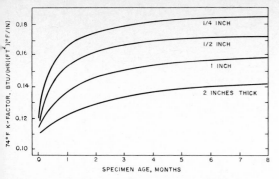

Figure VIII-9, effect of specimen thickness on K-factor of rigid 2 lb per cu ft fluorocarbon-blown urethane foam (specimens cut from unicellular slabstock and aged at 80°F).

become larger and tend to open as density is reduced below some threshold at a level which depends on current formulating and manufacturing technologies: these changes can increase radiant transmission and the fraction of air-filled cells respectively, thus contributing to higher initial and "equilibrium" K-factors.

The forces stimulating diffusion vanish when the pressure of each gas is constant throughout a system. Because this process literally requires infinite time, the fact that all cellular plastics can ultimately become air-filled has no practical significance. Refrigerated equipment, which serves for finite periods, does not freely expose cut inch-thick foam to the atmosphere. K-factor drift is essentially cancelled when foam takes its place in an insulating panel or jacket. It is accordingly found that pertinent design K-factors for poured-in-place or sprayed-in-place installations usually approximate those obtained *initially* from corresponding test specimens, while board exposure histories before installation tend to define the long-term operating efficiency of slabstock.

Moisture Resistance

Water vapor is always present in the atmosphere. Since condensate accumulation within thermal insulants could seriously detract from their performance (K=4.20 @ 74°F for water) designers of refrigerated equipment are especially concerned about this prospect.

Fibrous and granular materials do not provide a real obstacle to water penetration. By contrast, immersion tests indicate that no liquid enters the closed cells of those poly-

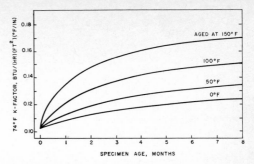

Figure VIII-10, effect of aging temperature on K-factor of rigid 2 lb per cu ft fluorocarbon-blown urethane foam (inch-thick specimens cut from unicellular moldings).

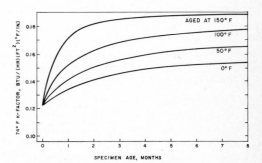

Figure VIII-11, effect of aging temperature on K-factor of rigid 2 lb per cu ft fluorocarbon-blown urethane foam (inch-thick specimens cut from unicellular sprayed material).

styrene and urethane foams which are strong enough to withstand imposed hydrostatic pressures.

Like other gases, water vapor can diffuse through solids under the influence of partial pressure gradients. The rates at which it passes through foams are very low (Table VIII-2) but not low enough to earn for these foams primary vapor barrier ratings. Because foams normally serve as cores of assemblies, such ratings are not essential. Equipment

Table VIII-2—Vapor Penetration Rates of Some Commercial Products

Material	Density, lb per cu ft	74°F WVP*
Gypsum wallboard	47-49	13-19
Glass foam	9-10	0.0
Mineral wool	6-18	100-120
Corkboard	7-11	2-10
Expanded polystyrene	1-2	1-4
Urethane foam	1.5-3	0.3-6

*Water vapor permeability, perm-inch = grains of moisture transferred per (hour) (square foot) (vapor pressure differential/inch of thickness).

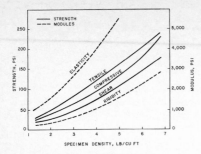

Figure VIII-12, average 75°F mechanical properties of rigid urethane foam.

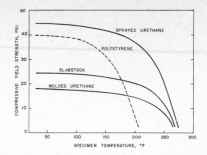

Figure VIII-13, effect of temperature on strengths of rigid 2 lb per cu ft foams.

designers can take advantage of each component's moisture-resistant qualities without insisting that any stand alone. Current refrigeration practices are conservative, and satisfied when one vapor barrier, often a sheet metal skin, is present on the moist (warm) side.

It is noteworthy, but not surprising, that the same factors control both water vapor and air diffusion rates. Their relative effects differ only in magnitude. Water vapor permeability is influenced significantly by polymer structure, foam density and closed cell content, temperature, and the "cell-layers-per-specimen" mechanism previously associated with K-factor drift.

Mechanical strength

Unusually large rigid foam boards can be handled and installed by one man. They are suitable substrates for direct application of plaster, mastics, and other coatings. The puncture resistance of sheet-metal and other thin skins improves significantly when backed with foam. Applied loads are distributed between two skins bonded together by a foam core, thus minimizing overall deflection and eliminating "oil-canning." The number and weight of structural parts in a foam-bonded assembly can also be reduced.

The mechanical properties of most commercial foam systems are roughly similar at room temperature; performance levels drop as continuing expansion progressively reduces the volume fraction of contained solid. Fig VIII-12 presents some typical order-of-magnitude relationships among various mechanical characteristics as functions of density.

Cell shape plays a prominent role in determining the exact strength acceptable for product design. Solid curves on Fig VIII-13 represent the same basic foam; only the slab product was isotropic. Both of the other processes caused cells to elongate to the same degree, but inherent differences of application required that sprayed and molded products be tested parallelly and perpendicularly to their respective rise directions. This strong effect corresponds to a twofold density change.

Differences between the polymers selected become more pronounced as temperature rises. Fig VIII-13 indicates that the thermoplastic polystyrene softens more readily than a thermoset urethane. More highly crosslinked urethanes will retain useful strengths at still higher temperatures. Other variations in molecular composition can influence polymer heat-distortion points and thus modify foam service maximum temperatures.

By definition, insulants for refrigeration are seldom exposed to environments much above 120°F. This is of interest mainly because, within a family of similar polymers, factors which improve temperature resistance tend to improve other foam properties also. This is most noticeable in WVP and some dimensional stability tests, and should by analogy extend to K-factor drift rates.

Friability

All of the curves on Fig VIII-12 would shift downward if polymer crosslinking were reduced below levels normally found in rigid urethane foams. Increased crosslinking, on the other hand, shifts the curves upward temporarily. Further increases extend the modulus trends, but tensile and then the other strength curves begin to fall off.

There is a limit to what may be expected from heat-resistant polymers, because excessive crosslinking produces foams which are brittle under service conditions. Solid fillers, such as powders, or coarse cells generally have similar effects in foams based on any polymer: they tend to increase their friability.

Thermal expansion

Solids contract when cooled. This fact must be considered in the design of heterogeneous assemblies which will be exposed to temperature fluctuations or gradients in service. Linear coefficients of thermal expansion for various commercial polystyrene and rigid urethane foams range between 4×10^{-5} and 8×10^{-5} per °F. The higher figure tends to occur at the lowest densities.

Durability

Chemical resistance—Polystyrene and the urethanes are not attacked by atmospheric gases at temperatures normally encountered in service. The polymers are inert to mildew and fungi and do not nourish insects or rodents. Their foams consequently have long working lifetimes without deterioration.

Polystyrene dissolves in many common organic solvents. Rigid urethanes resist greases and oils: they tend to swell in aromatic and oxygenated solvents but regain their original properties when dried. Both polymers are stable in water solutions of common detergents, salts, acids, and bases. Since foams respond in the same manner, their chemical resistance is adequate for most refrigeration applications (Table VIII-3).

Physical resistance—When fewer than about ⅔ of a foam's cells are closed, dimensional stability is a function of the base polymer's mechanical properties in the given environment. The unicellular structure of refrigeration-grade foams can be responsible for dimensional changes in milder environments.

Table VIII-3—Chemical Resistance of Expanded Plastics
(Immersed in Reagent for 30 Days)

Active materials	Urethane		Polystyrene		Polyethylene	
	Rating 75°F	Rating 125°F	Rating 75°F	Rating 125°F	Rating 75°F	Rating 125°F
Motor oil	E	E	G	F	G	F
Regular gasoline	G	—	N	N	N	N
Turpentine	E	—	N	N	N	N
Kerosene	G	G	P	N	N	N
Linseed oil	G	G	G	G	E	G
Benzene	E	—	N	N	N	N
Toluene	E	—	N	N	P	N
Methylene chloride	F	—	N	N	E	—
Ethyl alcohol	G	G	F	N	G	N
Methyl alcohol	G	G	F	P	E	E
Carbon tetrachloride	E	E	N	N	N	N
Methyl ethyl ketone	P	—	N	N	G	F
Acetone	P	—	N	N	G	G
Perchloroethylene	E	E	N	N	—	—
Water	E	G	E	G	E	E
Brine (saturated)	G	G	G	F	E	E
Sulfuric acid (concentrated)	N	N	N	N	E	G
Sulfuric acid (10%)	G	G	E	G	E	E
Nitric acid (concentrated)	N	N	P	N	G	N
Hydrochloric acid (concentrated)	N	N	F	F	E	E
Hydrochloric acid (10%)	G	G	E	E	E	E
Ammonium hydroxide (10%)	G	G	E	F	E	G
Sodium hydroxide (concentrated)	E	E	G	G	—	—
Sodium hydroxide (10%)	E	G	G	G	E	E

E—Excellent—The plastic was unaffected in any way for the duration of the test.
G—Good—A very slight clouding or discoloration of the plastic took place. Expected life: months to years.
F—Fair—Moderate effect on the plastic. Slight etching, some discoloration, and/or possibly some dimensional change or weight change. Expected life: weeks to months.
P—Poor—Considerable change in plastic. Expected life: days.
N—Not Recommended—Severe attack on plastic. In most cases, the plastic became soft in a few hours and was unusable within a few days or by the end of the test.

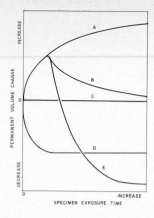

Figure VIII-14, typical foam stability curves.

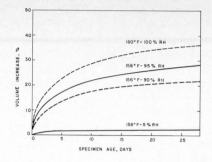

Figure VIII-15, foam stability curves showing influence of temperature and humidity.

Total pressures within closed-foam cells rise and fall with gas diffusion and temperature. Differences between these internal pressures and that of the atmosphere constitute pneumatic forces. Of course nothing happens when polymers are sufficiently rigid to withstand them (Fig VIII-14, curve C). More vigorous conditions encourage elongated cells to approach their preferred isotropic configuration: this cell-rounding process increases linear dimensions perpendicular to the foam rise by 0 to 2% in 2 days (at 160°F) to 100 days (at 70°F), usually without affecting the parallel dimension.

Table VIII-4 shows that fluorocarbon-blown urethanes are subjected to greater forces than air-filled polystyrene. Foams unable to resist these differentials will swell or shrink along curves A or D (Fig VIII-14) to relieve them. Cell walls too weak or brittle to flow sufficiently may rupture: test specimens then follow curves B or E, depending on whether or not the plastic "remembers" its original geometry. Foams based on polymers abnormally permeable to fluorocarbon can also yield B-type curves.

The solid content of a foam is highly significant. Cold-aging, for example, is a fairly realistic "go-no go" test in which foams are stable above characteristic thresholds but shrink abruptly, or rupture membranes, at lower densities.

Foam systems are commonly screened in the laboratory by cutting specimens for "accelerated aging" at elevated temperatures and humidities. The volume of refrigeration-grade polystyrene and urethane foam specimen normally increases about 0 ± 2% and 25 ± 15%, respectively, after 4 weeks at 158°F and 95% relative humidity. Urethanes should follow curves like those on Fig VIII-15 which, incidentally, reveal that high concentrations of warm water vapor exhibit a plasticizing effect. Mechanical properties at room temperature should change to correspond with the aged specimen's final density and cell shape.

No correlations exist between such aging and various types of service. Commercial foam-containing products are obviously stable. Not only are "accelerated" environments unrealistic for direct applications to refrigeration, but bond-in-place foams and adjacent structural components stabilize one another through reciprocal mechanical restraint which is not applied during laboratory tests.

Table VIII-4—Pressure Changes Within Dimensionally Stable Unicellular Foam Specimens

Blowing agent	Temperature, °F	Internal pressure, psia	Difference between internal and atmospheric pressure, psia (1)	Effect of time
Air	−20	12.2	− 2.8	Decays (approaches 0)
	+20	13.3	− 1.7	Decays
	80	15.0	0	None
	160	17.2	+ 2.2	Decays
CCl_3F	−20	1.4	−13.6	Decays
	+20	4.3	−10.7	Decays
	80	15.0	0	Rises and slowly decays
	160	17.2	+ 2.2	Rises and slowly decays

(1) Positive and negative figures promote swelling or shrinkage, respectively.   Initial internal pressure = 15 psia @ 80°F.

Section IX—RIGID URETHANE FOAM
PART I—CHEMISTRY AND PREPOLYMER TECHNIQUES
By Robert A. Stengard

1. WHAT RIGID URETHANE FOAMS ARE

Urethanes today come as rigid and flexible foams, elastomers, adhesives, fibers, paints and coatings. Some of the earliest commercial rigid urethane foams were made in the U.S. in 1952 and 1953. Since then, new isocyanates and other new starting materials for rigid foams have become available at an extremely rapid pace.

Rigid urethane foams are the reaction products of a polyisocyanate and a polyhydroxyl material. This reaction is carried out in the presence of catalysts, a surface active agent and a blowing agent, such as carbon dioxide or a fluorocarbon. The polyhydroxyl compound and the polyisocyanate react exothermically to form the polymer structure of the foam. Carbon dioxide or a fluorocarbon blowing agent expand the polymeric structure while it is being formed. The catalyst helps to control the speed of the reaction. The surface active agent aids in controlling the cell structure and allows the production of rigid urethane foams with fine uniform cell structure.

Rigid urethane foams include a large number of types having a wide range of physical properties. In general, they are characterized by having low elongation (usually less than 10 percent) in tension and a low elastic limit (usually less than 10 percent) in compression. They can be crushed and will have little recovery if compressed beyond their elastic limit.

Rigid urethane foams can be prepared in densities from less than 1 lb per cu ft to as high as 60 lb per cu ft. The high density foams (over 4 lb per cu ft) are used where structural strength is of importance; the low density primarily for thermal insulation. The majority of these foams are in the 1.5 to 2.5 lb/cu ft density range. The low density foams are sometimes referred to as semi-rigid urethane foams, because they have a little more flexibility than the high density foams and often some recovery if crushed beyond their yield points.

2. CHEMISTRY OF RIGID URETHANE FOAMS

The formation of rigid urethane foams involves several chemical reactions which do not take place in any given order but may occur simultaneously depending on temperature, catalysts and the ratio of the foaming ingredients.

(1) *Urethane reaction*

$$R\text{-}NCO + R'OH \rightarrow R\text{-}\overset{H}{\underset{}{N}}\text{-}\overset{O}{\underset{}{C}}\text{-}OR' + \text{heat}$$

Where RNCO is a polyisocyanate such as toluene diisocyanate or methylene bis (4-phenyl) isocyanate and R'OH is a polyhydroxyl-containing compound (polyols, glycols, polyesters and polyethers).

Both the isocyanates and the hydroxyl-containing compounds are polyfunctional*; they have several reaction sites per molecule, so that polymeric materials are formed.

(2) *Urea reaction*

$$R\text{-}NCO + HOH \rightarrow \left(R\text{-}\overset{H}{\underset{}{N}}\text{-}\overset{OH}{\underset{}{C}}\text{-}O\right) \rightarrow R\text{-}\overset{H}{\underset{}{N}}\text{-}H + CO_2$$

and: $R\text{-}NH_2 + RNCO \rightarrow R\text{-}\overset{H}{\underset{}{N}}\text{-}\overset{O}{\underset{}{C}}\text{-}\overset{H}{\underset{}{N}}\text{-}R$

(A substituted urea)

With water in the foaming composition, carbon dioxide is formed, as well as amines.

The amines react with more isocyanate to form a urea, and the carbon dioxide expands the foam while the polymeric structure is being formed.

(3) *Allophanate formation*

The hydrogen attached to the nitrogen on the urethane group is capable of reacting further with an isocyanate group to form an allophanate linkage.

$$R\text{-}O\text{-}\overset{O}{\underset{}{C}}\text{-}\overset{H}{\underset{}{N}}\text{-}R' + R''\text{-}NCO \rightarrow R\text{-}O\text{-}\overset{O}{\underset{}{C}}\text{-}\overset{}{\underset{O=C\text{-}N\text{-}R''}{N}}\text{-}R'$$
$$\overset{}{\underset{H}{}}$$

This is often used as a crosslinking mechanism.

*Functionality is defined as the number of reactive sites per molecule.

(4) Biuret formation

The hydrogens on the nitrogen atoms in the urea formed in equation (2) can react with isocyanate groups to crosslink through a biuret:

$$
\begin{array}{ccc}
\text{H} & \text{O} & \text{H} \\
| & || & | \\
\text{R–N–C–N–R'}
\end{array}
+ \text{R''–NCO} \rightarrow
\begin{array}{ccc}
\text{H} & \text{O} \\
| & || \\
\text{R–N–C–N–R'} \\
& & | \\
& & \text{O=C–N–R''} \\
& & | \\
& & \text{H}
\end{array}
$$

In the manufacture of rigid urethane foams expanded with an inert blowing agent such as Fluorocarbon-11 equation (1) is the only reaction of real importance: the moisture content of all ingredients is very low, so that equation (2) is only of minor significance.

In the manufacture of rigid urethane foams expanded with carbon dioxide, both equations (1) and (2) are important; the polymer is formed by both reactions and carbon dioxide blowing agent is formed according to reaction (2).

Reactions (3) and (4) are of relatively minor significance.

(5) Chain extension and crosslinking

Chain extension and crosslinking occur according to reaction (1) if polyfunctional starting materials are used. Equation (5) illustrates chain extension with a difunctional polyol and a diisocyanate. If the functionality is greater than two, crosslinking will occur.

$$\text{OCN–R–NCO} + \text{HO–R'–OH} + \text{OCN–R–NCO} \rightarrow$$

$$
\begin{array}{cc}
\text{H} & \text{O} & \text{O} & \text{H} \\
| & || & || & | \\
\text{OCN—[R–N–C–O–R'–O–C–N–R]—NCO}
\end{array}
$$

Prepolymer preparation

In the preparation of a rigid foam prepolymer an excess of isocyanate reacts with a polyol so that a high molecular weight isocyanate-terminated polymer is obtained, and the reaction occurs according to equation (5) by adding diisocyanate to the polyol molecule.

Heats of formation

The reaction of an isocyanate with an active hydrogen is exothermic, with a heat generation of from 20 to 35 Kcal/mol for urethane and urea formation, less for the allophanate and biuret.

An inert solvent can be used which will vaporize to form a gas which will expand the foam. Fluorocarbon-11, Fluorocarbon-12, Fluorocarbon-113 and Fluorocarbon-114 are suitable for expanding rigid urethane foams, since they volatilize in the right temperature range and are inert toward the urethane foam polymer structure.

Bond stability

The reactions of isocyanate groups can produce bonds with reactive hydrogen compounds; urethanes, ureas, amides, allophanates, biurets, as well as isocyanate "polymers", may be formed. These linkages vary in both hydrolytic and thermal stability. Since the degree of bond stability is of interest in the formulation of foams suitable for various specific end uses, a listing of the relative strengths of these bonds is shown in Table IX-1.

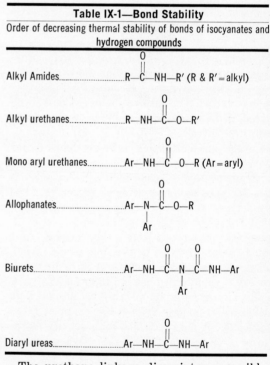

Table IX-1—Bond Stability

Order of decreasing thermal stability of bonds of isocyanates and hydrogen compounds

Alkyl Amides	$R–\overset{\displaystyle O}{\overset{\|}{C}}–NH–R'$ (R & R' = alkyl)
Alkyl urethanes	$R–NH–\overset{\displaystyle O}{\overset{\|}{C}}–O–R'$
Mono aryl urethanes	$Ar–NH–\overset{\displaystyle O}{\overset{\|}{C}}–O–R$ (Ar = aryl)
Allophanates	$Ar–\underset{\displaystyle Ar}{N}–\overset{\displaystyle O}{\overset{\|}{C}}–O–R$
Biurets	$Ar–NH–\overset{\displaystyle O}{\overset{\|}{C}}–\underset{\displaystyle Ar}{N}–\overset{\displaystyle O}{\overset{\|}{C}}–NH–Ar$
Diaryl ureas	$Ar–NH–\overset{\displaystyle O}{\overset{\|}{C}}–NH–Ar$

The urethane linkage dissociates reversibly to isocyanate and hydroxyl at elevated temperatures. This dissociation becomes appreciable in the case of alkyl aryl urethanes at 400°F, which represents the upper theoretical limit of continuous high temperature exposure for urethane foams.

3. RAW MATERIALS

Polyols

The polyol and the isocyanate are the principal ingredients in a rigid urethane foam. The choice of the polyol determines to a large extent the physical properties of a foam; e.g., whether it will be soft and flexible or hard and brittle and whether it will be permeable or impermeable to moisture and gases.

The functionality of polyols used for preparing rigid urethane foam affects the properties of the foam. For rigid urethane foam, polyols have a functionality of six or higher. This large number of reactive sites forms a three dimensional network which results in a stable rigid urethane foam.

Another important factor is the equivalent weight, which is the weight per reaction site, and is derived from the hydroxyl number reported as mg of KOH per gram of resin. Most of the polyols used today have equivalent weights of 80 to 160 (hydroxyl numbers in the range of 350 to 700). Polyols from one end of the range can be blended with polyols at the other end to obtain desired equivalent weight.

Most polyols used in rigid urethane foam preparation are hygroscopic. The equilibrium moisture content is generally high, by foam ingredient standards, and the rate of moisture absorption can be quite rapid. All polyols should be protected from contamination with water, since water as well as the polyol reacts with the isocyanates used in foam preparation.

Polyols are all subject to oxidation, some more than others; they should not be stored at elevated temperatures.

Castor oil and its derivatives

Castor oil was used for many of the early low density semi-rigid foams. It is a relatively low cost material. It must generally be blended with some other material to produce a satisfactory foam. If much castor oil is used in the polyol blend, the foams have flexibility, good resistance to heat, and a predominantly open cell structure. As the ratio of the castor oil in the polyol component decreases, an increasingly rigid, closed-cell foam is obtained. Castor oil and its derivatives are not widely used now. Polyesters and polyethers give better results.

Polyesters

Hydroxyl-terminated polyesters having an equivalent weight of about 125 have been used for preparing rigid urethane foams. These foams have a high percentage of closed cells and high strength properties combined with good resistance at elevated temperatures. Since the introduction of lower cost polyethers, less polyester-based rigid urethane foam has been made. Table IX-2 describes a typical polyester used for rigid foams.

Table IX-2—A Polyester for Rigid Urethane Foam

Viscosity, Brookfield,	
cps at 75°F	300,000
100°F	75,000
120°F	25,000
130°F	15,000
150°F	2,500
Hydroxyl number	440
Equivalent weight	128
Acid number, max	1.5
Water content, % max	0.15
Color, Gardner-Holdt, max	5
Weight per gal, lb	9.8

Polyesters are still used where foams with a high modulus are required. Their high viscosity makes their processing difficult, but it can be reduced into a workable range by heat or by the addition of an inert solvent such as a fluorocarbon blowing agent.

Polyethers

Foams prepared from polyether polyols are generally equivalent in properties to those prepared from polyesters.

Several types of polyethers are available for preparing rigid urethane foam. These polyethers are propylene oxide adducts of many different materials including sorbitol, sucrose, aromatics, diamines, pentaerythritol, phenol-formaldehyde condensates, and methyl glucocide. The polyether polyols cost less than the polyesters. Most have lower viscosity at the same equivalent weight, and, therefore, are easier to process. Some high viscosity materials are also available, but high viscosity polyols can be very difficult to handle. In addition, the higher viscosity polyols having high hydroxyl numbers contain more reactive sites per pound and will, therefore, require more isocyanate, producing a more costly foam. Since the lower equivalent weight polyols are generally more viscous, the choice of a polyol is a compromise between the physical properties desired in the foam and the ease of handling of the polyol. Fig. IX-1 shows the relationship of viscosity to equivalent weight for polyether polyols based on sorbitol.

Polyether polyols based on sorbitol having hydroxyl numbers between 450 and 550 (equivalent weights of about 112) are widely used because they represent a good balance between

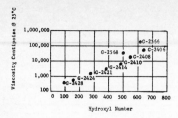

Figure IX-1, change in viscosity with hydroxyl number. Courtesy Atlas Chemical Industries Inc.

physical properties and polyol viscosity, or processing ease.

Polyether polyols used in rigid urethane foams range in functionality from triols to octols. Table IX-3 gives examples of various

Function-ality	Molecular weight	Hydroxyl Number	Equivalent weight	Viscosity cps at 25°C
Triol	440	340	160	32,000
Tetrol	300	770	75	44,000
Tetrol	500	448	125	1,470
Pentol	550	475	118	10,000
Hexol	760	490	115	8,000
Octol	—	443	127	250,000

Table IX-3—Polyether Polyols

functionality materials with some of their properties.

Table IX-4 describes a commercial sorbitol-based polyether polyol.

Table IX-4—Sorbitol-Based Polyether Polyol

Form @ 25°C	Light straw-colored, clear liquid
Specific gravity @ 25°C	Approx. 1.090
Density, lb/gal	9.1
Theoretical molecular wt.	760
Color, Hess-Ives	Approx. 5
Flash point °F	375
Fire point °F	395
Hydroxyl number	480-500
Normal ash, % max.	0.0025
Moisture, % max.	0.10
Viscosity @ 25°C, cps	7,500-10,000
Acid number, max.	0.5
Iodine number, max.	1.0
pH	4-7

Amine-based polyols

Amine-based polyols can be very helpful in improving cell structure and processibility of a foam. The amine used for making the polyether polyol is basic and even the polyol itself is basic which increases its rate of reaction with an isocyanate. In some foaming systems this helps to improve cell structure because the isocyanate-polyol reaction begins so rapidly that the blowing agent (Fluorocarbon-11) does not have time to separate

from the foaming mass.

An amine-based polyol that has been widely used is N,N,N′,N′,—tetrakis (2 hydroxy propyl) ethylenediamine, made by Wyandotte Chemicals Co., Wyandotte, Michigan (Table IX-5).

Table IX-5—Amine-Based Polyol

[N,N,N¹,N¹,-Tetrakis (2 hydroxylpropyl) ethylene diamine]

Form @ 25°C	Viscous water-white liquid
Specific gravity, @ 25°C	1.033
Density, lb per gal	8.6
Molecular weight	292
Moisture, %	0.05
Viscosity, @ 25°C cps.	44,000

Rigid urethane foams made with coal tar

Preliminary work shows that rigid urethane foams made with coal tar, up to about 20% by weight, are feasible for use in sound deadening, insulation, and void filling applications where certain physical properties are not critical.

The CP series of coal tar was used, since there is a distillation and viscosity specification for this type. The lowest viscosity grade of the CP series was used throughout this evaluation. Various catalyst systems were tried with more than 20% by weight of coal tar to prevent excessive shrinkage; however, none of these eliminated shrinkage completely. Therefore, the machine evaluation was carried out using 12 and 20% coal tar CP-422, based on total system. Tar CP-422 can be obtained from: Allied Chemicals Corp., Plastics and Coal Chemicals Div.; Reilly Tar & Chemical Corp., Indianapolis, Ind. and Koppers Co., Inc. Tar Products Div., Pittsburgh, Pa.

The physical property data of the batch-mixed and machine-mixed foams are shown in Table IX-6. Physical properties of a commercial polyether rigid slab stock foam are also shown in this table for comparison purposes.

The machine mixing of the two foams shown in Table IX-6 presented no processing problems. No adjustment of the mixing and metering systems was necessary and no special handling procedures were used. The foams were made using the normal operating methods for the manufacture of a prepolymer type rigid urethane foam.

Flame retardants

Polyols containing phosphorus, chlorine or combinations of the two are available for

Table IX-6—Properties of Batch and Machine-Mixed Foam Made with Coal Tar CP-422 and Prepolymer 164B-230

	Formulation number	
	267	268
Prepolymer 164B-230	100	100
"Freon 11"	31	31
Glycol (OH# approx. 650)	63	63
Coal tar CP-422	25	50
L-520	0.8	0.8
TMBDA	1.5	1.5

	Batch-mix		Machine-mix		Polyether Rigid slab stock
	267A	268A	267B	268B	
Density					
lb per cu ft	1.79	2.25	1.62	2.17	2.1
Physical properties					
Tensile strength, psi	42.1	44.2	46.1	41.0	53.3
Elongation, %	7.5	10.3	2.8	3.2	5.0
Closed cells					
%	84.4	84.6	71.6	70.6	89.7
Heat distortion, 100 gm./sq in., after 24 hours at					
121°C, % deflection	−0.7	1.0	−2.5	−4.1	0
150°C, % deflection	−7.8	−9.3	−10.0	−7.3	7.4
177°C, % deflection	−7.2	−25.5	−20.8	−33.6	−55.0
WVT—Dry cup method—7 days at 100°F—100% R H					
perm-in.	16.49	16.79	2.80	2.58	4.3
Water absorption—8 ft head for 7 days					
lb per sq ft	.09	.10	.09	.11	.07
lb per cu ft	4.3	4.9	4.2	5.2	3.4
Compressive strength					
Yield point, %	9	9	9	9	9
Yield point, psi	30.4	27.0	33.7	30.0	34.3
10% Deflection, psi	31.1	27.4	33.7	29.3	33.8
30% Deflection, psi	29.2	24.4	32.3	29.1	40.2
K-Factor—Btu/hr/sq ft/(°F/in.)					
Original	.160	.170	.153	.159	.136
Aged at room temperature for					
1 week	.166	.175	.169	.168	.135
2 weeks	.173	.192	.165	.170	.143
3 weeks	.173	.180	.165	.173	—
4 weeks	.173	.178	.167	.173	.146
Aged at 50°C for					
1 week	.170	.187	.167	.169	—
2 weeks	.162	.196	.166	.172	—
3 weeks	.176	.196	.170	.175	—
4 weeks	.174	.202	.170	.176	—
Flame test—ASTM D-1692					
			All completely consumed		
Dimensional stability					
Original size, in.	—	—	2 x 4 x 1	2 x 4 x 1	2 x 4 x 1
Size after 1 cycle,* in.	—	—	2 x 4 x 1	2 x 4 x 1	2 x 4 x 1
Size after 5 cycles, in.	—	—	2 x 4-1/16 x 1	2 x 4-1/16 x 1	2 x 4 x 1
Size after 10 cycles, in.	—	—	2-1/16 x 4-1/16 x 1	2 x 4-1/16 x 1	2 x 4 x 1
Size after 20 cycles, in.	—	—	2-1/16 x 4-1/16 x 1	2 x 4-1/16 x 1	2 x 4 x 1

*1 cycle = 16 hr at 100°F, 100% RH /Two hr at 15°F /6 hr at room temperature.

preparing rigid foams that have some degree of flame resistance. Some can be used without blending with other polyols; others, as recommended by their suppliers, should be blended.

The degree of flame resistance varies widely. Some foams are merely slow burning (as measured by ASTM D 1692), others burn only in contact with a flame, still others have low flame spread ratings (as measured by the radiant panel test ASTM E-162 or Tunnel Test ASTM E-84). The self-extinguishing qualities of flame resistant rigid urethane foams are obtained at a slight premium in cost or with a sacrifice in properties or processing ease (Table IX-7).

Table IX-7—Flame-Retardant Polyols

Material	Structure	Supplier	Eq. wt.
Hetrofoam 250	Polyester (contains chlorine)	Hooker	155
Fyrol #6	$(C_2H_5O)_2P(O)CH_2N$- (C_2H4OH+),	Victor Chemical	124
Fyrol #13	$ClCH_3P(O)(OCH_2 CH-)_3$ OH_2CH_3	Victor Chemical	170
Vircol 82	contains phosphorous	Virginia Carolina	260
Pelron 9733	—	Pelron	137
XPL3010	contains phosphorous	Atlas	142
XPL3011	contains phosphorous	Altas	110
Polyol 185	—	Wyandotte	129
Polyol 204	—	Wyandotte	—
Pyrostop PXU-110	contains phosphorous	Richardson	—
Niax BV375	—	Union Carbide	—

Isocyanates

The isocyanate is the second major component contributing to the polymeric formation of a rigid urethane foam. Isocyanate provides the reactive material which ties the polyol into a polymeric structure. The choice of the isocyanate affects the resulting foam properties.

Organic isocyanates were first made by Wurtz in 1848, but they remained a laboratory curiosity until the work of Hanford, Holmes, Rothrock and others in the early 1930's. They are the basis for the urethanes of today.

Most of the commercial isocyanates are made by reacting an amine or an amine salt with phosgene in the presence of an inert solvent. Using a toluene diamine as an example, the reaction is as follows:

$$CH_3C_6H_3(NH_2)_2 + 2\ COCl_2 \rightarrow$$
$$CH_3C_6H_3(NCO)_2 + 4HCl$$

A crude or polymeric isocyanate is obtained by distilling off the solvent, then a pure isocyanate, with little or no color, is produced by distillation under vacuum.

Starting with various nitrotoluenes (o, m, or p) or mixtures of them, TDI with different properties can be obtained. Aniline and formaldehyde are also frequent starting materials, resulting in diphenyl methane isocyanate (MDI).

Pure Isocyanates

A blend of 80% toluene 2,4-diisocyanate and 20% toluene 2,6-diisocyanate is a relatively low cost pure isocyanate, widely used in rigid urethane foams. Two other pure isocyanates, 100% toluene 2,4-diisocyanate, and a blend of 65% toluene 2,4-diisocyanate and 35% toluene 2,6-diisocyanate, are less widely used. These materials are described in Table IX-8.

Table IX-8—Pure Toluene Diisocyanates Used in Rigid Urethane Foams

	>97.5% 2,4 isomer[1] <2.5% 2,6 isomer	80% 2,4 isomer[2] 20% 2,6 isomer
Appearance	Water white liquid	Water white liquid
Specific Gravity, 77/39°F	1.22	1.22
Weight per gallon, lb	10.2	10.2
Purity, % min	99.5	99.5
Freezing point, °F	70.7	57.2
Total acidity, %	0.007	0.007
Hydrolyzable chlorine, %	0.015	0.015
Total chlorine, %	0.10	0.10
Boiling point, °F	484	484
NCH content, %	48.3	48.3
Equivalent weight	87	87
Odor	Sharp, pungent, characteristic.	
Solubility in aromatic hydrocarbons, chlorinated aromatic hydrocarbons, nitrobenzene, acetone, ethers and esters.	Soluble	Soluble

[1] Available as: Hylene® T (Du Pont)
Nacconate 100 (Allied)
Mondur TDS (Mobay)
[2] Available as: Hylene® TM (Du Pont)
Nacconate 80 (Allied)
Mondur TD-80 (Mobay)

The 80/20 blend of the 2,4 and 2,6 isomers has received much attention and a detailed description of it is given in Table IX-9.

Each of the isocyanate groups in the 2,4 and the 2,6 isomers have different reactivities. At room temperature the relative reaction rates are:

2,4 isomer   2,6 isomer

*After one group has reacted, the reactivity of the remaining group is 17.

As the reaction temperature increases, there is less difference in the relative reactivity of the various isocyanate groups.

80/20 toluene 2,4/2,6 diisocyanate is a mixture of two toluene diisocyanates having different freezing points. On freezing, fractional crystallization takes place with the higher melting 2,4 isomer crystallizing first. Freezing and thawing produce no change in the materials to interfere with their subsequent effectiveness.

Handling of isocyanates

The handling of toluene diisocyanate is covered in Bulletin SD-73 from the Manufacturing Chemists Association (MCA).

TDI is an irritating substance in either its liquid or vapor form.

Its characteristic odor and strong irritating effect on the eyes and upper respiratory passages are warnings of the presence of TDI vapors in the air. No one will voluntarily stay in a high concentration of these vapors.

A threshold limit for TDI vapor has not yet been fully determined, but preliminary tests indicate 0.1 ppm is safe. A concentration which can be smelled (approximately 0.1 to 1.0 ppm, varying with the individual) is too high for continuous exposure.

Portable calibrated indicators for the detection of TDI vapor are commercially available.*

The unit in Fig. IX-2 is capable of detecting levels as low as 0.01 ppm of TDI in air in less than 20 minutes.

Buildings in which TDI is handled or stored should be well ventilated. Totally enclosed systems should be used whenever possible for processes using TDI. A hood type ventilation unit should be situated over equipment where TDI vapors are present in the atmosphere. The hood face velocity should be at least 100 ft per minute per sq ft of hood opening.

Mine Safety Appliances, Pittsburgh, Pa.
Union Industrial Equipment Corp., Port Chester, N.Y.

Figure IX-2, test kit for measuring TDI content of air. Courtesy Union Industrial Equipment Corp.

Table IX-9—Properties of 80/20 Toluene 2,4/2,6 Diisocyanate

Specific heat, Btu/lb/°F	
@ 32°F	0.34
@ 320°F	0.45
Thermal conductivity @ 68°F, Btu/hr-sq ft-°F/ft	0.097
Flash point,	
Cleveland open cup	275°F
Tag open cup	270°F
Fire point, Cleveland open cup	285-290°F
Decomposition temperature	530°F
Gross heat of combustion, Kcal/mol	132
Latent heat of fusion, Btu/lb	29.2
Heat of vaporization @ 260°F, Btu/lb	144.9
Coeff. of expansion, in. per in. per °C	8.4×10^{-4}
Vapor density (air=1)	6.0
Electrical resistivity, reciprocal ohms at 1 Kc/in.	0.18×10^{-6}
Specific resistance, ohms	2.5×10^{6}

Temperature	Vapor pressure	Con. in air @ equilibrium
68°F	0.003 mmHg	0.00044 % by volume
104	0.070	0.0092
158	1.0	0.013
248	11.8	1.6
293	31.5	4.1

Temperature	Specific gravity	Viscosity	Density
16°C	1.227	—cps	10.240 lb/gal
17	1.226	—	10.231
18	1.225	—	10.223
19	1.224	—	10.215
20	1.223	3.20	10.260
21	1.222	—	10.198
22	1.221	—	10.190
23	1.220	—	10.181
24	1.219	—	10.173
25	1.218	2.90	10.165
26	1.217	—	10.156
27	1.216	—	10.148
28	1.215	—	10.140
29	1.214	—	10.131
30	1.213	2.65	10.123
31	1.212	—	10.115
32	1.211	—	10.106
33	1.210	—	10.098
34	1.209	—	10.090
35	1.208	—	10.081
36	1.207	—	10.073
37	1.206	—	10.065
38	1.205	—	10.056
39	1.204	—	10.048
40	1.203	2.15	10.040
41	1.202	—	10.031
42	1.201	—	10.023
43	1.200	—	10.014
44	1.199	—	10.006
45	1.198	—	9.998
50	1.193	1.75	9.956
60	1.183	1.45	9.873
70	1.173	1.20	9.789
80	1.163	—	9.706
90	1.153	—	9.622
100	1.143	—	9.539

In spray applications adequate ventilation is extremely important because air atomization can produce a high concentration of isocyanate vapors in the atmosphere.

TDI is not classified as a dangerous chemical and therefore is not subject to ICC regulations governing the transportation of hazardous articles. It is shipped in drums, tank trucks, or tank cars.

In general, plain steel equipment is satisfactory for contact with isocyanates. Tanks may be lined with heat cured phenolic coatings to prevent discoloration during storage. Aluminum is not recommended. Stainless steel pipelines and tanks are satisfactory but too costly unless an absolute minimum of discoloration must be maintained.

Urethane paints are not harmed by spills as much as are conventional coatings.

Polymeric isocyanates

Polymeric or undistilled isocyanates differ from the pure isocyanates by the presence of higher molecular weight (polymeric) isocyanates, or tars, which give these products a dark color and a higher viscosity. They have a lower isocyanate content. Foams can be made using these materials by either a prepolymer or one-shot technique.

Polymeric isocyanates offer an economic advantage over the pure isocyanates in foaming compositions. Flame resistant foams can be made more easily using them. They are particularly useful when a non-dripping, self-extinguishing foam is needed.

Table IX-10 shows the most important

properties of these polymeric isocyanates.

Same precautions should be used in handling the polymeric isocyanates as are used with the pure isocyanates. The polymeric isocyanates based on MDI, Methylene bis (4-phenyl) isocyanate, and PAPI, Poly aryl polyisocyanate, have lower vapor pressures and will generally be present in the atmosphere in lower concentration than TDI under the same conditions.

Other isocyanates are available, but none are presently of commercial importance for rigid urethane foams.

Catalysts

The reaction between an isocyanate and the hydroxyl group in a polyol will take place without a catalyst, but it is too slow. Without a catalyst, a foam may expand but it may not cure adequately to give good physical properties.

The urethane reaction in equation (1) can be catalyzed by basic materials. Tertiary amines such as triethylenediamine, tetramethylbutane diamine, diethylaminoethanol and triethylamine have been widely used.

Table IX-11 shows the relative order of reactivity of various catalysts in a model foaming system. These rates can be expected in

Table IX-10—Polymeric Isocyanates

	TDI	MDI	PAPI
Color	Dark brown	Dark brown	Dark brown
Specific gravity 25/25	1.27	1.24	1.23
Weight per gal, lb	10.6	10.3	10.0
NCO content, %	37-38	29-31	30.5-31.5
Equivalent weight	111-113	136-145	133-138
Sediment, %	<0.1	<0.1	<0.1
Hydrolyzable chlorine, %	<0.4	<0.2	<0.6
Total acidity, %	<0.4	<0.2	<0.4
Viscosity, @ 30°C, cps	70	100	350
Freezing point, °F (°C)	36 (2)	-23 (-10)*	
Flash point, °F (°C)	285 (140)	420 (216)	425 (219)
Fire point, °F (°C)	295 (145)	450 (232)	

*Determined on a quick-freeze test. On long standing at higher temperatures, crystallization will generally occur.
TDI = Toluene diisocyanate.
MDI = Methylene bis (4-phenyl isocyanate).
PAPI = Polymethylene polyphenyl isocyanate.

Table IX-11—Relative Reactivity of Catalysts (Urethane Reaction)

	Order of reactivity		Order of reactivity
Uncatalyzed	1	0.5% DBTDL	670
0.1% NEM	11	0.1% DBTDL + 0.2% TMBDA	700
0.5% NEM	22	0.1% DBTDL + 0.5% TEA	700
0.1% TEA	24	0.1% SnOct + 0.5% NEM	800
0.1% TMBDA	56	0.1% DBTDL + 0.5% NEM	900
0.5% TEA	74	0.1% DBTDL + 0.2% DABCO	1000
0.1% DABCO	130	0.1% SnOct + 0.2% TEA	1000
0.5% TMBDA	160	0.1% SnOct + 0.2% TMBDA	1000
0.1% DBTDL	210	0.1% SnOct + 0.2% DABCO	1000
0.2% DABCO	260	0.1% SnOct + 0.5% TEA	1000
0.3% DABCO	330	0.1% DBTDL + 0.5% DABCO	1410
0.3% DBTDL	340	0.1% SnOct + 0.5% TMBDA	1410
0.5% DABCO	390	0.1% SnOct + 0.5% DABCO	1510
0.1% DBTDL + 0.2% NEM	410	0.3% DBTDL + 0.3% DABCO	1780
0.1% DBTDL + 0.5% NEM	430	0.3% SnOct	3500
0.1% DBTDL + 0.2% TEA	530	0.3% SnOct + 0.3% DABCO	4250
0.1% SnOct	540	0.5% SnOct	4500
0.1% SnOct + 0.2% NEM	540		

NEM = n-ethylmorpholine
TEA = triethylamine
DABCO = triethylene diamine
TMBDA = tetramethylbutane diamine
DBTDL = dibutyltin dilaurate
SnOct = stannous octoate

full-size operation, although the mass effect may somewhat obscure differences in rates.

In rigid urethane foaming systems using the carbon dioxide formed by the water-isocyanate reaction, a balance of the relative rates between the urea and urethane reactions is necessary. If the urethane reaction is too slow, the gas will not be trapped and no foam will be formed. If the urethane reaction is too fast, the polymer will set up before the gas is formed and a high-density foam will result. Catalysts enable control of this reaction much less than the urethane reaction.

Tertiary amines alone can be used as catalysts but for some applications, such as spraying, more speed is desirable. Metal salts, particularly those based on tin, accelerate the foaming reactions. They can be used alone or in combination with the tertiary amine-type catalysts. Tin catalysts of importance for rigid urethane foaming are stannous octoate and dibutyl tin dilaurate. Stannous octoate will hydrolyze rapidly in the presence of a basic catalyst with loss of activity. Masterbatches containing stannous octoate and moisture are stable for only a few hours at room temperature. In some cases, particularly for making foam buns, the foaming machine is equipped to deliver several separate streams to the mixer. Here, stannous octoate catalyst can be delivered separately or in an inert carrier, such as a dry polymer or plasticizer.

Resin masterbatches containing dibutyl tin dilaurate may stay stable for months. Therefore dibutyl tin dilaurate is preferred for foaming systems packaged for use at other locations or in plants where resin masterbatch is not used immediately.

Other basic materials have been tried as catalysts, with little success. Materials as basic as caustic (NaOH) should not be used because they may cause violent reactions. Ferric acetyl acetonate (sometimes used as a catalyst in urethane coatings) in combination with a tertiary amine will work as a catalyst, but the foams may be pyrophoric at elevated temperatures.

"Delayed action" catalysts have been made. An organo-tin molecular sieve catalyst has been used experimentally but has not become of commercial significance.

Buffered amine catalysts, where the amine's activity is reduced by the presence of an acid, have also been used. One example is a diethylethanol amine water solution where one-third of the amine is buffered with hydrochloric acid. This catalyst was used with semi-rigid urethane foams based on castor oil and expanded with carbon dioxide.

Acidic materials can be used to retard the urethane reaction. Hydrogen chloride and benzoyl chloride have been used in combination with amine type catalysts to control reaction rates. A small percentage of acid can increase foaming time from 2.2 min. to 6 minutes.

Temperature can also be used to control urethane foaming reactions: higher temperatures accelerate the foaming reactions. Some delayed-action rigid urethane foaming systems have been made by premixing all of the foaming ingredients at very low temperatures (as low as $-300°F$). When these systems are heated, foaming of the mass takes place.

The vapors of tertiary amine catalysts are irritating and contact with the skin can cause dermatitis.

Tin catalysts can produce severe irritations by contact with the skin. Their vapors are also irritating. Care must be taken to insure that the materials in solid, liquid or vapor form do not come in contact with the human body.

Surface active agents

A surface active agent (surfactant) aids in the mixing of the foaming ingredients and helps to regulate the cell structure of the foam.

Castor-oil-based systems generally do not require a surfactant to produce a foam, but the inclusion of one will produce a foam with a finer cell structure and better physical properties.

Polyester- and polyether-based **rigid foams** generally require a surfactant whether they are expanded with carbon dioxide from the water-isocyanate reaction or with an inert blowing agent such as a fluorocarbon. Without surfactant the foam may collapse or will have a coarse cell structure.

Surfactants used in rigid foams range from ionic and non-ionic organic types to the silicones. Anionic surfactants, or those which contain active hydroxyl groups, should not be added to an isocyanate containing foaming component.

The most widely used surfactants are copolymers based on dimethyl polysiloxane and polyoxysiloxanes. Some of these silicones are prepared with ethylene oxide; others are made with ethylene and propylene oxides (SF-1034, made by General Electric, L-520 from Union Carbide, and DC-199 from Dow Corning).

	Fluoro-carbon-11	Fluoro-carbon-12	Fluoro-carbon-113
Chemical formula	CCl_3F	CCl_2F_2	CCl_2F-$CClF_2$
Molecular weight	137.38	120.93	187.39
Boiling point @ 1 atm., °F	74.78	–21.62	117.63
Freezing point, °F	–168	–252	–31
Viscosity @ 30°C, cps			
Liquid	0.405	0.251	0.619
Vapor (1 atm)	0.0111	0.0127	0.0104 (0.1 atm)
Surface tension @ 25°C, dynes/cm	19	9	19
Refractive index of liquid, $n_D^{26.5}$	1.1384	1.285	1.355
Flammability	nonflam-mable	nonflam-mable	nonflam-mable
Density			
Saturated vapor @ boiling point, gm/liter	5.85	6.33	7.38
Vapor @ 30°C & 1 atm, gm/liter	5.676	4.956	7.053[1]
Liquid, gm/cc			
Boiling point	1.479	1.487	1.510
10°C	1.511	1.364	1.599
20°C	1.488	1.329	1.576
30°C	1.464	1.292	1.553
Thermal Properties			
Heat capacity of liquid @ 30°C, cal/gm°C	0.209	0.235	0.218
Heat capacity of vapor @ 1 atm, cal/gm°C	0.135	0.145	0.161[1]
Heat capacity ratio, C_p/C_v	1.136	1.137	1.080[1]
Heat of vaporization @ boiling point, cal/gm	43.51	39.47	35.07
Thermal conductivity, Btu/hr/sq ft °F/ft			
Liquid @ 30°C	0.609	0.0492	0.0521
Vapor (1 atm)			
@ 10°C	0.00460	0.00509	0.00495
@ 20°C	0.00472	0.00533	0.00427
@ 30°C	0.00484	0.00557	0.00450
Hydrolysis, grams hydrolyzed per liter of water per year at 86°F and 1 atm of pressure	<0.005	<0.005	<0.005
Solubility in water @ 1 atm, 25°C, wt %	0.11	0.028	0.017[2]
Solubility of water, wt %			
@ 30°C	0.013	0.012	0.013
@ 0°C	0.0036	0.0026	0.0036
Solubility of oil	miscible	miscible	miscible

Table IX-12—Properties of Fluorocarbon Blowing Agents

[1] 60°C [2] at saturation pressure

Some silicones contain Si-O-C linkages and are hydrolytically unstable (e.g., L-520); others do not contain a silicon-carbon bond and are stable (e.g., DC-113 Dow Corning, L-530 from Union Carbide, SF-1066 made by General Electric). In general, higher viscosity silicone copolymers are more efficient and will give foams with finer cell structure. Surfactants are used at the 0.5 to 1% level in rigid urethane foams. With too little silicone, foam cell structure is large. Too much silicone does not affect the foam properties, but is wasteful.

One particular silicone usually works best in a particular foam system, producing the finest cell structure.

Two different types of silicones can be mixed with no difficulty, but occasionally a trace amount of one type in the presence of another type will produce a foam with large irregular cell structure. The solution is to wash the system with an inert material.

There is no health hazard connected with the use of silicones.

Blowing agents

Fluorocarbons—Most rigid urethane foams of low densities (below 4 lb/cu ft) are expanded with a fluorocarbon blowing agent and have an exceptionally high resistance to heat flow, because fluorocarbon blowing agents have low thermal conductivity (K factor). They also have low boiling points so that they are volatilized by the exothermic heat of the urethane reaction and expand the foam.

They act as a moderating agent and do not produce additional crosslinking into the foam. They are inert and are retained in the polymeric structure of the foam.

The exothermic heat of the reaction of an isocyanate with the hydroxyl group vaporizes the fluorocarbon. This moderates the foaming reaction, slowing down the gelling rate and making it easier to pour a large foamed section. Better quality foams with less scorching or charring in the center of a large pour can thus be obtained.

Fig. IX-3 shows the thermal conductivity of two of the most commonly used fluorocarbons, Fluorocarbon-11 and Fluorocarbon-12, compared to carbon dioxide and air, over a wide range of temperatures. Rigid urethane foams expanded with these gases have lower thermal conductivity than foams expanded with carbon dioxide or air.

Fluorocarbon-11, 12 and 113 can be used for

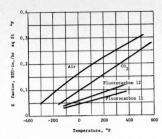

Figure IX-3, thermal conductivity of gases at various temperatures.

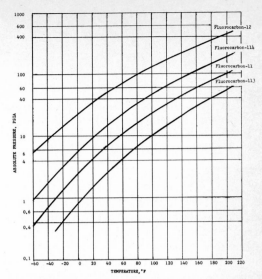

Figure IX-4, pressure-temperature relationships of fluorocarbon blowing agents.

expanding rigid urethane foams. Most frequently used is Fluorocarbon 11, because of its low cost and low boiling point (75°F). Fluorocarbon-12, which boils at −21°F is used in the frothing process (see p. 141). Fluorocarbons 113 and 114 cost more and are not as widely used. Fig. IX-4 shows the pressure-temperature relationship of fluorocarbon blowing agents. See Table IX-12 for physical properties of these fluorocarbons.

Handling of fluorocarbons

Fluorocarbon blowing agents are non-flammable materials and have a very low order of toxicity. Small drums of Fluorocarbon-11 are shipped in ICC 5B, ICC 5 or ICC 17E drums, and foaming composition components containing Fluorocarbon-11 should be shipped in the same types of containers. Fluorocarbon-12 is classified under ICC regulations as a non-flammable compressed gas, and, as such, must be shipped in ICC 4B 300 or ICC 4BA 300 containers. The last three numbers on these containers indicate the pressure rating in psi.

Care should be exercised in opening containers of Fluorocarbon-11, since this material boils close to room temperature.

Fluorocarbon-12, unlike Fluorocarbon-11, is a vapor at room temperature unless it is held under pressure. For the foaming processes it is used only from the container under pressure. It is available in a Pressureflow cylinder which can be hooked up directly to a mixing head through a flowmeter and throttling valve.

The air or nitrogen supply pressure to the Fluorocarbon cylinder must not exceed the ICC pressure rating, but an integral pressure relief valve set at 425 psi should relieve excessive pressure.

Carbon dioxide as blowing agent

Some low density foams and most high density rigid urethane foams used for structural purposes are expanded with carbon dioxide, produced by the water-isocyanate reaction, for easier processing and better density control. The amount of carbon dioxide generated is determined by the amount of water used in the foaming composition.

After the foam has formed, but before the polymer is completely set, it is very permeable to carbon dioxide, and often the diffusion of carbon dioxide out of the foam is more rapid than the infusion of air or moisture into the foam, causing foam shrinkage if the polymer structure is not sufficiently rigid. Low density rigid urethane foams expanded with carbon dioxide often exhibit a friability, on the surface or throughout the foam, because of the formation of short molecular weight units. This friability can be reduced by the use of higher equivalent weight polyols, and by the selection of adequate catalyst.

Fluorocarbons, carbon dioxide and isocyanate fumes are heavier than air and will settle in low places. Ventilation should exhaust the air from the low points.

Other blowing agents

Other blowing agents have been used experimentally to expand rigid urethane foams. Methylene chloride is of interest because of its low cost; however, it will soften urethane polymers and cause cracks in rigid foams expanded with it. Methylene chloride is not used in any practical process.

Hydrocarbon blowing agents such as propane, butane, and pentane have been tried. Because of their flammability and their value as fuels, they have not gained wide acceptance.

Additives

A great variety of materials have been used as additives: air, inert gases, dyes, plasticizers, metal oxides, plastics, organic fillers, wood-flower, clay, mineral talc, tall oil, coal tar and pitch for various purposes described below.

Nucleating agents

When large pours of foam are made by machine mixing, as in rigid foam bun produc-tion, addition of a nucleating agent may be needed to produce a fine cell structure. This nucleating agent can be air, added to the foam-ing composition at the mixer, or it can be a solid such as carbon black or talc, added to one of the foam ingredients. These additives are used in very small amounts, usually less than 1%. Physical strength properties, K fac-tor, and water pickup are improved.

Dyes and colorants

It is sometimes desirable to color one or both components of the foaming composition, for identification so that a resin component will not be put into a machine used for pump-ing the isocyanate component. Many dyes and colors are available. In general they should be dry to avoid upsetting the chemistry of the composition. Material added to an isocyanate-containing component should contain no active hydrogen groups which could react with the isocyanate. Colorants should be readily dis-persed in the foaming component and should not settle out on standing.

Organic fillers

Some of these materials, such as cornstarch, woodflour, etc., contain hydroxyl groups which can react with the isocyanate, but since they are solids, the reaction is very slow and they will act essentially as inert fillers. In general, the fillers will increase foam density and some-times give higher strength. These foams often have less resistance to moisture because some fillers are moisture sensitive.

Mineral fillers

Mineral fillers such as clays and talc have been used. Their behavior in rigid urethane foams is very similar to that of the organic fillers, but they have little effect on the mois-ture resistance of the foam. These fillers are more difficult to process since they are heavy and will tend to settle out of the urethane foaming composition. Agitators may have to be used. These fillers often increase the ap-parent viscosity of the foaming composition to such an extent that they are impractical to process. They may cause excessive wear of the pumps and the mechanical mixers used for blending the foam ingredients.

Metal oxides fillers

Metal oxides such as antimony oxide, and some inorganic materials such as ammonium phosphate impart a degree of flame resistance to rigid urethane foams. Heavier metal oxides have been added to modify electrical properties for uses such as radiation shielding and in radome work.

Plasticizers

Non-reactive liquids are used a) to reduce viscosity for improved processing, b) to im-prove flame resistance. The softening effect of the plasticizer is generally compensated by using a polyol of lower equivalent weight, so that a higher crosslinked polymer structure is obtained. These materials will also increase foam density and often adversely affect phys-ical properties.

Bulk fillers

Foams containing bulk fillers such as pheno-lic and styrene beads have usually been in-ferior to unfilled foams.

Fibers

Fibrous materials, principally synthetic fibers, such as nylon, acrylic and polyester, have been added to rigid urethane foams to give them better dimensional stability and higher strength properties. However, even small amounts of fibers will significantly in-crease the viscosity of the foaming composi-tion, making it more difficult to handle.

Reactive additives

Because of their low cost, there has been a great deal of incentive to add coal tar, pitch, blown asphalt and tall oil in rigid urethane foam. In every case, foam properties or proc-essing ease are sacrificed. Some compositions have been developed utilizing materials satisfactory for vibration damping.

Handling hazards

In general, there are very few handling problems or hazards associated with these additives outside of the problems already discussed. Because of the high viscosity that results from the use of some of these materials, they are difficult to pour and may be extremely difficult to process on conventional equipment.

4. TYPES OF FOAMING SYSTEMS

Rigid urethane foams can be prepared by three different techniques: 1) prepolymer, 2) semi-prepolymer, 3) one-shot.

Prepolymer technique

A polyhydroxyl compound is reacted with an excess of polyisocyanate to produce an isocyanate-terminated prepolymer, a material containing all of the polyol and all of the isocyanate to be used in the foaming composition. This prepolymer is reacted with water in the presence of the catalyst and a surface active agent to produce a foam. Conditions can be varied to control viscosity, isocyanate content and storage stability of the prepolymer and the final foam properties.

The prepolymer technique is used mostly with polyhydroxyl compounds having equivalent weight over 225, such as castor oil and its derivatives. Foams prepared from these materials have flexibility and are classified as semirigid. With polyols having lower equivalent weight, the semi-prepolymer technique is preferred because complete prepolymers prepared with these polyols are too viscous for usual processing equipment.

All prepolymer-based foams are blown with carbon dioxide from the water-isocyanate reaction. Foam density can be changed by varying the amount of water in the catalyst component. Table IX-13 gives typical formulation.

Semi-prepolymer technique

In the semi-prepolymer technique, approximately 20% of the polyol to be used in the foaming composition is pre-reacted with all of the isocyanate. The resulting material contains 28 to 31% of free isocyanate group, and is also called a prepolymer.

Foam is made by reacting this prepolymer

Table IX-13—Castor Oil-Based Prepolymer

	Parts by weight
Prepolymer, (14.5% NCO) Eq Wt = 290	
Castor Oil, Grade AA	85
PEG-200[1]	15
Toluene diisocyanate	100
Blend-Heat for 1-½ hrs at 120°C (250°F)	

Approx. foam density, lb per cu ft	2	5	10	16	20
Prepolymer	100	100	100	100	100
Catalyst #1	7	2	—	—	—
Water – 49%					
HCl (36% solution) – 9%					
Diethylethanolamine – 42%					
99.8% Glycerine (0.2% Water)	—	8	—	—	—
98% Glycerine (2.0% Water)	—	—	—	10	8
96% Glycerine (4.0% Water)	—	—	10	—	—
PEG-200	—	—	—	—	4
Diethylethanolamine	—	1.5	2	2	2

[1]Polyethylene glycol – Union Carbide Chemical Co.

with a masterbatch which contains the remainder of the polyol, catalysts, surface active agents, the blowing agent, and modifiers or additives. Sometimes one of the foaming ingredients, such as the blowing agent (if it is a fluorocarbon) or the surface active agent is included in the prepolymer rather than in the polyol masterbatch. Foams made by the semi-prepolymer technique may be expanded with either a fluorocarbon or carbon dioxide.

Foams prepared by the semi-prepolymer technique have been made from both polyesters and polyethers. Foam preparation for polyethers and polyesters is the same. These foams can be expanded with carbon dioxide or Fluorocarbon-11 (Table IX-14).

Table IX-14—Formulations for Polyether Foams

Blowing agent	Carbon dioxide		Fluorocarbon
Approx. density, lb per cu ft	2	6	2
NCO /OH ratio	—	—	1.10
	Parts by Weight		
Component A:			
30% NCO (equiv wt 140)	100	100	100
Component B:			
Polyether polyol (equiv wt 115)	46	65	74
Surfactant	0.75	0.75	1.00
Triethylenediamine	0.20	0.20	0.40
Fluorocarbon-11	—	—	36
Water (equiv wt 9)	2	0.6	—

Foams of various densities can be prepared with CO_2 by changing the amount of water, and therefore, the amount of polyol used so that the stoichiometry is not changed.

For high density foam (above 4 lb per cu ft), it may be necessary to reduce the catalyst level to prevent charring of the center of the foam section.

One-shot technique

In the one-shot technique all of the foaming ingredients are mixed together in one step in the mixer and allowed to react. (See Part II, this Section.)

Comparison of foaming systems

Table IX-15 shows some of the principal differences between the three types of foaming systems. All these techniques use a minimum of two components. In some cases it may be desirable to use more. In field operations, the number of components is generally held down to a minimum to minimize the equipment requirements. In the frothing technique, Fluorocarbon-12 is added as a separate liquid stream.

Higher viscosity and more reactive polyols can be used with the semi-prepolymer and one-shot techniques than with the prepolymer technique. The isocyanate content of the one-shot system is generally high and considerable heat is generated. Prepolymers have low isocyanate contents and will therefore generate less heat. A semi-prepolymer system falls about halfway between these two. A prepolymer system may develop a maximum temperature of around 200°F, the semi-prepolymer system about 250°F, and a one-shot foaming system 340°F or higher. This difference in exothermic heat developed can obviously limit the use of some foaming systems in combination with heat sensitive materials such as low melting thermoplastics.

5. PREPOLYMER PROCESSING

Prepolymers for rigid urethane foam can be prepared by batch or by continuous process. At present the continuous process is not of commercial significance and almost all rigid

Table IX-15—Comparison of Types of Foaming Systems			
	Prepolymer	Semi-prepolymer	One-shot
Usual number of Components	2	2	2
Isocyanate component	Reaction product of all polyol and all polyisocyanate	Reaction product of approx. ½ polyol + all polyisocyanate	Polyisocyanate
Polyol or catalyst components	Water + catalyst	Masterbatch of aprox. ½ polyol + catalyst, surfactant, blowing agent and additives	Masterbatch of polyol catalyst, surfactant, blowing agent and additives
Approximate ratio of isocyanate component to polyol or catalyst component	20 to 1	1 to 1	0.8 to 1
Viscosity of isocyanate component at room temperature	High (to over 100,000 cps)	Medium (generally under 4,000 cps)	Low (1 to 200 cps)
Viscosity of polyol or catalyst components	Low (1-10 cps)	Medium (generally under 4,000 cps)	Medium (generally under 5,000 cps)
Maximum exothermic temperature developed in foam—approx.	Low (to 200°F)	Medium (to 350°F)	High (to 400°F)
Processing ease: Range of mixing times (batch)	Up to 15 min	Up to 10 min	About 1 min
Range of foam times	Slow (2 min to 1 hr)	Slow to fast (30 sec to 30 min)	Fast (about 2 min)
Sensitivity	Most insensitive system to foaming conditions	Quite insensitive to foaming conditions— represents a good balanced system	Quite sensitive to foaming conditions.
Relative ease of machine mixing	Difficult	Very easy	More sensitive than semi-prepolymers.

urethane foam prepolymer is made by the batch process. Most of it is made by "cooking" or heating although a "no-cook" method is possible.

Raw materials

The polyols used in prepolymer preparation must be of high purity. Even small amounts of basic contaminants can result in complete gelation during preparation. A material containing hydrolyzable chloride, such as benzoyl chloride or hydrogen chloride, can be used to neutralize some of this basicity.

The water content of the polyols must be controlled for reproducibility from batch to batch and to obtain low viscosity prepolymers. If surfactants are used to control foaming in the reaction kettle they must be compatible with the entire foaming system, especially with other surfactants used in making the foam.

The batch process

The urethane reaction is exothermic, and generally the mixture is not cooled except to hold the temperature within reasonable limits. After the initial exothermic rise, the mass is heated to reaction temperature and allowed to "cook" for one hour at 160°F to 220°F. It is then cooled before discharge from the reactor into storage tanks or drums.

If the reaction mass is not cooled sufficiently after the "cook" cycle, it may continue to react and build up viscosity to a point where it will gel and be unusable. After cooling there is a slight "drift" in the isocyanate content of the prepolymer. Then, the material is stable under normal storage conditions when moisture and excessive heat are avoided. The quality of the raw materials must be maintained in storage and transfer; contamination, particularly by water, will lower the final isocyanate content and raise the final viscosity of the prepolymer.

The continuous process

In the continuous process, prepolymer is made by passing two accurately metered streams (polyol and isocyanate) through a scraped surface heat exchanger. The two streams are intimately mixed and simultaneously heated. The blended materials are held at the process temperature (250°F to 300°F) for a short time, about one minute, and then passed through a second scraped surface heat exchanger where they are cooled to room temperature. The prepolymer, now fully reacted, is collected in a hold tank for subsequent use (Fig. IX-5 and IX-6).

No-cook prepolymers

Prepolymers can be made by simply allowing the polyol-isocyanate mixture to exotherm. A small amount of tin catalyst is helpful in completing the reaction. End of reaction can be determined by studying the change in isocyanate content and viscosity with time. The percent NCO in a prepolymer can be measured using the procedure described in ASTM D-1638-60T (Section IV). If there is little or no change, after the initial drift, the reaction is complete and a stable material has been made. If the viscosity continues to increase and the NCO content to decrease the

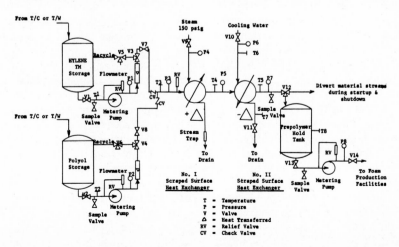

Figure IX-5, schematic flow sheet for continuous production of rigid foam prepolymer.

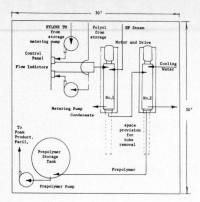

Figure IX-6, suggested equipment layout for continuous production of rigid foam prepolymer. No. 1 = Scraped surface heat exchanger for heating. No. 2 = Heat exchanger for cooling.

material will have a limited useful life. With polyols that contain basic materials or when they are made from amines, it may be difficult if not impossible to prepare stable prepolymers.

Molding and foaming in place

Molding and foaming in place includes all applications for rigid urethane foam where the mixed foam ingredients are poured into a mold or a cavity and allowed to either partially or completely fill the cavity.

Most of the rigid urethane foams prepared in place are based on the partial prepolymer technique, because of easy processability and relative safety. More latitude in formulating and processing is possible with this system than with the one-shot foaming compositions.

Poured-in-place or molding of a liquid urethane foaming composition is used to fill voids of irregular shape and reduces trim loss and handling costs. It is also less expensive to ship the liquid ingredients than the final bulky foam product.

Batch or machine mixing can be used. Batch mixing produces foam with more irregularities but has the advantage of simplicity. Machine mixing gives a more uniform, more consistent quality. A poured-in-place foam usually has higher strength in the direction of foam rise than in the direction perpendicular to foam rise. In thin sections, it may be cheaper to laminate slab foam because a poured-in-place foam would produce a high density skin. In thicker sections it is often more economical to pour in place than to laminate.

Batch mixing

Batch technique is used for filling small items such as small net floats and small insulated containers, also for large applications such as diving planes and rudders in submarines. The batch sizes can vary from a few grams to more than 50 lbs. Much of the early work was done by mixing the foaming ingredients with a paddle; mechanical stirrers are now used regardless of batch size.

Batch mixing is well suited where a limited number of voids are to be filled; it is simple, although not exactly reproducible. The ingredients must be very carefully weighed so that the exact amounts are used and the proper ratio maintained.

The mixer should be powerful enough to accept a slight change in load. Once a mixing procedure has been established and used satisfactorily, it must be adhered to, to obtain reproducible foams.

All batch mix foams are prepared by a non-froth technique; the incorporation of a blowing agent, gaseous at room temperature, cannot be incorporated into batch mixing at atmospheric pressure.

Machine mixing

Machine mixing is particularly desirable when a large number of voids are to be filled. If the voids are large, a continuous type mixer can be used. Since a continuous type mixer must be flushed at the end of a pouring cycle, it is generally not economical to use it for small cavities because of the amount of material being flushed out.

Continuous mixers are simple in construction and many have been designed by their owners. Production rates vary from as low as 2 to 3 lb per min to as high as 200 lb per min.

It is important that the ratio of the two or more foaming components be maintained at the proper level. Variations in the amount of materials or in the ratio pumped and metered should not exceed 1 to $1\frac{1}{2}\%$.

When a large number of small items are to be filled, an on-off mixer is convenient. It will produce foam as soon as the materials enter the mixer and there is no waste at the end of a fill cycle. In normal operation no solvent flush is required and there is no waste. At the end of a prolonged run where a series of molds have been filled, a solvent flush may be required, but the amount of material wasted

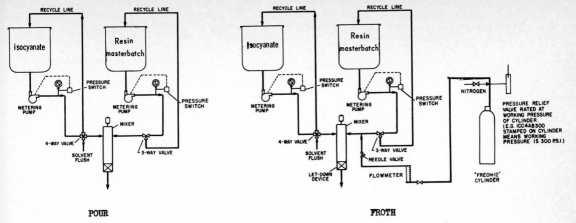

Figure IX-7, processes for rigid foam.

POUR   FROTH

is insignificant compared to that which would be lost with a continuous type mixer.

As the reaction between the isocyanate and the polyol proceeds, the reaction mass heats up and the reaction is accelerated as more heat is developed. A polymeric structure is being formed and the heat of reaction either volatilizes the fluorocarbon blowing agent or releases carbon dioxide, depending on the type of foaming system. This expansion occurs until all of the blowing agent is released and the polymeric structure becomes rigid. While cooling the polymeric structure will have hardened sufficiently to withstand the external atmospheric pressure ȯn the foam. The pressure in the cells of a rigid foam depends on the temperatures encountered during foaming and the rate of blowing agent generation, as well as the boiling point of the blowing agent. Generally this pressure at room temperature is about 10 to 12 psi.

6. THE FROTHING PROCESS

Frothed foams are pre-expanded with a blowing agent, which is a gas at room temperature, generally Fluorocarbon-12 (Fig. IX-7). The pressure must be sufficiently high for the Fluorocarbon-12 to remain liquid in the mixer. Fluorocarbon-12 is contained in a pressurized cylinder under constant nitrogen pressure of 250 to 300 psi. It is drawn off through a bottom outlet, or a dip leg, a safety valve, check valve, flow meter, needle control valve, into one of the foaming composition streams or directly into the mixer.

The foaming ingredients are mixed under pressure of about 100 psi then discharged to atmospheric pressure through a back pressure device which can be anything that will maintain a constant working pressure in the mixer.

Globe valves have been used, but an elastomeric diaphragm valve has been found to be more satisfactory, since it can be readily controlled by maintaining a constant air pressure on one side of the diaphragm against the working pressure in the equipment on the other side. This system is self-compensating: if there is any change in the flow of the foaming ingredients, the pressure on the air side of the diaphragm maintains a consistent operating pressure in the mixer. When the foaming mixture discharges from the back pressure valve to atmospheric, the Fluorocarbon-12 expands, producing a froth, generally at a density of 5 to 12 lb per cu ft instead of the normal high density of about 70 lb per cu ft. Fluorocarbon-11 continues to expand as heat is generated, to give a final foam density as desired, generally in the range of 1.5 to 2 lb per cu ft under normal operating conditions. The amount of Fluorocarbon-12 used determines the froth density, and the combination Fluorocarbon-12 and Fluorocarbon-11 determines the final density. Fluorocarbon-12 is slightly soluble in the foaming composition discharged from the mixer so all of it does not volatilize immediately. The usual operating range is 3 to 4 percent Fluorocarbon-12 based on the total foaming composition.

Froth foam has interesting properties and gives advantages in molding and foaming in place because of its low density:

1. Foaming pressures are reduced as much as 75 percent (Fig. IX-8).

2. Overall molded densities are lower with frothed foam: savings in materials can reach 15% (Fig. IX-9).

3. Because of its low density, froth foam can be deposited on poured foam that is still rising without causing it to collapse or shear.

4. With a froth system, a large cavity can

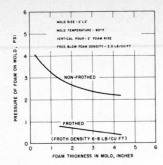

Figure IX-8, effect of frothing on foaming pressure.

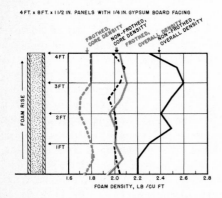

Figure IX-9, density profiles of frothed and non-frothed rigid urethane foam in sandwich panels.

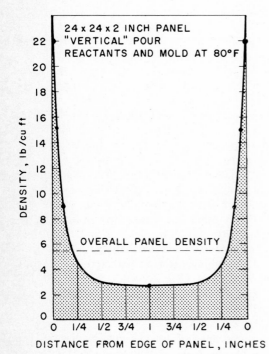

Figure IX-10, density profile of molded rigid foam panel.

normally be filled in a single pour.

7. MOLDING VARIABLES

In any molding operation, whether in the plant or foaming in place, many factors must be considered for reproducibility from pour to pour: for example, the amount of fill or packing, pressures involved in molding, mold release agents, mold temperature, the design of the mold itself, and the configuration of the void to be filled.

Overall densities

Figure IX-10 shows a cross-section of urethane foam molded between two flat surfaces such as panel facings, or a panel mold. The center core has a relatively uniform density, but there is a denser surface, which accounts for a large portion of the total weight even though it is a minor portion of the overall thickness. In any molding operation the weight of skin that can be tolerated must be carefully considered. In some cases, heavy skins are desirable for added strength. In other cases, they are of little value and efforts are made to minimize their thickness and weight. Several factors influence skin thickness: mold temperature, mold thickness, the way the mold is filled (horizontal or vertical pour), use of frothed or non-frothed system (Fig. IX-11).

Obviously there is more shear or drag on the sides of the mold in vertical foaming than in horizontal molding. This increases the density of the skin and the overall density

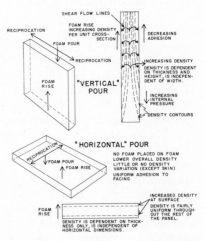

Figure IX-11, vertical + horizontal mold filling.

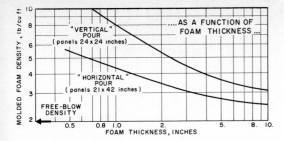

Figure IX-12, effect of pour direction on molded foam density.

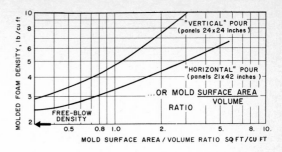

Figure IX-13, effect of surface-area-to-volume ratio on molded density.

of the molded section (Fig. IX-12). As the section thickness increases, there is less density difference between the two types of molding. Fig. IX-13 shows the effect on molded foam density of mold surface area to volume ratio.

The effect of mold temperature on foam density is shown in Fig. IX-14.

Fig. IX-15 shows that the temperature of the mold has relatively little effect on core density but has a significant effect on the density of the skin, particularly in a vertical type pour.

All of this seems to indicate that a horizontal pour is preferable to a vertical pour from the standpoint of lower overall densities in foam cross sections. However, it is more difficult to obtain good distribution of foaming compositions in horizontal pour. The equipment required for a horizontal pour is also costlier. Space requirement is greater and handling more difficult. As the temperature increases, there is less difference between the densities obtained by the two methods. For these reasons, most molded panel work is done today with a vertical type pour. The frothing process also results in lower skin densities.

Molding cycles

The temperature of the mold determines to a large extent the cycle of operation. At room temperature, mold residence times of one-half hour to as long as three hours are not unusual. If the mold temperature is increased to 120°F, mold time may be decreased to 10 to 20 minutes. At 160-170°F mold times may be as low as five minutes. For any given production rate, mold time determines the number of molds needed. Where expensive molds are required, it may be much more economical to use heat rather than extra molds to obtain the required production rate.

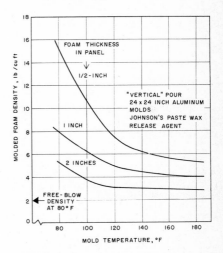

Figure IX-14, effect of mold temperature on molded foam density.

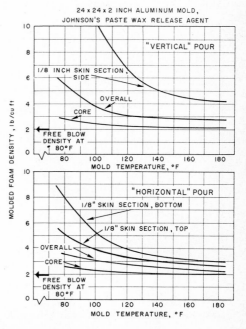

Figure IX-15, effect of mold temperature on foam skin density.

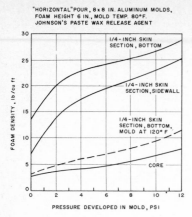

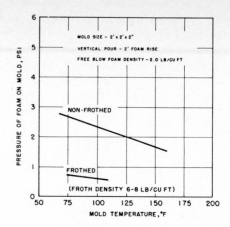

Figure IX-16, effect of mold pressure on foam density.

Figure IX-17, relationship between mold temperature and foaming pressure.

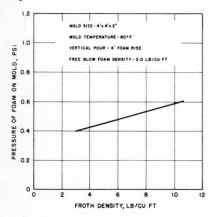

Figure IX-18, effect of foaming pressure on froth density.

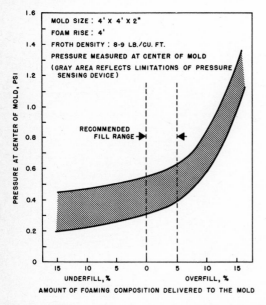

Figure IX-19, pressure developed in closed panel molding.

Molding pressures

Density & packing—The amount of material poured into a mold or cavity has some effect on the pressure developed, whether it is a froth or non-frothed foam, and will affect the overall molded foam density. The configuration of the mold, its thickness and the roughness of its surfaces all affect the pressures developed. Where foam rise is partially restricted because the mold is completely enclosed, excessive pressures can develop because of overloading. The mold may buckle and be destroyed by these pressures (Fig. IX-16).

The data were obtained by loading the mold lid to resist the pressures applied to the rising foam. The information can be used to estimate the pressure developed in the mold when the foam density is known compared to its "free blow" density. This data can be of help for designing molds to produce certain items.

The roughness of the mold surface has a considerable effect on the pressures developed. With rough or textured surfaces, the pressures developed in thin sections may be four to five times as high as those developed in molds with smooth facings, over which the foams can easily rise.

Frothed foam develops about one-fourth as much pressure as does non-frothed foam; therefore, lighter weight molds can be used. Fig. IX-8 also shows that the foam exerts less pressure in thick sections than in thin ones. Increasing mold temperature also reduces the pressure exerted by the rising foam (Fig. IX-17).

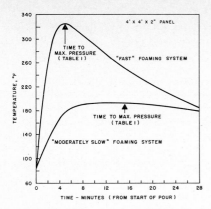

Figure IX-20, effect of foaming system on exotherm temperature in molded panel.

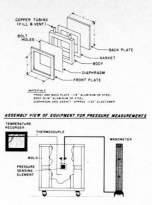

Figure IX-21, construction of pressure sensing element.

Pressure increases slightly with increasing froth density over the range of froth density studied (Fig. IX-18), because the higher the froth density the more post-expansion the froth undergoes to achieve low final foam density.

The amount of overfill or packing of a closed mold or void has considerable effect on the pressures developed (Fig. IX-19).

Experience suggests that an overfill of about 5% is close to optimum mold loading. Underfilling results in too little pressure build-up in the mold and may yield an item partly unfilled. Overfilling will generally give a better item, but its density will be higher and the pressure developed in the mold may be considerably higher. For example, an overfill of 5% with frothed foam will increase the pressure about 20% over that produced with an exact fill. An overfill of 12% will double the pressure; triple with a 15% overfill.

It is important that the froth be distributed evenly to prevent overloading of one section and underfilling of another section of the cavity. Excessive foam movement resulting from poor distribution can cause shear and localized higher foaming pressures and foam densification.

Time to maximum pressure—The time for maximum pressure to develop is important, because it determines how long the piece must remain in the mold. It varies across the face of the mold, but is usually longest in the center. The time can be varied by changing the foaming formulation from 1 to 4 min at the bottom of a mold, and from 5 to 15 min in the middle. Maximum pressure is defined as the pressure measured when there is no further increase in foam volume.

With some foaming systems time to maximum pressure coincides with time to maximum temperature (Fig. IX-20).

In one method of obtaining pressure measurements the pressure sensing elements (Fig. IX-21) are recessed into a piece of rigid foam so that the diaphragm of the sensing element is flush with the surface of the foam. The entire assembly is covered with a sheet of polyethylene. The sensing element and all connecting lines are completely filled with water to eliminate air, and connected to a mercury manometer. Heat from the foam mass will expand the water in the sensing element, causing a slight steady rise in pressure even after the foam has set. This slight rise in pressure is not considered when estimating maximum pressure.

Mold release agents

Urethane foams will release from a wide variety of surfaces. Release agents based on wax are often used (Table IX-16). Rigid

Table IX-16—Mold Release Agents Used With Rigid Urethane Foams	
Parting agent 1894 Ex S	Mitchell-Rand Mfg. Corp., Jersey City, N.Y.
Johnson's Paste Wax	Johnson Wax Company, Racine, Wis.
Chem-Trend P-2	Chem-Trend Inc. 4880 Route 23, Brighton, Mich.
"Perma Mold"	Brulin & Company, Inc., 2939-45 Columbia Ave., Indianapolis 7, Ind.
Mold release #3	American Latex Products Corp., 3341 El Segundo Blvd., Hawthorne, Calif.
Shanco 32-6 dispersion	Shanco Plastics & Chemicals, Inc., Tonawanda, N.Y.

urethane foams will release readily from highly polished surfaces such as chrome-plated metals, and very hard, non-porous surfaces, such as fired porcelain. Non-polar materials, polyethylene and TFE-fluorocarbon, can also be used. The choice of release agent depends on conditions involved in molding or poured-in-place operation. In some large voids a polyethylene film can be used particularly if it can be made to conform with the surfaces of the mold or void. In the case of small items, a highly polished surface, sometimes covered with a wax release agent, may be convenient. If the item is to be coated or painted, the mold release agent must be compatible with the paint or coating.

If molded items are to be adhered to other materials, care must be taken that the mold release agent used in the molding step is compatible with the adhesive which is used later.

8. SPRAYED URETHANE FOAMS

Rigid urethane foams can be applied by spraying-in-place on large surfaces. The foam adheres to most surfaces that have been cleaned of loose scale, oil, and grease. Urethane foam can be applied in thicknesses from 3/16 in. to 12 in. or more in multiple passes. Metering and handling of the foaming composition is the same as that used for poured-in-place or slab operations. Only difference is that in spray operation the foaming composition is broken up and delivered to the target by air, or pressure reduction in airless spraying. The foam formulation is modified to produce a faster rising and setting foam to prevent sagging or running of the foam on the target. This is accomplished by using more catalyst. Sometimes higher viscosity materials are included to prevent slumping or sagging.

Rigid urethane foam can be spray-applied as a liquid which foams rapidly and sets, or it can be applied as a frothed foam with discrete particles, which expands to the final foam density before setting.

Principal advantage of the spray type operation is it can be used to cover surfaces that would be impractical to cover with poured-in-place foam or with slab foam. Principal disadvantages: there is generally much overspray (except with airless or froth spraying) which means a loss of material and a fairly rough surface. The frothing technique allows more rapid application rates, less overspray, and less fumes; it requires somewhat more complicated foaming equipment.

Liquid foaming compositions are mixed and delivered to the target through one of three types of spray guns:

External mix with air atomization

With this type of gun, the foaming components are passed through the gun under pressure as separate streams; they are mixed and atomized simultaneously by an air blast in a specially designed nozzle. A large volume of air is required to give adequate mixing, resulting in much overspray. Since mixing is entirely external, the gun remains clean and does not plug.

Internal mix with air atomization

This spray gun differs from the external mix gun in that it mixes the foaming ingredients before they are discharged and atomized. Since the air is required only for atomization, a smaller amount is used and overspray is reduced. The materials are mixed inside the gun and facilities for flushing unreacted components are necessary to avoid plugging.

Internal mix with airless atomization

One form of internal mix gun blends the foaming ingredients by passing them through a labyrinth under high pressure, up to 3000 psi. Atomization is accomplished by the sudden drop in pressure across the nozzle. Overspray is negligible. Plugging can be a problem, and a solvent flush system is required.

The pumping and metering units for spray type applications can be very simple and have less capacity and a more limited operating range than those for pouring in place or slab applications, whether in the plant or in the field. Simplicity has been designed into the equipment so that it is more portable. Pumping and metering units for airless spray must be designed for high pressure and are not as simple.

Spraying rates

For most applications, outputs of 2 to 10 lb per min have been used. Equipment is available to mix and spray in excess of 20 lb per min but at this output it is difficult to distribute the foam properly and maintain a uniform thickness.

Foam thickness

Thicknesses up to 2 in. can be attained in

a single pass. Greater thicknesses are obtained with multiple passes because the foam would slump if applied too heavily in a single pass. The Industrial Insulation Committee of the Society of the Plastics Industry recommends that urethane foams be spray-applied within an ambient temperature range of 65°F to 100°F. Substrate temperatures should be in the same range. Those lower than 65°F should be sprayed with a flash coat to act as an insulator before applying subsequent layers of foam. Since moisture will affect the properties of rigid urethane foams, SPI recommends that the substrate be dry at the time of foam application. Wind velocities greater than 10 to 15 miles an hour may result in excessive heat loss and overspray, so caution should be used in high wind. The use of barriers is strongly recommended. SPI also recommends that the substrate be cleaned and, in the case of metals, treated with an adequate primer. If the insulation is to be subjected to temperatures below 32°F, a barrier coating having a rating of 0.05 perms per in. or less must be applied.

Urethane foam can also be applied by frothed spraying. In this technique, a froth foam is produced in the same manner as that for foamed-in-place operation. After the froth has been formed a specially designed nozzle is used to break up the froth into discrete particles which are then transported to the target by a stream of low pressure atomizing air. Once on the target, the particles expand to produce a frothed-sprayed foam in place. This type of equipment is still in the development stages but should be promising for those applications where a large amount of material must be applied at high delivery rates to large surface areas.

Since sprayed urethane foam must travel through the atmosphere to reach the target, the presence of moisture in the air is of even more importance than in other types of operation. When humidity is high the foaming composition must be specially formulated to compensate for high atmospheric moisture, otherwise poor foams with poor dimensional stability and possible shrinkage are obtained.

9. SLAB AND PANEL MANUFACTURING

Slab urethane foam is produced in the factory under very carefully controlled conditions and represents one of the most uniform foam products that can be obtained today.

Slab urethane foams are available in widths up to four feet, lengths to 12 feet and thicknesses from $\frac{1}{4}$ in. to 12 in. Rigid urethane foam can be cut and machined with conventional wood working equipment. It is the easiest form of urethane foam to inspect for quality. Even a visual inspection will give a good idea of its quality. It can be applied against any type of plastic, wood or metal surface, such as in panels where it is laminated to facing materials or in trailer truck bodies, where the foam can be inserted between the supporting members and cemented to the structure, if desired. Limitations of slab urethane foam: it does not conform to curved surfaces; it must be bonded with an adhesive for good adhesion to the substrate; it is bulky and cannot be shipped economically.

A large tonnage of rigid urethane foam goes into the manufacture of panels, which are two-layer or three-layer sandwiches of foam and another material, such as wood, plywood, asbestos or gypsum board, and metals, especially aluminum.

The method used for making rigid urethane foam panels depends on equipment available, type and size of panel to be produced, and anticipated volume. Three methods are available: laminating, foaming-in-place and spraying.

In laminating, an adhesive is applied to the board (facing) and to the foam slab. The sandwich is placed in a platen press or passed through rollers to form a panel. This process is probably the least expensive for producing panels of a thickness of one inch or less. It requires very little equipment.

For foaming-in-place, the frothing process is generally preferred because of the lower pressures developed. Foaming-in-place with froth may be the least expensive method for producing large quantities of panels in the two to six in. thick range. It is one of the more flexible methods of operation, because textured and non-rigid facing materials can be easily used.

The spray method is particularly suitable for panels where only one facing material is required and the other side of the panel has the foam exposed. However, three-layer sandwich panels can be made by spraying the urethane foam onto one facing of the panel, milling or cutting the foam to give a flat surface and laminating the other facing to the milled surface. If a thicker panel is desired, two facings with foam sprayed on each of them can be laminated together. In this case, there is only one adhesive line in the center of the panel. Spraying may be competitive with foaming-in-place on large panels but overspray must be kept to a minimum.

Production techniques affect the relative economics of panel manufacturing methods. For example, it is possible to combine the production of panels with slab stock manufacture by foaming-in-place (or spraying) onto a panel facing and building up a thick section of foam. The bottom, with the panel facing, can then be cut off and another facing adhered to it; the sawed-off foam can be used for slab stock. The cost saving made possible by such technique is considerable.

Adhesion problem

Urethane foams will generally adhere to wood especially where a mechanical interlocking can be obtained.

The adhesion of rigid foam to metal is not quite as good. If a steel surface has been freshly cleaned and roughened, adhesion may be adequate. Aluminum should be primed with a material that will give good adhesion even if moisture comes in contact later with the interface. The presence of any oils, greases, or rolling lubricants on the surface of the metal makes it extremely difficult to obtain good adhesion. Highly reflective metal surfaces, such as chrome-plated finishes, are also very difficult to adhere to and are sometimes used as mold release surfaces. Adhesion to metallic surfaces can be improved by the use of primers or surface treatments.

1. Surface treatments
   A. Bonderizing
   B. Phosphoric acid etching
   C. Anodizing (for aluminum)
   D. Sandblasting
2. Primers
   A. Vinyl
   B. Epoxy
   C. Alkyd and acrylic
3. Adhesives

Adhesion failures in panels can occur upon exposure to heat alone or heat combined with high humidity. It may result from poor dimensional stability of the foam.

In applications, such as freezers, involving low temperatures, there is a possibility of moisture penetration into the foam. Many coatings will give good adhesion, but few will give protection from corrosion if moisture is present. In laboratory tests, a vinyl wash primer has been used—it gave good adhesion and prevented corrosion of aluminum by moisture that had passed through the foam. Other materials, such as asphalt coating, offered some protection but were not as good.

Adhesives

Both thermosetting and thermoplastic adhesives have been used to laminate various facing materials to rigid urethane foam cores in panels. Thermosetting types include epoxy and phenol-resorcinol-based adhesives; thermoplastic types are elastomeric adhesives based on neoprene. The thermosets have better heat resistance than the thermoplastics, but poor initial tack. Thermoplastic neoprene-based adhesives have high initial tack, extensibility, to compensate for differences in coefficients of expansion, and resilience, to absorb shock loads in certain applications.

Rigid urethane foam has chemical and solvent resistance, so that solvent-based adhesives can be used. The solvent must be removed by evaporation before the adhesive joint is completed, because it cannot evaporate through the foam. Because rigid foam has good heat resistance, many sealants and adhesives can be applied hot.

Vapor barriers

Vapor barriers are required with urethane foams exposed to temperatures below 32°F. A recent SPI Industrial Insulation Subcommittee report states that "a water vapor transmission (WVT) rate of 0.05 perms or less is necessary to avoid moisture pick-up on exposure to temperatures of 32°F (0°C) or lower." A good quality rigid urethane foam has a WVT rating of 1 to 2 perm-in. Therefore, to attain the desired low moisture vapor transmission rate an additional water vapor barrier is necessary. Mastics, foils and films have all been used successfully as water vapor barriers with rigid urethane foam (Table IX-17).

Other foam processes

Semi-rigid or rigid urethane foams can be made from low density flexible foams by coating them with a solvent solution curable polymer. In essence, the low density foam serves as a support structure on which the reinforced foam is built. The cell size and thickness of the supporting foam and the viscosity and wetting ability of the impregnating liquid determine the ease of impregnation.

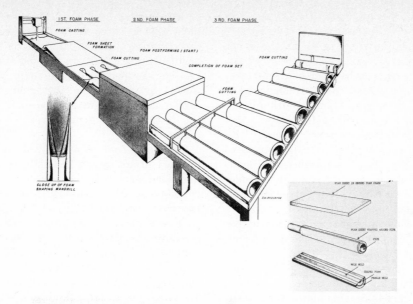

Figure IX-22, perspective view of postforming facilities for the continuous manufacture of urethane pipe insulation. Insert shows experimental methods used to post-form (shape) foam into pipe insulation.

11. STRENGTH PROPERTIES

The strength of a rigid urethane foam is influenced by many factors, such as catalyst, surfactant, type of mixing, foaming system, base polyol, isocyanate, each of which influence foam cell structure. But changes which do not modify the density will, in general, modify the properties only slightly.

The choice of a foam for a particular application should not be based on just one property. Often a property, such as very high compressive strength or low water vapor transmission, is obtained at the expense of some other property or processing ease. The selection should be made on functional requirements and will generally involve the best compromise of properties.

Density

Rigid urethane foams with densities below 4 lb per cu ft, used primarily for thermal insulation, are usually expanded with a fluorocarbon blowing agent such as Fluorocarbon-11. Some low density foams used for structural purposes are expanded with carbon dioxide produced by the water-isocyanate reaction. For processing ease, as well as density control, most high density foams are blown with carbon dioxide.

Compressive strength

Most rigid urethane foams have an elastic region in which stress is nearly proportional to strain. They do not entirely follow Hooke's Law (stress proportional to strain) because the curve is very slightly "S" shaped, but the deviation is not very great. In compression, the elastic region varies from 5 to 10% of the initial deflection (strain). In Fig. IX-23, initial stress is nearly proportional to strain, and there is elastic recovery. Beyond the yield point the foam has little elastic recovery. If a foam is compressed beyond this yield point,

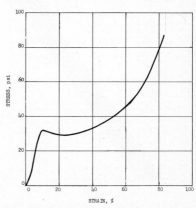

Figure IX-23, stress-strain curve in compression for rigid urethane foam (2 lb per cu ft density).

the cell structure is crushed. For low density foams (below 4 lb per cu ft) the stress required to crush the foam is about the same as the yield point stress. In this plateau, strain increases with little or no increase in stress. This plateau can extend to 70% compression (strain) in low density foams. With higher density foams the extent of the plateau decreases, and the stress required to crush the foam becomes greater as the strain increases. The curve in Fig. IX-23 is obtained at a loading rate of 2 in. per min on a one in. sample. At higher loading rates, higher strengths and a smaller plateau may be obtained.

Fig. IX-24 illustrates change in compressive strength with density. Most of the data below 4 lb per cu ft density are based on foams blown with a fluorocarbon blowing agent, and most of the data above 4 lb per cu ft density are based on carbon-dioxide-blown foams. No significant differences in strength values are noticed between foams made with the two types of blowing agents throughout the density range studied.

Most low density rigid urethane foams are anisotropic, that is, they are stronger in the direction of foam rise. The strength value in the strongest direction is shown in Fig. IX-24. Isotropic foams which have essentially the same property values in all directions can be made.

The anisotropic character of low density foams is generally more pronounced in molded items or panels where the foam rises through a long vertical distance: there, a foam may have almost twice as much strength in the direction parallel to foam rise as in the perpendicular direction. In molded items the directional properties of the foam can be minimized by overloading the mold, but then a higher density foam is produced. The use of the frothing process will produce a more isotropic foam.

The anisotropic character of the foam can be used to advantage in applications where a high load on the foam is expected in one direction, or one axis, and very little or no load on the other two axes. The use of slab foam in roof deck insulation is an example: there is a considerable load parallel to the foam rise, very little perpendicular to it.

In the generalized curve for the density-compressive strength relationship in Fig. IX-24, a particular foaming system falls in either the upper or lower portion of the gray area throughout the density range. If the density and compressive strength values for one foam are known, the compressive strength of that type at another density can be predicted from Fig. IX-24.

Temperature service limits

Rigid urethane foam with a density of 1.8 lb per cu ft or greater is generally serviceable at temperatures ranging from −320° to 225°F. Lower density foams have poor dimensional stability at temperatures below 40°F or higher than 170°F.

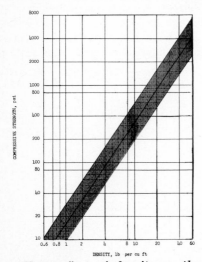

Figure IX-24, effect of density on the compressive strength of rigid urethane foam (90% confidence limits shown). Compressive strength $= 12.77D^{1.416}$.

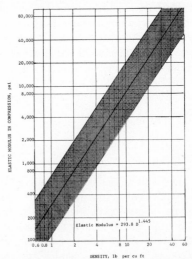

Figure IX-25, effect of density on elastic modulus in compression of rigid urethane foam (90% confidence limits shown).

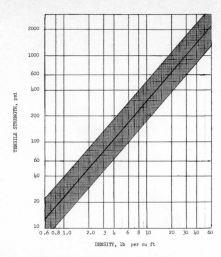

Figure IX-26, effect of density on tensile strength of rigid urethane foam (90% confidence limits shown). Tensile strength = $23.01D^{1.1115}$.

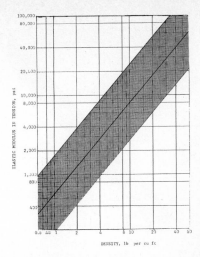

Figure IX-27, effect of density on elastic modulus in tension of rigid urethane foam (90% confidence limits shown). Elastic modulus in tension = $573.5D^{1.1508}$.

The mechanical strength of rigid urethane foam does not decrease much between room temperature and 200°F. Between 200 and 250°F there is some decrease in mechanical properties and dimensional stability. For these reasons a temperature of 210 to 225°F is recommended as upper limit for continuous service, with intermittent periods up to 250°F.

At the other end of the temperature scale, rigid urethane foam maintains its strength very well to temperatures as low as —320°F. Tensile strength and elongation decrease somewhat, but compressive strength at yield increases as the temperature is lowered. Rigid foam becomes less flexible at low temperatures. However, it can be hit with a hammer without shattering after immersion in liquid nitrogen at —320°F.

Elastic modulus in compression

A tangent modulus (see glossary, tangent to the stress-strain curve) is generally used, and data on elastic modulus in compression in Fig. IX-25 are based on a tangent modulus. These data follow the generalized expression for strength properties: log (elastic modulus) = A + B log (density), and the overall data can be expressed by the equation:

G_C = AD^B, where G_C is elastic modulus in compression, D is density and A and B are constants.

The elastic modulus in Fig. IX-25 is the highest value obtained by compressing the foam in the direction of foam rise. Values as low as 40% of this value can be obtained if the foam is compressed in the direction perpendicular to foam rise. If the foam is isotropic, the values at low densities will be somewhat lower and, of course, will be the same in both directions.

Tensile strength

The tensile strength of rigid urethane foams increases with density (Fig. IX-26). A generalized equation is:

S_T = AD^B, where S_T is tensile strength, D is density and A and B are constants.

With some foaming systems the elongation at break increases slightly with density; in other cases it decreases or remains nearly constant. The elongation can be changed within a limited range at any density by modifying the formulation.

Elastic modulus in tension

The elastic modulus in tension (G_T) increases with foam density as shown in Fig. IX-27. The change can be expressed by the generalized equation G_T = AD^B, where A and B are constants and D is density.

Values for elastic modulus in tension cover a wide range, which may result from differences in foam preparation, test method, edge effects, and sample sizes.

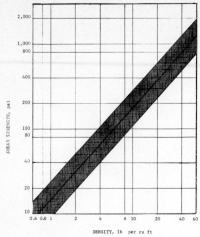

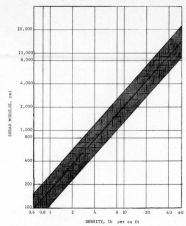

Figure IX-28, effect of density on shear strength of rigid urethane foam. Shear strength $= 14.9D^{1.077}$.

Figure IX-29, effect of density on shear modulus of rigid urethane foam (90% confidence limits shown). Shear modulus $= 169.9D^{1.0806}$.

Shear strength and shear modulus

Shear strength and shear modulus both increase with density and follow the same form of generalized equation as used for other strength properties. Data and equations are given in Figures IX-28 and IX-29.

Flexural strength and flexural modulus

Flexural strength and flexural modulus both increase with density and follow the same form of generalized equation as used for other strength properties. Data and equations are given in Fig. IX-30 and IX-31.

12. THERMAL PROPERTIES

Rigid urethane foams are thermosetting materials; however, they soften slightly with increased temperature, and harden somewhat at very low temperatures. Softening at high temperatures affects the foam in two ways: (1) loss in strength properties, and (2) change in foam dimensions (particularly low density foams). Low temperatures have generally very little effect on the foam strength properties; they make them a little harder and more brittle. Some very low density foams (particularly at densities below 1.5 lb per cu ft) will shrink considerably on exposure to low temperatures.

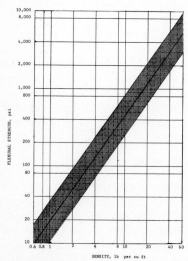

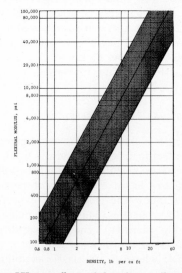

Figure IX-30, effect of density on flexural strength of rigid urethane foam. Flexural strength $= 18.99D^{1.3769}$.

Figure IX-31, effect of density on flexural modulus of rigid urethane foam. Flexural modulus $= 186.3D^{1.7587}$.

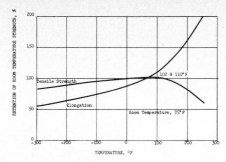

Figure IX-32, effect of temperature on tensile strength and elongation of rigid urethane foam. Density: 1.8 lb per cu ft. High crosslink density (calculated average distance between crosslinks = 350).

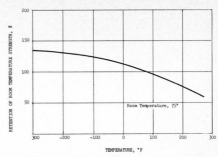

Figure IX-33, effect of temperature on compressive strength of rigid urethane foam.

All physical properties of rigid urethane foam are not affected in the same way nor to the same extent by a change in temperature (Fig. IX-32 and IX-33). Tensile strength reaches a maximum slightly above room temperature and decreases rapidly above that point with rising temperature. The tensile strength decreases very slowly at lower temperatures. The elongation at break, on the other hand, increases quite rapidly with temperature, indicating that the material is not entirely thermosetting. Compressive strength, unlike tensile strength, does not exhibit a maximum, but decreases with increasing temperature over the entire range from —320°F to 250°F. In general, the strain at the yield point in compression is not greatly affected by a change of temperature in the range of —100 to 250°F.

Shear strength, shear modulus and elastic modulus in compression follow the compressive strength curve closely. They all exhibit a similar decrease with increasing temperature.

Foam density also has an effect on the rate and extent of change of a physical property with temperature. The higher density foams change less with temperature than low density foams, particularly in compressive strength (Fig. IX-34). Tensile strength (Fig. IX-35) is not affected by temperature as greatly as compressive strength; shear strength and flexural strength (Fig. IX-36), although showing some change, are about intermediate between tensile and compression strengths. Elastic modulus in compression or tension shows about the same change with density. The shape of the stress-strain curve up to the yield point in compression changes very little with temperature.

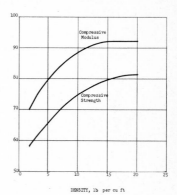

Figure IX-34, effect of density on compressive strength of rigid urethane foam at 160°F. Medium crosslink density (calculated average distance between crosslink = 400).

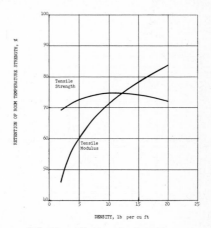

Figure IX-35, effect of density on tensile strength and tensile modulus of rigid urethane foam at 160°F.

Thermal conductivity (k-factor)

The thermal conductivity of urethane foams is greatly influenced by blowing agent, cell size, closed-cell content, and density of the

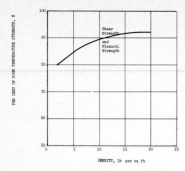

Figure IX-36, effect of density on shear strength and flexural strength of rigid ure-thane foam at 160°F.

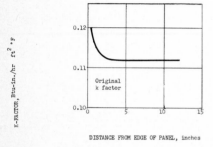

Figure IX-38, thermal conductivity of rigid urethane foam (blown with fluorocarbon-11) clad in aluminum panel and aged for one year at 70-120°F and 50-95% RH. Mean aging temperature was 75°F. Density of foam was 2 lb per cu ft.

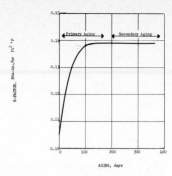

Figure IX-37, aging of rigid urethane foam with cut surfaces (blown with fluorocarbon-11). Aging conditions: 50% RH, 6″ × 6″ × ½″ sample size, mean temperature = 75°F, density = 2 lb per cu ft.

foam. Most foams used as thermal insulation have a density of about 2 lb per cu ft and are expanded with Fluorocarbon-11. With good processing technique they are made with a fine cell structure and are essentially closed-cell foams. Such foams will show some change in k-factor on aging depending on the exposure conditions. Fig. IX-37 shows a typical aging history for a cut foam slab exposed to 75°F, 50% relative humidity for 360 days. There is an initial period during which the k-factor rises rapidly followed by a leveling out period which can extend to years, during which the k-factor remains essentially constant. This phenomenon is true only in cut foams.

If the foam is totally enclosed, such as in a panel, there is little or no change in the k-factor in the body of the foam (Fig. IX-38).

The thermal conductivity of a rigid urethane foam is affected by temperature (Fig. IX-39).

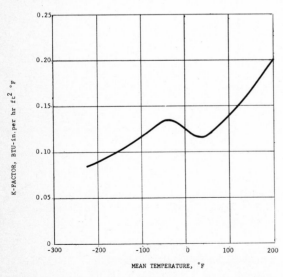

Figure IX-39, effect of temperature on the thermal conductivity of rigid urethane foam (blown with fluorocarbon-11).

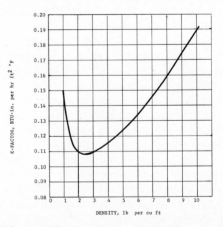

Figure IX-40, effect of density on thermal conductivity of rigid urethane foam (blown with fluorocarbon-11).

Below —80°F, the k-factor decreases with temperature. Above —80°F there is an inflection point with a minimum at about 45°F followed by a rapid rise. Carbon dioxide has a higher vapor pressure and thermal conductivity than Fluorocarbon-11 and is rapidly replaced by air because it permeates readily through the urethane polymer; therefore, a carbon-dioxide-blown foam shows no inflection point and has a considerably higher k-factor over the entire range.

Density also affects the thermal conductivity of rigid urethane foams (Fig. IX-40). A minimum thermal conductivity is evident in the density range of 2 to 3 lb per cu ft, with the conductivity increasing at higher or lower densities. Below 2 lb per cu ft, the increase in k-factor is caused by the difficulty in maintaining good cell structure and sufficiently high closed-cell content to prevent gas loss from within the foam cells. This gas loss causes convection currents and contributes to a heat loss by radiation effect. Above 3 lb per cu ft the conductivity increases because the conduction through the polymer becomes an increasingly important part of the overall thermal conductivity of both the foam and blowing agent.

Carbon-dioxide-blown foams show a change (similar to that for foams blown with Fluorocarbon-11) in k-factor with density (see Fig. IX-41). However, because of the higher thermal conductivity of the carbon dioxide, all of the k-factor values of these foams are at a higher level than those of foams blown with fluorocarbons.

Coefficient of linear thermal expansion

The coefficient of linear thermal expansion does not change much over the density range of 2 to 12 lb per cu ft. Most of the data indicate a value of 2.5 to 3.5 x 10^{-5} in. per in. per deg F for foams in the 1.5 to 4 lb per cu ft density range at room temperature. Higher density foams in the 8 to 12 lb per cu ft density range appear to have coefficients of linear thermal expansion of 3.0 to 4.0 x 10^{-5} in. per in. per deg F.

In the temperature range —190°F to 115°F, for low density foams, various investigators report values from 2.5 to 3.5 x 10^{-5} in. per in. per deg F.

Specific heat

Recent data have shown a value of 0.20 to

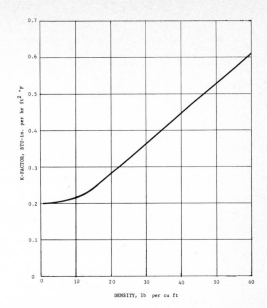

Figure IX-41, effect of density on K-factor of rigid urethane foam (blown with carbon dioxide).

0.25 Btu per lb °F for rigid urethane foams of 2 to 20 lb per cu ft density.

Change in weight at elevated temperatures

On exposure to elevated temperatures urethane foams will generally lose some weight, but the weight loss is very small. After allowing the foam to condition three days at room temperature with uncontrolled humidity during the summer, the total weight loss was only 0.5%. Approximately 2% of this weight loss was due to moisture absorbed from the atmosphere, lost on heating, then regained on exposure to room temperature and humidity. Another 0.5% loss was irreversible and probably consisted of volatile components of the foam.

Dimensional stability

Density, temperature, blowing agents, foaming systems, and polyols have an effect on the dimensional stability of a foam.

Rigid urethane foams are essentially closed-cell materials containing an inert gas as a blowing agent. At elevated temperatures the gas is heated, and since it is confined, the pressure in the foam cells increases according to Boyle's Law. The increase in pressure will cause the cells to increase in size slightly as the polymer softens, resulting in distortion. Since the foam cells are usually elongated in

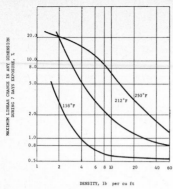

Figure IX-42, dimensional stability of rigid urethane foam, blown with fluorocarbon-11.

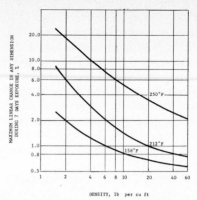

Figure IX-43, dimensional stability of rigid urethane foam, blown with carbon dioxide.

the direction of foam rise, an increase in pressure in the cells tends to make them more spherical, causing an uneven growth, or distortion, of the foam. As cells become more spherical, foam growth is larger in the direction perpendicular to foam rise than in the direction of foam rise.

On prolonged exposure to elevated temperatures, the blowing agent can be partially lost or diluted with air or water vapor; the cell walls are more permeable to these gases than to the fluorocarbon blowing agent. This may distort the foam, increase thermal conductivity by dilution of the Fluorocarbon-11, with a loss in the foam's insulating ability. If the foam structure is not very strong—particularly at densities below 1.8 lb per cu ft—the foam may swell so much on exposure to elevated temperatures that some of the foam cells are ruptured. Continued exposure to elevated temperatures will cause shrinkage as the polymer structure collapses, since there is no longer any internal pressure to maintain the cell structure. A 2 lb per cu ft density foam will begin to contract on exposure to elevated temperature after an expansion of about 30%, at which time some of the foam cells are ruptured. The piece may become dense and resemble no longer a foamed plastic.

At low temperatures, low density foams (under 1.8 lb per cu ft) will often exhibit shrinkage. The extent and rate of shrinkage is affected by the exposure temperature, the polymer structure, and the blowing agent. If the blowing agent is a gas that begins to condense below room temperature, the pressure inside the foam cells will be reduced and the foam will shrink if the polymer structure is not strong enough to withstand the external pressure of the atmosphere. Rigid urethane foams blown with Fluorocarbon-11 are a good example of this type of behavior. Gases that do not condense, such as carbon dioxide, will cause less reduction in pressure.

The permeability of the polymer to the blowing agent is reduced as the temperature is lowered. Since some strength properties, particularly compressive strength, increase with reduced temperature, a foam that is cooled quickly to a low temperature (below —40°) may exhibit no shrinkage other than that due to its thermal coefficient of expansion. If, however, the foam is cooled slowly, to a moderate extent—0°F to —20°F—it may shrink, because the polymer structure has not stiffened and cannot resist atmospheric pressure. Temperatures in the range of 0°F to —20°F are the most severe service conditions for low density rigid urethane foams.

The effect of density on the dimensional stability of polyether rigid urethane foams, blown with Fluorocarbon-11 or carbon dioxide, is shown in Fig. IX-42 and IX-43. At all temperatures the higher density foams are considerably more stable than the low density foams.

13. OTHER PROPERTIES

Closed cell content and cell size

Most low density rigid urethane foams (1.8 to 2 lb per cu ft range) have a closed cell content of 90% or greater. Below 1.5 lb per cu ft the closed cell content often decreases. Above 2 lb per cu ft the closed cell content usually increases quite rapidly and above 12 lb per cu ft is generally over 99% closed.

Slab foam made under closely controlled

factory conditions has very fine cell structure. Most of these foams have cell sizes in the 150 to 200 micron* range. At foam densities below 1.5 lb per cu ft it is difficult to maintain very fine cell structure and not unusual to have cell sizes in excess of 350 to 400 microns. At a density of 4 lb per cu ft, the cell structure is generally very fine and a 100 micron cell size is not uncommon. At densities over 10 lb per cu ft, cell sizes under 10 microns average are common (even for hand-mixed foams).

Field-applied foams and those mixed under batch conditions generally have coarser cell structure and more irregular cells than factory-produced foams which are generally sold in slab form. The cell size of these field-applied foams are often in the 300 to 400 micron range.

The average cell size of froth foams is a little lower than that of the comparable non-froth foam because the frothing agent acts as a nucleating source to produce a finer cell structured foam. But froth foams may contain some larger cells, because of trapped air or Fluorocarbon-12 that has not been blended into the foaming composition.

Water vapor transmission

The water vapor transmission (WVT) rating of foam is affected by the polymer, the cell size and the foam density (Fig. IX-44). Very few reliable WVT data are available for high density foams: a grey area is shown but WVT values outside of that area may possibly be obtained with certain foaming systems.

Water pickup on immersion

The amount of water that a urethane foam will pick up on immersion depends on the size of the sample, the type of surfaces, the method of production (molded or cut), and the immersion time, as well as the method used for removing excess moisture from the surface. Most water pickup methods used today are based on ASTM C-272. Some use an alcohol dip followed by gentle drying to remove surface moisture and alcohol. Other techniques involve merely wiping the surface moisture off with a paper towel or a cloth. The differences in test procedure give a very wide spread in water pickup values.

Most of the water pickup values reported in the literature are based on merely wiping the

Can also be expressed as cells per in.; 200 μ (microns) cells equal 127 cells per in.

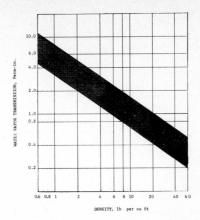

Figure IX-44, effect of density on water vapor transmission of rigid urethane foam.

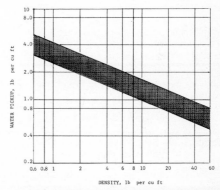

Figure IX-45, effect of density on water pickup of rigid urethane foam (based on 2″ × 2″ × 1″ sample).

surface of a cut foam that has been immersed in water for a specific period of time, generally seven days. The sample size is small, often 2″ x 2″ x 1″. Fig. IX-45 shows the general trend that can be expected for water pickup under this test method. The water pickup is mostly surface water on the foam.

Solvent resistance

Most urethane foams are very resistant to solvents and pick up very small amounts on immersion. Table IX-19 shows the weight gain of several types of polyether rigid urethane foams.

Electrical properties

The electrical properties of rigid urethane foams are affected by both temperature and foam density. Fig. IX-46 shows the effect of density on the dielectric constant and loss tangent (dissipation factor) of rigid urethane

Table IX-19—Solvent Pickup of Rigid Urethane Foams

Characteristics of foam tested:
  Density—2 lb per cu ft
  Closed cell content—>90% of foam volume
Test conditions:
  Specimen size—cylindrical pellets, 1 cu in. volume
  Immersion—one week at 75°F (24°C)

	Weight gain, lb. solvent per cu ft of foam[1]
Hydrocarbons	
Diisobutylene	2.6- 4.0
Hexane	2.2- 3.2
JP-4 Fuel	2.6- 3.8
JP-5 Fuel	2.4- 5.4
Xylene	3.2- 4.8
Halogenated Solvents	
o-Dichlorobenzene	4.2- 5.6
Trichloroethylene	13
Oxygenated Solvents	
Cellosolve acetate	7.2-12
Ethanol	6.4-13[2]
Glacial acetic acid	11-24
Glycol dimethyl ether	4.4-11
Methyl ethyl ketone	15-32[2]

[1]Several types of polyether based foams were tested. Since all types were not equivalent in their solvent pickup, a range of values is reported.
[2]Sample shrinkage.

Table IX-20—Sound Absorption Coefficient of Rigid Urethane Foams

Sound frequency cps	Absorption coefficient
125	0.12
250	0.18
350	0.20
500	0.27
1000	0.19
2000	0.62
4000	0.22
Noise reduction coefficient	0.32

foams. There is very little spread in the data on dielectric constant with various types of foams. Loss tangent varies considerably with the basic type of polymer used in preparing foam. The effect of temperature on both dielectric constant and loss tangent is shown in Fig. IX-47. The dielectric constant changes very little with temperature, whereas the loss tangent changes rapidly.

Sound absorption properties

Rigid urethane foams, even at low densities, have an essentially closed cell structure, normally over 90% of closed cells. In general, closed cell materials are not good sound absorbers. Rigid urethane foams are no exception. Table IX-20 shows the values of absorption coefficients for a rigid urethane foam as determined by the impedance tube method.

Even though urethane foams are not good sound absorbers their stiffness can often be used to advantage in noise control. They can be applied to sheet materials to reduce "drumming" or "oil canning" with the result that the noise level is lowered.

Flame Resistance

Rigid urethane foams are available in general purpose (non-SE) grade and self-extinguishing grade (SE.) The flame spread rating of an SE grade foam is considerably lower than that of a general purpose non-SE grade foam. Table IX-21 shows some flame spread ratings obtained on the ASTM E-84 type tunnel tests on both SE and non-SE grade

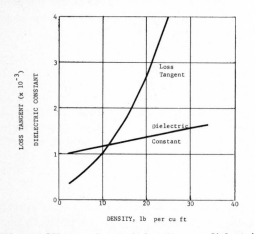

Figure IX-46, effect of density on dielectric constant and loss tangent on rigid urethane foam (frequency, 1-24 Kmc).

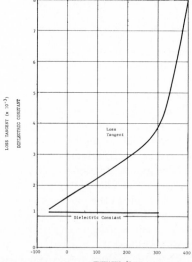

Figure IX-47, effect of temperature on dielectric constant and loss tangent of rigid urethane foam (halogenated foam).

RIGID URETHANE

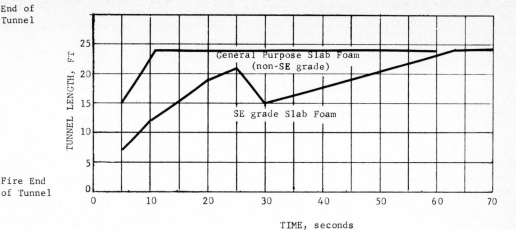

Figure IX-48, distance of maximum flame travel of rigid urethane foam (ASME-84).

foams. The flame spread rating with the SE grade foam was much lower than that of the general purpose grade foam. Values as low as 40 have been reported for other rigid SE grade urethane foam systems. The speed at which the flame travels and the maximum distance of flame travel are shown in fig IX-48.

Flame spread ratings obtained with the radiant panel test ASTM E-162 will not necessarily correlate with the results reported here for the tunnel test ASTM E-84.

In most applications, rigid urethane foams are covered with some type of facing material. The flame spread rating of the composite will be lower if non-combustible facing materials are used.

Vermin and fungus resistance

Urethane foam appears to be no more attractive to vermin than are other conventional insulations. High spot tests have shown that rats will nibble on rigid urethane foam but will not consume it even under starvation conditions. Autopsies performed on animals which nibbled on the foam revealed that the rats did not swallow the foam.

Laboratory tests indicate that fungi obtain no nutrition from rigid urethane foam; however, the foam is not toxic to the fungi. The foam will not support fungus growth, but will not kill active fungi transferred from other media (Table IX-22).

Only two rigid foam systems, one polyether and one polyester, were tested. Since there are many other foam systems for producing urethane foam, it is possible that some of the ingredients used will support fungus growth. The specific composition selected for a product should be tested to determine if a fungus problem exists.

Table IX-21—Flame Spread Ratings (ASTM E-84) (Unprotected Foam Slabs)						
Foam type	Facings	Flame spread rating[1]	Smoke developed[2]	Fuel contribution	Ignition time, minutes	Comments
SE grade	none	525	>200	Indeterminable	On contact	Foam almost totally burned away up to 16 ft. Surface charred 1/8 to 1 in. deep from 16 to 24 ft. Front 10 ft. of foam fell from tunnel roof after 1 min, 55 sec.
General purpose, Non-SE grade	none	3000	>200	Indeterminable	On contact	Foam completely burned to 18 ft, small portion remained from 18-24 ft at tunnel edges. Front 16 ft of foam fell from tunnel roof after 50 sec.

[1]A flame spread rating over 100 tells how much faster the flame spread was than that of red oak, i.e., 3000 means a flame spread 30 times as fast as that of red oak.
[2]Based on 0 for cement asbestos board and 100 for red oak.

Table IX-22—Fungus Resistance of Rigid Urethane Foam

Test A. Military Specification MIL-F-13927—Foam samples inoculated with fungi associated with degradation of textiles, rubber, leather, and similar products. The foam samples were inoculated with:

1. Asperigillus niger
2. A flevns
3. A terreus
4. Penicillium citrinum
5. Spicaria violacea
6. Trichoderma T1

Results—after 28 days' exposure, there was no growth on the specimens.

Test B. ASTM D 684-54 – Soil Burial
Results—after 28 days' exposure, no evidence of fungi on foam specimens. Cotton controls were totally degraded.

Test C. Federal Specification CCC-T-191B, Method 5760—samples on cotton wicks inoculated with the following fungi in a mineral salt solution:

1. Asperigillus clavatus
2. A niger
3. Chastomium globosum
4. Penicillium funo-glaucum
5. Trichoderma T1

Results—after 28 days' exposure, one type of fungus colony was growing on the sides of the rigid foam samples, but it is believed that this was an overrunning from the surface of the wicks underneath it.

Odor

Rigid urethane foam is relatively free from odor after it has been cured.

During the foaming reaction the odors of toluene diisocyanate and amine catalysts are present. On curing at room temperature or at elevated temperatures the odor is reduced very quickly to a low level. Selection of catalysts that either react with the isocyanate or have very low volatility will also help reduce the amine odor. Certain refrigeration industry reports indicate that refrigerators with urethane foam insulation impart a taste and odor to distilled water and unsalted butter but that it is practically negligible. In several cases, panels of experts have said that they actually preferred the taste imparted by urethane to that imparted by other insulation media.

14. USES

Rigid urethane foam is being used in a great variety of applications today; some because of the foam's excellent thermal properties, others because of its good strength. Principally, rigid foam is being used because of a unique combination of these properties—plus the fact that it can be foamed-in-place.

Rigid foam has been used extensively in construction applications. Castor-oil-based urethane foams have been used since September 1953. One installation was on a cooling water system. It still looks good and many more years of service life are predicted. A number of other installations of castor-oil-based foam date back to the period 1954 to 1956. All of these installations are still performing satisfactorily, with two exceptions: in one case the service temperature of $275°F$ was too high for the foam; in the other case failure was attributed to the lack of a vapor barrier. With vapor barriers, castor-oil-based foam has been performing satisfactorily in service conditions ranging from $-94°F$ to $+90°F$.

Experience with polyester-based foam blown with Fluorocarbon-11 dates back to 1956. Ex-

Table IX-23—Properties of Some Commonly Used Commercial Insulating Materials

	Urethane foam	Foamglass	Styrene-based foam Extruded	Styrene-based foam From beads	Cork	Glass fiber	Rockwool
Foamed-in-place	yes	no	no	yes with steam only	no	no	no
K factor, Btu/(hr) (sq ft) (°F per in)	0.11 to 0.16	0.38	0.24	0.22	0.28	0.24	0.32
Common commercial density lb per cu ft	1.5-2.5[1]	9	1.5-2.5	1.5-2.5	16	—	—
Temperature limits, °F	−320 to +225	−320 to +600	−320 to +170	−320 to +170	−320 to +200	−320 to +600	−320 to +1200
Flame resistance	SE[2]	NB[3]	SE[2]	SE[2]	SE[2]	NB[3]	NB[3]
WVT, perm in.	1.5-3	very low	1.5-3	1.5-3	high	v. high	v. high
Chemical & solvent resistance	good	good	poor	poor	good	good	good
Tensile strength, psi	40-80	—	40-70	30-60	—	—	—
Compressive strength at yield pt, psi	25-60	100	30-50	30	—	—	—

[1]Other densities of foamed urethane can be easily obtained.
[2]Self-extinguishing grades available.
[3]Does not burn.

RIGID URETHANE

perience with polyether slab stock, fire retardant type, dates back to 1960. All of these are performing satisfactorily. In all cases a vapor barrier was used. Use of vapor barriers is felt to be essential to long service life for rigid urethane foam. Typical examples:

(a) Use of urethane foam on the removable heads of refrigeration machines has resulted in considerably reduced maintenance costs. Previously, the insulation on these heads had to be replaced every time they were removed. Now it is an integral part of the equipment.

(b) Fire insurance regulations are becoming more strict regarding the isolation of floors in manufacturing buildings, to eliminate the chimney effect and spreading of fires. Foamed-in-place urethane has been used to good advantage around piping and equipment located in such floors. Not only is the fire hazard lessened, but the transmission of vibration is also greatly reduced (Table IX-23).

The number of confirmed and potential uses of rigid urethane foam is growing daily. The following list is not all-inclusive but shows some of the applications served by rigid foam today:

Amusement park figures, archery targets, armament cocoons, ball floats, boat bulkheads, boat flotation, buoys, burial vaults, casts for broken bones, cavity walls, Christmas decorations.

Ice buckets (complete units), igloos built on the spot, life preservers, mannequins, movable office partitions, nose cone insulation, curtain wall core, dock floats, doors (residential and industrial), duck decoys, encapsulating, exhibition displays, fish net floats, floating lids for gas storage tanks, flower decorations, hood insulation (automobiles), surf boards.

Thermal insulation of: heating and air conditioning equipment and ducts, chemical equipment, cold storage warehouses, dairy equipment, hot food containers, ice cream cartons.

Packaging: archaeologist specimens, missile components, furniture, moisture sensitive articles. Milk boxes, refrigerators and refrigerated transport, residential and industrial buildings, thermos jugs.

Perimeter insulation on housing, picnic coolers (complete unit), potting electrical circuits, radar domes and reflectors, relief pictures and maps, roofing material, sail boats, stage scenery, sound insulation, structural aircraft components, void filling, water shoes.

PART II—ONE-SHOT RIGID URETHANE FOAM
By Michael Seele

1. HISTORY AND MANUFACTURE

Non-existent a few years ago, the market for rigid urethane foam reached an estimated 29-million lb during 1962 and is projected to climb to 140-million lb by 1966.

The impressive place which this material has established for itself in the plastics market over such a relatively short period of time can be primarily attributed to its excellent thermal insulation properties (low K factor). Other outstanding properties, such as low moisture absorption, dimensional stability, chemical resistance, strength, and lightness also have contributed to its growth. The ability of rigid urethane foam to be poured "in-place" as a liquid has offered the design engineer many new applications for foamed plastic heretofore not practical or possible.

Several years ago, it was evident that there was a need to stimulate the rather sluggish growth rate of the rigid urethane foam market. The historical rate at which raw material prices were decreasing was not going to be enough to stimulate the growth of this remarkable material. Work began in the laboratory, and by early 1960 a commercial "one-shot" process for producing rigid urethane foam was ready for field development. The key to this process was a new polyisocyanate, a modified form of 80% 2,4 + 20% 2,6-toluene diisocyanate (TDI) (Allied's "Nacconate 4040").

A significant advantage of the one-shot process is its economics. Heretofore, most rigid urethane foam was produced by the "quasi-prepolymer" method. The important step of manufacturing a quasi-prepolymer from 80% 2,4 + 20% 2,6-toluene diisocyanate (TDI) and a resin is eliminated with the one-shot process. The one-shot process generally has the additional benefit of offering faster foaming and shorter cure time.

More recently, a modified p,p-diphenylmethane diisocyanate (MDI) was introduced by Mobay for the production of one-shot rigid urethane foam. Also suitable for the one-shot process is a Carwin product, polymethylene polyphenylisocyanate (PAPI). These products produce foams with excellent flame-retardant properties and which remain stable at relatively high temperatures.

Latest entry into the field of isocyanates comes from DuPont and is reported to be a modified form of 80% 2,4 and 20% 2,6 toluene diisocyanate (TDI) tradenamed "Hylene TRC."

The following outline will best explain the basic difference between the two accepted processes for producing rigid urethane foam, namely, the one-shot versus the quasi-prepolymer process.

Quasi-Prepolymer Process

Step 1:
Products—80% 2,4 and 20% 2,6 TDI and a portion of the resin.
Process—heat releasing reaction.
Result—quasi-prepolymer.
Resin can be either a polyester or a polyether. However, in recent years, polyethers have generally been used, because of their lower cost.

Step 2:
Products—remainder of the resin, catalyst, emulsifier and blowing agent.
Process—mechanical mixing.
Result—premix.
The blowing agent is generally Fluorocarbon-11.

Step 3:
Products—quasi-prepolymer and premix.
Process—mixing and reaction.
Result—rigid urethane foam.

One-Shot Process

Step 1:
Products—100% of the resin, catalyst, emulsifier and blowing agent.
Process—mechanical mixing.
Result—premix.

Step 2:
Products—premix, 100% isocyanate (such as Allied's "Nacconate 4040").
Process—mixing and reaction.
Result—rigid urethane foam.

Polyols

The following polyols can be used with most of the polyfunctional polyisocyanates (Mobay's Mondur, Allied's Nacconate and Carwin's PAPI) to produce one-shot foam:

- *Methylglucoside,* a product of Corn Products Co., makes a polyether; available in hydroxyl numbers from 400 to 600, with a wide range of viscosities.
- *Sorbitol-derived polyethers* range from 270 to 650 in hydroxyl numbers.
- *Sucrose-derived polyethers* have highest functionality available at present; they are octofunctional, give urethanes of great strength, rigidity and dimensional stability, although of low density. Their OH numbers vary from 350 to 550.
- *Amine-derived polyols,* either tetrafunctional or pentafunctional, are available from Wyandotte Chemical Corp., Union Carbide Corp., or Dow Chemical Co. They require a larger amount of modified isocyanate, therefore the foams they produce are more costly. Because of the presence of a tertiary nitrogen acting as a catalyst, they are particularly strong and stable.
- *Phosphorus-derived resins* are useful because of their great flame-retardant properties. They are available, with various phosphorus contents, and usable in varying proportions, from Virginia Carolina Chemical Corp., Victor Chemical Co., Wyandotte Chemicals Corp., Atlas Chemical Industries, and Union Carbide.
- *Polyesters*—Hooker Chemical Co. supplies an important group of polyesters based on highly chlorinated acid, instead of polyethers, to make one-shot rigid urethane foam, with excellent fire retardancy.

Catalysts

Catalysts are very important for the control of the foam produced; they minimize gas loss, prevent foam collapse, determine cell structure. Most commonly used catalysts are the tertiary amines and the tin compounds, alone or in combinations.

Silicones

Gas nucleation and bubble stability are promoted by the use of silicones, in proportions of 1 to 1.5 parts of silicone for 100 parts of polyols. The silicones are made by Dow Corning, General Electric and Union Carbide.

The one-shot technology offers an obvious economic advantage since it eliminates the cost of manufacturing the quasi-prepolymer. One-shot rigid foams can be processed on a variety of commercial foam machines, including those designed for froth foam. Hand batch methods are not recommended. In general, one-shot formulations are slightly more sensitive to changes in processing conditions, such as temperature and mixing, than most quasi-prepolymer formulations. One-shot foam production should only be handled under the direction of a competent technician. Actually, careful control should be maintained when processing either type system.

Producers of one-shot urethane foam have two alternatives: They can purchase all of their foam raw materials, make up their own premix, and thus produce foam at or near raw material cost. Or they can purchase a package system where, as an example, "Component A" is isocyanate, and "Component B" is the premix.

2. PROPERTIES

There are other advantages to one-shot foams besides their manufacturing economy. Both commercial production experience and laboratory tests have proved that the properties of one-shot foams are excellent, especially with respect to K-factor and dimensional stability. One-shot rigid urethane foams blown with Fluorocarbon-11 blowing agent have an initial K-factor of 0.11 to 0.12 at 70°F, putting them among the most efficient insulations commercially available. A given thickness of urethane foam provides the same insulating efficiency as approximately two and a half times the thickness of glass fiber or cork, and twice the thickness of polystyrene foam.

Nacconate 4040's low viscosity (50 to 150 centipoise at 78.8°F) gives the over-all one-shot system a lower viscosity and exceptional flowability. This flowability can contribute to faster and more economical production cycles by allowing for new product designs and production line foaming techniques. For example, a manufacturer of urethane foam-insulated household refrigerators was able to realize a savings on his production line because the one-shot system made it possible for the refrigerators to be filled faster, thus increasing the number of units which can be produced with a given number of fixtures. The one-shot systems generally foam and cure quickly, cutting production time in the fixture or mold significantly.

When used with flame-retardant reactive polyols or additive compounds, one-shot rigid urethane foams generally have superior self-extinguishing properties compared to quasi-prepolymer foams produced with 80% 2,4-and 20% 2,6-toluene diisocyanate (TDI). The one-shot foams have high melting points and consequently less tendency to drip and spread flames when ignited. Modified MDI and PAPI produce foams which are even superior in flame retardant properties to Nacconate 4040 foams.

In addition to the advantages described above, one-shot foam has all the well-known features of rigid urethane foam: strength, lightness, closed cells, the ability to adhere securely to substrates when poured-in-place, the ability to provide structural support, application versatility, and resistance to weathering, water, chemicals, solvents, oils, vermin and rodents. Urethane foam is unique in that it can be poured-in-place, molded, sprayed, or cut up into slab stock or boards after it has been made into buns. Boards can be nailed, glued or cemented to a variety of surfaces. One-shot rigid foams do all of these.

3. APPLICATIONS

As an insulation material, one-shot rigid urethane foam is presently finding its major commercial application in household refrigerators, freezers, panels for walk-in coolers, cold storage warehouses, curtain wall panels, refrigerated truck trailers, insulated railroad tank cars, and several other specialty applications. All of these applications are for poured-in-place foam. Either as pre-cut or molded shapes, one-shot foam is used for insulating pipes, industrial process equipment, roof decks, cold storage warehouses, and a host of other applications. Expansion joint fillers for highways and other concrete expansion joints is another interesting application for one-shot rigid foam. It is also finding increased use as an insulation sprayed on the underside of road bridges to reduce premature icing of bridges compared to the approach roads and thus provide safer driving conditions. It also helps prolong the life of the bridge decks themselves.

One-shot urethane foam can also be successfully used in the many commercial and military applications now being filled by rigid urethane foams. These include applications for packaging, aircraft, refrigerated cargo ships, ice cream truck bodies, beverage dispensing machines, refrigerated railroad boxcars, submarines, storage tanks, picnic coolers, underground storage areas and mines, and many others.

As a flotation material to increase buoyancy, rigid urethane foam is now being used in pleasure boats, floating docks, buoys, markers, and floating roofs in storage tanks for petroleum products. Rigid foam is also used to fill non-functional cavities and structural voids in ships which ordinarily require continual maintenance and coating.

Appendix—Typical one-shot rigid urethane foam formulations*

These systems range from a low cost non-flame retardant foam system suitable for refrigeration insulation, packaging, flotation, etc. through low cost self-extinguishing formulations and a non-burning system. While the non-flame retarded example shows Poly G-435 DM, a methylglucoside based polyether as the polyol, sorbitol and sucrose based polyols can be used equally well. In the non-burning area the HLR systems provide a high quality non-burning foam. Polyether systems employing Wyandotte Chemicals' experimental polyol 204 may also be utilized in preparation of non-burning foams at minimum cost, as may products from Atlas Chemical Industries, Union Carbide Corporation and Dow Chemical Company.

	Non-S.E.	S.E.	S.E.	S.E.	Non-Burning
Poly G-435 DM[1]	100				
G-2566[2]			78.6		
RS-450[3]		60		81.5	
X-204[4]		40			
HLR-250[5]					100
Vircol 82[6]			21.4	18.5	
DC-113[7]	1.5	2.0	2.0	2.0	1.25
Tetramethyl Guanidine[8]		1.5			
Tetramethyl Butanediamine[9]	1.7		1.5	1.5	
Triethylamine[10]	0.8	0.75			
F 11-B[11]	36	41	35	30	26
PAPI	110	110	130	90	86
NCO Index	1.05	1.05	1.03	1.03	1.0
Thru-put-lb per min	24	20	20	20	
Roto speed—rpm	5,000	5,500	3,450	3,450	
Temperature—°F					
Resin stream	90	90	83	120	129
PAPI stream	80	80	80	86	102
Cream time—seconds	16	13	11	5	
Rise time—seconds	44	70	60	50	
Tack free time—seconds	65	70	60	50	
Density—lb per cu ft	1.88	1.96	2.07	1.98	1.72
Compressive strength (parallel) psi	29	29	36	31	25.6
Dimensional stability					
Humid aging—158°F at 100% RH					
Volume change, %					
3 days	+5.0	+12.0	+6	+9	+6.9
7 days	+7.4	+15.0	+7	+9	+9.6
14 days			+6	+14	
28 days			+5 (56 days)	+14 (56 days)	
Dry aging—200°F					
Volume change, %					
1 day			+3 (230°F)	+4 (230°F)	
3 days	+2.7	+3.0	+3 (230°F)	+4 (230°F)	+2.8
7 days	+3.8	+4.0			+4.0
ASTM—1962-59T					
Distance burned, inches		1	1-3/16	1-1/8	½
K Factor—initial			0.125	0.125	0.125
Closed cells, %			90	90	91

*Courtesy Carwin Co., Div. of The Upjohn Co., North Haven, Conn.
[1]Olin Mathieson Chemical Corporation
[2]Atlas Chemical Industries, Inc.
[3]Dow Chemical Corporation
[4]Wyandotte Chemicals Corporation
[5]Hooker Chemicals Corporation
[6]Virginia-Carolina Chemical Company
[7]Dow Corning Corporation
[8]American Cyanamid Corporation
[9]Union Carbide Corporation, Chemicals Div.
[10]Union Carbide Corporation, Chemicals Div.
[11]E. I. du Pont de Nemours and Company, Inc.; Pennsalt Chemicals Corporation; Allied Chemicals Corporation; Union Carbide Corporation

PART III—CALCULATIONS AND STOICHIOMETRY

By Robert A. Stengard

1. CALCULATIONS

The isocyanate to hydroxyl ratio (usually called the NCO/OH ratio) has a pronounced effect on the physical properties of rigid urethane foams. For good quality foams, this ratio should be greater than one. The exact ratio to be used depends on the foaming conditions, the type of equipment used and the application. Calculation methods are outlined for various types of operations.

The basic chemical reactions involved in the formation of rigid urethane foam polymers are (a) reaction of isocyanate with hydroxyl groups to form urethanes, (b) reaction of isocyanates with water to form ureas and carbon dioxide. The heat from the urethane reactions can be used to volatilize an inert solvent such as a fluorocarbon to expand the foam. Foam reactions (a) and (b) are used to calculate the relative amounts of isocyanate resin or polyol, and water (with carbon dioxide expanded foam) required to produce a foam. The relationship between the amount of fluorocarbon and foam density has also been determined.

The following paragraphs cover the basic calculations involved in the preparation of foams prepared by the pre-polymer, semi-prepolymer and one-shot techniques.

The analytical information usually available is:

Isocyanate	Percent purity by weight, percent NCO, or equivalent weight.
Polyol	Hydroxyl No (as mg of KOH per gm) or equivalent weight. Acid No (as mg of KOH per gm) Water (percent by weight) Molecular weight (occasionally)

The equivalent weights (E) of water and the isocyanate groups are:

Water, (E_{H_2O}) = 9 (one-half of the molecular weight of water)

Isocyanate Group, (E_{NCO}) = 42 (the molecular weight of the isocyanate group)

In formulating urethane foams, the total moles of isocyanate groups used must be greater than the sum of the total moles of hydroxyl groups in the polyol including water and acid groups that may be present.

With most of the polyols (polyhydroxyl material) in use today, the acid number is very low (less than 1.0) and may be omitted in the calculations. If the acid number is high and cannot be neglected, it is added to the hydroxyl number. With good quality polyols designed for rigid urethane foams and not contaminated in any way, the amount of water present is so low that it can be neglected in most foam calculations. For example, using a polyol that has an equivalent weight of 110, and a water content of 0.1 percent, the error introduced in neglecting the water is 1 percent. In the preparation of high density foams, particularly at densities over ten lb per cu ft, by these techniques, even this amount of water must be included in the calculations because it is a source of some of the carbon dioxide that expands the foam.

In the preparation of prepolymers the water content must be considered because its presence will increase the prepolymer viscosity and reduce the isocyanate (NCO) content, i.e., equivalent weight.

The viscosity of a prepolymer varies inversely with its isocyanate content. It is, therefore, important that the prepolymers be designed to give workable viscosities within the handling limits of the equipment in which it will be used. Fig. IX-49 shows the relationship between viscosity and isocyanate content for

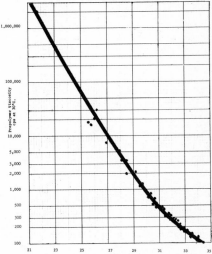

Figure IX-49, viscosity to free NCO-% relationships for rigid urethane prepolymers based on polyether polyols and toluene diisocyanates.

several prepolymers based on various polyether polyols and toluene diisocyanates.

Basic calculations

The following formulas may be used for calculating polyol, isocyanate, water and fluorocarbon concentrations for rigid urethane foams:

1. Equivalent weight (E_{polyol}) of polyol or hydroxy compound.

$$E_{polyol} = \frac{56.1 \times 1000}{OH\ No.}$$

56.1 is the molecular weight of KOH (OH No. is the milliequivalents of KOH per mole of polyol).

2. Equivalent weight of isocyanate (the isocyanate in this case is any isocyanate including isocyanate reaction products that contain reactive isocyanate groups such as prepolymer).

$$E_{iso} = \frac{4200}{Percent\ NCO}$$

4200 is 100 times 42 (the molecular weight of the NCO group).

3. Amount of isocyanate required to react with a polyol (for low density fluorocarbon expanded foams with negligible moisture in the polyol).

$$Wt\ isocyanate = \left(\frac{wt\ polyol}{E_{polyol}} \times E_{iso}\right)$$

(This must be calculated for each polyol if a mixture of polyols is used).

4. Amount of isocyanate required to react with water (in a polyol or added to foaming system in carbon dioxide expanded foams).

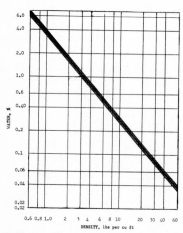

Figure IX-50, effect of water concentration on the density of rigid urethane foam. Water % = 3.706D⁻¹·¹²⁶.

$$Wt\ isocyanate = \left(\frac{Wt\ water}{9} \times E_{iso}\right) =$$

$$\left(Wt\ water\ added + Wt\ polyol \times \frac{\%\ Water}{100}\right)E_{iso}$$

$$\frac{}{9}$$

5. Total isocyanate used in foaming composition:

Wt isocyanate = (Sum of 3 and 4) × (desired NCO/OH ratio)

6. The theoretical equivalent weight and percent NCO of a prepolymer can be calculated as:

$$\%\ NCO = \frac{4200}{wt\ iso + wt\ polyol}\left[\frac{wt\ iso}{E_{iso}}\right.$$

$$\left. - \Sigma\left(\frac{wt\ polyol}{E_{polyol}}\right) - \Sigma\left(\frac{\%\ water \times wt\ polyol}{900}\right)\right]$$

$$Eq\ Wt = \frac{1}{wt\ iso + wt\ polyol}\left[\frac{wt\ iso}{E_{iso}} - \right.$$

$$\left. \Sigma\left(\frac{wt\ polyol}{E_{polyol}}\right) - \Sigma\left(\frac{\%\ water \times wt\ polyol}{900}\right)\right]$$

where Σ = sum of terms following between parenthesis, and 900 = 100 times 9 (the equivalent weight of water).

7. The amount of isocyanate required (theoretically) to obtain a certain percent NCO or equivalent weight prepolymer can be obtained with the equation in (6) by solving for the wt of isocyanate.

8. To adjust the NCO content of a prepolymer: Basis—100 parts of initial prepolymer of NCO content P and a final NCO content F. The weight of isocyanate to be added, I, is:

$$I = 100\left(\frac{F - P}{\%\ NCO_{iso} - F}\right)$$

9. If the foam is expanded with carbon dioxide from the water-isocyanate reaction, the amount of water required for a foam of any density can be determined from Fig. IX-50, which is based on experimental data. The amount of water shown includes the water that is present in the polyol or other foaming ingredients as well as added water. The relationship between the amount of water and the density of the foam can be reduced to the equation:

$$W = \frac{3.706}{D^{1.126}}$$

Where W = water content in percent
D = density of the foam, lb per cu ft
3.706 = constant
1.126 = constant

The amount of isocyanate is determined in equations 3, 4 and 5.

10. If the foam is expanded with Fluorocarbon-11, the amount of blowing agent can be determined from Fig. IX-51, which is based on experimental data. The equation for calculating the amount of blowing agent for any density is:

$$F = \frac{28.21}{D^{0.900}}$$

Where F = Fluorocarbon-11, percent
D = Density, lb per cu ft
28.21 = constant
0.900 = constant

Since the blowing agent is inert and does not react with the polyol or isocyanate no other calculations are required.

2. FOAM QUALITY

The quality of a rigid urethane foam, that is its ability to maintain dimensional stability under various conditions, and its mechanical strength are influenced to a large extent by the base polyol used. The average crosslink density is determined by the polyol and the NCO/OH ratio used, although the polyol is the most important.

In general, foams having low crosslink density have poor dimensional stability at low and high temperatures. Those having high crosslink density have good dimensional stability. However, if the crosslink density is too high, the foams may be brittle.

The crosslink density (Mc) can be calculated for a specific foaming system. This method does not include crosslinks contributed by an NCO/OH ratio over 1.0.

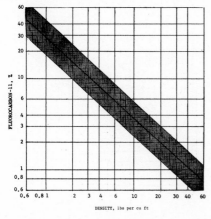

Figure IX-51, effect of fluorocarbon-11 concentration on the density of rigid urethane foam. Fluorocarbon-11 % = 28.21D⁻⁰·⁹⁰⁰.

$$Mc = \frac{\text{Total weight of polymer}}{\text{Moles of crosslinks}}$$

= average distance between crosslinks

For example:

	Parts by Weight Based on 1 MW of Resin
Polyol. Eq wt = 93.25 (8 OH groups per molecule)	748.0*
Catalyst	5.0
Surfactant	12.4
Blowing Agent (does not contribute to polymer structure in case of foams blown with fluorocarbons)	
Isocyanate	1317.0
Total wt of Foam	2082.4

The number of reactive sites available for crosslinking is two less than the number of reactive sites on a molecule since two sites are used for chain extension

$$Mc = \frac{2082}{6} = 347$$

Mechanical strength and dimensional stability of rigid urethane foam can be markedly improved by formulating the foam to an NCO/OH ratio of 1.05 to 1.10, rather than to an NCO/OH ratio of 1.00 or less. At low NCO/OH ratios (1.00 or less) mechanical properties and dimensional stability can be improved somewhat by heat curing. Dimensional stability can also be improved by using the frothing technique for expanding the foam. However, the improvement in properties brought about by increasing the NCO/OH ratio is much greater than that attributable to heat curing.

Figs. IX-52 to IX-55 show the effect of NCO/OH ratio on the strength properties and dimensional stability of rigid urethane foams made from a polyol having an equivalent weight of 94, a pure toluene diisocyanate, and blown with a fluorocarbon blowing agent. The foam densities varied from 1.4 to 1.5 lb per cu ft.

As the NCO/OH ratio of the foam formulation is increased from 0.95 to 1.10, compressive strength, deflection at yield, and tensile strength increase, while elongation decreases (see Figs. IX-52 to IX-55). For foams formulated to an NCO/OH ratio of 1.10, heat curing offers little advantage over room temperature curing.

The data shown were obtained on nonfrothed foams blown with Fluorocarbon-11 blowing agent. Frothed foam blown with a

*Equivalent weight of resin (93.7) × 8 = moelcular weight of polyol

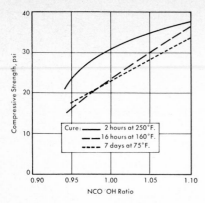

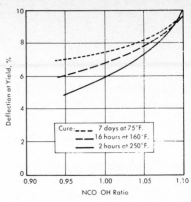

Figure IX-52, effect of NCO/OH ratio and cure on compressive strength at yield point.

Figure IX-53, effect of NCO/OH ratio and cure on deflection at compressive yield point.

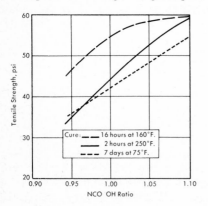

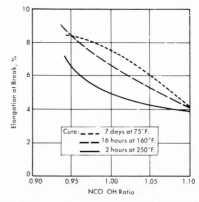

Figure IX-54, effect of NCO/OH ratio and cure on tensile strength.

Figure IX-55, effect of NCO/OH ratio and cure on elongation at break.

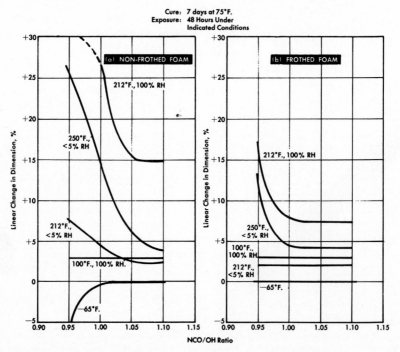

Figures IX-56 and IX-57, effect of NCO/OH ratio on dimensional stability.

blend of Fluorocarbon-11 and Fluorocarbon-12 shows similar trends, although the effects of NCO/OH ratio and heat curing are not as pronounced.

The dimensional stability of foams formulated to an NCO/OH ratio of 1.05 to 1.10 is consistently better than that of foams made with NCO/OH ratios of 0.95 to 1.00, under all exposure conditions studied (Figs. IX-56 & IX-57). Foams formulated to an NCO/OH ratio of 1.00 vary in dimensional stability because present metering equipment and formulating techniques permit the actual NCO/OH ratio to vary slightly and occasionally drop below 1.00.

Dimensional stability, as discussed here, refers to the resistance of the foam to swelling or shrinking; that is, the less a foam swells or shrinks in a particular environment, the more dimensionally stable it is. Factors that can affect dimensional stability of rigid urethane foam, other than those discussed here, are: catalyst, surfactant, type and amount of mixing, cell structure, foam density, foam age, and presence of molded skins or protective facings or coatings. The change in dimension is not the same on each of the three axes. Least change nearly always occurs in the direction of the foam rise, greatest change in the direction perpendicular to foam rise. Occasionally foams have been observed to shrink in the direction

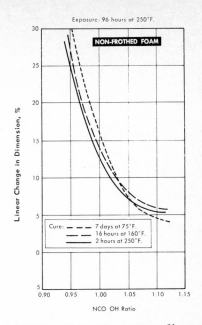

Figure IX-58, effect of cure on dimensional stability.

of foam rise while expanding in the direction perpendicular to foam rise.

Care must be taken that the *actual* NCO/OH ratio remains at the desired level. For example, the NCO content of a prepolymer may decrease with age by reaction with atmospheric

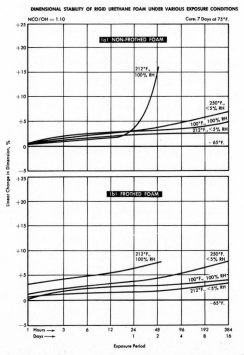
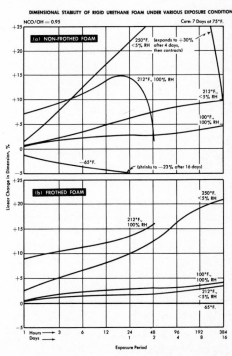

Figure IX-59, dimensional stability of rigid urethane foam under various exposure conditions.

moisture, if the prepolymer is not kept completely moisture free. Good dimensional stability can normally be maintained by formulating to an NCO/OH ratio of 1.05-1.10.

At NCO/OH ratios of 1.05 or less, frothed foam has better dimensional stability than non-frothed foam of the same density and NCO/OH ratio (see Figs. IX-56, 57, and 59). Even at an NCO/OH ratio of 1.10, frothed foam has somewhat better dimensional stability than non-frothed foam in high temperature, high humidity environments. (Compare the curves for a 212°F, 100% RH environment, in Figs. IX-56 and IX-57).

If a foam is formulated to an NCO/OH ratio of 1.05 or greater, curing conditions have very little effect on the foam's dimensional stability; foam cured at room temperature has dimensional stability as good as or better than foam which has been heat cured. At lower NCO/OH ratios, however, heat curing improves dimensional stability (Fig. IX-58).

Dimensional stability decreases (the foam swells more) as the temperature and humidity of the environment increase or as the exposure time to the environment increases. Swelling results from a combination of: (1) increased gas pressure in the cells due to expansion of fluorocarbon vapor and inward diffusion of air and water vapor, and (2) softening of the foam at high temperatures; pressure exerted by fluorocarbon, air and water vapor on the cell walls causes the softened foam to undergo plastic flow. Even the relatively stable foams formulated to an NCO/OH ratio of 1.10 are affected by exposure to high temperature and high humidity, as shown in Fig. IX-59. Carbon dioxide expanded foams will also distort at elevated temperatures because of gas expansion within the foam cells and softening of the polymer structure. Solvent vapors can also decrease dimensional stability by softening the foam.

Foams formulated to an NCO/OH ratio of 0.95 show considerably greater change in dimension than foams made with an NCO/OH ratio of 1.10 when exposed to the same environments. (See Fig. IX-59.) The 0.95 NCO/OH foams do not continue to swell with increasing exposure time in all environments; instead, they may swell initially and then contract. Closed cell measurements have shown that a foam which undergoes initial expansion and subsequent contraction contains a large percentage of ruptured cell walls.

Excessive shrinkage at low temperatures (below 75°F) also constitutes poor dimensional stability. Shrinkage results when the blowing agent condenses, leaving a partial vacuum in the foam cells, and the foam structure is not rigid enough to withstand the external pressure. This phenomenon was observed in the non-frothed foam formulated to an NCO/OH ratio of 0.95, when it was exposed at −65°F.

The NCO/OH ratio generally used for preparing slab foam in the plant is only slightly over 1.05. This gives an adequate margin of safety for this type of operation, and the small additional strength obtained by going to higher NCO/OH ratios is generally not worth the additional cost.

In plant molding operations a 1.05 NCO/OH ratio is generally satisfactory because adequate control over the ingredients can be maintained. However, in field applications where there is a possibility of moisture contamination of the isocyanate, fluorocarbon boil-off from the polyol masterbatch and variations in pumping and metering due to temperature differences, an NCO/OH ratio higher than 1.05 should be used. All of these errors will tend to lower the NCO/OH ratio into a range that could produce unsatisfactory foams. Therefore, the ratio often used for field application is about 1.10.

A higher NCO/OH ratio is generally used in spray application, whether in the plant or in the field, than in a pouring type operation. In factory operation, where humidity and temperature can be controlled, an NCO/OH ratio of 1.1 or less may be satisfactory, but if the spraying conditions are not controlled, and particularly if there is a variation in humidity, then an NCO/OH ratio of 1.15 or higher should be used. When spraying in the field under low humidity conditions, an NCO/OH ratio in the range of 1.10 to 1.15 can be used. If these conditions cannot be controlled, and there is a possibility of operation under high humidity conditions, an NCO/OH ratio as high as 1.2 should generally be adequate to produce a satisfactory foam. All of this assumes that good metering accuracy can be maintained. Even higher ratios may be desirable if metering accuracy cannot be controlled to ±2% and moisture contamination of the ingredients can occur. These considerations apply to both fluorocarbon and carbon dioxide expanded foaming systems.

Section X—FLEXIBLE URETHANE FOAM
By Paul G. Gemeinhardt
PART I—HISTORY AND INTRODUCTION

1. HISTORY

In 1937, Dr. Otto Bayer and coworkers discovered the diisocyanate addition polymerization reaction which marked the birthdate of a new and versatile class of organic chemical compounds known today as polyurethanes. The development of polyurethane adhesives, coatings and rigid foam (See Section IX) progressed slowly during World War II. It was not until the post-war years that the consumer potential of polyurethanes in the form of flexible foams was realized. Spurred on by the refurbishing of a war-torn country, chemists and engineers of the Farbenfabriken Bayer Laboratories, a branch of the former I. G. Farben Industrie, developed flexible foams based on the principle of the 1937 discovery. These systems were disclosed in 1952.

Until this time, interest in isocyanates and polyurethanes grew slowly in the United States. In 1950, E. I. duPont deNemours & Co. Inc. and Monsanto Chemical Co. started semi-commercial production of diisocyanates, primarily tolylene diisocyanate. DuPont, in 1953, announced a polyurethane foam and provided information on its method of preparation by the prepolymer route.

During 1952-1954, the Bayer diisocyanate-polyester flexible foam system was developed to a degree suitable for commercial production including the continuous processing machinery necessary for manufacturing. Prior to 1952, the polyurethanes were characterized by good properties but high prices. It wasn't until the development of flexible foam with their high strength at very low densities that large scale commercial use of polyurethanes seemed assured.

In 1954, Bayer and Monsanto formed the jointly owned Mobay Chemical Company to introduce the Bayer foam system and other related polyurethane technology to the U.S. This same year, Mobay announced, along with duPont and Allied Chemical Corp. (National Aniline Division), intentions for full-scale manufacturing of isocyanates, the building-blocks for polyurethanes. Thus, it was in 1954 that this country gave birth to a new industry —flexible urethane foams—based largely on Bayer know-how and utilizing equipment imported from Germany.

By 1956, the rapidly growing industry was no longer dependent on foreign imports to feed the supply lines of its continuous foam producing machines. Tolylene diisocyanate and polyester resin were in ready supply from domestic manufacturers. The 65/35% mixture of the 2,4 and 2,6 isomers of tolylene diisocyanate on which the original Bayer foam system was based was replaced by a cheaper 80/20% mixture which began pouring from American plant product lines. In addition, new polyesters and additives, such as catalysts, were introduced to meet the exacting demands of the isocyanate for producing the best foam capable of competing with highly successful competitive "foam rubber."

As the industry began to show semblance of maturity, however, it became apparent that the polyester-based systems could not hope to meet the competitive stature and needs of our economy. Their outstanding properties were commercially suitable for some applications, but polyester-based foam was lacking crucial properties and was too expensive as functional cushioning material. Despite improvements in compounding and development of ingenious fabricating techniques giving better humid aging, resiliency and cushioning characteristics, industry needed better and less expensive resins from which to build flexible foam. There followed investigations of polyesters based on dimerized linoleic acid (dimer acid) and polyethers.

Polyesters derived from dimer acid showed much promise for providing the softness, seating characteristic and moisture resistance needed for cushioning application. These systems were aggressively developed by Emery Industries, Mobay and others. But the advent of polyether resin prevented their reaching commercial status.

DuPont introduced the first semi-commercial polyether foam system in the U.S., based on poly-1,4-oxytetramethyleneglycol (Teracol 30). The properties of this foam were outstanding with regard to moisture resistance, resilience and softness, but its cost prohibited commercial use.

The commercial entry in 1957 of urethane grade polyether polyols derived from propylene oxide brought about a major change in polyurethane foam technology and market potential. Block copolymers of poly(oxypropylene)-poly(oxyethylene) glycols and similar block copolymers based on ethylenediamine were introduced by Wyandotte Chemical Corp. Urethane grade poly(oxypropylene) glycols and triols became commercially available from Dow Chemical Co., Union Carbide Corp. and Wyandotte. These materials were first offered to foam producers in the form of prepolymers in 1957 and very quickly gained in popularity because of their low cost and excellent properties.

In 1958, the large volume use of polyether resins was assured by the introduction of the "one-shot" foaming process permitting the elimination of the intermediate prepolymer step. For technical and economic reasons the use of polyether resins now exceeds that of all other resins, even though substantial quantities of polyesters are still in use today.

In a short span of nine years, the flexible urethane foam industry mushroomed to significant commercial importance in the United States as shown by the volume of foam produced, 150-million lb, in 1962. To give an overall picture of the flexible foam field, it is necessary to review the raw materials, chemistry, foam preparation, properties and applications.

2. RAW MATERIALS

The preparation of flexible urethane foams is based on carefully controlled reactions of diisocyanate with polyol and blowing agent (usually water). The control of foam formation from these basic components is governed by the presence of catalysts and foaming stabilizers (surfactants). Special foam properties can be obtained by including other additives such as fillers, plasticizers, pigments, flameproofing agents, color stabilizers, antioxidants and antihydrolyzates.

Isocyanates

Flexible foams have been prepared from a variety of aliphatic and aromatic diisocyanates. One of the first diisocyanates used for this purpose was hexamethylene diisocyanate.

This diisocyanate, when reacted with an adipic acid polyester and water, yielded foam having excellent color stability, a characteristic common to all aliphatic diisocyanates but not to aromatic diisocyanates. The use of hexamethylene diisocyanate did not pass the stage of academic interest, because of its low order of reactivity with polyol and water, even in a catalyzed state, and its high volatility, which increased its toxicity and handling hazards. Cost of manufacturing was also an important factor in determining which diisocyanate was to be used. For practical purposes, use of tolylene diisocyanate (TDI) has grown, and it is now used almost exclusively in the U.S. and abroad.

Various mixtures of the 2,4 and 2,6 isomers of tolylene diisocyanate shown below are in use for foam manufacture.

2,4 Isomer   2,6 Isomer

The original Bayer foam system first introduced in this country, employed 65/35% mixture of the 2,4 and 2,6 isomers. Today, this mixture is being used extensively abroad, whereas a lower cost 80/20% ratio is used almost exclusively in the U.S.

Major suppliers of tolylene diisocyanate in the U.S. are Mobay, duPont and Allied Chemical, who sell the material under the trade names Mondur, Hylene and Nacconate respectively. Announcements of intentions to produce TDI have been made by Nopco Chemical, Union Carbide and Olin Mathieson. Typical properties of the various types of TDI commercially available are summarized in Table X-1. Specifications reflected by the properties shown in that table were established by the American Society for Testing and Materials, under the guidance of the Flexible Foam Raw Materials Committee of the Cellular Plastics Division of the Society of the Plastics Industry. The ASTM has also established analytical procedures (D-1638-60T) for the following methods for TDI: isomer content, assay, acidity, hydrolyzable chloride, total chloride, freezing point, specific gravity, and color.

A review of the chemistry of the isocyanates with emphasis on their use in urethane polymer formation is given by J. H. Saunders and

Table X-1—Typical Properties of TDI Blends

Type (isomer ratio)	100	80:20	65:35
2,4 isomer, %	98.0 min.	80 ± 1	65 ± 2
2,6 isomer, %	2.0 max.	20 ± 1	35 ± 2
Amine equivalent, max.	87.5	87.5	87.5
Assay, % min.	99.5	99.5	99.5
Hydrolyzable chloride, % max.	0.010	0.005-0.007	0.010
Acidity (as HCl), % max.	0.010	0.003-0.004	0.010
Total chloride, % max.	0.1	0.05	0.1
APHA color, max.	25	15	25
Specific gravity @ 25/15.5°C	1.22 approx.	1.22 ± 0.01	1.22 approx.
Refractive index @ 25°C	1.566 approx.	1.566 ± 0.001	1.567 approx.
Flash point (Cleveland open cup) approx., °F	275	270	275
Fire point (Cleveland open cup) approx., °F	300	295	295

K. C. Frisch, "Polyurethanes, Part I—Chemistry" (Interscience Publishers, New York, 1962). See also Section IX of this Handbook.

Polyols

Two types of polyols (compounds containing alcoholic hydroxyl groups), namely, polyethers and polyesters, have gained commercial importance for flexible urethane foams.

Castor oil, a third polyol type, is the cheapest, but used to a much lesser degree. In its use for foams, the inherent stiffer character of the isocyanate castor oil urethane polymer is applied in areas where semi-flexible or even rigid foams are required.

Polyether polyols—Of the many polyether polyols known, those derived from propylene oxide are more widely used. The following illustrates a typical polyether glycol and a triol derived from glycerin:

Poly (oxypropylene) glycol

$$HO-CH-CH_2-O\ [-CH_2-CH-O-]_nH$$

Poly (oxypropylene) derivative of glycerin

$$H_2C\ [-O-CH_2-CH-O-]_nH$$
$$HC\ [-O-CH_2-CH-O-]_nH$$
$$H_2C\ [-O-CH_2-CH-O-]_nH$$

Since glycols and triols normally used have molecular weights of 2000 and higher, they are non-volatile, viscous liquids, relatively insoluble in water. They are soluble in common organic solvents such as alcohols, ketones, esters, and halogenated solvents.

When used for the preparation of foams, the polyether triols are used alone or in mixture with glycols. A 3000 molecular weight triol based on glycerin seems to have captured the major share of the polyether-based foam market. Special foam properties are achieved from the triol through the addition of varying amounts of a 2000 molecular weight glycol.

Of late, special effects, such as higher reactivity, have been achieved by terminating the basically poly(oxypropylene) polymer with primary hydroxyl groups through the addition of ethylene oxide. These "primary-hydroxyl-capped" polyether polyols have been found to require less catalyst when reacted with TDI than a comparable polyether containing all secondary hydroxyl groups, a saving in raw material costs as well as an improvement in foam properties.

The use of polyether polyols as chemical intermediates has shifted emphasis from purely physical properties to chemical properties. Today's "urethane grades" of polyether polyols are measured carefully for such properties as hydroxyl content, water content, acidity, acid content, carbonyl content, unsaturation, molecular weight, ash content, and color. ASTM (D-1638-60T) has reported analytical methods for most of these important properties (See Section IV).

Typical properties, of interest to foam producers, for representative polyether glycols and triols are listed in Table X-2.

Table X-2—Typical Properties of Commercially Available Polyether Glycols and Triols

Polyol	Glycol	Triol[1]	Triol
Molecular weight (approx.)	2000	3000	3000
Hydroxyl number (approx.)	56	56	56
Water, %	0.10	0.10	0.10
pH, H_2O /10MeOH	<7.0	<7.0	<7.0
Viscosity, cps. at 25°C	270	458	458
APHA color, max.	50	50	50
Specific gravity, 77/77°F	1.002	1.018	1.018
Pour Point, °F	−31	−23	−30
Flash point, °F	445	435	445
Fire point, °F	510	500	510
Refractive index, 77°F	1.450	1.452	1.452

[1]Primary hydroxy terminal groups.

Polyester polyols — The polyesters most suited for reaction with diisocyanates in the formation of flexible foams are those containing hydroxyl groups rather than *unsaturation*

Table X-3—Suppliers and Trade Names of Commercially Available Polyether Polyols	
Company	Trade name
Allied Chemical Corp.	Actol
The Dow Chemical Co.	Voranol
Jefferson Chemical Co.	Triol-G and Polypropylene Glycol
The Olin-Mathieson Corp.	Poly-G
Union Carbide Corp.	Niax
Witco Chemical Co.	Fomrez
Wyandotte Chemical Co.	Pluracol

Table X-4—Typical Properties of Commercially Available Polyester Polyols				
Trade name	Multrons			Fomrez 50
	R-68	R-70	R-18	
Supplier	Mobay	Mobay	Mobay	Witco
Approx. Molecular weight	2000	2000	2000	2000
Hydroxyl no.	45-52	50-57	57-63	49-55
Acid no., max.	1.2	1.5	1.5	2
Viscosity, cps., 25°C	12,000	15,000	20,000	17-22000
Water, % max.	0.1	0.1	0.1	—
Gardner Color, max.	1	1	1	1
Specific gravity @ 25/15.5°C (approx.)	1.19	1.19	1.19	
Refractive index @ 25°C (approx.)	1.475	1.475	1.475	—
Flash point (Cleveland open cup) approx., °F	570	570	570	
Fire point (Cleveland open cup) approx., °F	635	635	635	

so that cure proceeds by way of urethane *condensation*. Because it is not necessary to rely on reaction with a double bond of the unsaturated state, most of the polyesters are saturated, thus eliminating unnecessary complications.

The most common ingredients for the hydroxyl-terminated polyesters are adipic acid, diethylene glycol and trimethylolpropane. Other dibasic acids, as well as glycols and polyhydric alcohols, have been used for imparting special properties to polyester-based foams. For example, the greater hydrophobicity of dimerized linoleic acid ("Dimer" acid, a product of Emery Industries, Inc.) has been used to advantage for improving the hydrolytic stability of foam. Also, the greater flexibility and hygroscopic character of a 400-molecular weight polyethylene glycol has been used to improve the resiliency, low temperature properties and hygroscopic character of a urethane polymer. Despite these effects, the bulk of the polyester-based flexible urethane foams manufactured anywhere employs polyester derived from adipic acid and diethylene glycol.

Since the easiest control of urethane formation is obtained when the polyester contains only hydroxyl groups as reactive sites, the preferred polyesters are those with very low acid and water content.

Polyesters for flexible foam are very nearly linear so the amount of polyhydric alcohol used, from which slight branching is derived, is small. A typical polyester with molecular weight of about 2000 is a highly viscous, nonvolatile, water-white liquid.

Blowing agents

Carbon dioxide obtained *in situ* by the reaction of water with tolylene diisocyanate is the chief blowing agent for all commercially produced flexible foam. The amount of water and TDI used will determine foam density providing most of the gas formed is used to expand the urethane polymer. Because water participates in the polymerization reactions leading to the expanded, cellular urethane polymer, it has a very pronounced influence on the properties of foams. Much of this is due to the diarylurea linkages which are formed in the polymer backbone by the diisocyanate-water reaction. For better control of the foaming process, most foam manufacturers employ distilled or deionized water.

Other auxiliary blowing agents (inert solvents), which can be easily and controllably volatilized during the course of urethane polymer formation, can be used in addition to or as part replacement for the water in developing special foam properties. An example is the use of methylene chloride or trichloromonofluoromethane in either polyether- or polyester-based systems for softening the resulting foam. A number of other volatile solvents are known to have been used.

The "frothing process" recently developed at Du Pont utilizes refrigerants such as dichlorodifluoromethane, which volatilizes at below room temperature necessitating externally applied pressure to keep it in the foam ingredients.

Catalysts

The choice of catalyst for the preparation of flexible foams is governed by the type of polyol used. In polyether-based systems where one must counter the effect of low resin viscosity and reactivity (the latter due to the presence of all or a preponderance of secondary hydroxyl groups), very potent polymerization catalysts are required. For such systems, the stannous salts of dicarboxylic acids, for example stannous octoate, is preferred. Early foam technology used tertiary amines, but this general class, when used alone, has proven too inactive for controllable processing of one-shot polyether-based foams. They are used in conjunction with tin compounds since the latter have too low a catalytic effect on the TDI-water gas-forming reaction to be satisfactory by themselves. Thus, in the very popular one-shot polyether foam systems, a combination of tin compound and tertiary amine is used to tailor-make foaming and control processing characteristics. Some tertiary amines which are being used for this purpose are triethylenediamine (Dabco, a product of Houdry Process, Inc.), various derivatives of piperazine, morpholine and guanidine, as well as aliphatic amines such as tetramethylbutanediamine.

Generally, polyester-based systems process best with catalysts having a low order of activity and at most are more effective foaming catalysts than polymerization catalysts. Tertiary amines such as n-methyl, ethyl and coco morpholine and the dialkyl amines are used almost exclusively.

A second factor which governs the choice of catalyst is whether the method of foam preparation is one-shot or prepolymer. Since, during the foaming stage of a prepolymer system, the main reaction is that of gas formation (isocyanate groups and water), catalysts which give good control of carbon dioxide generation are preferred. Again, as in the polyester one-shot systems, tertiary amines are used.

Other factors controlling the choice of catalyst are odor, volatility, and compatibility with other foam ingredients. Odors resulting from residual catalyst usually cannot be tolerated in foam. Thus a catalyst having low or no odor is usually desired. One having high volatility enabling rapid dissipation from the foam can be used, but if the catalyst is too quickly dispelled, it will not be available for effecting final cure. Commonly used catalysts are listed in Table X-5.

Foaming stabilizers

As the term implies, foaming stabilizers are used to impart stability to the urethane polymer during the foaming process: they help in controlling the cell structure by regulating the size and to a large degree the uniformity of the cells. The choice of surfactant is governed

Table X-5—Common Catalysts for Flexible Urethane Foam

Chemical name	Supplier (Trade name)
N-Substituted morpholines	
N-methylmorpholine	Barlow Chemical Co.
	Jefferson Chemical Co.
	Union Carbide Corp.
N-ethylmorpholine	Baird Chemical Co.
	Jefferson Chemical Co.
	Union Carbide Corp.
	Barlow Chemical Co.
N-coco morpholine	Armour & Co.
	American Alcolac Corp.
Trialkyl amines	
Triethylamine	Pennsalt Chemical Co.
	Union Carbide Corp.
Dimethyl cetyl amine	Armour & Co. (Armeen)
Dimethyl soya amine	Armour & Co. (Armeen)
Dimethyl Lauryl amine	American Alcolac Corp.
Diethylcyclohexylamine	E. I. duPont de Nemours & Co.
N,N,N',N'-tetramethyl-ethylenediamine	Rohm & Haas
N,N,N',N'-tetramethyl-butanediamine	Union Carbide Corp.
Hydroxy amines	
N,N-diethylethanolamine	Pennsalt Chemical Co.
	Union Carbide Corp.
N,N-dimethylethanolamine	Pennsalt Chemical Co.
	Union Carbide Corp.
N-methyldiethanolamine	Union Carbide Corp.
	Dow Chemical Co.
Triethanolamine	Union Carbide Corp.
Tetrakis-(2-hydroxy propyl) ethylenediamine	Wyandotte Corp.
N,N'-Disubstituted piperazines	
Bis-(2-hydroxy propyl)-2-methylpiperazine	Wyandotte Chemical Corp.
1,2,4,-trimethylpiperazine	Wyandotte Chemical Corp.
N,N-dimethylpiperazine	Jefferson Chemical Co.
Others	
2,2,2-diazobicyclooctane	Houdry Process Corp. (Dabco)
Organo tin compounds	
Stannous octoate	Carlisle Chemical Co.
	Baird Chemical Co.
	Nuodex Products Co.
	M & T Chemical Corp.
	Witco Chemical Co.
Stannous oleate	Carlisle Chemical Co.
	M & T Chemical Corp.
	Nuodex Products Co.
Dibutyltin diacetate	Witco Chemical Co.
Dibutyltin dilaurate	Carlisle Chemical Co.
	Union Carbide Corp.
	M & T Chemical Corp.
Dibutyltin diethylhexoate	M & T Chemical Corp.
	Nuodex Products Co.

by factors such as polyol type and method of foam preparation.

The most commonly used surfactants for polyether-based foams are silicones such as the polyalkylsiloxane-polyoxyalkylene copolymers. Conventional polydimethylsiloxanes of relatively low viscosity (10 to 100 cs. at 25°C) have been used for polyether systems prepared and foamed as prepolymers. Generally, the silicones perform differently in polyester foam systems causing an unstable foaming situation rather than one of stability. Silicone oils, for example, can be used in very small amounts to enlarge the cell size of polyester foam. Stabilizers employed for polyesters are ionic, such as sulfonated castor oil and other natural oils, amine esters of fatty acids, long-chain fatty acid partial esters of hexatol anhydrides (Spans, produced by Atlas Powder Co.). Non-

Table X-6—Common Foaming Stabilizers for Flexible Urethane Foam

Type	Trade name	Supplier
Emulsifiers	Additive A-3	Mobay Chemical
	Additive A-7	,, ,,
	Additive A-9	,, ,,
	Witco 77-86	Witco Chemical
	Emulphor EL-719	General Aniline and Film
	Monosulph	Nopco Chemical
	Span 20, 40	Atlas Chemical
	Tween 80, 81	Atlas Chemical
Silicones	DC-200	Dow Corning
	SF-96	General Electric
	L-45	Union Carbide
Silicone copolymers	DC-199	Dow Corning
	DC-201	,, ,,
	DC-202	,, ,,
	DC-232	,, ,,
	SF-1034	General Electric
	SF-1066	General Electric
	L-520	Union Carbide
	L-521	Union Carbide
	L-530	Union Carbide
	L-531	Union Carbide

ionic surfactants work also, for example polyoxyalkylene derivatives of the Spans (Tweens, product of Atlas Powder Co.), the Emulphors (product of General Aniline and Chemical Co.), and polyoxypropylene-polyoxyethylene copolymers (Pluronic polyols, products of Wyandotte). In polyester systems, these materials help modify the viscosity of the polymer during foaming and frequently are used to provide additional control of reaction rates.

Miscellaneous additives

Other additives such as fillers, pigments, flame retardants, plasticizers and the like can be incorporated in flexible foams to impart special properties, but the use of fillers is slight since they rarely improve foam character and complicate the handling of ingredients during processing.

Pigments are used to impart a variety of colors to foam. These are usually handled as highly concentrated pastes which are fed into the resin stream prior to mixing with the other foam components.

Flame retardants, such as trichloroethylphosphate, are used to impart flame resistance but usually not without some deterioration of foam properties and increase in raw material cost.

3. FOAM SYSTEMS

Two basic systems can be used in the preparation of flexible foam: one-shot system and the pre-polymer system. The chief advantage of the one-shot system is the elimination of the prepolymer-forming step, but the advantages of a carefully controlled method of effecting urethane formation and foaming, as in the prepolymer system, cannot be overlooked.

The one-shot procedure involves the simultaneous mixing of all of the foam ingredients including diisocyanate, polyol, blowing agent, catalyst and foaming stabilizer (see Section X—Part II).

In the prepolymer system, all of the hydroxyl compound (polyol) is first reacted with the diisocyanate under carefully controlled conditions. This gives a product which, when combined with water, catalyst, and in some cases foaming stabilizer, produces a foam having a density dependent on the free isocyanate content of the prepolymer and the amount of water used (see Section X—Part III).

Chemistry of foaming

The preparation of urethane foam involves a complex chemical process, wherein the primary reacting groups are the highly unsaturated, very reactive isocyanate group ($-N=C=O$) and those containing labile hydrogen ($-H$). Because the reactive ingredients supplying the loosely held hydrogen atoms are hydroxyl-terminated resin and water, the primary reactions of a foam system produce urethane (I) and urea (III), the latter via an amine intermediate (II), as illustrated below:

$$-NCO + \quad -OH \longrightarrow \quad -NH\overset{\displaystyle O}{\overset{\|}{C}}O- \qquad (I)$$

$$HOH \longrightarrow \left[-NH\overset{\displaystyle O}{\overset{\|}{C}}OH \right] \longrightarrow$$

$$-NH_2 + CO_2 \qquad (II)$$

$$-NCO + -NH_2 \longrightarrow -NH\overset{\displaystyle O}{\overset{\|}{C}}HN- \qquad (III)$$

Since all of the primary reactants are at least difunctional, reaction (I) and the combination of (II) and (III) contribute to chain lengthening. Reaction (II) also yields carbon dioxide which serves as the primary blowing agent.

Crosslinking, which is necessary for maximum stability during foaming and best all around properties, can occur in several ways. The preferred method of crosslinking is by the addition of reactants containing polyfunctionality. In flexible foams, polyfunctional or branched resins are used.

Certain conditions, however, can promote further reaction of (I) and (III) with isocyanate to produce allophanate (IV) and biuret (V) as illustrated below. These reactions, when they occur, provide crosslinking sites, since diisocyanate is used.

$$-NH\overset{\displaystyle O}{\overset{\|}{C}}O- \longrightarrow \quad -N\overset{\displaystyle O}{\overset{\|}{C}}O- \qquad (IV)$$
$$\begin{array}{c} | \\ C = O \\ | \\ NH \\ | \end{array}$$

$$-NCO +$$

$$-NH\overset{\displaystyle O}{\overset{\|}{C}}HN- \longrightarrow \quad -N\overset{\displaystyle}{\overset{\|}{C}}HN- \qquad (V)$$
$$\begin{array}{c} | \\ C = O \\ | \\ NH \\ | \end{array}$$

The foaming behavior and properties of a foam system are largely governed by the rate and extent to which these reactions occur during foam preparation. In any urethane foam system the gas evolution (II) and the polymer growth (combination of I, III, IV, and V) must be matched so that the gas is trapped efficiently and the polymer has the right strength at the end of the gas evolution to maintain its volume without collapse or gross shrinkage.

PART II—ONE-SHOT SYSTEMS

In the one-shot system of foam preparation, the foam is made, as the term implies, by mixing all of the individual components at one time with no prereaction occurring. The various reactions normally occurring in a foam process, that is, chain-extension or polymerization by reaction of diisocyanate, polyol and water, and the formation of the blowing agent (CO_2) also from reaction of diisocyanate and water, are taking place simultaneously.

1. POLYETHER FOAM

It is the consensus that the advent of the one-shot polyether foam system late in 1958 guaranteed large volume applications of flexible foam in this country. These first systems employed 80/20 TDI, poly (oxypropylene) derivatives of glycerin of 3000 molecular weight, water, a combination of tetravalent tin compounds and tertiary amine catalysts, and a silicone foaming stabilizer (polyalkylsiloxane-polyoxyalkylene copolymer). The technology of the systems has improved since, but the basic systems are practically unchanged.

Effect of TDI variations

The 80/20 mixture of 2,4 2,6 isomers of tolylene diisocyanate is used almost exclusively in the production of one-shot polyether flexible foams, because it is the most readily available at lowest cost. Foam technology in the use of the 80/20 mixture had been so advanced, based on polyester foam developments, that at the time polyethers were introduced there was no reason for investigating other compositions.

Usually, the TDI is used in slight excess above stoichiometric amounts based on total hydroxyl content, to assure that at least stoichiometric amounts are used. The properties of foams can be varied by using more or less than stoichiometric amounts of TDI. As the excess is increased above a NCO/OH ratio of about 1.05 to 1, the foam develops a harsh or "boardy" feel which can be of use in some applications. Also, the compression modulus as well as the tensile strength increases with decreasing elongation. At less than stoichiometric amounts of TDI, the foam

Table X-7—Typical Formulations and Physical Properties for Commercial One-Shot Polyether Flexible Foams

	Formulation 1	2	3	4
Polyether triol 3000 M.W.	100	100	100	100
80:20 TDI	38	38	38	43
Stannous octoate	0.5			
Stannous oleate		1.0		
Dibutyltindiethylhexoate			0.1	0.2
Triethylenediamine			0.15	0.05
Ethyl morpholine	0.5 to 1.0	1.0	0.5	0.5
Tetramethyl-1, 3-butane-diamine	0.1			
Tartaric acid			0.05	
t-Butylcatechol				0.1
Silicone copolymer surfactant	1.0	1.0	1.0	1.0
Water	2.9	2.9	2.9	3.4
Index No.	100	100	100	100
Density, lb per cu ft	2.0	2.0	2.0	1.7
Tensile strength, psi	20.0	20.0	17.0	22.0
after autoclave aging, psi	18.5	19.0	14.0	18.4
Elongation, %	280	250	240	270
after autoclave aging, %	320	289	270	290
Tear strength, lb per in.			2.3	2.5
Compression set, 70°, %				
50%, 22 hr	3.0	3.0	5.0	6.3
90%, 6 hr	4.5	4.0	9.0	7.1
90%, 22 hr	7.0	6.0		
After autoclave aging (5 hr, 250°F)				
50%, 22 hr			6.0	5.5
90%, 6 hr	6.0	4.6	8.4	6.0
Compression deflection, psi				
25%/25% R*	.47/.36	.54/.46		
50%	.53	.63		
75%	1.21	1.44		
After autoclave aging (5 hr, 250 °F)				
25%/25% R*	.43/.33	.50/.44		
50%	.47	.58		
75%	1.13	1.33		
Indentation, lb per 50 sq in.				
Thickness, in.	2	2	2	4
25%/25% R*	27/24	32/28	26/22	29/26
50%/50% R*	37/33	41/37	35/30	40/36
65%/65% R*	54/49	61/54	51/45	53/48
75%/75% R*	88/76	97/84	84/71	80/70
Shear resistance	Good	Good	Good	Good

* R indicates one minute rest values.

Table X-9—Low Density, Soft One-Shot Polyether Foam Formulation

Polyether triol, 3000 M.W.	100
Trichlorofluoromethane	17.7
Stannous oleate	1.75
Ethylmorpholine	0.5 to 1.0
Silicone copolymer surfactant	2.0
Water	3.6
TDI, 80/20	42.5

becomes more difficult to process because of slower cure with tendencies toward splitting, voiding or collapsing.

A summary of the effect of TDI index (expression used for indicating the amount of TDI used with respect to the stoichiometric amount and equated as Index=Actual TDI/

Table X-8—Firm One-Shot Polyether Foam Formulation and Physical Properties

	Composition 1	2
Polyether triol, 3000 MW	85.0	85.0
Quadrol[1]	15.0	15.0
TDI, 80/20	47.5	42.2
Water	2.3	1.8
Silicone copolymer surfactant	1.5	1.5
N, N'-Dimethylpiperazine	0.9	0.9
TDI index	100	100
Density, lb per cu ft	2.3	2.7
Tensile strength, psi	18.7	19.3
Elongation, %	65	60
Compression set, 22 hr, 50%	7.9	12
Compression deflection, psi		
25%	1.31	2.02
25% R*	1.09	1.69
50%	1.80	2.80
75%	4.80	7.30

* Denotes one minute rest
[1] Wyandotte Chemicals Corp. (tetra kis [2-hydroxy propyl] ethylenediamine)

Table X-10—Typical Physical Properties of Low Density, Soft Polyether Foam

Aging condition	None	Autoclave 5 hr, 250°F	Dry oven 140°C 2-1/2 days
Density, lb per cu ft	1.1		
Tensile strength, psi	9.0	8.5	
Elongation, %	220	280	
Compression set, 70°C, % of original height			
90%, 6 hr	4.5	6.7	
90%, 22 hr	7.0		
50%, 22 hr	3.5		
Compression deflection, psi, at			
25%/25% R*	0.18/0.95	0.15/0.12	
50%	0.21	0.17	
75%	0.40	0.33	
Indentation load, lb per 50 sq in.	2" thick	4" thick	4" thick
25%/25% R*	11/9	14/13	10/9
50%/50% R*	14/12	20/18	14/13
65%/65% R*	18.5/16.5	27/25	21/19
75%/75% R*	30/25	43/38	33/29
Shear resistance	Poor		
Cell size, cells per inch	30 to 35		

* one minute rest value

FLEXIBLE URETHANE

Theoretical TDI) on the load bearing properties of a typical one-shot polyether foam system is given in Table X-16.

Because the amount of TDI used in a given foam formulation is important in governing final foam properties, much depends on the exact calculation of the amount required. This calculation is based on the total hydroxyl content of the polyol and water constituents. A method for determining the amount of TDI necessary is shown in Table X-17.

Extreme excess, such as could occur in case of resin pump failure or of depletion of supply

Table X-11—Formulations and Typical Properties for Super-Soft Foam Based on Polyethers with Different Hydroxyl Numbers

Hydroxyl No.	160	134	108
Polyether triol 3000 M.W.	—	25	50
Polyether triol 1000 M.W.	100	75	50
Stannous octoate	0.125	0.15	0.17
Triethylene diamine	0.125	0.15	0.15
N-Ethylmorpholine	0.1	0.1	0.1
Silicone copolymer surfactant	2.0	2.0	2.0
Water	4.0	4.0	4.0
TDI, 80/20	47.7	47.7	47.3
Index No.	75	80	85
Density, lb per cu ft	1.6	1.5	1.5
Tensile strength, psi	11	12	12
Elongation, %	200	190	200
Tear strength, lb per in.	1.7	2.0	2.2
Rebound resilience, % (Goodyear-Healy pendulum at 75% penetration)	25	31	35
Compression set, % 90%, 22 hr, 70°C (158°F)	15	15	15
Indentation load, lb per sq in. (4″ thickness)			
25% deflection	14	16	20
50% deflection	20	23	28
65% deflection	26	30	36

Table X-12—Typical Molding Formulation for One-Shot Polyether Foam

Triol (primary OH), 3000 molecular weight	75 parts by wt
Diol, 2000 molecular weight	25 ″ ″ ″
Refrigerant 11	10 ″ ″ ″
Resin mixture	110.1
TDI, 80:20	54
Activator I	1.32
Stannous octoate	0.12 or less
Carrier (dioctylphthallate)	10 to 1 mixture with stannous octoate
Activator II	
Triethylenediamine	0.15
Silicone copolymer surfactant	3.0
Water	4.5

Table X-13—Typical Self-Extinguishing Polyether Foam

Polyether triol, 3000 M.W.	100
Stannous octoate	0.35
Dibutyltin dilaurate	0.05
Water	3.5
Dabco	0.09
Silicone L-520	1.6
Fluorocarbon 11	9.0
TDI, 80/20	43.5
"Firemaster T23P"[1]	15
Index No.	103

	Control	Self-extinguishing
Density, lb per cu ft	1.7	1.5
Tensile strength, psi	12	12
Elongation, %	180	200
Tear strength, lb per in.	2.3	2.4
Compression deflection, psi		
25% deflection	0.40	0.35
50% deflection	0.55	0.43
Rebound resilience, % (Goodyear-Healy pendulum at 75% penetration)	40	43
Compression set, % 90%, 22 hr, 158°F (70°C)	10	10
Extinguishing time, sec	Completely consumed	3.2
Distance burned, in.	Completely consumed	1.1
Self-extinguishing	No	Yes

[1]Michigan Chemical Corp.

Table X-14—Typical Formulation and Physical Properties for One-Shot Polyether Foam that can be Flame- and Heat-Laminated

Niax Triol LF-70[1]	100 Parts by wt.
TDI, 80/20	42.6 ″ ″ ″
Activator I	4.7
Water	3.0
Triethylenediamine	0.1
Silicone copolymer surfactant	1.4
N-ethylmorpholine	0.2
Activator II	0.75 to 1.0
Stannous octoate	0.15 to 0.20
Niax diol PPG-2025[1]	0.60 to 0.80
Index No.	105
Density, lb per cu ft	1.85 ± 0.1
Tensile strength, psi	15 to 20
Tear strength, lb/in.	2.5 to 3.0
Elongation, %	300 to 400
Indent, lb/50 sq in., 4 in. at	
25% deflection	26 ± 2
50% deflection	39 ± 3
65% deflection	52 ± 4
Cell count, cells per inch	80 ± 20

[1]Union Carbide.

Table X-15—Typical Formulation for Sponge-Like One-Shot Polyether Foam

Polyether triol, 3000 M.W.	100
80/20 TDI	38
Stannous octoate	0.3 to 0.5
Catalyst 16[1]	0.05
N-ethylmorpholine	1.0
Silicone copolymer	1.0
Water	2.9
Special Silicone additive[2]	0.02 to 0.04% by wt. of polyol

[1]Mobay Chemical Co.

[2]Dow Corning Corp., Silicone Additives C-2-0145 or C-2-0146; best results obtained by dispersing silicone in the resin.

Table X-16—Effect of TDI Index on Indent Load Deflection of One-Shot Polyether Foam

TDI index	100	104	108
Indent, lb per 50 sq in., 2 inch at			
25% deflection	13.5	17	18
50% deflection	20.5	26.5	28
65% deflection	31.5	38	39
75% deflection	52	56	60

of resin, can lead to dangerously high temperatures of the improperly proportioned mix and must be avoided.

Effect of polyol variations

Since the polyol makes up the bulk of the weight of final foam product, it is not surprising that it is influential in determining foam properties. As a general guide, polyethers used in a one-shot system give soft, highly resilient foam with excellent moisture stability. They do not generally show the high

Table X-17—Method for Determining TDI Requirement
(Basis: 100 parts resin)

$$\text{TDI eq. resin} = (\text{Hydroxyl number} + \text{acid number}) \times \frac{87 \times 100}{56 \times 1000}$$

$$= (\text{Hydroxyl number} + \text{acid number}) \times 0.155$$

$$\text{TDI eq. water} = (\text{Water in resin} + \text{free water}) \times \frac{174}{18}$$

$$= (\text{Water in resin} + \text{free water}) \times 9.67$$

$$\text{TDI theor.} = \text{TDI eq. resin} + \text{TDI eq. water}$$

$$\text{Index number} = \frac{\text{Actual amount of TDI used}}{\text{TDI theor.}} \times 100$$

Table X-18—Formulations and Typical Physical Properties for One-Shot Foams Prepared from Polyether Triols of Various Molecular Weights

	Formulation						
	No. 1	No. 2	No. 3	No. 4	No. 5	No. 6	No. 7
Voranol CP-3000[1] (MW 3000)	100	100					
Voranol CP-4000[1] (MW 4000)			100	100	100		
Voranol CP-5000[1] (MW 5000)						100	80
Voranol CP-3001[1] (MW 3000)							20
TDI Index (80/20)	105	105	105	105	108	105	105
Water	2.9	3.6	3.6	3.6	3.6	3.6	3.6
Refrigerant-11	0	0	0	6.0	10.0	0	0
Silicone copolymer surfactant	1.0	1.0	1.0	1.2	1.4	1.0	1.0
Triethylenediamine	0.25	0.25	0.15	0.15	0.15	0.15	0.15
Stannous octoate	0.35	0.35	0.50	0.50	0.50	0.60	0.40
Density, lb per cu ft	2.0	1.6	1.6	1.4	1.2	1.6	1.6
Tensile strength, psi	19	16	18	16	13	18	19
Elongation, %	>300	>275	>325	>275	>225	>325	>325
Resiliency, cm[2]	55	50	48	45	42	48	50
Compression set, %[3]	<10	<10	<10	<10	<10	<10	<10
Load bearing, RMA[4]							
at 25% deflection	26	24	28	20	13	30	28
at 65% deflection	52	50	56	41	26	62	56

[1]The Dow Chemical Co.

[2]Resiliency—obtained by dropping 8.36 gram steel ball on 2″ thick sample from 100 cm height.

[3]Compression set at 75% deflection, 22 hours at 158°F., 30 minute recovery.

[4]RMA—Rubber Manufacturers Association stiffness index. It is obtained by placing a circular metal plate of 50 sq in. on a 2-in. thick piece of the foam under test, having a diameter at least 2 in. larger than the metal plate; then setting a given weight on the plate and measuring the deflection, or measuring the weight for given deflections.

strength of prepolymer or one-shot polyester systems, nor are they as resistant to solvents and chemicals.

The most widely used polyethers for flexible foams are triols having molecular weight of about 3000. In general, triols of higher molecular weight (4000 and above) give greater difficulty in cell size control, and produce foams exhibiting higher modulus but lower resiliency (Table X-18).

Polyols of higher functionality (3 and above) yield foam with increased compression modulus, but decreased tensile strength, tear strength and elongation. Decreasing the functionality tends to give lower compression modulus while increasing other properties.

A method that has become popular for varying the functionality as well as the molecular weight of the polyol constituent is the blending of a glycol of 2000 molecular weight with a triol in order to effect certain changes in properties. Straight glycols are not generally used in one-shot systems because of difficulty in processing.

Preliminary studies of relations between molecular structure (governed predominantly by polyether polyol) and mechanical properties in polyether and polyester foams have been reported.

In these studies, the silicone oil was of the poly-(dimethylsiloxane) type. The calculated molecular weight per branch point (M_c) was based on the functionality and molecular weights of the components used as were the percentages of aromatics, urethanes and ureas.

Data in Table X-20 show the combined effects of reducing the degree of cross-linking (increasing molecular weight per branch point), aromatic content and urethane content in softening the foam, increasing strength properties while decreasing solvent and chemical resistance.

Similar trends are shown (Table X-21) for a series prepared with polyether triol plus glycols.

The Clash-Berg torsional stiffness curves shown in Fig. X-1 for foams prepared from polyether triols show the same trends noted

Table X-19—Physical Properties of One-Shot Polyether Foams from Mixtures of Glycol and Triol

Polyether triol 3000 MW	100	80	60	40	20	—
Polyether diol 2000 MW	—	20	40	60	80	100
TDI, 80/20%	38	38	38	38	38	38
Water	2.9	2.9	2.9	2.9	2.9	2.9
Ethylmorpholine	1.0	1.0	1.0	1.0	1.0	1.0
Silicone copolymer surfactant	1.0	1.0	1.0	1.0	1.0	1.0
Stannous oleate	1.5	1.5	1.5	1.5	1.5	1.5

	orig.	aged*	orig.	aged*	orig.	aged*	orig.	aged*	orig.	aged*
Density, lb per cu ft	2.4		1.9		1.9		1.9		2.0	
Tensile strength, psi	22.3	21.6	21.3	14.9	26.0	16.8	22.0	9.2	17.2	6.9
Elongation, %	250	305	380	325	375	380	415	160	325	89
Compression set, %										
6 hr 90%	3.7	5.0	6.4	4.8	6.2	7.1	6.6	7.0	6.5	12
22 hr 50% based on original thickness	4.9		5.6		5.7		5.6		6.1	
Comp. deflection, psi at										
25%	.74	.65	.53	.51	.46	.36	.38	.33	.43	.36
25% R**	.64	.44	.44	.42	.39	.30	.32	.28	.35	.30
50%	.90	.79	.61	.60	.55	.42	.46	.40	.52	.45
75%	.87	1.75	1.36	1.41	1.38	1.06	1.16	1.08	1.34	1.17
Load indentation, lb per 50 sq in. (2 in. thick)										
25%	34		27		28		24		26	No
25% R**	30		23		24		21		22	data;
50%	47		35		36		32		34	properties
50% R**	41		31		32		28		30	too
65%	68		52		50		46		49	weak
65% R**	60		46		45		40		42	to
75%	108		82		80		77		81	test
75% R**	92		69		69		65		67	

*Autoclave, 5 hr, 250°F, 12 to 15 psi   **R = 1-minute rest

for the data in Table X-20: steady progression toward better low-temperature flexibility with increasing molecular weight.

With higher aromatic and urethane contents, the modulus increases sharply at higher temperatures. Similarly, when two foams with approximately equal aromatic and urethane contents are compared, the one with the higher M_c value retains its flexibility at lower temperatures.

Foams were prepared by the one-shot method from a poly (oxypropylene) triol and tetrol with tolylene diisocyanate and water, using a poly-oxyalkylene-polysiloxane copolymer as a foam stabilizer. Fig. X-2 shows the relations between the molecular weight per branch point, the tensile modulus, the elongation and the volume swell in dimethylacetamide. The molecular weight is related to the relative contents of urethane and aromatics in the foam.

A plot of the reciprocal of the compression

Table X-20—Relationship Between Structure and Physical Properties for Polyether Urethane Foams
(Pure triol systems)

Weight per branch-point	1650	2175	3375	3900	5175	6525[a]
Aromatic, %	16.2	14.9	12.6	11.2	11.0	11.0
Urethane, %	10.5	8.3	5.3	4.5	3.4	2.7
Urea, %	7.9	7.6	6.6	6.6	6.7	6.6
Density, lb per cu ft	2.4	2.2	2.5	2.5	2.8	2.4
Tensile strength, psi	30.0	21.0	18.0	20.0	22.0	15.0
Tensile mod, 100% elong, psi	—	16	12	10	7	6
Elongation, %	100	130	155	200	295	340
Compression strength, psi						
25%	1.9	0.9	0.5	0.5	0.5	0.3
25% R[b]	0.7	0.6	0.5	0.4	0.4	0.3
50%	2.8	1.3	0.7	0.7	0.7	0.4
75%	8.3	4.3	2.1	1.9	1.6	0.9
Compression set, %	7.0	3	4	3.0	—	14
Rebound elasticity, %	16	15	44	49	42	—
Yerzley resilience, %	N.A.[c]	N.A.[c]	47	63	50	—
Point load indent, sec.	7100	130	1	1	1	—
Swell index, vol. %	145	170	237	240	350	—

[a]Prepolymer prepared under different conditions.
[b]Measured after one minute rest.
[c]Not applicable.

Table X-21—Relationship Between Structure and Properties of Polyether Urethane Foams
(Triol plus diol system)

Av. mol. wt. per branch-pt.	1650[a]	2175	2400[a]	2985	3385	3700	4480	5500	6170	7580[a]	8280	10225	15185[a]
Aromatic, %	16.2	14.9	13.4	15.1	14.7	12.0	12.4	12.4	12.5	11.9	11.9	14.6	12.3
Urethane, %	10.5	8.3	7.3	8.8	8.1	4.8	4.4	4.5	4.5	3.6	4.8	7.9	6.0
Urea, %	7.9	7.6	6.8	7.2	6.9	6.9	7.0	6.6	6.6	7.3	6.8	6.6	7.0
Density, lb per cu ft	2.4	2.2	2.7	2.2	2.6	2.3	2.9	2.7	2.6	2.5	2.3	2.2	2.2
Tensile strength, psi	30.0	21.0	—	26.0	28.0	18.0	25.0	20.0	20.0	21	18	24	21.0
Elongation, %	100	130	—	125	180	180	185	235	260	280	225	270	375
Compression-strength, psi													
25% def.	1.9	0.9	1.1	1.2	1.7	0.6	0.7	0.7	0.6	0.5	0.5	0.5	0.4
50%	2.8	1.3	1.5	1.7	2.4	0.9	1.0	0.9	0.9	0.7	0.7	0.7	0.4
75%	8.3	4.2	3.6	5.2	6.6	2.0	2.7	2.0	2.4	1.7	1.6	1.7	1.0
Compression set, %	7.0	3.1	—	30	15	—	3.0	—	—	8	5.0	3	6
Rebound elasticity, %	16	15	18	20	20	38	32	—	28	—	—	25	—
Yerzley resilience, % at 30% deflection)	N.A.[b]	N.A.[b]	11	30	22	30	38	—	51	—	—	21	—
Swell index, vol. %	145	170	—	175	205	270	237	—	350	—	—	390	—

[a]The catalyst concentration in this run was different from the standard amount.
[b]Not applicable.

Table X-22—Effect of Structural Factors and Branching on Torsional Stiffness (Clash-Berg)			
Weight per branch point	3375	3385	10,225
% aromatic (C_6H_3—)	12.6	14.7	14.6
% urethane (—NHCOO—)	5.3	8.1	7.9
Temp. °C at modulus 50 psi	−37	−10	−35
Temp, °C at modulus 100 psi	−40	−30	−45

deflection values at 25% deflection versus M_c is shown in Fig. X-3 for 2.2 to 2.5 lb per cu ft density. The deviation from a linear relation is probably the result of variations in the aromatic and urethane contents of the foams. Similar relations were obtained at higher densities, with the higher density foams having greater compression strength.

There seems to be no correlation between compression set and molecular weight per branch point for values within the range of 2000 to 15000.

The trends established for polyesters are in general agreement with those obtained for the polyether series. At similar weights per branch point, the polyester foams are firmer than those obtained from polyethers. Fig. X-5 shows the low-temperature flexibility of a flexible and a semi-flexible polyester foam, the former begin considerably stiffer at a given temperature than a more cross-linked polyether foam shown on Fig. X-1. A greater degree of intermolecular forces due to the presence of the ester linkages in polyester foams and greater flexibility in the polyether chain are considered to be the principal reasons for the greater compression strengths and greater apparent moduli of the polyester foams at certain temperatures (Table X-23).

Effect of blowing agents

One method for generating a blowing agent

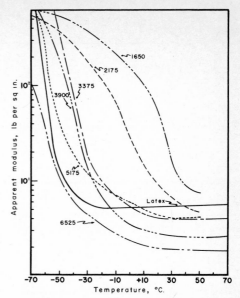

Figure X-1, Clash-Berg torsional curves, showing variations of flexibility in function of temperature, for various molecular weight formulations.

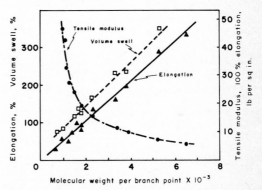

Figure X-2, relation between calculated molecular weight per branch point and properties of polyether foams.

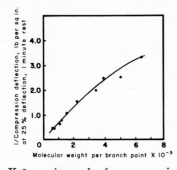

Figure X-3, reciprocal of compression, deflection related to calculated molecular weight per branch point, for polyether foams.

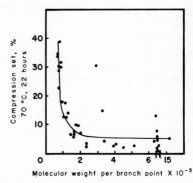

Figure X-4, compression set related to calculated molecular weight per branch point for polyether foams.

Table X-23—Relationship Between Structure and Physical Properties of Polyester Urethane Foams

Weight per branch point	410	474	538	755[a]	1370	2170	2460	3760	4220	4760	6070	6700	8900	15,200
Aromatic, %	21.8	18.7	22.7	16.6	15.9	15.3	14.7	14.4	14.2	13.8	14.0	13.9	13.8	12.6
Urethane, %	16.6	11.1	17.3	7.7	7.9	6.8	5.8	5.2	4.7	4.5	4.4	4.2	4.0	3.7
Urea, %	5.2	4.0	5.0	4.8	6.8	7.0	7.1	7.2	7.2	7.1	7.3	7.3	7.3	7.1
Density, lb per cu ft	2	2	2	2.8	2	2.1	2	2.3	2	2	2.4	2	2.3	2.0
Tensile strength, psi	55	21	55	35	27	27.9	26	27.2	29	20	34.3	33	28.7	25
Elongation, %	10	—	10	60	160	145	270	300	300	200	450	380	385	350
Comp. strength at yield (10%), psi	20	9.1	20	8.7	—	—	—	—	—	0.7	—	—	—	0.6
Compression set, %	—	—	—	47	26	—	18	—	9	5	—	14	—	5

[a]Contains 4.0 pbw. plasticizer. Calculations based on actual componente other than plasticizer.

Table X-24—Effect of Varying Water Content on One-Shot Polyether Flexible Foams

	Run No. 1	2	3	4
Polyether triol 3000 M.W.	100	100	100	100
80/20 TDI	38	44.7	48.3	58
Water	2.9	3.6	4.0	5.0
Catalyst 16[1]	0.05	0.05	0.05	0.05
N-ethylmorpholine	1.0	1.0	1.0	1.0
Stannous octoate	0.3 to 0.5	0.3 to 0.5	0.3 to 0.5	0.3 to 0.5
Silicone copolymer	1.0	1.0	1.0	1.0-1.5
Density, lb per cu ft	2.0	1.7	1.6	1.3
Tensile strength, psi	20	20	18.4	17.1
Elongation, %	240	260	210	225
Compression set, 90%, %	5.5	5.2	6.2	7.0
Indent, lbs per 50 sq in., 2″				
25%	34	30	32	28
2% R[2]	30	26	27	23
50%	44	38	41	37
50% R	39	33	36	31
65%	62	53	57	21
65% R	56	47	49	43
75%	99	87	88	80
75% R	86	72	74	61
Shear resistance	Good	Good	Fair to good	Fair

[1] Mobay Chemical Co.
[2]R denotes one minute rest

Table X-25—Effect of Varying Water Content on the Load-Bearing Ability of One-Shot Polyether Foam

Water, phr[1]	Density, lb per cu ft	Load bearing, lb per 50 sq in. [2]
3.0	1.90	43
3.5	1.70	37
4.0	1.50	36
4.5	1.35	35

[1] Parts per 100 parts of resin
[2] Load creating a 25% deflection on 4 inch thickness

in flexible foams, including one-shot polyethers, is the formation of carbon dioxide *in situ* from reaction of water and TDI. Thus, the amount of water in a system governs the foam density providing there is sufficient TDI present to complete the reaction with water.

In addition to providing the blowing agent, water serves another purpose. Reaction of water with isocyanate also produces a primary amine which reacts further with isocyanate to form urea. Such a sequence of reactions occurs in a foam system leading to the incorporation of the stiffer, stronger urea linkage in the backbone of the urethane polymer formed. The amount of water used influences substantially the density and other properties (Table X-24).

It is interesting to note that even as the foam is blown to lower density by increasing the amount of water and TDI, there is no marked reduction of the load-bearing ability. This is shown by the data in Table X-25.

Because of the stiffening action obtained when water is used alone, it has become common to utilize inert blowing agents (volatile

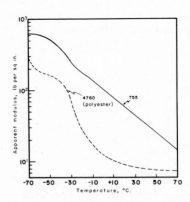

Figure X-5, effect of molecular weight per branch point on Clash-Berg torsional stiffness of polyester urethane foam.

Table X-26—Effect of Varying Amounts of Inert Blowing Agent on Properties of One-Shot Flexible Foam

Formulation:

Polyether triol, 3000 M.W.[1]	70	Stannous octoate	0.35
Polyether diol, 2000 M.W.[1]	30	Dibutyltindilaurate	0.075
Triethylenediamine	0.10	TDI, 80/20	43.7
N-Ethylmorpholine	0.30	Water	3.5
Silicone L-520*	2.0	Refrigerant 11	Variable

TDI index = 103

Physical properties:						
Refrigerant 11, parts per 100 polyol	0	2.5	5.0	7.5	10	15
Density, lb per cu ft	1.6	1.5	1.45	1.4	1.35	1.25
Elongation, %	430	350	450	360	380	330
Tensile strength, psi	21	19	19	14	15	12
Tear strength, lb per in.	4.0	3.0	3.5	2.5	3.5	2.5
Rebound resilience, % (Goodyear-Healey pendulum at 75% penetration)	40	40	40	40	40	40
Compression set, % (90%, 22 hr, 158°F)	<10	<10	<10	<10	<10	<10
Indentation, lb per 50 sq in. (4" thickness)						
25% deflection	36	33	30	27	24	18
50% deflection	51	48	41	38	33	27
65% deflection	66	63	51	50	45	37

*The silicone was set at a high enough level to handle the maximum amount of Fluorocarbon-11 which was added in this experiment.
[1]Use 0.05 to 0.10 part tartaric acid per 100 parts of polyol in all formulations containing dibutyltin salts.

solvents) for better control of foam softness. Two inert blowing agents generally used are trichloromonofluoromethane and methylene chloride. They do not contribute in any way to the physical characteristics of the urethane polymer, and can be used in combination with or as part replacement for water, giving excellent control of density while maintaining desirable softness. They are not used, however, without forfeiting certain other properties (see Table X-26).

Table X-27 reveals the effect of the inert blowing agent on the properties of one-shot polyether foams of equal density. Table X-28 shows how a very soft foam can be prepared by judicious choice of the amount of both water and inert blowing agent.

A secondary benefit resulting from the use of inert blowing agents is the reduction in the amount of heat build-up in large-volume foaming. This, of course, affects the cure of the foam but not seriously, unless too much volatile solvent is used. Because of the cooling and the overall lowering of reaction rates, systems employing inert blowing agents may require additional catalyst and foaming stabilizers in order to hold desirable foaming conditions. This is true particularly when methylene chloride is used, due to its higher latent heat of vaporization. Typical formula-

Table X-27—The Effect of Fluorocarbon-11 on Properties of Equivalent Density One-Shot Polyether Foams

	With Fluorocarbon-11 added	No Fluorocarbon-11 added
Polyether: 3000 MW triol with primary hydroxyls	50	50
4000 MW triol	50	50
Silicone stabilizer	1	1
Stannous octoate	0.4	0.4
Triethylenediamine	0.15	0.15
Water	3.5	4.2
TDI, 80/20	44	51
Refrigerant 11	7	None
Machine mixed at agitator speed of 2400 rpm Delivery rate—50 lb per min		
Properties (cured 1 hr at 121°C (250°F))		
Density, lb per cu ft	1.42	1.42
Indentation load, 2 in. thick, lb per 50 sq in.		
at 25% deflection	22	29
at 50% deflection	27	36
at 65% deflection	36	47
at 75% deflection	53	71
Compression set, %, after 22 hr at 158°F		
at 50% deflection	3	4
at 90% deflection	5	6

tions for foams prepared by a combination of water and methylene chloride and their properties are shown in Table X-30.

Effect of catalysts

The catalyst serves to drive the reactions between isocyanate, resin and water at such rates that the foam rises and cures fast enough to prevent collapse of foam. Therefore, catalyst type and concentration must be carefully chosen to provide a suitable balance of reactions. Foam producers rely on catalysts for giving them fast production cycles with relatively short periods of storage of the foam prior to its disposal. In fact, it is largely due to the catalysts that large volume production of one-shot polyether foam is possible without oven cure.

Table X-28—Super Soft One-Shot Polyether Foam Using a Combination of Blowing Agents

Polyether triol 3000 MW	80	parts by wt
Polyether glycol 2000 MW	20	,, ,, ,,
80/20 TDI	26.3	,, ,, ,,
Stannous oleate	1.5	,, ,, ,,
N-ethylmorpholine	1.0	,, ,, ,,
Catalyst C-16[1]	0.15	,, ,, ,,
Silicone copolymer stabilizer	1.0	,, ,, ,,
Fluorocarbon 11	15	,, ,, ,,
Water	1.8	,, ,, ,,
Density lb per cu ft	1.8	
Tensile strength, psi	7.0	
Elongation, %	285	
Tear strength, lb per in.	1.0	
Comp. set, 90%, 6 hrs	5.8	
Indent, lbs per 50 sq in., 2 in. thick at		
25% deflection	7.4	
25% R[2]	6.8	
50% deflection	10.5	
75% deflection	15.4	
	25.5	

[1] Mobay Chemical Co.
[2] R denotes one minute rest

Table X-29—Cooling Effect of Fluorocarbon-11 in Resilient One-Shot Polyether Foam Slabs

(Starting temperature of foam intermediates was 24°C.)

Fluorocarbon-11 in Foam formulation, parts/100 parts resin	Max. exotherm temp. in slab, °C.	Time to reach max. exotherm temp., sec.
0	107	200
2.5	106	260
5.0	102	300
7.5	99	300

The catalysts most commonly used in one-shot polyether systems are tertiary amines and tin compounds such as stannous octoate, stannous oleate, dibutyltin diethylhexoate and dibutyltindilaurate.

Using different methods of evaluating the effects of catalysts, Britain and Gemeinhardt and Hostettler and Cox, independently observed the remarkably strong catalytic effect of many metal compounds. The work showed in particular the remarkable effect of the tin catalysts and was instrumental in the development of one-shot polyether foam systems. (See Journal of Applied Polymer Sciences, 4, 207, 1960 and Industrial & Engineering Chemistry, 52, 609, 1960.)

It has been established that tin catalysts are many times more powerful for the isocyanate-hydroxyl reaction than the tertiary amines, but not strong catalysts for the isocyanate-water reaction in a foam system. Thus tin catalysts are used to force the reaction between isocyanate and polyether polyol at such a rate that viscosity of the fluid polyether resin is rapidly increased, trapping and holding the gas formed by catalytic effect of the tertiary amine on the isocyanate-water reaction. One tertiary amine, triethylenediamine (Dabco), is a sufficiently strong catalyst to effect a one-shot polyether foam but

Table X-30—Typical Formulations and Properties for Polyether Foams Prepared with Water and Methylene Chloride

Triol 3,000 MW	100	100	100
80/20 TDI index	103	103	103
Water	3.6	3.6	3.6
Triethylenediamine	0.1	0.1	0.1
N-ethylmorpholine	0.5	0.5	0.5
Silicone copolymer	1.5	1.5	1.5
Trichloromonofluoromethane		Variable	
Stannous octoate	0.35	0.35	0.3
Methylene chloride	None	4.5	9.0
Density, lb per cu ft	1.6	1.4	1.2
Tensile strength, psi	23.4	14.7	14.6
Elongation, %	320	235	230
Compression set @ 158°F, %			
22 hr −90%	7.5	6.6	5.5
ILD-lb per 50 sq in.			
2" thickness			
25%	29	20	15
65%	49	34	27
25% return	19	13	12
4" thickness			
25%	36	28	19
65%	68	55	42
25% return	24	19	14

the difficulties of processing have been too great for satisfactory commercial production with Dabco as the sole catalyst.

The effect of tin catalysts is shown in Table X-31 where the order of reaction is listed for some of the more common catalysts used with respect to the water-isocyanate reaction. In Table X-32 are listed the order of activity for the reaction between hydroxyl and isocyanate for various concentrations of typical tin compounds. It is evident, from Table X-32, that a synergistic action exists between tin catalysts and tertiary amines.

The amount of catalyst used has a great influence on the processing characteristics and the foam structure of one-shot polyether systems. Using a standard recipe, such as recipe 1 shown in Table X-7, the rise time (measure of the time elapsed between initial mixing of the foam ingredients and the completion of its rapid expansion) is a function of the combined amine and tin catalyst concentrations (Tables X-33 and X-34).

While the amine catalysts are generally considered to be the primary agents promoting carbon dioxide formation, the contribution of the tin catalyst, partly as it affects the rate of temperature rise, cannot be neglected. From these data, it is apparent that rise time is independent of cell size.

The effect of tin catalyst concentration on foam structure is illustrated in Fig. X-7. It shows that at comparable catalyst levels, the membranes of a large-cell foam are more stable than those in a foam having smaller cells. As a direct result, lower tin catalyst levels are necessary to achieve an open-cell foam as the cell size is increased. Also, the range throughout which an open-cell foam can be made is narrower with the large-cell foam.

It appears that the optimum catalyst level is that slightly above the level which gives a stable foaming, open cell foam. At this level, the ease of processing and foam properties are at their maximum levels.

Table X-31—Order of Catalytic Activity: Isocyanate-Water Reaction with Same Weight Concentration

0.1 part per 100 parts resin	Order of activity compared to stannous octoate
2,2,2-Diazabicyclooctane (Dabco)	2.7
N,N,N',N'-Tetramethyl-1,3-butane diamine	1.6
Triethylamine	1.5
Dibutyltin dilaurate	1.3
N-Ethyl morpholine	1.1
Stannous octoate	1.0

Table X-32—Order of Catalytic Activity[1]

Catalyst	Concentration, parts per hundred parts of resin	Order of activity relative to rate of an uncatalyzed reaction
Stannous oleate (SnOle)	0.1	25
Dibutyltin dilaurate (DBTDL)	0.1	280
Dibutyltin di-2-ethyl hexoate (DBTDEH)	0.1	300
DBTDL	0.2	430
DBTDEH	0.2	460
SnOle	0.2	590
DBTDL	0.3	6.0
DBTDEH	0.3	650
DBTDL	0.5	720
DBTDEH	0.5	830
DBTDL	0.1 + 0.1 TED*	860
DBTDEH	0.1 + 0.1 TED	870
SnOle	0.3	910
Stannous octoate (SnOct)	0.1	1270
SnOle	0.5	1820
SnOct	0.1 + 0.1 TED	2110
SnOct	0.2	2500
SnOct	0.3	3380
SnOct	0.5	4450
SnOct	0.5 + 0.1 TED	5140

*Triethylenediamine.
[1]For isocyanate-hydroxyl reaction

Table X-33—Effect of Tin Catalyst Concentration on Rise Time
(Tetramethylbutanediamine level at 0.1 part)

Sample	1	2	3	4
Stannous octoate per hundred parts of resin	0.15	0.35	0.60	0.35
Rise time, sec.	138	94	79	92
Cell size, cells per in.	30	30	30	60

Table X-34—Effect of Amine Catalyst Concentration on Rise Time
(Stannous octoate level at 0.3 part)

Sample	1	2	3	4
Tetramethylbutanediamine, parts per 100 parts of resin	0	0.1	0.2	0.3
Rise time, sec.	140	106	94	83
Cell size, cells per in.	60	60	45	60

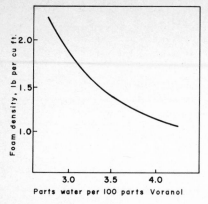

Figure X-6, effect of water content on density of one-shot polyether foams.

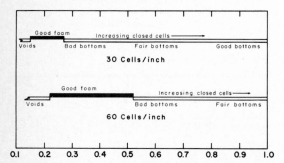

Figure X-7, foam character with relation to stannous octoate concentration.

The composition of the catalyst system will influence foam properties as shown on Table X-35 for foams prepared at constant densities.

The tin catalysts preferred for one-shot polyether foam systems are the stannous salts of dicarboxylic acids, such as stannous octoate and stannous oleate. Early in the development of these systems it was learned that certain tin compounds particularly those containing alkyl groups attached directly to tin, such as dibutyl-tin-diethyl-hexoate, promoted an oxidizing degradation of the ether bond in the polyether urethane polymer at temperatures exceeding 120°C. Since higher temperatures are formed during the foaming of large blocks of foam, these catalysts could not be used satisfactorily. Stannous compounds do not promote such degradation and are therefore preferred.

Most commercial polyether one-shot foam is produced using a combination of tin and tertiary amine catalysts for reasons given above. Catalysts are used in concentrations varying between 0.1% and 2.0% of the total reactants, to obtain the foaming characteristics desired.

Effect of stabilizer

These are compounds selected to stabilize the foaming mass during and following the re-

Table X-35—Control of Polyether Foam Indentation Load by Catalyst

	1.8 lb per cu ft			1.5 lb per cu ft			1.3 lb per cu ft		
Polyoxypropylene triol (MW 3000)	70	70	70	70	70	70	70	70	70
Polyoxypropylene diol (MW 2000)	30	30	30	30	30	30	30	30	30
Dabco	0.10	0.10	0.10	0.10	0.10	0.10	0.10	0.10	0.10
N-Ethylmorpholine	0.30	0.30	0.30	0.30	0.30	0.30	0.30	0.30	0.30
Silicone L-520	1.3	1.3	1.3	1.7	1.7	1.7	1.7	2.0	2.0
Stannous octoate	—	0.30	0.50	—	0.25	0.05	—	0.25	0.05
Dibutyltin dilaurate*	0.25	0.05	—	0.25	0.05	—	0.25	0.05	—
TDI, 80/20	41	41	41	42.8	42.8	42.8	44	44	44
Water	3.3	3.3	3.3	3.4	3.4	3.4	3.5	3.5	3.5
Fluorocarbon-11	—	—	—	5	5	5	10	10	10
TDI index=103									
Elongation, %	400	310	390	300	270	250	450	300	380
Tensile strength, psi	20	19	21	16	15	16	19	15	16
Tear strength, lb per in.	3.3	3.3	3.6	2.9	2.4	2.6	3.3	2.5	3.3
Rebound resilience (Goodyear-Healey pendulum at 75% penetration), %	42	43	43	40	43	42	41	42	42
Compression set, % (90%, 22 hr, 158°F)	<10	<10	<10	<10	<10	<10	<10	<10	<10
Indentation load, (4″ thickness) lb per 50 sq in.									
25% deflection	35	39	43	30	36	38	24	27	30
50% deflection	48	57	62	41	49	53	32	36	41
65% deflection	65	76	84	56	64	68	45	47	52

*0.05 to 0.10 part of tartaric acid per 100 parts of polyol was used in all formulations containing dibutyltin salts.

lease of blowing agent.

Stabilizers most commonly used for one-shot polyether systems are copolymers of polydialkylsiloxanes and polyoxyalkylene ethers, such as L-520, a product of Union Carbide Corp. They contain the silicon-oxygen-carbon linkage which is susceptible to hydrolysis, and care must be exercised in their use. Recently, nonhydrolyzable silicones, based mainly on the direct silicon-carbon linkage, have been developed for use in foam systems. These can be brought in contact with water with little regard for the storage life of the mixture.

The silicone surfactant performs three important functions in a foam system: it contributes to bubble formation, growth and stability. It is used in varying amounts according to the desired density, the processing conditions under which the foam is being made and type of blowing agent employed. Generally, one part per 100 parts resin is used, but it has been found advantageous to add another 0.2 part for each 0.5 part of water above the usual amount (3.5 parts) and another 0.25 to 0.50 part for each 5 parts of inert blowing agent used.

It is usually not necessary to use more of the silicone surfactant than will give the desirable control of foaming stability and cell-size regulation. Too little or too much can be detrimental to foam properties (Table X-36 and Fig. X-8).

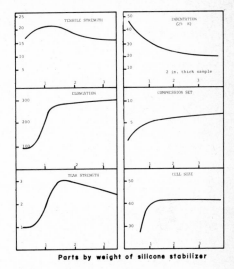

Figure X-8, effect of various silicone stabilizer concentrations on the properties of one-shot polyether foam.

Table X-36—Effect of Varying Amount of Silicone Stabilizer on Properties of One-Shot Polyether Foam						
	Parts by weight					
	1	2	3	4	5	6
3000 MW Polyether triol	100	100	100	100	100	100
TDI, 80/20	48.3	48.3	48.3	48.3	48.3	48.3
Stannous oleate	1.1	1.1	1.1	1.1	1.1	1.1
N-ethyl morpholine	1.0	1.0	1.0	1.0	1.0	1.0
Catalyst 16[1]	0.2	0.2	0.2	0.2	0.2	0.2
Water	4.0	4.0	4.0	4.0	4.0	4.0
Silicone stabilizer	0.3	0.7	1.0	1.5	2.0	5.0
Cell size (cells per inch)	Irreg.	32	42	44	44	44
Density, lb per cu ft	1.9	1.9	1.8	1.7	1.6	1.6
Tensile strength, psi	13.5	14.7	19.7	20.6	18.3	17.6
Elongation, %	95	120	215	250	255	265
Tear, ppi	1.2	1.1	1.8	2.9	2.8	2.3
Comp. set, 22 hr, 90%, %	4.8	6.1	6.3	5.9	6.8	8.3
Comp. deflection, psi at						
25%	.69	.77	.59	.51	.43	.35
25% R[2]	.59	.63	.48	.42	.35	.29
50%	.84	.85	.64	.55	.45	.38
75%	1.64	1.91	1.46	1.12	.92	.75
Load indentation, lb per 50 sq in., 2 in.						
25%/25% R[2]	51/45	49/42	38/33	33/28	26/33	23/20
50%/50% R[2]	73/65	63/55	47/41	41/35	33/29	28/24
65%/65% R[2]	104/91	86/75	65/57	54/47	44/38	37/33
75%/75% R[2]	166/144	132/112	103/87	82/69	69/57	58/49

[1]Mobay Chemical Co.
[2]R = one-minute rest

Effect of miscellaneous additives

Flexible polyether foams are not usually extended with fillers; however, special effects and properties can, in rare cases, be achieved by their use. Loading of foams with as much as 50% by weight of inexpensive barytes (barium sulfate) increases foam density to the 3 to 4 lb per cu ft range without seriously affecting hydrolysis or dry-heat aging. Soft-filled, high density flexible foams have weight and hand particularly desirable in some cushioning applications; stiffer types are for high-load-bearing and shock absorbing materials (Tables X-37 and X-38).

A large number of commercially available fillers were screened to determine the following factors:

1) Low cost
2) High bulk density
3) Low viscosity building properties when blended with polyether resins
4) Inert chemical behavior
5) Low water content
6) Uniformity of product and particle size

Of the materials screened, barytes, a finely ground form of the natural mineral barite, best fills the requirements to date. The following summarizes properties of Barytes No. 1 (C. K. Williams and Co., Easton, Pennsylvania):

$BaSO_4$	98 to 99.5% by weight
Water content	0.03% by weight
Specific gravity	4.40
Oil absorption	8
Particle size distribution	1 - 20 microns (median 6 - 7)

Barytes No. 1 can be dispersed in common polyether resins using standard mixing equipment. Addition of the filler to the polyether with continuous agitation has been most convenient, although the reverse procedure could be used as barytes has little tendency to cake. When thoroughly dispersed, barytes settles slowly from polyether mixtures and continuous agitation throughout foam production

---

Table X-37—Formulations and Physical Properties of High Density Flexible Urethane Foams Based on 3000 Molecular Weight Triols, Loaded with Baryte Filler.

				Parts by weight					
3000 M.W. triol	100			100			100		
Barytes No. 1[1]	100			100			100		
Water	2.0			2.5			3.0		
Refrigerant 11	7.0			3.0			—		
N-ethylmorpholine	1.0			1.0			1.0		
Triethylene diamine	0.05			0.05			0.05		
Stannous octoate	0.4			0.5			0.5		
Flexol 10-10[2]	0.4			0.5			0.5		
Silicone copolymer	1.0			1.0			1.0		
80/20 TDI Index	108			108			108		

	(a)	(b)	(c)	(a)	(b)	(c)	(a)	(b)	(c)
Density, lb per cu ft	3.6			3.4			3.2		
Tensile strength, psi	10.2	10.9	8.95	13.2	13.4	10.9	12.3	12.4	10.3
Elongation, %	175	165	230	165	155	220	100	90	120
Tear strength, lb per in.	1.3			1.5			1.2		
Compression set 158°F, %									
22 hr 50%	2.9	2.0	5.9	3.9	2.4	4.6	3.8	2.2	4.3
22 hr 90%	90	90	90	90	90	90	7.7	7/37	11/90
4″ ILD, lb per 50 sq in.									
25%	35	32		46	43		59	55	
25% R	32	28		41	39		52	49	
65%	79	77		101	101		125	124	
65% R	73	71		92	93		112	112	
Return 25%	22	21		26	26		30	29	
25% R	24	23		30	29		35	34	
Rotary shear	Good			Good			Good		
% softening	33			33			42		

(a) Original, (b) Aged 22 hours, 140°C, (c) Autoclave, 5 hours, 250°F, 15 psi.
[1]C. K. Williams and Co. [2]Union Carbide Corp.

runs is recommended. Care should be taken not to whip any air into the polyol/filler blend. The effect of Barytes No. 1 content on the viscosity of mixtures with 3000 molecular weight triol is shown in Fig. X-9. Concentrations as high as 70% by weight can be obtained at viscosities below 5000 centipoise at room temperature.

Blends containing equal weights of polyether resin and filler are approximately 1.6 times more dense than the polyether resin alone.

Mixtures of polyether and Barytes No. 1 can be pumped by gear pumps used for polyether metering. Flushing of the lines and pumps with a non-filled resin or a solvent is recommended.

In continuous production, some pump damage due to the erosive action of the barytes may occur. Pumps should be inspected and calibrated frequently until the producer is sure of the magnitude of the problem.

During investigation of high-density flexible urethane foam systems, compression set values as high as 90% have been most troublesome. Improvements have been obtained in most cases by long curing cycles at either ambient or elevated temperatures, but in either case, other problems of storage and production scheduling appeared. To obtain a full picture of compression set in high density foams, variation in set with percent compression was studied for foams of Table X-37 containing 100 parts by weight of Barytes No. 1 per 100 parts of polyol. The results are shown in Fig X-10. Compression set values remain low until approximately 75% compression, then rise rapidly. If compression sets of filled high-density and unfilled low-density foams are compared on a constant load rather than a constant deflection basis, the load which produces 90% compression of a low-density foam will produce less than 75% deflection of a high-density foam. At this compression, the set is satisfactorily low.

Table X-38—Formulations and Physical Properties of High Density Flexible Urethane Foams Based on Triol-Diol Blends and Loaded with Baryte Filler

	Parts by weight								
3000 M.W. triol	75			75			60		
2000 M.W. diol	25			25			40		
Barytes No. 1[1]	100			100			100		
Water	2.5			2.5			2.5		
Refrigerant 11	6.0			9.0			3.0		
Methylene chloride									
N-Ethylmorpholine	1.0			1.0			1.0		
Triethylene diamine	0.05			0.05			0.05		
Stannous octoate	0.7			0.7			0.7		
Silicone copolymer	1.0			1.0			1.0		
80/20 TDI Index	108			108			108		

	(a)	(b)	(c)	(a)	(b)	(c)	(a)	(b)	(c)
Density, lb per cu ft	3.0			2.6			3.2		
Tensile strength, psi	11.2	10.6	9.0	9.8	8.9	7.9	13.5	15.5	9.4
Elongation, %	165	165	190	165	160	190	200	165	185
Tear strength, lb per in.	1.5			1.3			2.0		
Comp. set 158°F, %									
22 hr 50%	3.9	2.9	4.9	5.7	3.9	6.1	4.2	3.2	4.2
22 hr 90%	90	80	14.4/90	90	90	76	90	76	38/90
4″ IDL, lb per 50 sq in.									
at 25%	37	33		31	27		46	40	
25% R	33	30		28	25		41	36	
65%	81	77		66	63		100	94	
65% R	73	70		60	58		90	85	
Return 25%	21	19		17	16		25	22	
25% R	23	21		19	18		29	25	
Rotary shear	Good			Fair			Good		
% softening	36			49			42		

(a) Original, (b) Aged 22 hours, 140°C, (c) Autoclave, 5 hours, 250°F, 15 psi.
[1]C. K. Williams and Company

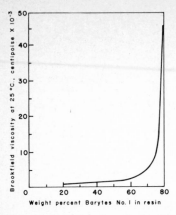

Figure X-9, change in viscosity with percent (by weight) of Barytes No. 1 in a 3000 molecular weight polyether polyol.

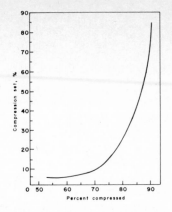

Figure X-10, change in compression set of high density-filled flexible urethane foam in function of percent compression at 158°F for 22 hours.

Production of very soft-filled foams having low 90% compression set properties has, thus far, been difficult. If high 90% compression set values can be tolerated, soft foams can be produced most effectively by lowering foam density in conjunction with low water concentrations and relatively high auxiliary blowing agent concentrations.

Other additives such as antioxidants, light stabilizers, antistatic agents, etc. have been incorporated in polyether flexible foams with varying degrees of success. Investigations are continuing to find the most effective additives that will have the greatest benefit on polyether foams.

Polyether foams can be colored with inorganic pigments when the need arises, but this is rare. It is achieved by blending the proper amount of pigment to the resin, or a masterbatch or pigment paste can be added by metering it into the resin line a short distance from the mixer. In-line mixers have also been used for premixing the paste with the resin.

Polyether foam can be flame-proofed by addition of 8% to 10% by weight of compounds containing halogen and/or phosphorous such as trichloroethylphosphate. Usually this is done at some expense of other foam properties. The formulation and physical properties of a flame-proofed one-shot polyether foam have been shown in Table X-13.

2. POLYESTER FOAM

The first flexible urethane foam system introduced in this country and used commercially was based on polyesters. Generally, polyester-based systems tend to give foams with high compression and tensile moduli and exhibit excellent resistance to oxidation, chemicals and solvents. But the inherent stiffness of polyester-based systems made them unacceptable for large volume cushioning application. This, combined with higher cost, has prevented polyester foams from reaching truly significant commercial stature with respect to the overall foam market.

The initial Bayer system was based on a combination of a 65/35 ratio of 2,4 and 2,6-tolylene diisocyanate and a polyester with a certain degree of branching (Multron R-18, product of Mobay Chemical Co.). For commercial reasons, the 80/20 ratio of 2,4 and 2,6 isomers was preferred in the U.S. This change in the composition of the TDI necessitated a change in the basic structure of the polyester. Although the change was slight (reduced branching), it was instrumental in the development of a basic technology permitting the large scale production of foam, as known today. The bulk of the polyester foam produced in this country now is based on 80/20 TDI, polyesters derived from adipic acid, diethylene glycol and polyhydric alcohol such as trimethylolpropane, water as the blowing agent, tertiary amine catalysts and organic nonionic and anionic surfactants as foaming stabilizers.

Although polyesters have been largely replaced by polyether resins for flexible foam manufacture, they still remain an important factor in Europe and for special applications in the U. S.

The processing characteristics and prop-

Table X-39—Typical Formulations and Physical Properties for 1.5 lb per cu ft Density One-Shot Polyester Foam

	Parts by weight		
Polyester[1]	100	100	100
80/20 TDI	53.5	53.5	53.5
N-ethylmorpholine	2.0	1.5	1.2
N-cocomorpholine	—	1.5	—
Armeen DM16D[2]	—	—	0.5
Additive A-3[3]	1.0	1.0	1.0
Witco 77-86[4]	1.5	1.5	1.5
Water	4.3	4.3	4.3

Tensile strength, psi	24-26
Elongation, %	250-300
Compression set, 50% 22 hr, %	10-15
Compression deflection, psi	
10%	0.60-0.65
25%	0.65-0.75
50%	0.70-0.85
70%	1.10-1.30

[1]Multron R-68, Mobay Chemical Co.
[2]Armour Co.
[3]Mobay Chemical Co.
[4]Witco Chemical Co.

Table X-40—Typical Formulations and Physical Properties for a 2 lb per cu ft One-Shot Polyester Foam

	Parts by weight			
Polyester[1]	100	100	100	100
80/20 TDI	43	43	43	43
N-ethylmorpholine	2.0	1.5	1.2	1.8
N-cocomorpholine	—	1.5	—	0.5
Armeen DM16D[2]	—	—	0.5	0.3
Additive A-3[3]	1.0	1.0	1.0	1.0
Witco 77-86[4]	1.5	1.5	1.5	1.5
Water	3.3	3.3	3.3	3.3

Tensile strength, psi	25-30
Elongation, %	250-350
Compression set, 50% 22 hr, %	2-10
Compression deflection, psi	
10%	0.55-0.65
25%	0.65-0.75
50%	0.70-1.00
70%	1.40-2.50

[1]Multron R-68, Mobay Chemical Co.
[2]Armour & Co.
[3]Mobay Chemical Co.
[4]Witco Chemical Co.

Table X-41—Typical Formulations and Physical Properties for a 3-lb per cu ft Density One-Shot Polyester Foam

	Parts by weight		
Polyester[1]	100	100	100
80/20 TDI	32.5	32.5	32.5
N-ethylmorpholine	2.5	1.75	1.0
N-cocomorpholine	—'	1.75	—
Armeen DM16D[2]	—	—	0.5
Additive A-3[3]	1.0	1.0	1.0
Witco 77-86[4]	1.5	1.5	1.5
Water	2.3	2.3	2.3

Tensile strength, psi	25-35
Elongation, %	300-400
Compression set, 50% 22 hr	2-6
Compression deflection, psi	
10%	0.65-0.75
25%	0.65-0.75
50%	0.80-1.0
70%	1.50-2.50

[1]Multron R-68, Mobay Chemical Co.
[2]Armour & Co.
[3]Mobay Chemical Co.
[4]Witco Chemical Co.

erties of one-shot polyester-based foams are governed, as in polyethers, by the composition and amounts of the various ingredients used. These effects will be discussed in detail.

Effect of TDI variations

The initial Bayer polyester system, which

Table X-42—Formulation and Typical Physical Properties for High-Density One-Shot Polyester Foam

	Parts by weight
Polyester[1]	100
80/20 TDI	20.4
N-ethylmorpholine	2.0
Armeen DM16D[2]	0.5
Additive A-3[3]	1.0
Water	0.9
Index No.	120

		Autoclave aging 5 hr 250°F 100% RH
Density, lb per cu ft	6.0	—
Tensile strength, psi	17.7	12.3
Elongation, %	235	740
Tear strength, ppi	2.2	—
Compression set 70°C, %		
50% 22 hrs	4.1	47.0
90% 6 hrs	2.3	86.0
RMA 2" Piece		
25%/25% R	62/55	
50%/50% R	119/101	
65%/65% R	229/168	
75%/75% R	428/726	
Compression deflection, psi		
25%/25% R	0.86-0.76	
50%	1.31	
75%	4.51	

[1]Multron R-68, Mobay Chemical Co.
[2]Armour & Co.
[3]Mobay Chemical Co.

formed the basis for flexible urethane foam technology in this country, employed a 65/35 mixture of the 2,4 and 2,6 isomers of TDI and a polyester with a certain degree of branching. As stated previously, for commercial reasons the 80/20 TDI was preferred in the U. S. Unfortunately, with the same polyester, catalyst and emulsifier system used with the 65/35 ratio, the 80/20 ratio gave severe foam shrinkage due to closed cells. A change to a somewhat less branched polyester gave foam without shrinkage when using 80/20 TDI. Thus the effects of relatively minor changes in the composition of the TDI with respect to a given polyester system were discovered at a very early stage of the development. Generally, in a given formulation the use of 65/35 TDI will result in a more open cell foam having slightly higher density and compression modulus than when the 80/20 TDI is used. Typical formulations and physical properties for polyester foam prepared with 65/35 TDI are shown in Table X-45.

Table X-43—Formulation for Sponge-Like One-Shot Polyester Foam

	Parts by weight
Polyester[1]	100
80/20 TDI	38-47.5 (80 to 100 Index)
N-ethylmorpholine	2.5
Additive A-3[2]	1.0
Witco 77-86[3]	1.5
Water	3.7
Glycerine	1.0-2.0
Density, lb per cu ft	1.8

[1]Multron R-68, Mobay Chemical Co.
[2]Mobay Chemical Co.
[3]Witco Chemical Co.

Table X-44—Formulations and Physical Properties for Die-Cuttable One-Shot Polyester Foam

	Parts by weight			
Polyester[1]	100	100	100	100
80/20 TDI	47	47	47	47
N-ethylmorpholine	2.75	2.0	1.8	1.8
N-cocomorpholine	—	2.0	—	0.5
Armeen DM16D[2]	—	—	0.4	0.3
Witco 77-86[3]	1.5	1.9	1.9	1.5
Additive A-3[4]	1.0	1.5	1.5	1.0
Water	3.5	3.5	3.5	3.5
Density, lb per cu ft	2.0	2.0	2.0	2.0
Tensile strength, psi	26.9	24.9	28.4	25.5
Elongation, %	250	270	335	300
Compression set, %				
90% 22 hr	13.0	7.8	38.0	13.0
Tear strength, ppi	2.6	2.4	2.5	3.0
Compression deflection, psi				
25%	0.77	0.65	0.63	0.67
25% R	0.51	0.50	0.47	0.52
50%	0.92	0.70	0.94	0.76
75%	2.70	1.73	4.37	2.47

[1]Multron R-70, Mobay Chemical Co.
[2]Armour & Co.
[3]Witco Chemical Co.
[4]Mobay Chemical Co.

Table X-45—Typical Formulations and Physical Properties for One-Shot Polyester Foams Prepared with 65/35 TDI

	Parts by weight	
Polyester[1]	100	100
65/35 TDI	45	45
Catalyst C-3[2]	—	2.7
N-ethylmorpholine	2.25	—
Additive A-3[2]	—	1.1
Witco 77-86[3]	1.5	—
Additive A-7[2]	1.0	1.5
Additive A-9[2]	1.15	1.5
Water	2.0	1.5
Tensile, strength, psi		17-23
Elongation, %		150-250
Compression set, 50% 22 hr, %		4-6
Compression deflection, psi		
10%		0.65-0.80
25%		0.65-0.80
50%		0.80-0.95
70%		1.50-1.87

[1]Multron R-18, Mobay Chemical Co.
[2]Mobay Chemical Co.
[3]Witco Chemical Co.

Studies of the effect of TDI isomer ratio on the properties of one-shot polyester foams showed that the foaming time increased progressively by changing from the 65/35 TDI to 100% 2,4-isomer. The foam height increased with increasing 2,4 isomer content, reaching the maximum with 100% 2,4 TDI. The reaction exotherm, however, was greatest for the 65/35 TDI (100°C) and the lowest for 100% 2,4 TDI (87-92°C). These effects are shown in Table X-46.

The amount of TDI necessary for the development of good physical properties, especially humidity aging, is at least equivalent to the theoretical based on the total content of hydroxyl groups present. Generally, a slight excess of 3-10% is used. Too much (>10%) can lead to processing problems and deterioration of foam properties as can too little TDI (95% of theoretical equivalent to an index number of 95).

Table X-46 — Effects of Varying TDI Isomer Ratios on Physical Properties of Medium Density Flexible Polyester Urethane Foams

%2,4 TDI	% 2,6 TDI	Density (lb/cu ft)	Compression set, %	Tear, lb/in.	Tensile, psi	25% Deflection lb/10 sq in.	Rebound, (Schoppe)	Elongation, %
65	33	4.3	14.2	5.2	37.9	16	23	223
68	32	3.75	14.3	4.25	38.0	14	22	246
71	29	4.25	14.5	3.7	27.9	11.25	43	248
76.5	23.5	5.7	19.5	3.15	20.3	8	38	257
79	21	4.0	11.4	3.3	21.2	8.25	44	255
81	19	3.3	11.6	4.5	23.0	8	23	233
83.5	16.5	3.4	10.3	4.2	23.3	11	39	195
86	14	3.4	13.5	4.0	31.6	10.75	31	230
88	12	4.3	14.3	3.3	28.6	11.25	43	225
90	10	5.0	16.3	3.0	20.9	9.5	26	233
100	0				shrunk very badly			

Effect of polyester variations

Polyesters most commonly used for one-shot flexible foam are derived from adipic acid and diethylene glycol. Normally, they contain slight but varying degrees of branching obtained by the addition of a polyhydric alcohol such as trimethyolpropane at the time of the esterification.

The degree of branching even though slight has a marked influence on the character of the foam obtained. Too much under any given condition will lead to closed cells and severe foam shrinking. Too little will lead to improper developing of gel strength resulting in foam splitting or collapse. Generally as the degree of branching in the polyester decreases within limits, compression modulus and hydrolytic stability will decrease while tensile modulus, tear strength and compression set will increase.

Table X-47—Variation of Polyester One-Shot Foam Density with Water and TDI

Density	1.7	2.0	2.5	3.5	4.0	6.0	10.0
Water, phr	3.8	3.6	3.1	2.5	1.8	1.0	0.5
TDI, phr	47.4	45.4	40.3	34.2	27.1	18.9	13.9

Usually the amount of water contained in the polyester is 0.1% or less and need not be considered when calculating the TDI requirement for foaming. All of the polyesters are hygroscopic, however, and may absorb up to 2% of their weight of moisture from the air. When the water content of the polyester exceeds 0.3%, it should be compensated for by a corresponding reduction of water used in the system.

Effect of blowing agents

As in one-shot polyether systems, carbon dioxide formed in situ by reaction of TDI and water, is the chief blowing agent for one-shot polyester foam.

The amount of water used in the foam formulation governs the final density providing there is a corresponding amount of TDI. This control of density by the amounts of water and TDI used is shown in Table X-47.

If the water is increased without a corresponding increase of TDI, density will decrease to some extent, but the foams will be characterized by low tensile and compression moduli, high compression set, and poor hydrolytic stability. Too little water results in higher density than desired and slow curing.

Small amounts of inert blowing agent, such as trichloromonofluoromethane and methylene chloride, can be incorporated in one-shot polyester foams to decrease density and load bearing properties. Concentrations of 2-5 parts per 100 parts polyester imparts considerable softness. Because they affect the overall exothermic heat, the use of blowing agents necessitates adjustments in catalysts and surfactants.

Effect of catalysts

Tertiary amines (N-methyl and ethyl morpholine, N-cocomorpholine and dimethyl cetyl amine) are generally used in one-shot polyester systems. N-ethyl morpholine can and is frequently used by itself. The other two are usually used individually in combination with N-ethyl morpholine or in combination of all three.

The use of a single catalyst adds simplicity

to the system; however, for maximum development of some properties, such as die-cuttability, a combination is used. A mixture of N-ethyl morpholine and N-cocomorpholine produces foam that can be die-cut without edge sealing.

Normally about 1.5-2% catalyst by weight of the total reactants will provide the most desirable foaming and gelation rates and the best overall properties. Increasing the catalyst concentration above this level tends to affect cell size and structure and decreases the density and compression modulus. Too little catalyst causes an increase in density and generally complicates the processing of the system.

The more active catalysts usually associated with the foaming of one-shot polyether systems are too strong for most polyester systems causing closed cells and severe shrinkage.

Effect of surfactants

Emulsifying surfactants are used to promote intimate contact of all foam components when mixed. This insures greater uniformity of cell size and, in addition, stabilizes foaming, promotes open cells, and controls shrinkage. Typical compounds used are: Witco 77-86 (a blend of nonionic and anionic surfactants, Witco Chemical Co.), Emulphor EL-719 (non-ionic surfactant, General Aniline and Film Corp.), and Additives A-3, A-7, and A-9 (sulphonated castor oils, Mobay Chemical Co.).

Additive A-3 in addition to its emulsifying characteristics retards shrinkage by promoting open cells. In some systems, an excess, however, may produce smaller cells coupled with foam voids and cracks. Additives, such as A-7 and A-9, retard the rate of foam surface cure and help in preventing voiding and side-splitting of foam blocks. Too much will prolong the cure and will promote closed cells, resulting in foam shrinkage.

In most systems Witco 77-86 can be used as replacement for A-7 and A-9 or both. Emulphor EL-719 has occasionally been used satisfactorily by itself as the only surfactant.

Generally, 2-3% surfactant, based on the total weight of reactants, is used for optimum results.

Effect of miscellaneous additives

Mineral oils can be used to increase the cell size and, in some systems, to retard shrinkage. The use of this additive should be restricted to systems with cell sizes greater than 60 cells/inch, since the mineral oil may cause an irregular type of structure at smaller cell sizes. Normal concentration range is 0.05-0.20 parts per 100 parts of resin.

Table X-48—Typical Formulation and Physical Properties for Flameproofed One-Shot Polyester Foam

Formulation	Parts by weight	
Polyester[1]	100	
80/20 TDI	39.4	(index no. 105)
N-ethylmorpholine	3.0	
Additive A-3[2]	1.0	
Witco 77-86[3]	1.5	
Water	3.0	
Tricresylphosphate	4.0	

Physical properties	
Density, lb per cu ft	2.0
Tensile strength, psi	21
Elongation, %	200
Tear strength, lb/in.	4.5
Compression set, 50%, 70°C, %	10
Compression deflection, psi at	
10% deflection	0.60
25% deflection	0.63
50% deflection	0.85
70% deflection	1.95
Inflammability	Self-extinguishing

[1]Multron R-68, Mobay Chemical Co.
[2]Mobay Chemical Co.
[3]Witco Chemical Co.

Table X-49—List of Pigments Used in One-Shot Polyester Foams

	Supplier
Red	
Vulcan Pink G (PR 477)	Verona
Permanent Carmine FBB Extra	Verona
Permanent Carmine FR Extra (PR 398)	General Dyestuff
Yellow	
Vulcan Fast Yellow 5G (PR 478)	Verona
Benzidine Yellow OTYT-564-DT (PR 518)	DuPont
Green	
Heliogen Green GA and GB (PR 483)	General Dyestuff
Phthalocyanine Green GV (PR 483)	Verona
Resoform Brilliant Green GP	General Dyestuff
Blue	
Heliogen Blue GV and BNC (PR 481)	General Dyestuff
Phthalocyanine Blue BV (PR 481)	Verona
Resoform Brilliant Blue BP	General Dyestuff
Black	
Philblack A	Phillips Chemical Co.
Pigment Fast Black TW	Verona

The flameproofing of polyester foams can be accomplished with tricresyl phosphate or trichloroethylphosphate. However, tricresyl phosphate may be preferred since some foams produced with it have better humidity aging. A maximum of 4.0 parts per 100 parts of resin should be used; above this concentration the humidity aging is adversely affected. A typical self-extinguishing formulation is shown in Table X-48.

Much of the one-shot polyester-based foam commercially produced is pigmented to various shades in a variety of colors. Generally, the pigment, in paste form, is fed into the main resin stream of a production foam machine just prior to mixing the resin with the other foam components.

The type of pigment, its concentration and method of introduction will depend largely upon the specific requirements and operational set-up. In the selection of a pigment, particular attention should be given to the uniformity, the type of surface-active agent used, intensity of color, and any particular effect upon foaming characteristics. Several of the pigments which have been used successfully are listed in Table X-49.

Acidic modifiers, such as oleic acid and a mixture of refined fatty acids from tall oil, have been very helpful in one-shot polyester systems for control and promotion of open cells.

The use of fatty acids in combination with a small amount of inert blowing agent improves the "hand" and softness.

The acidic modifiers have proven to be of great benefit in the preparation of fine-cell foam (70 pores per inch), using triethylenediamine catalyst.

PART III—PREPOLYMER SYSTEMS

The first large-scale use of prepolymer systems was for the manufacture of polyether-based flexible foam, superior to polyester-based foams because of greater appeal as cushioning materials at substantially lower cost. By the time one-shot systems were introduced, prepolymer systems had reached a high level of commercial importance. But they were forced into obsolescence by the one-shot systems which afforded even greater economy. Today, prepolymers are used almost exclusively for the preparation of semi-rigid and rigid foams.

The prepolymer system of foam preparation consists of two steps. In the first step, a partial polymer is formed by reaction of diisocyanate and polyol under carefully controlled conditions. Usually, sufficient diisocyanate is used so that the prepolymer terminates in isocyanate (—NCO) groups. As in one-shot systems, tolylene diisocyanate (80/20 isomer mixture) has been the chief diisocyanate used commercially. The second step is effected to further the polymerization and cause foaming of the prepolymer by addition of water. Catalysts and foaming stabilizers are employed in the second step to regulate the foaming rate and cell size respectively. Reaction with water leads to the formation of urea linkages in the final polymer structure and provides carbon dioxide which acts as the blowing agent. Thus, in a pre-polymer system, the two main reactions normally occurring in a urethane foam process are carried out independently, allowing for better control of each.

There are two methods for the preparation of prepolymers. In the *one-step method,* all of the TDI required for foam preparation is added at one time to the polyol and the reaction conditions are mild. The combined effect of large excess TDI and moderate reaction temperature leads to the formation of a relatively simple TDI-polyol adduct in solution with diisocyanate. The procedure gives a narrow distribution of low molecular weight polymers and the viscosity of the prepolymer is not too different from the viscosity of the starting resin. Polyesters, which normally exhibit moderately high viscosities, are converted to prepolymers by this method.

In the *two-step process* there is first a reaction of TDI with polyol, using less TDI than is ultimately needed for foam preparation. This first step often utilizes an NCO/OH ratio of 1.1 to 1.5/1 with reaction temperatures up to 140°C. These conditions provide long chains terminating in isocyanate groups which are diluted with the second step addition of TDI to raise the isocyanate content of the prepolymer to the desired level for foaming. The two-step process forms higher molecular-weight segments than the process where all of the TDI is added initially, and gives a prepolymer with a considerably higher viscosity than the viscosity of the resin reactant. This procedure is commonly used for converting the more fluid polyether glycols to prepolymers.

1. TWO-STEP PROCESS

The two-step process has been used almost exclusively for the preparation of polyether prepolymer for flexible foam. The most common polyether resin used has been polypropylene glycol of about 2000 molecular weight and the diisocyanate has been the 80/20 mixture of the 2,4 and 2,6 isomers of tolylene diisocyanate. It is generally agreed by the numerous investigators of these systems that the most important facet of the preparation is the control of the crucial "viscosity-building" first step. Poor control of this step can result in gelation and total loss of product. A successful prepolymer is one that develops gel strength quickly during foaming in order to minimize the occurrence of an unstable condition leading to foam fissure or collapse. It is possible to achieve the desirable stability during foaming by forming high molecular weight straight chain urethane polymers, such as by reacting near stoichiometric quantities of diisocyanate and glycol. This is risky because such systems are prone to gel and, if successful, the usual high viscosity of the prepolymer limits its practical use.

Better methods for developing prepolymer stability during foaming are known and have been widely used. These are based primarily on building branch points in the prepolymer structure so that crosslinking occurs as the prepolymer is expanded with the blowing agent. The safest way of achieving this is by the addition of controlled amounts of polyols, such as triols and tetrols, with the glycol. A triol, for example, introduces a single branch point under mildest condition with minimum risk of gelation. A second, but less safe, method involves the promoting of side reactions, such as allophanate and biuret (when water is present) by choice of processing conditions. These side reactions are favored at temperatures exceeding 100°C or in the presence of a catalyst but are difficult to control.

Biuret branching: The key point in the two-step method of prepolymer preparation lies in the adjustment of the glycol to a fixed concentration of water, made by adding sufficient water to the glycol to raise the water content

to 0.4%. The mixture is agitated under a blanket of nitrogen for 30 minutes at 95 to 104°F after which the first addition of TDI is made. Procedure highlights for the preparation of three such prepolymers are summarized in Table X-50.

Table X-50—Polyether-TDI Prepolymers with Biuret Branching

	Run No.		
	A-1	A-2	A-3
Polypropylene glycol, MW 2000	100	100	100
Total water	0.4	0.4	0.4
1st addition of TDI (80/20):			
NCO/OH ratio	1.25/1	1.25/1	1.25/1
NCO/H₂O ratio	1/1	1/1	1/1
Reaction time, min	90	15	75
Reaction temp, °C	120	140	120
2nd addition of TDI (for 9.5% NCO):			
Reaction time, min	25	25	23
Reaction temp, °C	80	80	120
Drumming temperature, °C	40	40	40
Properties			
Brookfield visc, cps at 86°F	20,000	20,000	11,000
NCO %	9.5	9.5	9.5

Allophanate branching: The essential functionality for gel strength during foaming is developed, in this method, by the reaction of additional diisocyanate with the labile hydrogen of the urethane bond after a second addition of diisocyanate has been made. Two techniques have been used successfully to achieve this: 1) reaction at a fixed temperature after the first and second additions of TDI and 2) reaction at two temperatures after the first addition of TDI with no additional reaction following the second TDI addition. Typical formulations using these techniques are summarized in Table X-51.

Urethane branching: A method of developing functionality in prepolymer systems involving the least risk of gelation is by employing triols and tetrols with the glycol in forming an all-urethane prepolymer. The use of these materials increases the chain branching and cross-linking sites in the prepolymer. Caution must be used to avoid building too highly branched prepolymers which can adversely affect foam properties. Neutral or basic (containing tertiary nitrogen) polyols of low or high molecular weight may be employed to produce these prepolymers. The choice of specific polyol, however, will govern the properties of the prepolymer, particularly viscosity. For example, a low molecular weight polyol will produce the highest viscosity and small changes in the amount will produce a large change in the viscosity as well. Large quantities of such polyols can and probably will cause gelation.

The reaction conditions used in this method are the mildest of all the methods described. Reaction temperatures are generally below 100°C. Table X-52 summarizes formulation information for three typical all urethane prepolymers.

The reproducible formation of polyether prepolymers by any method is dependent on a number of process variables. In a typical two-step process, viscosity is used as the chief means for following a prepolymer-forming reaction; therefore, these variables have the greatest influence on the crucial viscosity-building first step.

Table X-51—Polyether-TDI Prepolymers with Allophanate Branching

| | Run No. | |
Procedure	B-1	B-2
Step 1		
Polypropylene glycol M.W. 2000	100	100
Water (total), %	0.15	0.15
80/20 TDI (1st addition)		
(NCO/OH ratio)	1.05/1	1.05/1
(NCO/H$_2$O ratio)	1/1	1/1
Reaction temp, °C	120	80
Reaction time, min.	120	120
Step 2		
TDI addition (to obtain 9.5% NCO)	ca. 25	None
Reaction temp, °C	120	140
Reaction time, min.	60	120
Final Step		
TDI addition (to obtain 9.5% NCO)	None	ca. 25
Drumming temp, °C	40	40
Properties		
Brookfield viscosity, cps., 86°F	6500	17,000
NCO, %	9.5	9.5

Table X-52—Polyether-TDI Prepolymers with Urethane Branching

| | Run No. | | |
	C-1	C-2	C-3
Polypropylene glycol M.W. 2000	75	100	100
Non-basic triol M.W. 2500	25		
Non-basic triol M.W. 134		3	
Basic tetrol M.W. 294			0.5
Water (total), %	0.15	0.15	0.15
80/20 TDI (1st addition)			
(NCO/OH ratio)	1.05/1	1.05/1	1.05/1
(NCO/H$_2$O ratio)	1/1	1/1	1/1
2nd TDI addition	for 9.5% NCO	for 9.5% NCO	for 9.5% NCO
Brookfield viscosity, cps., 86°F	5300	18,000	6300
NCO, %	9.5	9.5	9.5

Table X-53—Foam Formulation for Polyether-TDI Prepolymers

	Parts by weight
Prepolymer (9.5% NCO)	100
Silicone oil (50 ctks)	0.5
N-thylmorpholine	1.0
Triethyl amine	0.3
Water (10% excess)	2.25

Table X-54—Physical Properties of Polyether-TDI Prepolymer Flexible Foams

| | Biuret-branched | | | Allophanate-branched | | Urethane-branched | | |
	A-1	A-2	A-3	B-1	B-1	C-1	C-2	C-3
Gel strength during foaming	Good	Good	Good	Fair	Good	Fair	Fair	Good
Density, lb per cu ft	2.5	2.3	2.1	2.4	2.4	2.2	2.1	2.3
Tensile strength, psi	20	19	16	18	18	15	12	19
Elongation, %	400	400	425	350	320	320	200	450
Compression-deflection, psi								
25% deflection	0.38	0.38	....	0.33	0.33	0.45	0.53	0.44
50% deflection	0.56	0.56	....	0.49	0.52	0.55	0.68	0.56
Compression set, SPI Method A, 22 hr., 70°C.								
50% deflection, %	6	9.5	7.0	6	6	6	5	6
90% deflection, %	8	8.0	8.0	10	15	8	8	20

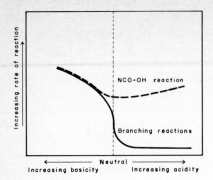

Figure X-11, general effect of strong acids and bases on prepolymer formation.

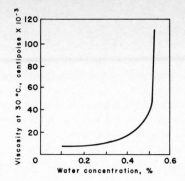

Figure X-12, effect of water concentration on prepolymer viscosity.

Effect of raw materials

Exacting raw material control is essential if one is to achieve reproducibility of pre-polymer manufacture.

Top on the list of variables, which must be watched in both the polyethers and the di-isocyanate used, is the *degree of neutrality*

Table X-55—Effect of TDI Acidity on Prepolymer Formation

Acidity*	Prepolymer	Exotherm, °C
0.00	Gelled	100 to 130
0.00	"	"
0.05	"	"
0.40	"	"
1.27	Liquid	50 to 60
9.30	"	"
11.9	"	"
14.2	"	"

*Expressed in microequivalents of acid per gram of prepolymer.

with respect to basic and acidic impurities found in the major constituents. Any impurity of this type in polyether (as residual basic catalyst or catalyst-neutralization product) or in diisocyanate (as acid resulting from resi-

Table X-56—Effect of Acid Catalyst on Prepolymer Formation

Acidity*	Prepolymer	Exotherm, °C
0	Liquid	58
216 HCl	"	69
580 HCl	"	82
0	"	59
28 H₃PO₄	"	59
54 H₃PO₄	"	67
107 H₃PO₄	"	80

*Expressed in microequivalents of acid per gram of prepolymer

dual or carbamyl chloride) has tremendous bearing on the reactions in a prepolymer preparation.

Table X-57—Typical Specifications for Polyether Glycol (2000 M.W.) Used in Prepolymer Systems

Acid, % max	0.2
Color, APHA max	75
OH no., corrected	52.0 to 59.0
Na, K max ppm	10
Terminal unsaturation, max milliequivalent	0.04
Water, % max	0.1
pH (10 g in 60 ml isopropanol and H₂O, 10:1) @ 25°C	4.0 to 6.0
Volatility, % max	0.2
Carbonyl content	report value
Saponification no.	report value

The presence of *water,* as a variable associated with the polyol component, has an important bearing on the properties of pre-polymers as well as on the reproducibility in manufacturing. The effect of varying water concentration on the viscosity of a prepolymer based on polypropylene glycol (2000 M.W.) is shown in Fig X-12. This explains the difficulty in reproducing prepolymer viscosity as the water content varies; therefore the water content of polyethers used in prepolymer manu-facturing is adjusted to a constant level (usu-ally 0.1%) by manufacturers.

The effect of *equivalent weight* of the polyol, is important. Although satisfactory prepoly-mers can be made from a variety of polyether glycols and polyols, their choice and concen-trations must be made judiciously to achieve good control of prepolymer formation and foaming. The concentration of lower molecular-weight polyols, when used with glycol, has a greater influence on prepolymer viscosity than the concentration of higher molecular-weight polyols. The effect is even greater when polyols containing tertiary nitrogen are used because of their added catalytic effect. When these are used, lower reaction temperatures and shorter reaction times generally counteract the catalytic nature of these materials.

Variations in polyol *functionality* and *molecular weight* greatly influence also the properties of flexible foams prepared from prepolymers.

Effect of isocyanate-hydroxyl ratio

Other things remaining constant, the ratio of isocyanate to hydroxyl (NCO/OH) has a direct bearing on the viscosity-build of a prepolymer system. The maximum viscosity is approached as the ratio nears 1. However, since it is not practical, from the standpoint of handling, to prepare prepolymers of too high viscosity and because risk of gelation is greater, an excess of TDI is generally used. In the two-step process, the choice of NCO/OH ratio for the crucial viscosity-building first phase will nearly set the degree of safety with respect to gelation involved in the preparation. Generally, ratios of 1.2 to 1.5/1 are used with the higher ratio insuring maximum safety against gelation. Such changes can be made without major change in foam properties. The effect of the NCO/OH ratio on the viscosity of a polypropylene glycol prepolymer, in which the amount of water present was adjusted to 0.4%, prepared at a temperature of 120°C for 90 minutes is shown by Fig X-13.

Effect of catalyst

There have been reports of the intentional use of catalysts for effecting short reaction times or continuous prepolymer preparation. The use of organo-tin compounds, such as dibutyl tin dilaurate has been reported. Sodium salts of phenols and disodium phosphate (a possible residual impurity in polyethers) are strong catalysts leading easily to gelation, whereas N-ethylmorpholine is not. Generally, highly basic compounds cause rapid gelation of prepolymer. Among the metals, lead, ferric, stannic, stannous, cobalt, titanium, vanadium and copper compounds caused the most rapid gelation at rates approximating the order given.

Effect of reaction time and temperature

The reaction time necessary to develop specific prepolymer properties, such as viscosity,

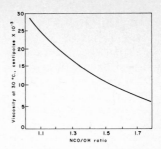

Figure X-13, influence of NCO/OH ratio on prepolymer viscosity.

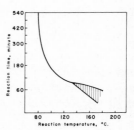

Figure X-14, relationship between reaction temperature and time in prepolymer formation.

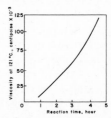

Figure X-15, effect of reaction time on prepolymer viscosity.

is a function of the reaction temperature. This is illustrated on Fig X-14 for the preparation of a polypropylene glycol (2000 m.w.) prepolymer to a viscosity of 100 stokes at 25°C.

In the absence of catalysts, reaction temperatures below 100°C will lead primarily to chain extension or *linear* polymer formation through urethane and urea groups. Temperatures above 100°C lead to allophanate and biuret reactions causing significant formation of *branch* sites. *Thus the choice of reaction temperature or time relates directly to the degree and rate of viscosity build in prepolymer manufacturing.* Fig X-15 shows the effect of reaction time on prepolymer viscosity, when polypropylene glycol (2000 m.w.) and TDI are reacted at an NCO/OH ratio of 1.25/1 at a temperature of 121°C.

In summarizing the effects of reaction conditions, the selection of reaction time and temperature in prepolymer manufacture is a carefully considered compromise involving the shortest processing time combined with the highest degree of safety possible.

Processing technique

Substantial quantities of polyether prepolymer were manufactured prior to the change-over to one-shot foam systems, therefore the techniques of large scale prepolymer manufacture were fairly well established.

In the interest of reproducibility, the amount of TDI used should be calculated for each batch based on the actual analytical requirements determined for the resin.

Type 316 stainless steel is the recommended material of construction for a prepolymer reactor. Other tanks for handling isocyanates and resin, such as weigh tanks, hold tanks or blend tanks may be constructed of aluminum or nickel or may be plastic-lined. Special consideration must be given to the solvent used and its effect on plastic-lined vessels.

The reactor should be jacketed for steam heating and water cooling. This provides an easily controlled heating medium which does not produce localized hot spots, which are objectionable, and at the same time permits quick cooling to stop a reaction at a desired point. Prepolymer reactions which require extended heating should have the time-temperature cycle controlled by a programmer to get the best manufacturing reproducibility from batch to batch. This has been found to be an important aspect of reproducibility.

Agitation is quite important. Satisfactory performance in 2000 gallon, 6'6" diameter reactors has been experienced with two 35-inch diameter turbines, having 45 degree pitched blades on the same shaft, rotating at either 84 rpm or 100 rpm and both turbines pumping the same direction, either upward or downward. The lower turbine is located 8 inches above the bottom of the reactor, and the other one 4 feet above the first. Four baffles 6½ inches wide are located symmetrically around the perimeter of the vessel.

Positive pressure (1 to 4 psig) nitrogen blanketing is recommended for vessels where isocyanates are reacted or held, mainly to insure against contamination by moist air. Carbon dioxide would serve the purpose but it is considerably more soluble than nitrogen, and in the case of foam prepolymers the foaming characteristics are affected by dissolved gas, so nitrogen is used.

Filtration of prepolymers with viscosities of the order of 2000 to 3000 cps @ 60°C is accomplished satisfactorily with Ful-Flo filters. Moyno pumps are used for high capacities and Bar-Mag pumps for pilot plant use.

Blending is a strong contributing factor to the reproducibility from lot to lot of foam prepolymers. Three to five batch blends have much better foaming reproducibility than that experienced between individual batches. Blending of polyether prepolymers may be accomplished by pumping from the bottom of the blend tank to the top, permitting the liquid stream to flow down the walls of the tank to the liquid level (free fall should be avoided to reduce gas entrapment), with enough pumping to circulate the contents of the tank four times. A blending temperature of 50°C is satisfactory and part of a blend may be held during process at this temperature for a week without change, if properly stabilized.

Packaging of NCO-terminated polymers may be done in baked-phenolic-lined steel containers. If a solvent is employed the effect of the solvent on the lining of the container must also be considered.

To gain a more positive control over the side reactions in the manufacturing process and to produce a storage-stable product, an acidic stabilizer is recommended: 0.03% of benzoyl chloride, based on the weight of polyether, is added prior to reaction of the polyether resin with the diisocyanate. The same amount is added to the prepolymer at the end of the reaction to insure good storage stability. Other acidic substances, such as phthalyl chloride or hydrogen chloride may find use as stabilizers in special cases.

Color stability during processing has been achieved by adding 0.3% propylene oxide to the polyether prior to reaction with TDI.

The reproducibility of foam cell size from batch to batch of prepolymer, and the silicone oil requirement present difficult problems in foam prepolymer production. Prime mechanical variables are the heating-cooling cycle and the mixing. In addition, the amount of dissolved gas is extremely important since it affects the formation of the foam. This can be illustrated by vacuum-degassing a prepolymer and then trying to foam it. "Boiling" i.e., failure to trap the gas, will result (this has been demonstrated several times with Mobay prepolymers).

The recommended procedure of maintaining 1 to 4 psig nitrogen pressure, and using 0.10% water in the polyether insures that there will be an adequate amount of dissolved gas.

To insure uniformity of production, the prepolymer should always be handled in the same way: vacuum or higher pressure to assist in material transfer should never be used.

A typical procedure followed by Mobay for batch manufacturing of polyether prepolymer is as follows:

Flush the reactor with nitrogen, charge polyether, adjust water content to 0.10%, add 0.03% benzoyl chloride and 0.3% propylene oxide and agitate 30 minutes. Add TDI at an NCO/OH ratio equal to 1.4 and agitate 2 hours below 30°C to insure thorough mixing. Heat to 110-115°C and maintain in that range until the viscosity measured at 73°C is at the desired value, plus or minus 50 cps. Then add TDI to produce a final NCO = 10.5%. Cool immediately by applying water to the jacket. When the temperature is below 100°C add 0.03% benzoyl chloride. Drum out or blend at 50°C, using a pump to discharge the prepolymer, and pumping through a Ful-Flo filter, pore size No. 13.

A catalyzed pilot plant preparation has been described by Union Carbide Corp. (Techn. Bulletin on Niax catalyst) employing dibutyltindilaurate as the catalyst in amounts of 0.025 and 0.05 parts by weight. Processing time was reduced by about 50-75% when using this catalyst.

2. ONE-STEP PROCESS

Prepolymers of polyester are usually prepared by the one-step process, wherein all of the TDI ultimately required for foaming to a desired density is reacted at one time. Preparation may be accomplished by adding the polyester to the isocyanate, or the reverse order of addition. Both procedures have worked equally well but because the latter is simpler from the standpoint of handling, it is preferred. As in the two-step process, the viscosity of the final prepolymer can be varied by choice of reaction temperature and time. In fact, those factors having influence on the formation of prepolymer in the two-step process would be influential in the control of prepolymer formation by the one-step process as well.

A typical procedure for the preparation of a polyester-based prepolymer by the one-step method is described as follows: The polyester is placed in a properly cleaned and dry reactor equipped with agitator and provisions for heating and cooling. All of the TDI is added at room temperature with stirring under a blanket of dry nitrogen. The reaction mixture is allowed to exotherm but not exceed 90°C. At first sign of decrease in reaction temperature, heat is applied and the reaction mass is heated to 90°C. The reaction temperature is then held at 90°C for one hour with continuous agitation. After this time the reaction product is cooled and transferred to clean, dry, airtight storage containers.

The ratio of isocyanate to polyester is determined by the hydroxyl number of the polyester and the density of foam desired. The NCO content of the prepolymer is related to the foam density if CO_2 is the sole blowing agent as indicated in Table X-58.

The utilization of blowing agent is less efficient in a polyester prepolymer system than a polyether.

Table X-58—Relation Between NCO Content and Foam Density in Polyester Prepolymer Systems

Density, lb per cu ft	NCO content, %
2	13.5
3	11-11.5
4	8 approx.

The approximate amounts of TDI required to produce polyester prepolymer foams having densities of 2 and 3 lb per cu ft are given in Table X-59.

Table X-59—TDI Requirement for Polyester Prepolymer Foams

Foam Density, lb per cu ft	TDI, phr Polyester (OH no. 57-63)	Polyester (OH no. 45-42)
2	50-53	47-49
3	40-42	39-41

Typical formulations and physical properties for two polyester prepolymers are shown in Table X-60.

3. FOAMING PREPOLYMERS

The foaming of prepolymer systems requires the addition of blowing agent, catalyst and foaming stabilizer to the prepolymer. Miscellaneous additives, such as fillers, pigments, flameproofing agents and the like can be incorporated in a prepolymer system in much the same manner as in a one-shot system. Their effects are similar also.

A polyether prepolymer having an isocyanate content of 10 to 10.5% can produce foam with a density of about 2 lb per cu ft. Since carbon dioxide is the common blowing agent used, the amount of water added to the prepolymer will directly control the density. When the isocyanate content of a prepolymer is less than 10%, additional TDI is usually added to the prepolymer at the time of foaming to produce foam at a density of 2 lb per cu ft.

Typical formulations for prepolymer polyether flexible foams with physical properties are given in Tables X-61 and X-62.

Typical formulations and properties for prepolymer polyester flexible foam are shown in Table X-63.

Effect of prepolymer variations

The isocyanate content of the prepolymer governs the density of the resulting foam when water is used in the system. Generally for a polyether prepolymer system, an isocyanate content of 10-10.5% will produce a foam density of 2 lb per cu ft if close to theoretical amount of water used. When the isocyanate content is less than 10%, it is customary to add TDI for producing low density foam. Since this introduces an unnecessary handling step, the use of prepolymers having at least 10% NCO is preferred.

The viscosity of the prepolymer will largely govern the amounts of catalysts and foaming stabilizers required for good controllable foaming. Prepolymers having high viscosities, for example 20,000 cps, are remarkably stable during foaming and are thus less dependent on catalyst and surfactant for foaming stability. It is possible, in fact, to stabilize foaming by viscosity only, eliminating entirely the need for surfactant. Such systems are highly viscous and cause a greater demand on pumping and mixing.

Table X-60—Typical Formulations and Physical Properties for Polyester Prepolymers

Prepolymer type	1	2
Recipe, parts by weight:		
Polyester (OH no. 57-63)	100	
Polyester (OH no. 45-52)		100
80/20 TDI	53.4	39
Properties		
NCO, %	13.4	8.6
Viscosity, cps.	11,350 (at 25°C)	1250 (at 73°C)

Table X-61—Typical Formulations and Physical Properties for Prepolymer Polyether Flexible Foam

	1	2	3
		Parts by weight	
Prepolymer[1]	100	100	100
Catalyst 16[2]	0.6	0.2-0.3	0.2-0.3
N-ethylmorpholine		3.0	3.0
Water	2.4 (10% excess)	2.4	2.6
Silicone oil (50 ctks.)	0.6-1.2	0.6-1.2	0.6-1.2
	Physical properties (samples cured overnight at 180°F)		
Tensile, psi	18-23	18-23	18-23
Elongation, %	250-350	250-350	250-350
Tear, lb/in. 50% Defl.	2.5-3.0	2.5-3.0	2.5-3.0
Compression Set, 50%, 70°, %	7-11	3-7	5-10
Compression, Deflection, psi			
@ 25%	.30-.41	.41-.56	.34-.41
@ 25%, 1 min rest	.25-.35	.33-.47	.28-.35
@ 50%	.42-.60	.54-.72	.44-.60
@ 75%	1.09-1.42	1.34-1.68	1.0-1.2
RMA lb/50 sq in, 2″ slab			
@ 25%	17-27	25-32	18-27
@ 25%, 1 min rest	15-23	21-28	16-24
@ 50%	29-40	39-49	31-40
@ 50%, 1 min rest	26-35	32-42	27-34

[1]Mobay Chemical Co., Mondur PG-56, NCO = 10.0-10.5%, Visc. = 8500-12,000 cps. at 25°C.
[2]Mobay Chemical Co.

Effect of blowing agent

As in one-shot systems, the majority of prepolymer foam is produced with carbon dioxide as blowing agent, resulting from the reaction of free NCO with water.

It has been customary to use an excess (10%) of water in all prepolymer systems to obtain the best foam properties. Less than stoichiometric amount results in higher compression modulus and lower strength. Too much water (20% excess) on the other hand will use up too much of the available NCO in producing carbon dioxide leaving an incomplete water-isocyanate reaction. This is usually accompanied by serious deterioration of foam properties.

Effect of catalyst

The most common catalysts for prepolymer systems are tertiary amines, such as the trialkylamines, substituted morpholines and piperazines. The choice of catalyst can have major influence on foam properties and cure. Active catalysts, such as triethylamine, cause rapid foaming but slow cure to ultimate foam properties. Foams prepared from active catalysts are usually cured at elevated temperature in order to develop acceptable properties. Less active catalysts, such as N-ethylmorpholine, produce slower foaming but are generally more effective in promoting foam cure. It has been customary to use a combination of fast and slow catalyst for achieving the best overall processing conditions of foaming and cure leading to acceptable foam properties. A typical combination can be a mixture of triethylamine and N-ethylmorpholine used in amounts of 0.2 to 0.5 and 2 to 3 parts by weight respectively.

Choice of catalyst will also be governed by its volatility and odor. The more volatile catalysts are driven out of the system by the heat of the foaming reaction and thus are not available to benefit the cure. If odor is objectionable, the odor of the volatile catalysts must be dissipated at a faster rate.

Catalysts containing hydroxyl groups, such as ethyldiethanolamine, can be used. They are generally the least active, become chemically bound in the foam polymer structure and are not lost by volatilization. Their odor level is also greatly reduced leaving little or no amine odor in the foam.

Effect of foaming stabilizer

Polydimethyl siloxanes (silicone oils) of low viscosity (100 ctks.) are the preferred foaming stabilizers for polyether prepolymer foam systems. The silicone oils have a profound effect

---

Table X-62—Typical Formulation and Physical Properties for Soft Prepolymer Polyether Flexible Foam

Prepolymer[1]	100
80/20 TDI	7.5
Catalyst 16[2]	0.2
N-Ethylmorpholine	2.0
Water (10% excess)	2.4
Silicone oil (50 ctks.)	0.75-1.5

Physical properties (samples cured overnight at 180°F)	
Tensile Strength, psi	14-23
Elongation, %	300-450
Tear, lb/in 50% deflec.	2.1-3.6
Compression set, %	5-10
Compression deflection, psi	
@ 25%	.28-.42
@ 25%, 1 min rest	.24-.33
@ 50%	.38-.57
@ 75%	.99-1.48
RMA, lb/50 sq in, 2″ slab	
@ 25%	14-23
@ 25%, 1 min rest	12-20
@ 50%	21-32
@ 50%, 1 min rest	19-29

[1]Mobay Chemical Co., Mondur PG-48, NCO = 6.5-7.0%; Visc. = 10,000-15,000 cps. at 25°C.
[2]Mobay Chemical Co.

Table X-63—Typical Formulations and Physical Properties for Prepolymer Polyester Flexible Foams

	Recipe No.	
	I	II
	Parts by weight	
Prepolymer I[1]	100	
Prepolymer II[2]		100
N-cocomorpholine	2.8	
N-ethylmorpholine		1.1
Additive A-9[3]	0.6	
Additive A-7[3]	0.6	
Additive A-3[3]		0.7
Witco 77-86[4]		0.7
Water	2.1	1.8
Density, pcf.	2.3	4.0
Tensile Strength, psi	31.6	46
Elongation, %		565
Comp. set, 50% defl.,70°C, %	7.5	11
Comp. defl. psi at 50% defl.	1.82	1.7

[1]Mobay Chemical Co., prepolymer based on formulation I, Table X-60.
[2]Mobay Chemical Co., prepolymer based on formulation II, Table X-60.
[3]Mobay Chemical Co.
[4]Witco Chemical Co.

on the cell size of most polyether prepolymer systems. Generally, as the amount of silicone oil used is increased, the cell size decreases up to a point where the cell size becomes too small and the foam collapses. Because of the fine control of cell size achieved by the silicone oil, it has been the practice to feed it separately in production of foam for better control.

The preferred proportions of silicone oil for most prepolymer systems range from 0.3 to 0.7 parts per 100 parts of prepolymer. The actual amount used, however, will be governed by specific processing conditions. The temperature of the prepolymer when foamed will influence the effectiveness of the amount of silicone oil used. As the prepolymer or foaming temperature increases, more silicone oil is required to produce a specific effect.

Silicone oils have one detrimental effect on polyester prepolymer systems leading to foaming instability resulting in boiling and collapse. Usually, emulsifiers of the anionic and nonionic type, such as are used in one-shot systems, are the best stabilizers for these systems.

Effect of cure

Unlike one-shot systems, prepolymer foams usually require a post-cure at elevated temperature if foam properties are to be developed quickly. This is due primarily to the lower exotherm temperatures encountered in the processing of prepolymer systems. Certain catalysts, such as N-ethylmorpholine, are effective in promoting cure and when used, curing temperatures may be lower. Generally, each manufacturer has established optimum curing conditions consistent with his plant. As a rule, several hours at temperatures of 150-200°F are very helpful in effecting final foam cure.

Effect of crushing

Most prepolymer foams have a relatively high percentage of closed cells. Consequently, the foams require flexing in order to rupture some cell membranes and prevent shrinkage. Initial flexing or crush should be to approximately 50% of the initial height as soon as the foam has reached a state of cure that allows crushing without tearing or loss in block height. Additional crushing to 20% of the original height completes the opening of cells and insures good resiliency. As a guide, most foam can be crushed after about 10 to 20 minutes at 170 to 180°F without damage to the foam. If crushing is delayed until the foam is more completely cured, then it will be more difficult and some closed cells may remain, shrinkage can occur and recovery from indentation will be slower.

Foam properties most affected by crushing are load bearing, compression set and resiliency; load bearing and compression set are reduced whereas resiliency is improved.

PART IV—FOAM PRODUCTION AND TROUBLE-SHOOTING

1. GENERAL

Two basic methods are used commercially to make flexible foam: free-rise foaming or slab process, and molding. Both employ the pour system and differ only in the manner by which the foam is poured. For slab production, pouring is effected continuously, whereas pouring is done intermittently in most molding operations.

Other methods for producing flexible foam are known, such as frothing and spraying, but these are still in the development stage.

The success of a foam production depends largely on the equipment used. Improvement in the design of the mechanical equipment for manufacturing flexible urethane foam has undergone rapid development over the years. See Section III, parts I and II.

In principle, a foam machine consists of two parts, a *pumping* unit which must be capable of accurately metering two or more components and a *mixer* capable of blending and efficiently mixing the various components.

A single *pumping* or metering unit consists essentially of a storage tank, a pump, a pump drive system, miscellaneous valves, instruments, piping, and in the case of isocyanate or resin units, a heat exchanger. A schematic flow diagram for a two-component metering system is shown in Fig. X-16.

Numerous types and makes of pumps are available. Gear pumps and piston type pumps with an accuracy of ±0.5% are adequate. In multi-component machines where recycle of a component is not required, high pressure liquid-fuel injection pumps have been found very acceptable for low viscosity components.

These are commonly used on the Mobay-Hennecke slab foam machines. To vary the proportion of one or more components, variable speed drives change the pump speed or the length of stroke is changed in piston-type pumps.

The *mixing* is equally as important for satisfactory foam production as the metering of the various components. Many types of mixers are available and each manufacturer of foam-processing equipment has a variety to choose from.

Two general categories of mixers are available for flexible foam production. The continuous mixers usually provide low shear type of mixing and are capable of operating continuously for long periods of time for slab foam production. They include an agitator with pin-like projections on a central shaft. The intermittent or "on-off" mixers are commonly used in molding. They provide high shear mixing, are self-cleaning and operate on an on-off cycle such as is required for molding operations.

An intermittent mixer having no moving parts has been developed by Bayer based on the use of Bosch (fuel injection) pumps and nozzles. Low-viscosity components are mixed by the high injection pressure and velocity at which they enter a very small mix chamber.

The housing of mixers can be cylindrical or tapered in shape. The latter is used in conjunction with the on-off mixer because of its self-cleaning characteristics. Outlet nozzle design can be varied in diameter and length to control the hold-up time in the mixing chamber.

2. POURING FOR SLAB PRODUCTION

Continuous pouring is the chief method for making foam in slab production.

In a typical continuous-pour slab producing machine, two or more components are accurately metered to the mixer where they are intimately mixed. The mixing head traverses at right angles to a continuous moving conveyor and liquid foam mixture is deposited on the conveyor in a pattern of nearly parallel lines which merge before initiation of foaming. The free-fall distance of the liquid mixture to the conveyor must be held to a minimum in order to prevent splashing and the trapping of air bubbles when the liquid makes contact with the conveyor. This is simply accomplished by fitting an extension of proper length to the discharge opening of the mixer. Release paper, which is dispensed mechanically by the drive mechanism of the conveyor, is used for lining the conveyor and side guides to prevent contact of the liquid with the conveyor. The conveyor is usually set at a slight angle (5° to 10°) to the horizontal to prevent the liquid from the mixer from falling into the rising foam.

Conveyor systems for typical slab-foam-machines range from 50 to 100 feet in length and travel at speeds up to 20 feet per minute. Generally, one-shot polyether systems require the highest speeds because of their lower viscosities and greater tendency to flow during the latent stage or up to the creamy state. As the viscosity of the liquid foam mixture increases, such as in polyester systems, the speed of the conveyor may be reduced.

As the continuous slab of foam leaves the conveyor of the foam machine, heat in the form of live steam, or from electrical heaters, can be applied to the top of the foam block to facilitate surface cure and loss of tackiness. The foam is then immediately transferred to a secondary conveyor, the speed of which is synchronized with the speed of the first con-

Figure X-17, bird's eye view of a continuous production of flexible urethane foam. Courtesy Burkart Mfg. Co.

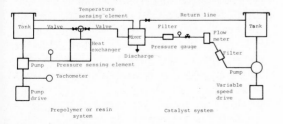

Figure X-16, two-component metering systems for foam production.

veyor and it is conveyed several hundred feet more, away from the foam machine.

At some point, just beyond the end of the first conveyor, the continuous block of foam is usually sectioned. Straight cuts can be achieved without stopping the conveyor by vertical cutters moving in the same direction as the conveyor at the same speed. Crushing and curing ovens can be strategically located in the line if the need arises without disrupting the forward movement of the foam.

Flow rates in slab production usually range from 100 to 200 lb per min but they can be higher. Blocks measuring 80 inches wide and 2 to 3 feet thick can be produced.

A typical commercial slab producing machine is pictured in Fig. X-17.

The success of any chemical process is only as good as the control provided for it. This is particularly true for a urethane foam process which is often difficult to carry out because the variables are so many. The most profitable flexible foam production operations are those where a concerted effort has been made to provide the necessary process control.

Raw material control, which is largely the responsibility of the supplier, is vital for reproducible foam production. So are reliable and accurate proportioning, efficient mixing and cleanliness of operation. Usually, very exacting temperature control is provided for the major foam constituents—resin and isocyanate—and in some cases the temperature of the minor constituents is also controlled. The objective of this control is not necessarily tied to any given temperature since foams can be formulated over a wide temperature range. But the control must hold the temperature, whatever it may be for a given formulation, within very narrow tolerances. Such control, in the order of ± 2 degrees F, provides consistent operation without the need for juggling formulation during a run to counteract the effect of varying temperature. The effect on foam properties of varying resin and isocyanate temperatures is shown in Table X-64. Note that, as the temperature of the materials increases, the amount of tin catalyst used decreases.

Opinions on the effect of varying environmental conditions (room temperature and humidity) are mixed. Those who feel strongly enough that changes in environmental conditions during foaming affects processing characteristics have enclosed their foaming operation in air-controlled shelters.

There is good evidence that climatic or seasonal changes influence the natural curing of foam and its properties.

Most continuous pour foam machines are equipped to meter at least four components. The resin, except for prepolymer systems, is usually metered by itself as is the isocyanate. If more than one resin is used, a blend is made by mixing them in the feed tank; the mixture then constitutes the resin component. The additive components, catalysts, surfactant and water are usually handled as one component by blending. In cases, such as one-shot polyether systems, where problems of compatability arise, they may be separated into two components. There is a growing tendency in slab production to meter separately as many of the foam intermediates as practical. This allows great freedom for changing formulation during the run, simply by changing delivery of one pump.

Table X-64—Effect of Materials Temperature on Foam Properties

Formulation	A	B	C	D
Resin (polyether triol, 3000 MW)	100	100	100	100
Silicone fluid	1	1	1	1
Stannous octoate	0.4	0.3	0.2	0.1
Triethylenediamine	0.15	0.15	0.15	0.15
Water	3.75	3.75	3.75	3.75
80/20 TDI	45	45	45	45
Index no.	110	110	110	110
Temperature of foam intermediates, °F				
Polyether resin	80	90	100	120
TDI	80	90	100	120
Foam properties (Cured one hour at 250°F. and one day at 75°F.):				
Density, lb per cu ft	1.80	1.80	1.90	2.10
Tensile strength, psi	10	13	14	14
Elongation at break, %	140	180	160	140
Resilience, Yerzley, %	31	30	44	57
Compression set, %, 22 hr at 158°F				
Original at 50% deflection	2	2	2	3
at 90% deflection	3	3	3	5
After 24 hrs at 220°F and 100% R.H.				
at 90% deflection	5	4	5	12
Load deflection, 2″ thick, lb per 50 sq in.				
Original at 25% deflection	32	32	32	36
at 50% deflection	40	40	45	51
at 65% deflection	56	51	64	72
at 75% deflection	83	72	92	106
65/25 Index	1.75	1.59	2.00	2.00
After 24 hr at 220°F and 100% R.H., % change from original				
at 25% deflection	−4	−9	−14	−17
at 50% deflection	−2	−5	−14	−22

The cell size in slab production is partly controlled by the energy input of the mixer; energy input is controlled by the velocity of the components entering the mixer, by mixing speed or by a combination of speed and shear.

The design of the outlet nozzle of the mixing head affects the degree of hold-up in the mixing chamber and has been shown to have an important influence on foam quality. The outlet nozzle has to be considerably smaller than the diameter of the mixing head itself, in order to prevent the liquid mix from being distributed over too large an area. Ideally, the mix should leave the mixing head as a smooth column of liquid at a point not more than a few inches above the mold surface, in order to avoid splashing and entrapping of air. The use of tubular extensions to the mixing head is an obvious method of achieving this, but care has to be exercised in the choice of the tube, as it has been demonstrated that the cell size of foam is affected to a considerable extent by the diameter of the outlet tube. An increase in the diameter of the outlet nozzle causes a decrease in the cell size of the foam. The foam may be very sensitive to these changes in diameter, and a minor alteration sometimes has an appreciable influence on foam structure. By giving careful attention to the design of the outlet nozzle, one can be sure that the foam strutcure will be uniformly fine from the start to the end of a long run. If, on the other hand, there is a pressure build-up in the head, foam structure can become coarser after a few feet of foam have

been made. Not all foam formulations are equally sensitive to these changes, and in some cases it appears that there may be a critical pressure, above which pressure has little influence on cell size. In general, pressures in the mixing heads are small.

Table X-65—Effect of Outlet Nozzle Size on Cell Size of One-Shot Polyester Foam

Nozzle diameter	Cells per inch
20 mm	85
12 mm	70
9 mm	40
7 mm	20

Another factor having an important effect on foam structure is the presence of air. In large amounts, air can cause complete collapse of the foam; at lower levels, mixed cell size results. Usually air, as a contaminant in any of the foam ingredients or by unintentional introduction into the mixing head, is not desirable.

The variation in physical properties through the profile of a continuously poured block of foam are slight for a properly formulated, well processed system. Generally, greatest variation will occur near the top and bottom. Properties measured from samples taken at different levels through the profiles of typical slab produced one-shot polyether and polyester foams are shown in the Tables X-66 and X-67.

Knowledge of corrective measures to be taken when difficulties occur in slab produc-

Table X-66—Variation in Physical Properties through the Profile of a Block of One-Shot Polyether Foam

	Top			Block height: 20 in.				Bottom
Sample	1	2	3	4	5	6	7	8
Density, lb per cu ft	1.6	1.6	1.6	1.6	1.6	1.6	1.6	1.7
Tensile strength, psi	21	20	20	21	21	21	20	23
Elongation %	360	370	360	350	340	340	330	340
Tear strength, lb per in.	3.4	3.2	3.8	3.1	3.8	3.3	3.7	3.0
Compression set, 90%, %	9.0	7.0	7.0	5.0	6.0	6.0	7.0	28
Indent lb 50 sq in. at								
25%	25	29	31	33	36	36	35	34
25% R[1]	22	25	26	28	31	31	30	32
50%	32	37	38	39	44	44	42	43
50% R[1]	28	32	33	35	39	38	37	38
65%	44	60	51	54	61	62	59	62
65% R[1]	38	52	45	48	54	55	52	54
75%	64	113	80	85	96	104	96	99
75% R[1]	55	91	68	73	83	87	82	85

[1]R denotes one minute rest.

tion is important to the producer, and trouble-shooting guides are extremely useful. Typical examples of such guides for the production of polyester and polyether one-shot flexible foams follow.

3. TROUBLE-SHOOTING GUIDE FOR POLYESTER FOAM PRODUCTION

Holes

One of the most common problems encountered in the manufacture of polyester foam is holes. Specific causes of holes are many, but they can be generally categorized as contamination, air, and/or poor mixing.

Contamination, the major cause of holes, can be defined as the presence of any material incompatible with the foaming system, such as dirt, grease or other foreign material. To insure against contamination, strong emphasis must be put upon cleanliness and good housekeeping. Contamination may come from:

1) Dirt in any of the feed streams, polyester, TDI or activator,

2) Dirty mixing chamber,

3) Dirt on the paper mold,

4) Dirt falling into the foam from off the machine, or drips from leaking injector nozzles,

Table X-67—Variation in Physical Properties through the Profile of a 10″ Block of One-Shot Polyester Foam

Block height: 10 in.

	Top—		→Bottom
Sample, from top	2-4″	4-6″	6-8″
Density, lb per cu ft	1.7	1.7	1.9
Tensile strength, psi	28.7	29.9	34.9
Elongation, %	303	345	360
Compression set, %			
6 hr 90%	10.0	9.6	11.0
22 hr 90%	19.0	23.0	21.0
Compression deflection, psi			
25%	0.63	0.63	0.69
25% R	0.48	0.48	0.52
50%	0.72	0.71	0.60
75%	2.02	1.78	1.92
Indentation 2″ thickness, lb per 50 sq in.			
25%/25% R	45/36	46/36	49/38
50%/50% R	59/48	58/47	65/52
65%/65% R	88/70	87/70	96/77
75%/75% R	152/114	147/113	—
Tear strength, lb per in.	3.0	3.4	3.5
Shear 100,000 cycles (Mobay Rotary Shear Tester)	Good	Good	Good

5) Improper cleaning of the mixing head when the machine is used to foam other systems such as polyether one-shots,

6) Improper cleaning of equipment used in the preparation of the activator,

7) Incomplete removal of solvents used to clean the mixing head, especially if dimethylformamide has been used,

8) Build-up of rust or scale on the walls of activator tanks,

9) Pigments incompatible with the foaming system,

10) Improper cleaning of a newly installed pipe,

11) Pipe dope or cutting oil used in the frabrication of lines,

12) Excessive oil or water from air compressor,

13) Use of certain types of rubber hose for flexible lines. The use of rubber hose should be discouraged.

Air, to a certain degree is necessary for nucleation as evidenced by the fact that a polyether prepolymer resin de-gased under heat and vacuum will not foam properly. However, the amount of air may become excessive and will cause formation of holes. The amount of air or gas that can be tolerated depends on the formulation and foam structure of a system; a large-cell foam is less susceptible to the development of holes by air than a fine-cell foam. For best results the amount of air trapped into the resin due to handling must be held to a minimum. Some operating procedures may result in trapped air. They are:

1) Handling resin from drums carelessly.

2) Absence of a dip pipe in resin tanks. With a dip pipe, the resin stream does not have to fall through a vapor space when the tank is charged.

3) Poor pump packings, or poor flange gaskets on the suction side of the resin feed pump.

4) Formation of a vortex in the resin feed tank as the result of polyester feed pump suction.

5) Air trapped in the activator mix. With some activator formulations the viscosity of the mix is high and therefore additional time is needed for the mixture to de-gas.

6) Air sucked in around the mixing head agitator packing or simmer rings.

7) Splashing in the lay-down pattern.

8) Too fast a traverse travel, resulting in trapped air along the pour pattern.

9) Too large a discharge nozzle.

Poor mixing will generally result in clusters of holes which may be predominant along the line of the pour pattern. Specific causes are:

1) Poor mixing of the activator.

2) Improper functioning of the injector or Bosch nozzle.

3) Improper mixing in the mixing head, caused by too low an agitator speed or too high a throughput.

Voids

Voids or splits in a polyester foam block can rupture either the top, bottom or side surface and/or be completely contained as internal splits. Sometimes the location of the void is indicative of one of the specific causes listed below.

1) *Top voids*
   a) Cell size too small,
   b) Dirt in any of the feed streams, polyester, isocyanate or activator. This dirt can cause a hole which may expand to a void,
   c) Dirty mixing chamber,
   d) Too high resin temperature; this decreases the cell size and may result in voids,
   e) Drippings of TDI, resin, activator, etc., upon the surface of the rising foam,
   f) Too low catalyst level,
   g) Low activator rate,
   h) Too fast surface cure,
   i) Too much over-lap or under-flow; that is, presence of one foaming layer on top of another which is at a different stage of foaming.

2) *Bottom voids*
   a) Dirt on paper mold,
   b) Irregular conveyor surface,
   c) Paper wrinkles.

3) *Side voids*
   a) Catalyst level too low,
   b) Traverse stopping too close to the edge, or pausing too long before reversal,
   c) Too slow conveyor speed,
   d) Too steep conveyor angle,
   e) Wrinkles in the sides of paper mold,
   f) Too slow traverse travel,
   g) Low TDI index,
   h) Misalignment of side guides.

4) *Internal splits*
   a) Cell size too small,
   b) Catalyst level too low,
   c) Temperatures too high.

Striations

A striation is a distinct line of unusual cell structure in the foam which parallels the direction of the head travel. In some foam applications, this physical appearance detracts from the quality of the foam and therefore must be maintained at a minimum. Some of the more common causes of striations are:

1) Poor blending between clear pour, initial reaction zone and foam rising zone,

2) Too steep foaming angle—resulting in too much under-flow or channeling of liquid,

3) Conveyor speed leading to confusion of reactions zones,

4) Insufficient mixing,

5) Head traverse speed inadequate,

6) Failure of injection nozzle resulting in poor mixing,

7) Return stops of traverse head too close to the edge of the mold,

8) Excessive foam fall resulting in splashing,

9) Improper mixing of activator,

10) Poor pigment distribution,

11) Too low polyester temperature (below 60°F),

12) Too large discharge nozzle—resulting in foam build-up,

13) Pre-reaction line in pour; this occurs when there is foam build-up in the discharge nozzle. This build-up may also be caused by faulty mechanical devices used to control the cell size,

14) Intermittent introduction of air causing striations of small cells,

15) Contamination in any one of the feed streams,

16) Excessive block width,

17) Too much emulsifier,

18) Foam density too low; higher density foams are less susceptible to striations,

19) Cell size too small; the smaller the cell, the greater the striation,

20) Dirty mixing chamber.

Irregular cells

The term "irregular cells" is used to describe a structure wherein adjacent cells are distinctly different in size. Fine cell foams (60 cells per inch) are more susceptible to the formation of irregular cells than are coarser cell foams. Some of the common causes of irregular cells are:

1) Cell size too small,

2) Improperly mixed activator,

3) Excess air included with any of the feed streams,

4) Dripping injection nozzles or poor spray pattern,

5) Plugged nozzle relief lines,

6) Overheated mixing chamber,

7) Low agitator speed,

8) Mixing head too small,

9) Dirty mixing chamber,

10) Contamination in any feed stream.

Shrinkage

The shrinkage in a polyester foam system which has a minimum of closed cells is approximately 2 to 4%. As the number of closed cells increases, the shrinkage becomes progressively worse. The first sign of shrinkage is a wrinkling of the top skin. In some cases where there are traces of closed cells near the surface, these have been eliminated by spraying steam on the surface of the block immediately at the end of the rising period. Some of the formulating techniques which can be used to reduce or eliminate shrinkage are:

1) Decrease TDI Index to 100,

2) Increase emulsifier,

3) Reduce catalyst,

4) Reduce cell size if a smaller cell size can be tolerated.

Control of cell size

The cell size at a constant throughput and agitator speed can be controlled by varying the back-pressure in the mixing head. This back-pressure can be changed by either changing the diameter or the length of the discharge nozzle. Cell size is inversely proportional to nozzle diameter.

Another method involves changing the agitator speed. In most cases, the cell size will respond to changes in agitator speed, but that response is governed by the mixing head design: in some machines, the cell size will increase with increasing agitator speed while with others the reverse may be true. Some pigments will cause a decrease in cell size. Increasing emulsifier will result in smaller cells. Increasing isocyanate will increase cell size. Air will result in a decrease in cell size but may cause irregular cells.

4. TROUBLE SHOOTING GUIDE FOR POLYETHER FOAM PRODUCTION

The production of one-shot polyether flexible foam is generally less sensitive to overall operating conditions than the production of polyester-based foam. This is due primarily to the greater stability of one-shot polyether systems during foaming, making them almost insensitive to many of the processing variables. In addition, polyether foam undergoes less scrutiny with respect to holes, fine cell size, irregular cells, striations and so forth. Thus its production appears to be much more trouble-free.

Boiling

Boiling denotes an unstable system with loss of blowing agent and deterioration of foam structure. When this occurs, check the following:

1) Effectiveness of silicone copolymer surfactant used as foaming stabilizer; if it is all right, try a higher concentration.

2) Effectiveness of tin catalyst since boiling can be caused by lack of polymerization leading to gelation; if it is all right, try a higher concentration of catalyst.

3) Gross misproportioning of one of the major constituents or defect in supply of tin catalyst.

4) Gross malfunctioning of mixer.

Collapse

Collapse usually occurs soon after the foam has reached maximum rise when polymerization leading to gelation is unduly slow. Chief cause is faulty proportioning of foam constituents. Collapsing of foam can be corrected by:

1) Proper balancing of the polymerization reaction by raising the amount of tin catalyst to the level insuring proper gelation. This can usually be done without significant effect on foaming characteristics, such as cream and rise times.

2) Reducing the amine catalyst. This can also be helpful in synchronizing foaming and polymerization. It is usually accompanied by longer cream and rise times.

Settling

Slight settling (⅛″ to ¼″) just after maximum rise is normal and desirable for greatest porosity. Excessive settling indicates that the reaction rates are slightly out of balance and can be corrected by:

1) Increasing the tin catalyst concentration slightly.

2) Reducing the amine catalyst concentration slightly.

3) Increasing the silicone copolymer foaming stabilizer.

Table X-69—Effect of Fluorocarbon on Foam Strength Properties at a Constant Water Level				
Recipe, parts by weight	1	2	3	4
3000 MW triol (sec. OH)	100	100	100	100
80/20 TDI	48.3	48.3	48.3	48.3
Fluorocarbon-11	0	5	10	15
Water	4.0	4.0	4.0	4.0
Stannous oleate	1.0	1.0	1.0	1.0
Catalyst C-16[1]	0.05	0.05	0.05	0.05
N-ethylmorpholine	1.0	1.0	1.0	1.0
Silicone copolymer	1.0	1.0	1.0	1.0
Properties				
Density, lb per cu ft	1.6	1.4	1.3	1.2
Tensile strength, psi	21.0	17.0	15.0	12.0
Elongation, %	235	225	220	185
Indent load deflection				
lb per 50 sq in. at 25% R	33	28	24	20

[1]Mobay Chemical Co.

Table X-70—Effect of Fluorocarbon on Foam Strength Properties at Constant Density			
Recipe, parts by weight	1	2	3
3000 MW triol (sec. OH)	100	100	100
80/20 TDI			
Fluorocarbon-11	5	10	15
Water	3.6	3.2	2.7
Stannous oleate	1.0	1.0	1.0
Catalyst C-16[1]	0.05	0.05	0.05
N-ethylmorpholine	1.0	1.0	1.0
Silicone copolymer	1.0	1.0	1.0
Properties			
Density, lb per cu ft	1.5	1.5	1.5
Tensile strength, psi	16.0	12.0	10
Elongation, %	225	195	180
Indent load deflection			
lb per 50 sq in. at 25% R	31	26	19

[1]Mobay Chemical Co.

The catalysts normally used in molding are triethylene diamine and stannous octoate. Triethylene diamine controls the gas evolution rate and assists in developing better foam surfaces. It must be maintained at minimum level to insure good compression sets.

There is a relationship between stannous octoate concentration, cell size, and physical properties in one-shot polyether foam. A low stannous octoate concentration and a medium-to-large cell-size leads to low compression set.

Many systems with a stannous octoate concentration over 0.15 parts by weight have given poor compression set properties, regardless of cell size (Fig X-18).

The tin catalyst concentration required for optimum foaming is an inverse function of the cell size. With smaller cells, the polymer is distributed over a much larger area and requires additional stability (more catalyst) in the early gelation stage. Thus, cell size in-

directly controls compression sets; if too small, a higher tin concentration may be necessary.

The silicone co-polymer is a surfactant essential in the production of one-shot urethane foam. It contributes to the stability of the system, improves flow characteristics of the rising foam and to a lesser degree, controls cell size. The optimum silicone level is the amount necessary to produce the smallest cell size desired. When the silicone is increased above this level, lower load bearing, higher tear and higher elongations result. However, when the silicone level is decreased, larger cells, lower tensile strength, lower tear strength and higher load-bearing will occur.

In discussing the various mechanical aspects of molding, a drawing (Figure X-19) of a typical molding line is helpful in following each phase of the operation.

The mold is an important variable in the process. Because of the high surface area-to-

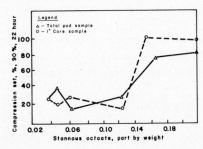

Figure X-18, compression set of molded flexible foam versus stannous octoate concentration.

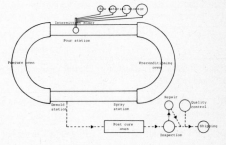

Figure X-19, sketch of typical topper pad molding line.

volume ratio, lower foam exothermic temperatures are developed in molding, and there is a need for additional heat. The mold must withstand internal pressures without distortion, and, in addition, it should have good heat transfer properties and a smooth surface to aid in the release of the foam product. Aluminum, steel, some thermoset plastics and metal-filled thermoset plastics have been used successfully, but sand-cast aluminum molds are the most used. With this type of mold the intricate contours of an object can be molded easily. Aluminum also has excellent heat transfer properties allowing quick addition of heat in the precure oven.

The function of the mold-conditioning oven is to lower the temperature of the mold coming from the curing oven to the normal foam-pouring temperature of 110° to 120°F. This conditioning temperature can be reached in two different ways. One is by the use of temperature-controlled recirculating air or water. The second, and most satisfactory, is by force-cooling the mold to a temperature below that required, and then warming it slightly to pouring temperature. Force-cooling can be accomplished with refrigerated air or with cool water spray and evaporation.

There have been investigations on the effect of pouring foam in hot molds (up to 190°F) in order to shorten mold cycles and to facilitate cure (Table X-71).

The exotherm temperature of a molded topper pad is much lower than that of a free rise foam bun and auxiliary heat must be provided to complete the cure. This is accomplished in the precure oven by maintaining in the object the same time/temperature relationship that would be developed by the exotherm in a free-rise foam. The length of the cure cycle and the

Trouble-Shooting Guide for Production Molding of One-Shot Polyether Foam	
Problem	Cause and corrective measures
1. Mold underfilled on one side	Generally if the mold has an unsymmetrical shape pouring closer to the underfilled section will help.
2. Splits repeating at a specific point	A corresponding hot spot either on the mold or the lid. Too much fill at the point where the splits appeared.
3. 1/4" of large cells in the foam just under the skin	Heat induction too fast during initial seconds of cycle resulting in some defoaming. Delayed entry of the mold into cure oven will slow the temperature rise to desired amount. Molten release agent.*
4. Loose skins	Too low a Dabco catalyst level usually results in poor skin cure. Index not in optimum range, resulting in poor skin cure.
5. General splits and voids	Too low a tin catalyst level will cause this. Cell size changed which necessitates catalyst adjustment. Mold surface too hot at pour, which disturbs the foaming balance.
6. Blisters on pad surface	Hot spots on the mold resulting in local defoaming. Pools of release agent which plasticize the foam. Silicone copolymer content too low resulting in poor foam stability.
7. Leather-like skin	Too much overfill—high density skin Severe over-indexing Mold too hot at pour
8. Uncured pad surface	Mold cycle time too short, resulting in poor foam cure. Mold cycle temperature too low, resulting in poor foam cure. Isocyanate index not in optimum range.
9. Closed cells	Too high tin catalyst level or too low amine level. Cell size increases which necessitates a drop in the tin catalyst level.
10. Varying internal densification from mold to mold	Surface temperature change at pour. Cell size change resulting in varying foam stability.
11. Holes on outer surface but skin cured in pockets	Air due to splashing on lay-down. This may be difficult to correct.
12 Pockets just below skin on top of pad	No solution as yet but might be due to a vortex or occluded air in the head of an intermittent machine.

*Some release agents, due to a variety of ingredients, have a very wide melting point range and may be slightly molten at foam pour; this is not easily identified on a mold by visual inspection.

type of heat used depend on the size and shape of the mold, the foam properties desired and the heat transfer characteristics of the mold. The precure-oven heat sources may be direct-radiant or convection heat, or, most frequently, a combination of both. Shorter cure cycles can be achieved with full radiant heat, but the expense of such an oven may be high. Conventional 400 to 500°F forced-air ovens are satisfactory, but cure cycles are somewhat longer. Here, the foam is elevated to the desired temperature rapidly with the radiant heaters, and maintained at this temperature through the remainder of the cure cycle by forced hot air.

Ease of release, skin condition and overall appearance of the molded part are greatly dependent on the temperature of the inside mold surface at the time of demolding. Satisfactory molded-foam appearance will be obtained as long as the inside mold surface temperature is at least 200°F. Below 200°F, there is a tendency toward loose skin and foam adhesion to the mold.

No satisfactory permanent mold release agent has been developed to date. It must be reapplied after each pour. The most satisfactory agent is a special blend of waxes in a solvent carrier which is designed to melt slightly below the demolding temperature. The release agent is solid during the pour and gelation parts of the cycle; it does not react with the liquid foam ingredients. But as the mold approaches the demolding temperature, the release agent becomes liquid and allows the foam to be easily stripped from its mold. This type of mold release agent is normally sprayed

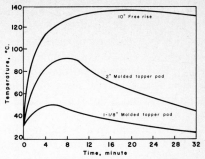

Figure X-20, effect of foam thickness on exotherm.

Table X-71—Effect of Mold Temperature at Time of Filling on Properties of Molded Polyether Foam

Mold temperature, °F	100	150	170	190
Density, molded, lb per cu ft	2.38	2.08	2.04	2.00
Tensile strength, psi	25	22	20	20
Elongation at break, %	350	245	230	230
Indent load deflection, 2 in. thick, lb per 50 sq in.				
at 25% deflection	32	30	29	24
at 65% deflection	83	75	70	62
65/25 index	2.6	2.5	2.4	2.6
Compression set*, %, after 22 hr at 158°F, at 90% deflection	46	12	10	15

*Tested after 2 days post-cure at room temperature (75°F)

upon the mold at a minimum temperature of 200°F. At lower temperatures, the solvent carrier has a tendency not to flash off completely, and to interfere with skin cure.

A demolded topper pad, being much thinner than a slab-stock bun, dissipates heat rapidly. Thus, topper pads are normally given an addi-

Table X-72—Formulations for One-Shot Resilient Foam Molding

Ingredient	Topper pad		Snap-on Topper pad		Bus seat		Furniture Cushion		
	A	B	C	D	E	F	G	H	I
3000 MW triol	75	60	75	60	75	60	75	70	60
3000 MW triol with primary OH groups	—	20	—	20	—	20	—	—	20
2000 MW diol	25	20	25	20	25	20	25	30	20
L-520 silicone fluid	2.0	2.0	3.5	3.5	2.5	2.5	2.5	2.5	2.5
Triethylene diamine	0.20	0.20	0.20	0.20	0.20	0.20	0.25	0.25	0.20
Supplementary amine catalyst	0-0.5	0-0.5	0-0.5	0-0.5	0-0.5	0-0.5	0-0.5	0-0.5	0-0.5
Stannous octoate	0.20	0.15	0.20	0.15	0.25	0.20	0.20	0.25	0.15
Fluorocarbon	0-7	0-7	0-7	0-7	0-7	0-7	0-10	0-10	0-10
Plasticizer[1]	—	—	—	—	—	—	0-5	0-5	0-5
Water	4.0-4.4				3.8-4.4		3.8-4.2		
TDI (isocyanate index)	104-106								

[1]Ester type plasticizers such as didecyl phthalate or dioctyl phthalate.

tional cure or post-cure of 1 hour at 250°F. To promote rapid build-up of good physical properties, this post-cure commences as soon after demold as possible. Certain topper pads, with low tin catalyst concentrations and high precure oven temperatures, have developed good properties without a post-cure, but at present, this is the exception.

A typical procedure for the molding of a topper pad made up from the formulation shown in Table X-73 is shown Fig. X-19. The conditions are listed in Tables X-74 and X-75. Filling the mold was accomplished by making a single pass down the mold center in approximately 8 seconds. The mold lid was placed in position and the mold run into the precure oven which required about 30 seconds. After the mold was held in the precure oven for the desired time, it was removed. The pad was then stripped from the mold and post cured.

Table X-73—Formulation for Molded Topper Pad

	Parts by weight	
Resin: Mixture:		
Polyether triol (primary OH), 3000 MW	75	
Polyether, diol, 2000 MW	25	
Fluorocarbon-11	11	
Formulation:		
Resin mixture	111	
TDI, 80/20	53	
Activator I	1.32	
Stannous octoate (stabilized)		0.12 or less
Carrier[1]		10 to 1 mixture with stannous octoate
Activator	7.65	
Triethylenediamine		0.15
Silicone copolymer		3.0
Water		4.5

[1]A plasticizer used to permit increased metering accuracy of the tin catalyst.

Table X-74—Machine Conditions for Molding of Topper Pad

Machine type	Mobay M-13—stationary head
Resin rate, gm per min	6000
Agitator speed, rpm	5000
Mixer size—dia × length, mm.	
at top of tapered mixer	50 × 70
Mixer capacity, cc	25
4-port-mixer	1—Resin blend, Fluorocarbon-11, 2—TDI, 80/20 3—H₂O, amine catalyst, silicone copolymer 4—tin catalyst, carrier
Nozzle extension ⎱ Nozzle length ⎰	Adjusted for pre-selected cell size
Mold description	1/4" aluminum with inserted wooden lid for 2-3/8" thick automotive topper pad
Mold dimensions	
length × width, in.	53 × 20-1/2

Table X-75—Molding Conditions for the Manufacture of a Topper Pad

Isocyanate index	100-103
Resin mixture, temp, °F	100±5
TDI, temp, °F	Ambient-80
Activator, temp, °F	Ambient-80
Release agent (sprayed on mold)	N-1[1]
Agitator speed, rpm	5000
Foam discharge nozzle size	to give 40-45 cells per inch
Cell size, cells per inch	40-45
Mold surface temp. at charge, °F	110 ± 10
Mold cycles which were used, min.	
Radiant heat	10
450°F. Circulating hot air	12
350°F Circulating hot air	14
250°F Circulating hot air	18
Mold temp at time of release, °F	190 minimum
Delay between demold time and post cure, min	5 maximum
Post cure, temp, °F	250
Post cure, time, hr	2 minimum
Crushing	Preferable
Degree of crushing, % compression	50 minimum
Time of crushing	After post-cure

[1]Trade name, Chem-Trend Corp.

Table X-76—Physical Properties of Molded Polyether Foam Topper Pads

Pad No.	1	2	3	4
Precure temp, °F	Radiant[1]	450°F[2]	350°F[3]	250°F[4]
Pad density, lb per cu ft	1.5	1.5	1.5	1.6
Tear strength, lb. per in.	2.8	2.0	2.0	1.9
Tensile strength, psi	19	17	17	16
Elongation, %	280	230	215	210
Compression set, %				
22 hr—90%				
1" core sample	10 to 20	10 to 20	10 to 20	10 to 20
Indent, lb per 50 sq in.				
25% 1-min rest	18	18	19	20
65% 1-min rest	45	45	51	51
Hydrolysis aging				
7 days, 190-195°F.				
over water				
% of original defl.	81	78	75	73

[1]Inside face of mold at release, °F.—275 w/10 min. cure cycle.
[2]Inside face of mold at release, °F.—265 w/12 min. cure cycle.
[3]Inside face of mold at release, °F.—230 w/14 min. cure cycle.
[4]Inside face of mold at release, °F.—190 w/18 min. cure cycle.

PART V—FOAM PROPERTIES

Flexible urethane foams, produced commercially, may be classified into two basic groups: polyester and polyether foams. Each of these groups involves different formulations and produces different characteristics and properties in the urethane foam end product.

A flexible urethane foam is made up of interconnecting cells separated by very thin and usually broken membrane-like walls; the skeleton structure consists of heavy seams, commonly referred to as ribs, at the cell juncture. Since the bulk of the urethane polymer is in the rib structure, it is the rib which has the greatest influence on foam properties and

accounts for the distinctive qualities of the foam. Photomicrographs of flexible foams of small, medium and large cells, using transmitted and reflected light, are shown in Fig. X-21, 22, and 23.

1. MECHANICAL PROPERTIES

The mechanical properties of flexible foam include: density, tensile strength, elongation, tear strength, compression set and resiliency or rebound. Standard methods of measurements have been adopted for these and are described by ASTM Methods D 1564-63T. Description of the tests is given in Section

Figure X-21-T, magnified view of small cell size urethane under transmitted light.

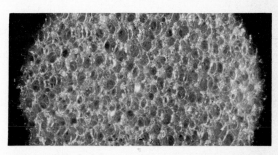

Figure X-21-R, magnified view of small cell size urethane under reflected light.

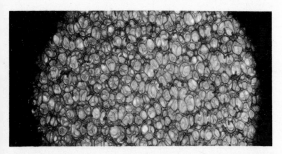

Figure X-22-T, magnified view of medium cell size urethane under transmitted light.

Figure X-22-R, magnified view of medium cell size urethane under reflected light.

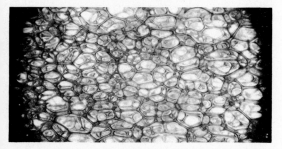

Figure X-23-T, magnified view of large cell size urethane under transmitted light.

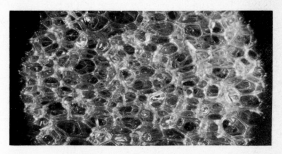

Figure X-23-R, magnified view of large cell size urethane under reflected light.

Table X-77—Typical Mechanical Properties for Flexible Urethane Foam
2 lb per cu ft Density, Slab Stock

	Polyester (adipate)	Polyester (dimer acid)	Polyester (adipate prepolymer)	Polyether	Polyether (Prepolymer)
Tensile strength, psi	25-30	18-25	35-40	12-20	20-28
Elongation, %	250-350	200-300	450-550	150-250	375-450
Tear strength, lb per in.	4-6	4-6	8-10	1.5-2.5	4-6
Compression set, %, 70°C					
50% deflec. (based on orig. height)	5-15	7-15	5-15	2-5	5-10
90% deflection	10-20	10-20	10-20	3-7	5-15
Rebound, %	20-30	35-45	30-40	30-55	30-50
Indentation (RMA), lb per 50 sq in.					
at 25% deflection	40-50	8-20	50-75	20-40	12-35

Table X-78—Typical Mechanical Properties of Flexible Foams at Various Densities
(Adipic Acid Polyester System, Slab Stock)

	Foam density, lb per cu ft			
	1.5	2	3	4
Tensile strength, psi	24-26	25-30	25-35	30-40
Tensile elongation, %	250-300	250-350	300-400	300-400
Tear strength, lb per in.	4-6	4-6	4-6	5-7
Compression set, 70°C, % (based on original height)	10-15	2-10	2-6	2-6
Compression-Deflection, psi				
at 10% Deflection	0.60-0.65	0.55-0.65	0.65-0.75	0.75-0.80
at 25% Deflection	0.65-0.75	0.65-0.75	0.65-0.75	0.80-0.85
at 50% Deflection	0.70-0.85	0.70-1.0	0.80-1.0	1.0-1.3
at 70% Deflection	1.1-1.3	1.4-2.5	1.5-2.5	2.0-2.8

Table X-79—Effect of Cell Size on Mechanical Properties of Flexible Polyester Foam

	Cell size, aver diam, in.			
	0.01 to 0.02	0.015 to 0.03	0.025 to 0.035	0.04 to 0.05
Density, lb per cu ft	2.1	2.0	2.0	1.9
Tensile strength, psi	34.7	30.5	30.0	18.8
Elongation, %	310	340	335	250
Compression set, (based on orig. thick.), % 70°C 22 hr /50%	10.0	6.8	5.0	4.7
Compression deflection, psi				
10%	0.93	0.90	0.91	0.80
25%	0.95	0.89	0.87	0.80
50%	1.15	1.03	0.94	0.90
70%	2.28	2.02	1.75	1.38

IV of the Handbook.

Flexible urethane foams are characterized by high mechanical strength at low density and exhibit low compression set and a high degree of resiliency. A unique feature is that they can be formulated over a wide density range with added versatility in varying the indentation load deflection. Their real commercial appeal, however, stems from the fact that good overall mechanical properties can be obtained at very low density, which upsets many old ideas correlating weight with quality.

Typical mechanical properties for several types of flexible foam having an average density of 2 lb per cu ft are given in Table X-77.

The mechanical properties are considerably influenced by density (Table X-78). These changes in density were effected by varying the amount of water and diisocyanate used. Tensile, elongation, tear strength and compression set all improved slightly as the density was increased. The softness or load bearing properties were nearly independent of density at 10-25% deflection. As would be expected, the denser foams exhibited high load bearing, capacities at the 50-75% levels.

A correlation of mechanical properties with cell size has indicated that a smaller cell structure favors higher tensile strength, elongation, and tear strength, and a tendency toward somewhat higher compression set and load bearing strength at 70% deflection (Table X-79).

One of the early limitations of adipic acid polyester foams was the "plateau" effect in compression: a steady increase of load on the foam did not cause much change until a yield point, at about 10% deflection, was reached. Then, with a small increase in loading, the foam was suddenly deflected to about 50 or 60%. Beyond that point, deflection slowed down while more load was applied.

In the manufacture of cushioning products, "coring" has been very effective in altering this compression-deflection behavior. Fig. X-24 illustrates the effects of three different coring

designs. Molding the foam with cone-shaped cores (Curve D) gave a very soft cushion with an essentially linear stress-strain curve, and little drift at the 25% and 50% deflection points. Long, sharp cones of foam gave softer cushions than did shorter, flatter cones. Similar conditions existed with pyramid-shaped cores.

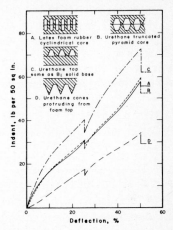

Figure X-24, indentation characteristics of adipic acid polyester urethane cushions compared with commercial foam rubber cushion.

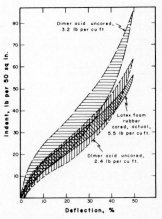

Figure X-25, indentation hysteresis characteristics of dimer acid polyester urethane and latex foam rubber molded cushions.

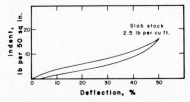

Figure X-26, indentation characteristics of dimer acid polyester urethane foam.

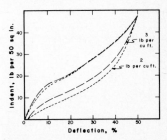

Figure X-27, indentation characteristics of polyether urethane molded cushions.

Molded cushions with truncated pyramid cores (Curve B) gave results nearly identical to those of a commercial latex foam cushion with cylindrical cores (Curve A). Stiffer cushions with nearly linear curves were obtained by reducing the amount of coring (Curve C). As the percentage of foam in the cushion increased, that is, as the core volume decreased, the drift at the indent rest points increased. The drift with sample C approached that of slab stock.

In contrast to the *adipic acid* polyester foams, *dimer acid* polyester foams gave rubber-

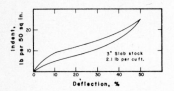

Figure X-28, indentation characteristics of polyether urethane foam.

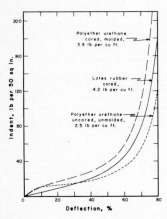

Figure X-29, indentation characteristics of auto topper pads.

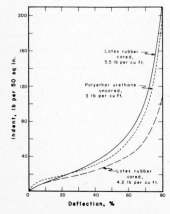

Figure X-30, indentation characteristics of molded cushions.

like indent curves without coring. Fig. X-25 gives typical indentation curves for molded 2.4 and 3.2 lb per cu ft dimer acid polyester cushions. The denser cushion was prepared from the same formulation as the lighter cushion simply by charging more prefoam mixture into the mold. This 2.4 lb per cu ft cushion had essentially the same indent curve as a latex cushion, whereas the 3.2 lb per cu ft cushion was somewhat stiffer. Each cushion had somewhat greater *hysteresis* than the latex cushion, resulting in a more stable feel of the cushion in use.

Slab stock from the dimer acid type foam, a free-rise foam with skin removed, was much softer than the molded cushions with skin intact (Fig. X-25).

Polyether foams have essentially the same indentation behavior as the dimer acid polyester foams. Fig. X-27 shows typical indent behavior of 2 and 3 lb per cu ft polyether cushions, very similar to that of latex cushions. Again, the hysteresis of these foams is greater than that of a latex cushion, giving a more stable feel in use. Fig. X-28 shows that the same formulated slab stock is softer largely because of the absence of skin on the trimmed slab.

The indentation behavior of a foam in the range of 50 to 80% deflection may be used to indicate whether "bottoming" may be expected when used for seating. To avoid bottoming, the load bearing characteristics of the foam should increase fairly rapidly beyond about 50% deflection, and very rapidly at 70 to 80% deflection. Fig. X-29 and X-30 compare polyether foams with latex foam in that respect.

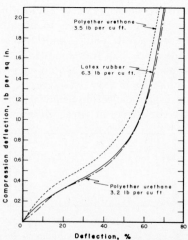

Figure X-31, compression-deflection characteristics of urethane and latex foams (2 in. x 2 in. x 1 in. blocks).

Table X-80—Compilation of Threshold Aging Periods for Polyester Foam

THRESHOLD AGING PERIODS, (Days)

Sample	Temp. °C	% R.H.	Tensile strength						Compression set						Compression-deflection, (25%)					
			(A)	(B)	(C)	(D)	(E)	(F)	(A)	(B)	(C)	(D)	(E)	(F)	(A)	(B)	(C)	(D)	(E)	(F)
α	80	100	6.5	6.0	2.6	2.5	—	—	4.7	5.5	2.1	2.7	—	—	5.6	5.0	4.5	4.0	—	—
β	70	100	17	17	10	5.1	17	14	17	16	6.0	5.5	17	17	16	15	10	10	~22	~20
γ	60	100	33	24	14	12	37	30	32	28	14	15	33	30	35	24	22	21	35	~40
δ	50	100	76	72	50	33	88	72	85	80	40	40	85	80	80	73	60	40	80	>>150
ϵ	40	100	185	180	100	85	200	180	190	185	80	80	>>200	200	190	185	~120	85	>>300	195
η	30	100	>>225	>>230	250	100	>>250	~180	>>300	>>300	>>300	>>200	>>250	>>300	>>300	>>300	>>300	>>200	>>300	>>300
θ	80	70	9.0	6.5	3.4	3.0	13	7	6.5	4.5	3.6	3.5	13	8.5	9.0	6.0	4.5	3.6	15	10
κ	70	70	22	19	11	8.0	24	17	20	16	9.0	10	27	21	24	18	14	14	31	29
λ	50	50	185	180	100	65	210	130	160	145	72	100	220	160	200	180	130	110	210	220
μ	23	50	>>600	>>1230	>>600	500	>>1230	>>600	>>600	>>600	>>600	>>600	>>600	~600	>>1230	>>1230	>>1230	>>1230	>>1230	>>1230
τ	AMB (New Martinsville, W. Va.)	AMB	>>1800	>>1800	1600	1100	>>1800	~1300	>>1800	>>1800	>>1000	~1000	>>1800	~1000	>>1800	>>1800	~1400	~1000	~1500	~1300
χ	AMB (Florida)	AMB	830	900	690	500	1200	550	900	950	~600	~500	1200	~500	900	950	~700	520	~1200	600
ψ	100 (1-5%)	AMB	—	—	—	—	200	150	—	—	—	—	>>400	>>300	—	—	—	—	>>400	>>300
3	80	50	20				13		20				18		20				23	

>> Means greater than this value. ⎫ Both in above table and in graphs.
~ Means about this value. ⎭

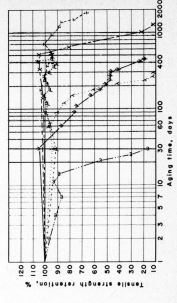

Figure X-33, tensile behavior of polyester foam vs. time of aging.

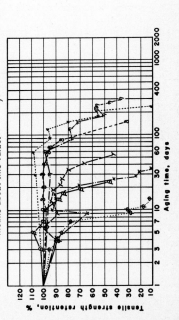

Figure X-32, tensile behavior of polyester foam vs. time of aging.

2. PERMANENCE PROPERTIES

A material's usefulness depends on the length of time its mechanical properties hold up under actual conditions of use. Thus the performance of foam exposed to heat, moisture, light, oxygen and so on, measured under accelerated conditions for expediency, is important information to ascertain the expected life of a foam product.

Hydrolysis resistance

Hydrolysis resistance, or humid aging, as it is sometimes called, is the foam's ability to resist the effects of a combination of heat and moisture. A variety of conditions can be used to determine it.

Polyester-based foams are more sensitive to the effects of humid aging than polyether-based foams. Steingiser and coworkers recently reported the following findings after five years of study of both types of foam, exposed to a variety of conditions.

All samples were cut from the center of foam blocks to insure sample uniformity. After curing, 7 days at 65-75°C for polyester, 16-24 hours at 70°C for polyether prepolymer, and at least one day under ambient conditions for one-shot polyether, all samples were precompressed by rolling three times to 25% of their original height. Specimens from a given block were thoroughly mixed and determinations were made on 3 to 5 specimens for constant deflection compression set, compression load deflection, density, ultimate tensile strength and tensile elongation. All aged specimens were dried at 70°C (ambient humidity) for 4 hours or for a minimum of 24 hours at 23°C and 50% RH prior to testing.

A new term, the "Threshold aging period (TAP)" was defined as the time at which rapid loss of property began under the con-

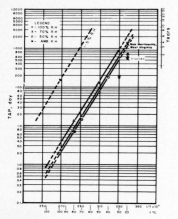

Figure X-34, Arrhenius plot of tensile changes for polyester foam.

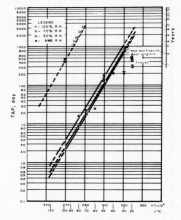

Figure X-35, Arrhenius plot of compression set changes for polyester foam.

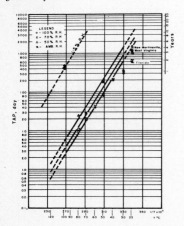

Figure X-36, Arrhenius plot of compression-deflection, 25% changes for polyester foam.

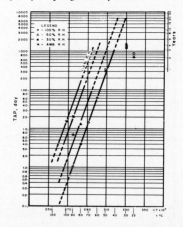

Figure X-37, Arrhenius plot of tensile changes for polyether foam.

Table X-81—Property Retention and Oxidation Resistance of Urethane Foams
Aging at 100°C., Amb. R.H.—Circulating Air Oven

Sample Type	Aging Time, Months	Str. psi	Tensile Str. Retention %	Elong. %	Compression Set % Thick, 70°C 22 Hrs 50%	Compression-Deflection, psi 25%	25% Retention, %
Adipic Acid Polyester Multron R18 2.1 lb per cu ft	0	19.9	—	215	7.0	1.04	—
	1	19.8	100	200	3.2	1.21	116
	2	19.3	97	205	3.6	1.01	97
	3	17.5	88	185	2.8	1.39	134
	4	18.7	94	175	3.2	1.40	134
	5	17.1	86	160	2.5	1.31	126
	6	15.8	79	150	2.5	1.29	124
	7	15.5	78	140	2.5	1.21	116
	8	16.1	81	145	2.8	.96	92
	9	15.2	77	135	2.4	1.43	137
	10	15.3	76	140	2.5	1.34	129
	11	14.0	70	130	1.8	1.25	120
	14	11.0	55	120	—	—	—
	15	9.9	50	120	—	—	—
Adipic Acid Polyester Multron R68 2.2 lb per cu ft	0	30.0	—	365	10	.71	—
	1	31.5	105	420	4.3	1.01	142
	2	26.5	88	355	7.2	.76	107
	3	22.7	76	325	4.0	1.00	141
	4	22.6	75	265	6.0	.97	136
	5	19.2	64	220	12	.96	135
	6	16.7	56	210	5.0	.94	132
	7	15.7	52	160	5.0	.89	125
	8	14.5	48	170	6.0	.70	99
	9	14.1	47	145	4.3	.95	134
	10	14.1	47	155	5.2	.91	128
	11	12.1	41	120	4.3	.80	113
	14	7.1	24	75	—	—	—
	15	6.0	20	70	—	—	—
Polyether Prepolymer PG-44 2.2 lb per cu ft	0	21.3	—	295	7.5	0.27	—
	1	20.4	96	295	4.1	0.31	115
	2	17.4	82	250	4.4	0.32	118
	3	15.3	72	215	3.9	0.36	133
	4	14.3	67	175	4.7	0.34	126
	6	12.4	59	150	4.0	0.38	140
Polyether Prepolymer PG-48 2.3 lb per cu ft	0	22.8	—	490	10	0.22	—
	1	17.8	78	450	4.5	0.21	95
	2	15.5	68	375	4.0	0.21	95
	5	8.2	36	185	3.1	0.23	105
	10	7.7	34	140	3.0	0.22	100
	24	4.3	19	75	3.8	0.22	100
Polyether Prepolymer PG-50 2.5 lb per cu ft	0	30.5	—	450	14	0.32	—
	1	26.6	87	465	7.2	0.33	103
	2	24.7	81	385	5.1	0.34	106
	5	16.5	54	270	4.2	0.34	106
	10	10.6	35	170	3.8	0.37	115
	24	6.2	20	90	6.8	0.29	91
Polyether Prepolymer PG-56 2.2 lb per cu ft	0	24.8	—	345	14	0.39	—
	1	22.9	92	405	6.2	0.28	72
	2	21.0	85	350	5.1	0.33	85
	5	13.9	56	260	4.4	0.28	72
	10	10.0	40	155	4.7	0.33	85
	24	5.3	21	80	6.0	0.30	77

Products of Mobay Chemical Co.

dition of exposure. The logarithm of the TAP value was then plotted versus the reciprocal of the absolute temperature, and an "apparent energy of activation" of the degradation process was determined. In addition, the extrapolation of this plot to normal conditions of 20 to 30°C and 40 to 60% relative humidity produced life expectancy data for the foams. Fig. X-32 and 33 show typical sets of aging curves of tensile strength changes for polyester foam (Table X-80). TAP values are generally higher for polyether based foam, as expected.

Whereas the expected life expectancy for the best polyester foam tested was in the range of 4 to 14 years, that for polyether foam was estimated at 10 to 30 years. Polyester foam based on dimer acid have superior hydrolytic stability than adipic acid polyesters.

Oxidation resistance

Oxidation resistance of flexible urethane foam, in general, has been found excellent. Adipic acid polyester foams normally have superior resistance to oxidation than dimer acid polyester and polyether foams. Polyether foam based on propylene oxide are more oxidation-resistant than those containing ethylene oxide.

Steingiser and coworkers have reported oxidation resistance of a variety of flexible foams under different conditions (Tables X-81, X-82 and X-83). These data reveal the superiority of polyester foam. However, none of the polyether foams contained known antioxidants; they could be expected to improve if proper oxidation stabilizers were added. In all

Table X-82—Property Retention and High-Temperature Dry Air Aging of Flexible Polyether Foams (140°C)

Sample type and Formulation	Aging period, days	Indentation, lb/50 in.² indentor 4-in. thickness of foam					
		25% R	% Ret.	50% R	% Ret.	75% R	% Ret.
PG-48 polyether prepoly-	0	16	—	24	—	58	—
mer, (2″ thick)	1	13	81	18	75	47	81
	3	11	69	16	67	42	72
	6	11	69	15	62	40	69
	11	4	25	8	33	31	53
3000 MW triol, one-shot	0	25	—	37	—	75	—
stannous octoate, (stand-	0.1	23	92	35	92	69	92
ard for heat aging)	1	25	100	36	97	75	100
	5	21	84	30	81	61	81
	50	14	56	20	54	45	60
3000 MW triol, one-shot	0	32	—	48	—	101	—
low dibutyltin dilaurate,	1	32	100	48	100	104	103
tartaric acid, (standard	7	26	81	39	81	88	87
for heat aging)	25	22	69	33	69	73	72
3000 MW triol, one-shot	0	30	—	48	—	95	—
96 index, stannous octoate	1	23	77	33	69	77	81
	7	19	63	27	56	62	65
3000 MW triol, one-shot,	0	28	—	44	—	92	—
92 index, stannous octoate	1	23	82	33	75	79	87
	7	17	61	25	57	55	60
3000 MW triol, Dabco,	0	22	—	30	—	68	—
fluorocarbon-11	1	21	95	29	97	68	100
	6	20	91	27	90	66	97
3000 MW triol, one-shot,	0	41	—	59	—	117	—
0.1 dibutyltin dilaurate,	1	35	85	51	86	110	94
0.1 tartaric acid	7	30	73	41	69	88	75
3000 MW triol, one-shot,	0	26	—	33	—	76	—
0.1 dibutyltin dilaurate,	1	19	73	27	82	63	83
0.05 t-butyl	2.9	19	73	26	79	70	92
catechol	17	15	58	19	58	49	64

Product of Mobay Chemical Co.

cases, urethane foams were shown to be equal to, or better than, latex foam rubber.

3. DYNAMIC FATIGUE RESISTANCE

There are certain correlations between rotary shear resistance and certain mechanical properties for a series of foams of a single type. This is illustrated in Fig. X-38, 39, 40, 41. Those properties appearing to have most influence on rotary shear resistance are tensile modulus and elongation. Factors, such as cell size and degree of cross-linking which have a great effect on tensile strength and elongation, are involved also. Steingiser also shows correlation of rotary shear testing with actual use.

Correlation in laboratory tests between rotary shear, static constant load and slow flex has also been shown by Steingiser and coworkers (Table X-84).

Table X-83—Tensile Properties of Flexible Foams as a Function of Fade-O-Meter Exposure

Sample type and formulation	Exposure time, hours	Tensile Strength, psi	Elongation, %
Standard polyester foam	0	20.1	200
	20	22.5	190
	80	15.3	165
	140	12.1	130
Standard polyester foam	0	30.8	375
	20	22.9	290
	80	16.9	265
	140	14.3	250
Standard polyether foam	0	25.6	250
	20	22.0	220
	80	15.3	180
	140	12.8	155
Dimer acid polyester foam, one-shot	0	21.7	200
	20	18.3	130
	80	12.8	85
	140	11.4	85
Dimer acid polyester foam, prepolymer	0	18.2	150
	20	18.7	110
	80	13.9	90
	140	11.4	80
Ethylene oxide capped polypropylene glycol prepolymer foam	0	11.0	330
	20	11.8	190
	80	11.4	180
	140	9.2	180
Poly (oxybutylene) glycol prepolymer foam	0	17.4	200
	20	9.1	100
	80	5.0	80
	140	4.4	75

Table X-84—Laboratory Tests of Per Cent Softening, Polyether Foam*

	Sample K		Sample L		Sample M	
Recovery Time	1/2 hr	24 hr	1/2 hr	24 hr	1/2 hr	24 hr
Static Constant Load Test	33	10	36	8	33	13
Slow Flex Test	34	23	28	19	30	17
Rotary Shear	38	33	44	36	36	31

*SPI Round Robin test samples. Density 1.5 lb per cu ft. Softening reported as per cent of original 25% indent values.

These data have indicated that rotary shear combines more of the elements of actual use wear than other methods. In addition to showing softening which the other tests do also, rotary shear measures permanent cell structure breakdown as reflected by the slower recovery of loss in load bearing after test.

Good correlation has been reported between rotary and linear shear as shown in Table X-85.

Table X-85—Shear Testing Round-Robin Between Ford and Mobay*

	A	B	C	D
Rotary Shear 100,000 cycles				
% softening at 25% ILD	36	36	18	18
Rating	Good	Good	V. Good	V. Good
Linear Shear Tester* 40,000 cycles	30	33	12	17
% softening at 25% ILD**	24	22	9	15

*1 hr recovery.
**24 hr recovery.
***All samples supplied by Ford Motor Co., Engineering section. Rating of best load bearing retention: "C" > "D" > "B" > "A".

Finally, correlation was found also between rotary shear and a standard durability test (U. S. Testing Laboratory Durability Tester for mattresses) as shown in Table X-86.

4. SOLVENT AND CHEMICAL RESISTANCE

The solvent or chemical resistance of flexible urethane foams is excellent. Generally, polyether foams undergo greater swelling than do the polyesters; however, after drying both types of foams regain their original properties. One-shot polyether foams tend to be the weakest in the wet state because of their generally lower mechanical strength properties.

Solvents such as hydrocarbons and linseed oil cause little swelling of the polyester foams, whereas aromatics, chlorinated solvents, esters, ketones and alcohols cause severe swelling. Water and aqueous solutions do not swell these foams. The polyether foams are swollen by ether, gasoline and turpentine, in addition to the aromatics, chlorinated solvents, esters, ketones and alcohol. Aqueous solutions cause no swelling of the polyether foams.

Solvent and chemical resistance of polyester and polyether foam in a variety of solvents and chemicals is shown in Tables X-87 and X-88.

5. LOW AND HIGH TEMPERATURE FLEXIBILITY

Low and high temperature flexibility of flexible urethane foams has been reported by Saunders and others in terms of Clash-Berg torsional stiffness (Fig. X-42).

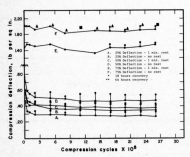

Figure X-38, flex fatigue resistance of adipic acid polyester foam 2 lb per cu ft density.

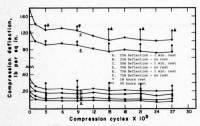

Figure X-39, flex fatigue, dimer acid polyester urethane foam.

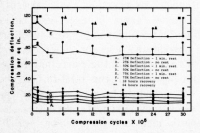

Figure X-40, flex fatigue, polyether urethane foam.

The modulus which was calculated from this test should represent a qualitative basis for comparison of other properties, such as indent characteristics. The adipic acid polyester foams were found to begin stiffening significantly at about —10 to —25°C. The dimer acid foam stiffened gradually, but in the temperature range of —10 to —30°C it reached any given modulus at a temperature about 15-20° lower than the adipic acid polyester foam. The polyether foam showed an additional advantage of about 10°C, e.g., reached an apparent modulus of 2000 psi at —40°, compared to —30° for dimer acid and —10° for adipic acid polyester foam. The latex foam reached this modulus at —53°C.

6. SOUND ABSORPTION

The sound absorption characteristics of flexible urethane foam are comparable to commercial acoustical materials as shown by Stengard in Table X-89 when using the impedance tube method. Other investigators are in general agreement with Stengard. Factors controlling sound absorbency of foams are: foam thickness and density degree of open

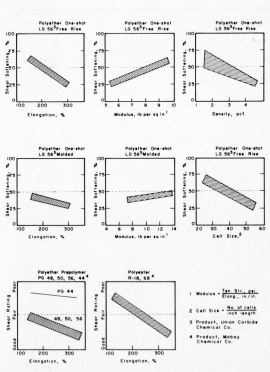

Figure X-41, relationship between rotary shear characteristics and certain physical properties of foams.

Table X-86—Polyether Foam Mattress Intercomparisons Between U.S. Testing Laboratory Durability Tester and Mobay Rotary Shear Tester

Foam Description	Density, lb per cu ft	Mobay rotary shear % Softening*	Rating	U. S. Testing Lab. % Softening*	Rating
One-shot slab stock 3000 MW triol	1.9	31	Good	37	Good
One-shot slab stock 3000 MW triol	1.5	38	Good	36	Good
One-shot slab stock 3000 MW triol	1.1	64	Poor	66	Poor
One-shot slab stock 3000 MW triol, fluorocarbon-11	1.1	49	Fair	37	Very Soft Initially
Prepolymer slab stock PG-56[1]	2.1	—**	Poor	37	Good ***
Prepolymer slab stock PG-44[1]	2.0	—**	Very Poor	∾ 90	Very Poor

*Softening expressed as % of original 25% indent loading.
**Numerical data not taken initially when method was first developed; only a visual examination of cell breakdown, set, softening determined the rating.
***Note: In actual end use, these systems softened badly within a year's time and clearly were no longer serviceable.
[1]Product of Mobay Chemical Co.

cell and cell size. Ball and Paffrath showed that the presence of thin non-porous skins, such as is normally formed on sprayed foam, does not impair absorbency. In fact, under certain conditions, the sound absorption quality is improved.

7. THERMAL CONDUCTIVITY

Flexible urethane foams have low thermal conductivity (K-factor) and in this respect are comparable to many well known commercial building and insulating materials (Table X-90).

Table X-87 — Solvent and Chemical Resistance of Polyester Urethane Foams System: 3 lb per cu ft Adipic Acid Polyester Foam

Solvent or chemical*	Change in tear strength, % Wet	Dry**	Swelling
Linseed Oil	−20	Unchanged	Slight
Turpentine	−45	"	"
Ether	−40	"	"
Gasoline	−55	"	"
Mineral oil	−50	"	"
Benzene	−80	"	Heavy
Chlorobenzene	−90	"	"
Carbon tetrachloride	−75	"	"
Ethyl acetate	−90	"	"
Acetone	−75	"	"
Ethyl alcohol	−85	"	"
Water	−35	"	None
Sea water	−40	"	"
Salt, 10%	−35	"	"
Detergent solution	−30	"	"
Soap solution	−30	"	"

*Immersed 50 days at room temperature.
**Dried for 24 hr at 40°C.

Table X-88—Solvent and Chemical Resistance of Polyether Urethane Foams System: Modified Polypropylene Glycol

Solvent or chemical*	Change in tensile strength, % Wet	Dry**	Swelling
Turpentine	−73	0	Heavy
Ether	− 5	0	"
Gasoline	−64	+ 8	"
Mineral oil	+ 6	0	Slight
Benzene	−30	− 4	Heavy
Carbon tetrachloride	−37	+ 7	"
Ethyl acetate	−27	−15	"
Acetone	−63	0	"
Ethyl alcohol	−90	−10	"
Water	−47	− 8	None
Salt, 10%	−43	− 8	"
Detergent solution	−40	− 8	"
Soap solution	−43	+ 5	"
Sodium carbonate, 10%	−36	0	"
Sodium hydroxide, 10%	−35	+ 5	"
Nitric acid, 10%	−43	0	"

*Immersed 50 days at room temp.
**Dried 24 hr at 40° C

8. FLAME RESISTANCE

Flexible urethane foam, which has not been made flame-proofed, will support combustion but at a slower rate than latex foam rubber and many other commonly known materials. Urethane foams can be made self-extinguishing and even non-burning (ASTM D-1692-59T) by the addition of special flame-proofing agents, usually at the expense of other properties.

Table X-89—Sound Absorption Characteristics of Flexible Urethane Foams and Architectural Acoustical Materials

	Weight lb per sq ft	NRC[1] Specification range
Urethane foams*		
Flexible polyether urethane foam (2.7 lb per cu ft)	0.22	0.60-0.70
Flexible polyester urethane foam (3.2 lb per cu ft)	0.26	0.75-0.85
Flexible castor oil based urethane foam (2.0 lb per cu ft)	0.17	0.70-0.80
Architectural acoustical materials* *		
Regularly perforated cellulose fiber tile	1-1.5	0.70-0.80
Random perforated cellulose fiber tile	0.96-1.5	0.70-0.80
Fissured cellulose tile (3/4 in. thickness)	0.77	0.60-0.70
Perforated mineral fiber tile	1.7	0.65-0.75
Fissured mineral fiber tile (15/16 in. thickness)	1.45	0.65-0.75
Textured mineral fiber tile	0.96	0.65-0.75

Sample thickness is one inch unless otherwise specified.
*The urethane foam samples have all cut surfaces with no skins.
**From "Sound Absorption Coefficients of Architectural Acoustical Materials." Published by Acoustical Materials Association, 335 East 45th St., New York, N.Y.
[1]Noise reduction coefficient.

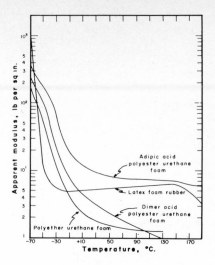

Figure X-42, torsional stiffness properties of flexible foam (Clash-Berg).

Table X-90—Thermal Conductivity of Some Building and Insulating Materials

Material	Den. lb per cu ft	°F	K*
Asbestos	29.3	32	1.08
Alum. Foil, 7 Air Spaces /2.5 in.	0.2	100	0.300
Cork Board	10.0	86	0.300
Felt, wool	20.6	86	0.48
Fiber Insulating Board	14.8	70	0.336
Glass fiber	0.5	75	0.29
	9.4	86	0.270
Mineral wool	19.7	86	0.288
Polystyrene rigid foam	1.8	40	0.25
Flexible urethane foam	2.3	75	0.24
Slag wool	12.0	86	0.262
Wallboard, insulating type	14.8	70	0.336
Wool, Animal	6.9	86	0.252

*K = BTU /hr /sq ft / °F /in.

PART VI—APPLICATIONS

Applications for flexible urethane foams have multiplied at an incredible rate since their debut in 1955. One of the factors involved in the wide scale acceptance is the ease by which urethane foam can be fabricated. Horizontal table splitters slit sheets of foam down to a thickness of 1/16 in. Cylinders of foam fashioned from continuously poured blocks can be "peeled" to form thin, continuous sheets. Ingenious cutting devices have been designed for profile cutting and splitting of foam to form sine, triangle, trapezoid and other pro-

files in variable heights and dimensions (Fig. X-43). It can be quilted to fabrics with ordinary equipment, cut by hot wire to form continuous strip mouldings (Fig. X-44) and other shapes, post-formed in simple jigs (if effected early enough) or in heated presses to a variety of useful parts, and surface-embossed for decorative effects. In addition, flexible foam can be sewn, tacked, stapled, shredded for filler, hog-ringed, grommeted, dyed, silk-screened, glued, heat-sealed and flame-laminated to fabric. These properties make flexible urethane foam

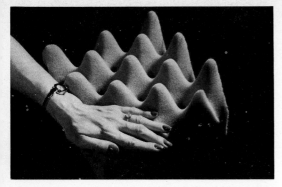

Figure X-43, coring by profile cutting is unique way of altering cushioning characteristics of flexible urethane foam.

Figure X-44, flexible urethane foam is cut cleanly by a hot wire to fashion many interesting and useful shapes.

an inmportant material for cushioning, packaging, laminates, sound and thermal insulation, and filtration applications. Common applications for flexible urethane foam are:

Polyether Based	Polyester Based
Furniture	Textile laminates
Public seating	Carpet and rug
Transportation	underlay
Bedding	Filtration
Sound insulation	Casketing
Thermal insulation	Packaging
Packaging	Grooming aid (hair
Household sponges	curlers, etc.)
Industrial sponges	Novelties
Gasketing	

1. COMFORT CUSHIONING

Furniture

Urethane foam has made its greatest penetration in the furniture market, because of its lower cost, versatility, lightness, greater strength, easy bonding with adhesives, and compatibility with textiles. Traditionally-expensive furniture is now available at medium prices because arms and backs can be sculptured and tufted more economically. Urethane foam keeps the fabric welting in place and allows application of zippers to upholstery. For padding and filling materials, urethane foam in slab stock can be applied easily, faster than animal hair and textile filling.

This simplicity of fabrication has made urethane foam especially well suited to mass production of furniture in designs that are easily cut from slab stock (Fig. X-45).

Used in a variety of ways, it can be surrounded by Dacron or in-quilted batting. Rubber webbing bases with loose urethane foam seats and back cushions are employed in very comfortable high-fashion modern and early-American groupings at a price nearly anyone can afford.

Another important advantage of urethane foam in the furniture industry is its ability to be foamed in place. A technique for mass-producing fully-molded urethane foam upholstered chairs in a single operation involves the use of polyether type foam, cured in a mold around a supporting frame of tubular metal construction. The process calls for positioning the basic tubular frame in a chair mold cavity. Urethane chemicals are poured into the mold and expand immediately to completely envelop the steel frame in foam, in only a few minutes. The chair is completed by applying upholstering material and inserting four legs. In addition to the obvious economies, the chairs are light in weight, provide good support for the back, and will not mar walls or other surfaces, since there are no hard exposed edges.

Urethane foam is responsible for the growing trend in *all-plastic* chairs. Rigid plastic shells, fashioned to any shape in inexpensive molds, are supplemented by foam cushioning

Figure X-45, urethane foam is especially well suited as cushioning material, for the modern Scandinavian and Italian styles shown. Courtesy Crest, Inc.

made with or without an integral skin. This can easily be a one-step operation by molding the foam directly to the plastic shell.

Transportation

The use of urethane foam in the automobile and truck industry is increasing rapidly in such applications as headliners, sun visors, padded dashboards, seat cushioning (Fig. X-46), carpet and mat backing, door seals, and weather stripping.

The polyether type foam has the resiliency and comfort characteristics so necessary in automobile seating. At the same time, its ability to be foamed in place is a major advantage. Popular among U. S. manufacturers are molded urethane foam topper pads which can be economically mass-produced in a variety of sizes and thicknesses.

Unitized seating, whereby the springs are made an integral part of the foam cushion by molding in a single step, is being developed.

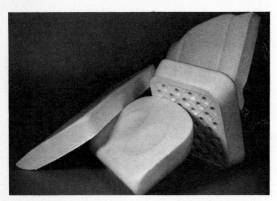

Figure X-46, fully molded cushions of urethane foam for the transportation industry.

Figure X-47, molding of truck seat cushion of urethane foam, burying support springs in the foam, is a process developed by Bostron Corp.

A urethane-cushioned truck seat, manufactured by Bostrom Corporation (Fig. X-47), employs the spring-action principle of a torsion bar applied to the suspension mechanism. A quick turn of a handle adjusts this seat for smooth, vibrationless driving for drivers of all weight.

Urethane foam is being used in aircraft where its weight-saving advantages are important. The modern jet airliners use urethane foam for seat cushioning, mattress padding, protective padding on hat-racks, sides of planes and berth covers, carpet underlay, and cushioning in cockpits (Fig. X-48). In the new large jets, urethane seating reduces the weight by about 1000 lb.

Public seating

Flexible urethane foam is making inroads in public seating for theatres, auditoriums, offices, and churches. Here, requirements in seat design are: comfort, attractive appearance, compactness, economy, durability, freedom from odor, ease of cleaning, and resistance to fire, dampness, fungus and vermin.

Bedding

Urethane foam mattresses are finding ready acceptance because of their durability, non-allergic character, freedom from odor, ease of cleaning, and resistance to solvents, oils and perspiration. A distinct advantage is the light weight permitting ease of turning and handling. A urethane foam mattress weighs 75% less than a comparable inner-spring and 50% less than a foam rubber mattress. In hospitals and military installations, urethane foam is

Figure X-48, "X" marks the spots where urethane foam is used to provide comfort and safety in the cockpit of a Boeing jet aircraft.

being used because of its ability to withstand steam sterilization and its non-inflammability.

Other bedding uses include various combinations of specially profiled cut foam for pillow fabrication, shredded foam as filler for pillows, quilts, and comforters, and pads for covering conventional mattresses.

2. PACKAGING

The use of urethane foam in packaging techniques is almost limitless. It can be molded to virtually any shape, fabricated by slicing, coring, die-cutting, heat-sealing, and sewn to meet the most intricate requirements of package design.

Industry has become aware of the outstanding shock absorbency offered by urethane foam. In a qualitative test conducted early in the development of packaging uses, it was found that a ⅛-in. thick urethane foam in a double layer was comparable to a double layer of ½-in. thick cellulose batting. In another "drop" test, urethane foam proved to be dramatically superior in shock absorption to four other standard packing materials, and almost 100% more effective than rubberized curled hair. Other features are its insulating qualities, nonabrading surface, low compression set, and resistance to attack by bacteria, rodents, insects, and fungus.

Unique and sophisticated forms of packaging are possible with urethane foam. Delicate instruments for the electronic and missile fields are protected by carefully engineered molded foam packages, or they can be incased in polyethylene bags or wax around which the urethane is foamed.

3. LAMINATES

Laminates are formed by bonding urethane foam directly to fabric, plastics, and other flexible substrates. By far, the biggest use of such laminates is as garment lining where flexible urethane foam offers a very high insulating quality, yet is breathable and light in weight. Additional advantages include excellent hand and drape, outstanding crease and wrinkle resistance. Foam-lined garments can be washed and dry cleaned, and sell within the textile industry's current pricing structure. At the same time, the foam lining upgrades the final product so that less expensive fabrics, such as cotton, can often successfully replace more expensive and heavier woolen goods.

The insulating properties of urethane foam

Figure X-49, fragile electronic tube cradled safely in a bed of flexible urethane foam, which was foamed in-place around the part.

lining has been checked in laboratory tests. It was found that a ⅛-in. thickness of urethane is comparable to a 14-16 ounce wool batting. Foam interlining is being used in almost every style of clothing, such as coats, jackets, parkas, sportswear, dresses, suits, and innerwear.

Although processes have been reported whereby foam laminates can be produced continuously in a single operation, two older methods seem preferred. In the "flame-lamination process," thin (3/32-in.) sheets of foam are passed over a bank of flame jets which heats and melts the foam surface leaving it soft and tacky. In this state, the foam is then bonded by pressure to the fabric. This can be done at speeds up to 200 feet per minute. The flame laminating process is most adaptable to polyester type foam although recently polyether foams have been successfully employed. The other method uses adhesives, applied to the surface of the foam, to bond the lining to the fabric.

Other possible laminating applications are: foam to vinyl for sound-deadening wall coverings, foam to terry cloth for bathroom mats, foam to vinyl or neoprene for outdoor shelter coverings, lining of shoes for added comfort and shape retention, foam-backed draperies, lightweight foam-lined blankets, and foam-backed paper for insulated bags.

4. SOUND AND THERMAL INSULATION

Flexible foam, being of open cell structure, is an excellent sound absorption medium. If desired, it can be coated with such decor effects as wall tile and coverings without harming sound absorption characteristics.

In addition, urethane foam is a good absorber of heat. Its thermal conductivity (K-factor) is about 0.25 Btu/sq ft/in/°F/hr, which is comparable to many commonly used

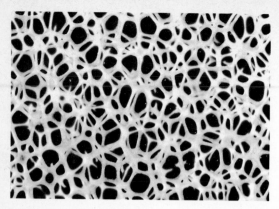

Figure X-50, magnified view of urethane foam with cell walls leached out so that only connecting ribs remain. Courtesy Scott Paper Co.

Figure X-51, urethane foam fashioned to a variety of shapes for use as household and industrial sponges.

insulating materials, such as rock wool, glass wool, balsam wood, cork and other synthetic foams.

This combination of sound and thermal insulating properties coupled with strength, ease of assembly, and low overall cost makes urethane foam attractive for a wide range of building applications (see Section V).

5. FILTRATION

The filtering characteristics of urethane foam can be improved by special processes. Scott Paper Co. has developed a process in which cell walls are leached out so that only connecting ribs remain (Fig. X-50). This foam is finding increased use as an air filter medium in central ventilating systems, as air intake filters for automobile carburetors, in air conditioners, and in warm air furnaces. Because of the open cell structure, the filter foam can hold considerable quantities of dust and other air contaminants. It is useable for liquids as well. Variations in cell size lead to a whole range of filter possibilities of differing "mesh" and the filters are reusable, since they can be washed (Fig. X-50).

6. MISCELLANEOUS

Carpet Underlay

Flexible urethane foam, as cushioning supports for rugs and carpeting, can give inexpensive carpeting the luxurious feel of costly, thickly tufted wool. Its tendency to provide

enough friction to prevent crawling and slipping has been a boon to the "throw" rug market.

Urethane foam carpet underlay has not yet reached its full potential primarily for reasons of cost: the bulk of the carpet underlay market is supplied by inexpensive jute and rubberized curled hair. The key to accelerated growth of urethanes in this area will be made by continuing developments of suitable methods and equipment for applying foam directly to the back of carpeting.

Sponges

The high abrasion and tear resistances of urethane foams make them ideal for use as household and industrial type sponges. Variations in cell size give urethane sponges a high degree of abrasive cleaning action. In addition, they are resistant to chemicals, acids and solvents, and remain soft when dry (Fig. X-51).

The water absorbency of urethane sponge can be improved by incorporating chemical compounds of a more highly hydrophilic nature than the ingredients more commonly used. Urethane foam sponge can be impregnated with a variety of cleaning materials and polishing waxes for specialty applications.

Others

Other applications for flexible urethane foams are sporting goods, household and industrial novelty uses, footwear, horticulture, medical, and military.

Section XI—MOLD DESIGN AND POUR PATTERN CONSIDERATIONS FOR URETHANE

By Herbert Brabandt, Jr.

The purpose of this section is to point out some of the pitfalls involved in mold design and to present some idea of the considerations which must go into the design of a mold and related equipment to produce a quality end product.

Conversion from one type of molding operation to another is often complicated to the point of being impossible. For example to convert from slab stock insulation of refrigeration panels to a pour-in-place method, new molds, fixtures, and jigs would have to be designed, because new foaming pressures would be involved. Likely, if a panel application is originally handled by the frothing technique, a minimum of jigs and panel supports would be required; but if it is later necessary to switch to a conventional foaming system, then much heavier molds, jigs, and/or panel supports would be necessary because of the increased foaming pressures which tend to distort the panel.

Panel jigs

Panel jigs are designed to withstand the particular pressure involved, and to hold the panel absolutely rigid while the foam is curing. A typical example may be as follows: 2 lb per cu ft rigid urethane foam at 12 to 15% packing (this refers to overfill), when dispensed into a mold with a cross section of two inches, may generate pressures up to 300 lb per sq ft in an 8 ft rise. This figure may be even greater in other applications, and in order to keep mold deflection at a minimum, the use of very sturdy jigs is necessary.

Mold material

The inner material from which a mold may be fabricated greatly influences the final mold surface temperature. For example, molds constructed of low heat-conducting material, such as plywood, will retain the reaction heat much more efficiently than a metal mold. Metal molds dissipate heat rapidly and cause an increase in skin density and mold cycle time.

With plywood, the mold cycle time is shorter and there is a more uniform density gradient from the skin to the core. By pre-heating the mold, the effect of various high conductivity mold materials may be counteracted.

Mold dimensions and configurations

Governing factors are: finished product thickness, geometrical shape, height of rise, and amount of material required.

The maximum cross-section is generally limited by the quantity of liquid mix that can be dispensed within the handling time. If a mixing head backed by metering equipment is used, this time is a function of throughput and cream time. If the foam is hand batched, it is a function of the maximum amount of material that can be thoroughly mixed and poured within the handling time.

Minimum cross-section is dependent upon the height of rise. As the cross-section dimension is reduced, frictional forces (shear) tend to restrict the rise of the foam, thus increasing its density at the bottom of the part being foamed. The gas pressures within the foam are relatively constant at a given thickness and the pressures on the walls of the mold are greater when thinner sections are poured. For cross-sections of less than one inch, it is usually best to resort to the horizontal laydown-sandwich skin method, although panels have been foamed by the froth technique 3/8 inch thick by four feet high, with a six lb per cu ft material, into highly heated molds.

The configuration of the mold is important in a closed mold operation. Although the proper amount of material may be dispensed into the mold, if it is not properly vented to allow the air displaced with foam to escape, air pockets will result. Small holes in the top of the mold should be located furthest from the filling point to allow the air to escape. For example, if the main portion of the liquid mix is dispensed at the center of the bottom of a cube-shaped mold, the vent holes would best be located in the top corners.

It is necessary to calculate the volume of each mold. Once the mold is properly preconditioned temperature-wise, and properly vented, in the case of a closed mold, the amount of material that will fill it can be calculated knowing the foam density, and neglecting losses due to vaporization of the blowing agent.

Some of the panel-type plywood knock-down molds may require a good deal of time to assemble. The actual pour time may be a small fraction of the overall mold preparation time. This is not good. For efficient production operation, the mold should be designed so that its assembly and pre-conditioning require a minimum of time.

Mold pre-conditioning

Mold release agents—There are numerous ways of effecting release of a part from its mold. The particular method of release used depends upon the overall operational requirements. In rare cases, mechanical pushers are built into the mold to effect release upon its opening. The ultimate in mold release is a mold, which has its own built-in release, for example a mold made of some material, such as polyethylene, or some highly polished metal which possesses low adhesive properties. Unfortunately, this is fairly expensive and the proper construction of this type of mold requires a technical knowledge common only to experienced mold-makers and designers. One variation of this method, which is receiving much attention, is the coating or laminating of the molds' inner surfaces with a uniform film of polyethylene. Experience must be acquired before success can be guaranteed.

One form of mold release in wide use today on less intricate parts, mostly with flat surfaces, is release-paper and polyethylene film. Special silicone-treated papers, waxed paper, and thin plastic film or sheeting are available for this purpose. Untreated brown wrapping paper may be used sometimes, for example in continuous slab production. The paper is then removed with a thin skin of foam on it in the trimming process. This method is limited to molds with flat surfaces and may require too much wasted time in the case of large closed molds.

Probably the most common method of release today is the grease or wax-coating method, using silicones, oils, greases, waxes, etc. applied with a cloth or brush or sprayed on. Care must be exercised, so that the mold and

foam temperatures do not affect the release agent selected.

In some cases, it is desirable for the mold release to serve as protective coating for the finished product, or as a finish coat to enhance its appearance. A recent development is a type of polymeric release agent which forms a skin that serves the above purposes, and is an excellent barrier against moisture or vapor transmission. This is highly desirable in products which may be in contact with water. This release agent is applied to the mold surface in liquid form; it forms a thin skin and bonds itself to the finished foam product. Another advantage of this particular product is that it can be colored with organic oil dyes. It is manufactured by North Shore Laboratories Corp., Salem, Mass., under the name of "Niksun." Niksun No. 1 is used in applications where rigid foams predominate, Niksun No. 2 is used more commonly with the flexible foams.

Another method which is still under development is that of actually blending the release material into the foam mix. This cannot be used in all cases, but where the physical characteristics of the product are not critical, its use will reduce labor costs of mold preparation considerably. A large amount of this release agent is required and this may adversely affect cell structure.

Mold preheating—Preheating the molds is necessary in most cases for various reasons. Mold surface temperature affects the overall density of a molded part. The exothermic reaction of the foaming process produces heat. If the mold surfaces are cold, they may dissipate this heat unevenly and the result is a non-uniform product with a high density layer at the mold surface. This high density layer, which may be 1/16th inch thick, is actually unexpanded, or partially expanded, foam. In a high surface-to-volume product, such as building panels, this may represent 50% of the material, and may result in an underfilled mold. Preheating the mold surfaces not only minimizes the thickness of the foam skin, but also helps to complete the reaction, and reduces the cure time.

The mold surface preheat temperature may range from 100 to 150°F, depending upon the materials used. Smaller cross-sections—½″ to 1″—may be more favorably produced, density-wise, by using higher mold temperatures, possibly up to 180°F; however, care must be taken not to overheat the mold surfaces, else a premature gel may result. The cost of heating above 150°F may be substantial and always merits investigation. The amount of time the mold should be heated, from 10 to 30 minutes, will depend upon the size of the mold, material of mold, and the method of heating.

Methods of heating include banks or rows of infra-red lamps, electric heating blankets, hot air blowers, or temperature-controlled ovens. Better control and higher efficiencies are obtained with ovens and electric heating blankets; however, for a small operation where precise temperature is not essential, infra-red lamps or hot air blowers may perform satisfactorily.

Pour patterns

Filling of a mold may be accomplished by one of many different methods, depending on geometrical configuration of the mold, including surface-to-volume ratio and cross-section width vs. height of rise; size of object under consideration and ease of handling mold; throughput capacities of metering equipment and mixing head; total amount of material to be dispensed; cream time of the mix; rise time; and physical properties tolerances.

Puddling

Puddling is the dispensing of the liquid mix into a mold or cavity, using no particular method or pattern of distribution. It may be the dumping of a batch mix or the continuous dispensing of mix into one general spot. This method is used where there is a low mold surface-to-volume ratio and a minimum amount of wetting is necessary. By wetting is meant the covering of the mold's surface with liquid mix. The puddling method is somewhat limited in shot size, because all the foam must be dispensed before the cream time has elapsed; therefore it is commonly used for small parts or where high throughput equipment is available.

If liquid mix is deposited on top of material which has started to expand, there may be damage to the cell structure and physical properties of the finished product may be affected. For an application of the puddling method to a large part, variables which may be adjusted are either chemical (to increase the cream time) or mechanical (to increase the throughput of the equipment).

Defined patterns

When the liquid mix cannot be dispensed into the mold by puddling, it is necessary to resort to a pour pattern. This may be accomplished either by moving the mixing head so that the foam is not all deposited in the same spot of the mold, or by moving the mold, which may be mounted on casters, past a stationary mixing head. In slab production, there is a definite pour pattern formed by a combination of traversing mixing head and moving conveyor. The reciprocating motion produces parallel ribbons of liquid mix. The spacing of the ribbons vary with throughput and conveyor speed. When the maximum ribbon spacing is two inches from center to center for an 8 lb per min throughput, it might be increased up to four or five inches for a higher throughput. Distribution should be smooth and uniform to keep the lateral flow of the foaming mix at a minimum. Care should be taken to avoid trapping air in large pockets and it is best to keep the foam travel, or ribbon spacing, at a minimum.

The pour pattern method eliminates dispensing on top of rising foam, gives a better distribution of the liquid mix, and provides more surface wetting, thus yielding a more uniform end product.

The type of pattern used depends largely upon the configuration of the mold; but the one most generally used is the "multiple linear traversing method" which is, in effect, the formation of a multiple "S" pattern.

In a closed mold operation, where the material is dispensed into the bottom of the mold, after which the top is positioned, the amount of material must be predetermined. Then a pour time is established for a given throughput, and the pour pattern must be completed in that length of time, to get even distribution of material. It will help to mark off the mold, in sections, with chalk or some other marking device; by using a watch with a sweep second hand and glancing at the chalk-marks, it is easier to get a better distribution of material in the mold. The idea is to dispense into each chalk-divided section, in the corresponding time, the proper amount of liquid mix.

Panels

Practically every panel involves the pouring of a high surface-to-volume ratio. Essential factors in pouring panels are: maintaining uniform physical properties and preventing the panel from bulging at the sides as a result of foaming pressures (See Section IX, Part 1).

Section XII—EXTRUDED EXPANDED POLYSTYRENE

By R. N. Kennedy

1. HISTORY AND MANUFACTURING

The concept of cellular polystyrene may be dated to the time of the introduction of styrene monomer and the plastic, polystyrene. The Swedish inventor, Munters, referred to a patent filing date of August 21, 1931 in his U. S. Patent No. 2,023,204 issued December 3, 1935 on the product, "Foamed Polystyrene." During this period, polystyrene as a molding and an extrusion material was in the early stages of development. Thus, it is not surprising that cellular polystyrene did not become commercially available until the early 1940's.

In 1942, The Dow Chemical Company started research to develop a process for production of a cellular polystyrene by a process now known as the "extrusion process." The material from this process was introduced in July of 1943. Work on other methods of making polystyrene foam took place in the late 1940's in Germany by Badische Anilin & Soda Fabrik and in England by the Expanded Rubber Company, Ltd. The process for making cellular polystyrene by molding expandable polystyrene granules containing a solvent blowing agent was originated in Germany in the early 1950's and entered the United States market in 1954 (See Section XIII—Expandable Polystyrene).

The first product made by The Dow Chemical Company was used by the U. S. Coast Guard and Navy as a buoyancy medium in lifesaving equipment and by the Quartermaster Corps as insulation. This material, trademarked "Styrofoam®," was in the form of large logs and contained large cells ($\frac{1}{4}$ in. diameter). During the war period, it was also submitted to industry. Manufacturers of domestic refrigerators and concerns consuming insulation in refrigerated spaces expressed interest in the product. As a result of this interest, it appeared that the low temperature insulation market would probably be a major outlet and thus work was started to improve its thermal characteristics. The low temperature insulation market for cellular polystyrene developed slowly and did not consume any

sizable volumes until the late 1940's. In the meantime, other markets such as in the display and novelty fields, the floral market and as buoyancy in metal boats matured more quickly.

During the maturing of this product many changes took place in the types of material offered and sizes available. A flame resistant product was introduced in 1952. Colored materials for the novelty and floral trade and higher density materials were also put on the market in the early 1950's. New types of extruded cellular polystyrene products have been put on the market each year, generally tailoring the properties and size of the material to a particular end use such as a polystyrene foam board with skins of another material, such as aluminum, for perimeter insulation and special materials for the buoyancy and floral fields.

Manufacturing process

Styrene monomer (vinylbenzene) is one of the most widely used chemical "building blocks" in forming high polymers or plastics. Coal and crude oil are the raw materials for benzene and ethylene respectively, which are reacted to form the vinylbenzene or styrene monomer. Annual U. S. production capacity for styrene monomer is estimated at 2.405-billion lb (OPDR. p. 3, March 11, 1963). Approximately 36% of this capacity is employed in the production of molding and extrusion grade plastics. Other major markets are in the rubber and coatings industries and broad use as a chemical intermediate is also significant.

Polystyrene plastics are produced by mass, suspension, and solution polymerization techniques giving maximum versatility in design of these materials, copolymers, and foams and films.

Extruded polystyrene foam is made by the free expansion (nearly 40 volumes) of a hot viscous mixture of polystyrene, blowing agent and other additives through a slit-like orifice. The solvent blowing agent is added in liquid form to a chamber containing the polystyrene and other additives, and the system is kept at elevated pressures and temperatures until extrusion (U. S. Patent No. 2,669,-751; U. S. Patent No. 2,740,157). The temperatures are controlled closely prior to and during the extrusion process. After the foam has been expanded, it is cooled slowly to prevent formation of undue stresses which cause rupturing of the cell walls. When the material is sufficiently cooled, it is cut to standard lengths and thicknesses. An annealing step follows the cutting operation to assure that the final material will be of uniform quality.

The expansion during the production of extruded foam is quite different from that of the expandable beads during molding (See Section XIII—Expandable Polystyrene). The extrusion process starting material is a viscous solution under pressure and at elevated temperatures. As the material flows through the slit-like orifice the pressure is reduced to atmospheric where the blowing agent rapidly expands the polystyrene. During expansion, the polymer temperature is lowered below the second order transition point, causing the foam structure to freeze rather than collapse. This is the temperature below which molecular rotation in a plastic becomes negligible: it is often associated with a brittle point or a softening point. The soluble blowing agent plays a double role. It facilitates extrusion by plasticizing the polymer thereby lowering the polymer viscosity and then upon evaporation, when the pressure is reduced, the cooling action leads to increased viscosity resulting in hardening of the foam structure.

2. PRODUCTS COMMERCIALLY AVAILABLE

Extruded cellular polystyrene has been successfully produced in densities from 1.2 to 6 lb per cu ft. A range in sizes and shapes can be made varying from ¼ in. to 25 in. in thick-

Figure XII-1, types of extruded polystyrene foam boards; showing a range of commonly used thicknesses and widths.

ness; from 6 in. to 48 in. in width and to any length that can be conveniently handled. All possible combinations of the above width and thicknesses are not available since a maximum cross-sectional area of extrusion exists for each size of extrusion equipment. In general, the wider widths are only available in thinner sections.

Extruded foam polystyrene is available in both flame-retardant and nonflame-retardant formulations. It is available in various colors. It can also be produced in a wide range of cell sizes.

The Dow Chemical Company, Midland, Michigan, is the major producer of extruded polystyrene foam; Ludington Plastics, Inc., Ludington, Michigan, makes specialty items such as rods and small boards.

Table XII-1 gives a general description of the various products available. Several of these products are shown in Fig. XII-1. These are primarily classified according to the characteristics that have a major effect on properties.

	Table XII-1—Commercially Available Extruded Polystyrene Foams				
Designation	Average density lb/cu ft	Flame retardant	Average cell size, millimeters	Appearance and color	Forms
A	1.9	Yes	0.5	Blue	Cut boards
B	1.9	Yes	1.0	Blue	Cut board and rough billets
C	1.8	No	2.0	White or colored	Cut board and rough billets
D	2.9	No	Small	White	Cut boards
E	4.3	No	Small	White	Cut boards
F	2.6	Yes	Small	Blue	Boards with extruded skins
G*	1.7	No	10.0	Clear	Cut boards

Copolymer of styrene and methyl methacrylate

Table XII-2—Mechanical Properties at 75°F

Type	Compressive strength psi	Tensile strength psi	Shear strength psi	Flexural strength psi	Compressive modulus psi	Bending modulus psi	Shear modulus psi
ASTM Test	C1621-59T		C273-53	C203-55T	C1621-59T	C203-55T	C273-53
A	30	70	40	70	1500	2500	900
B	30	60	30	60	1000	2500	900
C	16	54	32	52	1000	1150	1100
D	65	105	58	80	4000	5000	2500
E	130	178	88	160	5050	5500	3300
F	30	—	—	—	—	—	—
G	10	—	—	16	—	—	—

The portion of this chapter on physical properties and applications will use alphabetical designations in discussing the various foams, for convenience sake. These alphabetical designations are not industry-wide.

3. PROPERTIES OF EXTRUDED POLYSTYRENE FOAM

Properties of extruded polystyrene foam as with most foams are a function of the base plastic, the density, type of cells—open or closed—and cell size. The base plastic governs to some extent all of the properties but it affects mostly such characteristics as resistance to burning, resistance to solvents including water, and change of properties with temperature and aging. The density and cell wall size and orientation primarily control the mechanical properties. The type of cells, open or closed, and gas within the cell affect the thermal conductivity and water resistance characteristics.

Mechanical properties

The mechanical properties of the various polystyrene foams listed in Table XII-1 are shown in Table XII-2. Mechanical properties vary with density (the higher the density the greater the strength). Cell size and cell orientation and a skin on the surface of the foam also affect these properties. A typical stress-strain curve for various polystyrene foams in compression is shown in Fig. XII-2. Polystyrene foams with larger cells show a definite yield at around 3% while the smaller celled products do not show a definite yield. The compressive strength as listed in Table XII-2 is taken at 5% for materials with smaller cells. Expanded polystyrene is a thermoplastic; thus its mechanical resistances decrease slightly as the temperature is raised to the heat distortion temperature. When that temperature is reached, the cellular structure collapses. Mechanical properties are not affected adversely at sub-zero temperature. For example, compressive strength at liquid nitrogen temperature (−320°F) is approximately 25% higher than at room temperature.

Thermal properties

Thermal conductivity ("k" factor)—The

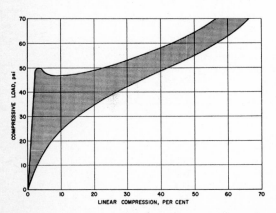

Figure XII-2, compressive stress-strain relationship for extruded polystyrene foams.

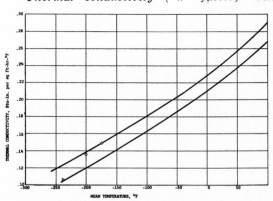

Figure XII-3, thermal conductivity of Type A extruded polystyrene foam vs. mean temperature.

thermal conductivity of extruded polystyrene foam at relatively low densities is a function of cell size and mean temperature. The average thermal conductivity of the various types of extruded cellular polystyrene at mean temperatures of 40°F and 75°F are shown in Table XII-3.

Table XII-3—Thermal Conductivity ("k" Factor)

Type	Average "k" factor (Btu-in./sq ft-hr-°F)	
	40°F Mean temp. average	75°F Mean temp. average
A	.24	.26
B	.28	.30
C	.28	.30
D	.23	.25
E	.23	.25
F	.24	.26
G	—	.50

The thermal conductivity of Type A polystyrene foam as a function of mean temperature is shown in Fig. XII-3.

Heat distortion temperature—This is the highest temperature at which no distortion by heating alone takes place. All extruded polystyrene foams are very similar, being dependent upon the base polymer. The heat distortion temperatures are in the range of 165°F to 175°F.

Linear thermal coefficient of expansion—The value for all types is 0.000035 per °F between 0°F and 80°F.

Specific heat—It is, for all types, 0.27 Btu per lb per °F at 40°F.

Water resistance properties

Extruded cellular polystyrene absorbs negligible amounts of water because of its closed-cell structure and the inherent resistance of the base plastic to water. Four water resistance characteristics of extruded polystyrene foams are:

Capillarity—None.

Water Absorption—Water absorption of extruded polystyrene foams after being completely submerged under a 10 foot head of water for 48 hours is 0.08 lb per sq ft for types A, B, D, E and F; it is 0.12 lb per sq ft for types C and G. Water pickup under these conditions is on the open surface cells and thus is dependent upon cell size and the presence or absence of a skin on the surface.

Water vapor transmission—The values obtained in accordance with ASTM E-96-53T,

column Method E, are 0.8 perm for type F, 1.2 perms for types A, B, D, E and 1.8 perms for type C. Perm refers to grams of water per hour transmitted through one sq ft of substance, one inch thick, under a partial vapor pressure differential of one inch of mercury.

Electrical properties

The electrical properties of cellular polystyrene approach those of air because of the excellent electrical properties of the base plastic, polystyrene. The dielectric constants and power factors of the cellular polystyrene are directly proportional to density ranging from values of air to those of the solid polystyrene. Table XII-4 gives electrical properties of ex-

Table XII-4—Electrical Properties

Types	Dielectric constant (10^2 to 10^3 cps)	Power factor (10^3 to 10^8 cps)
A,B,C,F,G	<1.05	<0.0004
D,E	<1.07	<0.0004

truded polystyrene foam.

Sound absorption

Cellular polystyrenes are not considered to be efficient sound absorbing materials. They are practically equal to wood, plaster, brick and other common building materials in sound absorption in the lower frequencies. They are somewhat better than these materials at higher frequencies. The sound absorption values in Table XII-5 were obtained by the

Table XII-5—Sound Absorption of 1", Type A Foam

	Sound absorption coefficient	
	Mounting #4	Mounting #7
125 cps	0.01	0.38
250	0.03	0.25
500	0.05	0.17
1000	0.14	0.15
2000	0.49	0.09
4000	0.19	0.15
NRC	0.18	0.16

ASTM Reverberation Room method.

Light stability

Cellular polystyrene is degraded by direct sunlight. The degree of degradation is dependent upon formulation and density. Flame retardant formulations and low density unpigmented materials have less light stability. All polystyrene foam should be kept covered when stored out-of-doors.

Light transmission properties

The light transmission of cellular poly-

Table XII-6—Light Transmission of Extruded Polystyrene Foam		
	Transmission (%)	
Thickness (in.)	Type C	Type G
¼	45	
½	30	
1	15	63
1½	10	
2	5	55

styrene is dependent upon thickness and cell size. The values in Table XII-6 were obtained by a method which would be equivalent to the transmission of light if the foam were used as a window.

Burning characteristics

Extruded polystyrenes Type A, B and E are formulated to be flame retardant and may be characterized by the following tests:

1. ASTM D16292-59T, "Flammability of Plastic Foams and Sheeting." Rating: "Self-extinguishing by this test."

2. Military Specification MIL-P-16591D, "Plastic Material, Cellular Polystyrene." Rating: "Class 2—Fire retardant."

3. Federal Specification HH-I-524, "Insulation Board, Thermal." Rating: "Type II, Class 2—Self-extinguishing (flame retardant)."

4. ASTM E84-59T, "Surface Burning Characteristics of Building Materials"—(Tunnel Test). Rating: In one in. thickness, flame spread range = 10 to 25.

Nonflame-retardant extruded polystyrene foams may be characterized as to the burning rate by ASTM Test D1692-59T: Type C—6 in. per min. Type D—6 in. per min. Type E—2½ in. per min. Type G—6 in. per min.

When heated, extruded polystyrene foam tends to melt away from the source of heat thus reducing the likelihood of ignition. Generally an open flame is necessary to start these materials burning. They are not a fire hazard when installed between noncombustible materials such as a masonry wall and plaster, because free access to air is needed for continued burning.

The ignition temperatures of polystyrene foams are relatively high compared to cellulosic materials. The flash ignition temperature is in the neighborhood of 700°F while the self-ignition temperature is 800°F.

Miscellaneous properties

Extruded polystyrene foams can be expected to retain their properties indefinitely unless exposed to direct sunlight or physical damage.

Extremes of temperature from sub-zero to 170°F do not affect them.

Polystyrene foams have no odor when wet or dry and do not sustain mold growth. They contain nothing of food value and consequently do not attract rodents or vermin.

4. FABRICATION TECHNIQUES

Mechanical fabrication

Expanded polystyrene foam may be fabricated with common power driven wood working tools. No special techniques are required. General rules to be followed:

The power tool should be operated at a high rate of speed and the feed rate of the foam should be low. This results in many thin cuts giving the foam a smooth surface and prevents the tearing action which might accompany the use of a thick cut.

Tools must be kept sharp for maximum cutting efficiency.

The cutting blade or tool should form an angle of approximately 110° with respect to the surface of the foam stock for maximum cutting efficiency. This results in a lifting action in removal of the foam rather than a tearing action and gives a smooth cut.

Cell size may affect the fabrication properties of expanded polystyrene. Small cell products usually require more cuts per inch of length to give the smooth surfaced cuts normally obtainable with larger cell materials. This may be accomplished by increasing the number of teeth on the cutting tool, increasing the peripheral speed of the tool, or by decreasing the rate of the feed.

Sawing—The high speed band saw is perhaps the most widely used piece of cutting equipment for fabricating rigid foams. Special adaptation of the machine is not required, and many types of saw blades may be used. However, the results obtained with each type of blade will vary with the size and set of the teeth and the pitch of the blade. The set of the teeth should be sufficient to insure removal of the "sawdust" from the cut. The highest rates of cutting are attained with ordinary metal and wood cutting blades, but these blades also give a fairly rough surface. A skip-tooth blade, as designed for plastics, gives a fairly smooth surface with a lower rate of cutting. Very smooth surfaced cuts may be obtained with a double edge scallop blade but the rate of cutting with this type of blade is very low.

Although a great deal of latitude is indicated in the choice of a blade, the fabricator must adhere closely to a particular blade thickness which is determined by the size of the band saw pulley. The blade thickness should be 0.001 of the pulley diameter in inches. For example, a 12 inch diameter pulley would require a blade having a thickness of approximately 0.012 inch.

A metal cutting blade ⅝ inch in width and 0.022 inch in thickness and having a pitch of 10 or more teeth per inch, operating at a band speed of 10,000 feet per minute with a foam feed rate of 90 feet per minute, has been found suitable for cutting large quantities of foam.

High density foams may be cut with most conventional blades. However, if a smooth surfaced cut is necessary, a blade with very little set and lubricated with a soap solution is required.

Planing—Planers are commonly used for finishing rough planks of extruded polystyrene foam. High peripheral speeds with low feed rates are necessary in using the planer to insure a smooth surfaced cut. A planer found to be useful for finishing has six blades parallel to the axis of a spindle rotating at 3,600 rpm. A feed rate of 90 feet per minute yields 20 cuts per inch of length. An alternative planer design uses a lawn mower type blade.

Shaping and routing—Symmetrical objects such as balls and bells are formed by feeding a rotating flat blade having the desired contour into the foam. Drill presses are commonly used for this operation. Symmetrical objects may also be formed with the use of a lathe, in which case the flat blade is fed into a rotating piece of foam.

Nonsymmetrical pieces may be formed with shapers, routers, sanders, milling machines, multiple wood carving machines, or carved by hand. Cavities may be obtained with a flat blade router. Narrow cuts or slots are made with circular saws, high speed milling tools, or dado blades.

Grinding—The hammermill and the rotating blade mill are two types of equipment which may be used to grind rigid foams. The hammermill is available in two types which produce entirely different forms of ground foam. The rigid hammermill gives shredded material, while the swing hammermill gives balls or pellets. The rotating blade mill produces a pellet which can be controlled to some extent as to size by the feed rate. The blade size, however, determines the degree of latitude available in the feed rate. Densities of ground foam vary according to the density of the foam and the form in which it is ground.

"Sawdust" in mechanical fabricating operations

"Sawdust" produced in the mechanical fabrication of plastic foams is not considered a health hazard but it may present certain problems. "Sawdust" in contact with the skin can be rather annoying, particularly if the worker is perspiring. It is also quite irritating if allowed to come in contact with the eyes. Thus, employee comfort can be maintained by the proper control of fabrication conditions. A pneumatic pickup system at the point of cutting is recommended for "sawdust" removal. Proper use and maintenance of such a system will also greatly improve housekeeping conditions.

Hot wire fabrication

Extruded cellular polystyrene is a thermoplastic material and thus is susceptible to softening and melting upon exposure to heat. This property is utilized in fabrication by hot wire cutting which involves the melting of the cell structure. A hot wire cut surface is different in appearance from that of a mechanically cut surface. This is due to the formation of a thin layer of plastic over the cell structure of the foam as it is melted by contact with the heated wire. This effect may be desirable in some instances due to the added strength afforded by the thin covering layer of solid plastic.

The principle of operation is relatively simple. A low voltage current is applied to a nickel-chrome resistance wire, which heats the wire in proportion to the applied current and the resistance of the wire. Temperature control of

Table XII-7—Wire Sizes & Voltage—Current Requirements for Hot Wire Cutting

Size of wire	Voltage drop, volts/foot	Current, amperes
No. 35	13 to 15	1.44 to 1.74
No. 25	6.2 to 8.6	3.0 to 4.0
No. 20	4.4 to 5.6	6.4 to 8.0
No. 15	2.5 to 4.0	12 to 18
No. 10	2.0 to 3.5	24 to 36
¼″x⅛″	1.5 to 2.0	75 to 110

Note: These are not minimum or maximum figures. They are intended only to assist in determining the size transformer to be used with each size of wire. The transformer voltage output should be equal to the voltage drop of the cutting wire. Its current rating should be equivalent to the stated value in the table.

the wire may be obtained with a variable voltage transformer. Amperage and voltage drops per foot of wire length for various wire sizes are listed in Table XII-7 to assist the fabricator in determining the size transformer required.

Feed rates in hot wire cutting are considerably lower than those in mechanical cutting. Multiple wires spaced as desired are therefore utilized in production operations whenever possible. The factors affecting feed rate in hot wire cutting are the temperature of the wire and the density of the foam. The feed rate must be low enough to prevent distortion of the wire or wires which would result in uneven cuts. Automatic feeding devices are required to obtain flat, level surfaces on long, straight cuts. The temperature of the wire may be controlled for more efficient operation by use of a variable voltage transformer in conjunction with a low-voltage high-amperage transformer. Some smoke is produced during a hot wire cutting operation and should be removed from the immediate area by the use of proper ventilation or local exhaust systems.

Plane surfaces may be cut with a taut, small diameter wire. The wire may be spring loaded to maintain a taut condition. Curved surfaces, such as pipe covering, require a heavy wire or ribbon formed to the desired shape. Symmetrical objects may be fabricated by rotation of either the foam or the formed wire. Electrical resistance-heated metal dies may be used for cutting complete shapes from the foam in a single operation.

Heat forming

Heat forming by softening and shaping requires a temperature slightly above the heat distortion temperature of polystyrene foam (190°F to 200°F). The source of heat may be radiant heating panels, banks of infrared lamps, woven electric heaters, or a series of strip heaters. The polystyrene foam should be heated from both sides simultaneously to insure a more uniform temperature through the piece. After heating polystyrene foam to the proper temperature, it is placed in a mold and formed by pressure applied to the mold with an air cylinder. The mold may be of the matched male and female type, or a male mold may be used in conjunction with a cavity which is slightly larger than the piece to be formed. Heating cycles in the range of 30 to 90 seconds have proven satisfactory for one inch

thick material. Suitable mold materials include wood, plaster of Paris, and metals.

5. BONDING TECHNIQUES

Many authorities on adhesives contend that bonds are formed as a result of specific adhesion, with mechanical adhesion having little if any effect on bond strengths. They maintain that the sanding of a smooth surface does not promote mechanical adhesion, but in reality exposes a greater surface area for specific adhesion. While this may be true for smooth surfaced materials, foam plastic materials do provide a high degree of mechanical adhesion in forming bonds due to their unique cellular structure which gives an interlocking action between the cells of the foam and the adhesive. Bond strengths are further enhanced if the adhesive has specific attraction for the materials being bonded.

Polystyrene foams may be bonded to a variety of other materials by many different types of adhesives; however, because of the inherent characteristics of polystyrene foam, certain precautions must be observed and care must be taken when selecting adhesives for any given application. The following discussion reviews the various types of adhesives and related problems of each when used with polystyrene foam.

Drying adhesives

Adhesives which reach the bonded state by evaporation of a liquid are known as "drying type adhesives." The liquid may be water, an organic compound or a mixture of organic compounds. The final adhesive may be a solution, suspension or emulsion of resin, rubber or asphalt, but in all instances the liquid must evaporate to effect full strength of the bond.

Evaporation proceeds through the glue line in nonporous structures or through the glue line and the bonded substance in vapor-porous materials.

Although extruded cellular polystyrene is nonporous, it may be bonded to porous materials with little difficulty using drying type adhesives because the liquid component of the adhesive may evaporate through the porous member. However, where the foam is to be bonded to another nonporous material with a drying adhesive, some means to allow the adhesive to dry must be incorporated in the structure. This is usually done by applying

This table lists the types of adhesives which may be used for bonding polystyrene foam to itself, metal, wood, or masonry. The adhesives are listed, insofar as possible, in the order of decreasing effectiveness for each class of adhesive. However, the order may change for specific applications. Selection of an adhesive type should be on the basis of finding the best combination of properties as required for a particular application.

Adhesive class	To polystyrene foam adhesive type	To metal adhesive type	To wood adhesive type	To masonry adhesive type
Drying adhesives	Pressure-sensitive rubber emulsion Rubber solvent Resin solvent Rubber emulsion Resin emulsion (small areas only)	Pressure-sensitive rubber emulsion Rubber solvent Rubber emulsion	Pressure-sensitive rubber emulsion Rubber solvent Rubber emulsion Resin solvent Resin emulsion Asphalt emulsion	Rubber emulsion Asphalt emulsion Rubber solvent Resin solvent Resin emulsion
Setting adhesives	Epoxy Phenolic Resorcinol-phenolic Resorcinol Urea Latex modified portland cement mortar Portland cement mortar Mineral cement Internal setting asphalt	Epoxy Internal setting asphalt Latex modified portland cement mortar	Phenolic Resorcinol-phenolic Resorcinol Urea Epoxy Internal setting asphalt Latex modified portland cement mortar	Latex modified portland cement mortar Portland cement mortar Mineral cement Internal setting asphalt
Hot melt adhesives	Asphalt, wax	Asphalt, wax	Asphalt, wax	Asphalt, wax

the adhesive with a notched trowel, or by applying the adhesive in spots rather than continuous between the two members. These types of applications will allow drying to proceed through the adhesive line.

Open time, the time lapse between applications of the adhesive and joining of the parts, may be used with success in many applications of this nature to preclude most of the drying problem after the bond is formed. This method is useful only with tacky adhesives. Adhesive is usually applied to both surfaces and allowed to reach maximum tackiness. The bond is then formed by placing the surfaces tightly together. Bonds formed in this manner should be tested for sufficient strength prior to large-scale use.

Setting adhesives

Adhesives which reach full bond strength through the medium of chemical reaction are called "setting type adhesives." This group includes portland cement and plaster of Paris among the inorganic compounds, and organic adhesives such as phenolics, epoxies, and resorcinols. These latter compounds harden by a chemical mechanism as do cement and plaster, but the hardening consists of an entirely different process known as polymerization. Catalysts, i.e., compounds which accelerate a chem-

ical reaction but do not alter its course, are widely used with the organic setting type adhesives to hasten the hardening process. Accordingly, two-part adhesives which must be mixed and used shortly thereafter are commonly encountered in this group. Since these adhesives have a limited pot life they should be mixed in small quantities that can be used before setting takes place. Drying problems are absent or of little consequence when using a setting type adhesive.

Hot melt adhesives

Adhesives which must be softened with heat and applied in such softened state are termed "hot melt adhesives." A list of such materials would include asphalts, waxes, rubbers and naturally occurring resins. Practical limitations such as poor specific adhesion, high unit cost, thermal degradation, and operational difficulties reduce this group to asphalt and wax-based materials.

Hot melt adhesives which have a workable fluidity at temperatures below 300°F may be employed as bonding agents for extruded polystyrene foam. The dip application of hot melts requires temperature control which may not be available to the fabricator. The most satisfactory method of application is by a roll coater which permits a broader temperature range in the tank.

The following gives general information on hot melt temperatures to be used with the various methods of application:

1. Roll coater—tank temperature to be no higher than 400°F.
2. Vat dipping—vat temperature to be no higher than 300°F.
3. Pouring or mopping—adhesive temperature to be no more than 200°F.

Selection of an adhesive

Selection of an adhesive and its method of application requires consideration of several factors:

1. Vapor porosity of materials to be bonded.
2. Bond strength requirements:
   (a) Initial bond strength
   (b) Final bond strength
3. Area to be bonded.
4. Type of application desired (brush, spray, trowel, push-box).

Table XII-8 lists specific adhesive types for various bonding applications.

Bonding foam to foam

Considerable time may be required to achieve complete dryness of a drying adhesive on large areas. Spot or serrated applications which provide many voids for evaporation are therefore recommended. Open time may also be used to aid drying of large areas. Small areas (i.e., glue line width two inches or less) may be bonded without employing spot or serrated applications, and usually open time is not required.

The possibility of solvent attack must not be overlooked when using drying adhesives as many are based on aromatic or chlorinated hydrocarbons (e.g., benzene, chlorobenzene), ketones and esters (e.g., methyl ethyl ketone, ethyl acetate) which are particularly strong solvents for polystyrene foam. Adhesives containing petroleum naphthas are borderline cases in that they may attack the foam. Open time should always be allowed for these adhesives to partially, or wholly reduce solvent attack. Residual solvent may cause difficulty at elevated operating temperatures, and tests should be conducted to detect such effects prior to large-scale use.

Setting type adhesives offer the best means of preventing incomplete or slow drying and solvent attack. Most setting adhesives contain little, if any, solvent, and these are limited to water and the lower alcohols. Setting adhe-

sives generally do not have high initial bond strength, but the ultimate bond strength is usually very adequate.

Hot melt adhesives may be used for bonding polystyrene foam to polystyrene foam if care is exercised to limit the dip time to a few seconds in order to prevent distortion, shrinking and softening. The major advantage of hot melt adhesives is that they do not present drying problems. However, operational difficulties should be studied before using hot melt adhesives in large-scale installations.

Bonding polystyrene foam to metals

Polystyrene foam lends itself well to bonding with metals for many important applications. The problems encountered in this type of adhesion are similar to those encountered in bonding the foam to itself and all other nonvapor-porous materials. Open time may be required and bonding may be limited to small areas or serrated or spot applications when employing drying type adhesives. Open time is the time lapse between the application of the adhesive and the joining or mating of parts. Setting adhesives again preclude much of these shortcomings and work well with present metal fabricating methods.

Metals should be cleaned prior to bonding. This is true for all bonded materials, but it is particularly important that metals be free of any surface grease, oil and dirt to overcome the inherently poor specific adhesion of many adhesives on metals. Sanding with fine grit sandpaper is of value for removal of the oxidized film on most metals. Sanding also exposes more surface area, thus yielding greater ultimate strength.

Bonding polystyrene foam to wood

Polystyrene foam may be bonded to wood with little difficulty from drying because wood is vapor-porous. However, plywood seldom offers this advantage due to the presence in most plywoods of phenolic glues between the plies. Spot or serrated applications are sometimes necessary on plywood for this reason, and open time of 15 to 30 minutes to aid drying may be helpful. Solvent attack must again be avoided to achieve strong and long-life bonds.

Wood has high specific adhesion for most phenolics, ureas, melamines and their relatives. Setting type adhesives are accordingly the most satisfactory for bonding polystyrene foam to wood. This type adhesive presents the additional advantage of requiring little or no open time.

Bonding polystyrene foam to masonry

The vapor porosity and rough surface of masonry simplifies the bonding problem. Portland cement mortar is an ideal adhesive for bonding to masonry. It is low in cost and is cheaply and easily applied by push-box.

Many other adhesives—hot melts, cold setting and emulsions—will successfully bond to masonry when effectively applied.

Bonding polystyrene foam to cloth and paper

Polystyrene foam may be easily bonded to both cloth and paper since these materials are highly vapor porous. Most drying adhesives may be used if they do not contain strong solvents for polystyrene.

Bonding polystyrene foam to glass and plastics

The use of drying adhesives with these materials presents a problem of specific adhesion in addition to the usual problems of drying and solvent attack to the foam. In general, pressure sensitive adhesives give the most satisfactory results when bonding polystyrene foam to these materials, although rubber solvent adhesives and resin solvent adhesives have been used on occasion.

6. COATINGS FOR POLYSTYRENE FOAM

Coating of polystyrene foam may be desirable:

1. To protect from physical damage and weathering.
2. To protect from solvents or other materials which cause degradation.
3. To retard the rate of burning.
4. To beautify and decorate.

Coatings which serve to protect from physical damage and weathering are used chiefly in construction and flotation. Decorative coatings are generally used in the novelty and display fields. There are, of course, coatings which may be used for both protection and decoration.

Problems

Solvent attack to the foam constitutes the major operational problem in coating polystyrene foam. Coatings containing aromatic or chlorinated hydrocarbons, ketones and esters dissolve polystyrene foam and consequently should be avoided. This problem is not as critical as with adhesives since coatings present one open surface for evaporation of the solvent. Hence, a material considered borderline with respect to solvent attack as an adhesive would in many instances pose no serious solvent problems when used as a coating. Spray application and the use of thin coats further reduce solvent attack potential. Elevated temperatures reduce drying time but should be considered with caution because of the increased action of the solvent.

Pinhole-free coatings are generally desired to insure protection of the foam, and several coats may be required to obtain complete coverage, thus increasing labor and material costs.

Physical-damage-resistant coatings

Physical strength and hardness are the major requirements of coatings. Portland cement plaster, latex modified plasters, mineral cements, and filled asphalt emulsion are particularly useful for protecting polystyrene foam from physical damage.

Epoxy coatings, although expensive, give good protection from physical damage.

Water-dispersed texture paints, sand-filled water-dispersed paints, sand-filled latexes, and other water-dispersed coatings may be used to protect polystyrene from physical damage.

Increased strength properties may also be gained by incorporating reinforcing cloths or meshes with all these materials.

Materials available in sheet form, such as plywood, metals, masonite, asbestos cement board, reinforced polyester, etc., may be laminated to polystyrene foam to serve as protection from physical damage.

Weather-resistant coatings

The surface of polystyrene foam degrades when exposed out-of-doors. Multiple coats of water-dispersed exterior paints or coatings will prevent such degradation. However, since some protection of the foam from physical damage in addition to weather resistance is usually necessary, portland cement plaster, latex-modified plasters, and asphalt emulsions are often used as weather-resistant coatings. These materials may be painted for decorative purposes.

Solvent-resistant coatings

The function of this type of coating is to

protect the polystyrene foam from attack by aromatic and chlorinated hydrocarbons, ketones, esters, and various other organic compounds. Care must also be exercised to obtain complete pinhole-free coverage. It is usually necessary to apply several coats in order to achieve this end, and cost may be high.

Epoxy coatings are effective for protecting polystyrene foam from attack by polyester resins. Shellac, and vinyl latexes such as saran, have also been used with some success for this purpose.

Unfortunately, no universal solvent-resistant coating has been found to be entirely suitable. Each solvent resistance application is unique, however, and possibly one of the many commercial synthetic resins might be useful in a specific case.

Fire-retardant coatings

Polystyrene foam internally flame-retarded is a convenient and economical solution for applications requiring such characteristics; however, at times it may be necessary to use a fire-retardant coating.

Fire-retardant coatings achieve success by blanketing the foam, which thus delays the spread of, or extinguishes, the flame. These coatings do not prevent the foam from distorting, shrinking, or melting due to exposure to heat. The degree of protection afforded depends upon the thickness of the coating and the ratio of foam surface area to volume.

Intumescent paints and coatings, inorganic compounds such as potassium silicate or waterglass, inorganic cements, vinyl coatings, and many commercially available fire-retardant solutions may be used as coatings.

Decorative coatings

Paints—Water-dispersed paints may be applied to polystyrene foam for decorative purposes. Some commercial oil paints may be applied if care is observed. In general, enamels, varnishes, and most outdoor house paints cannot be used with polystyrene foam due to solvent attack. Appropriate tests should be conducted in any doubtful cases prior to large-scale use.

Dyes and pigments—Polystyrene foam may be attractively tinted with many water-soluble or alcohol-soluble dyes and pigments or combinations thereof. Phosphorescent, luminescent, and fluorescent pigments may also be used in decorating. Black lighting in displays offers a unique method for obtaining striking effects. A suitable binder such as shellac may be blended with dyes and pigments to provide increased wear resistance.

Miscellaneous decorative coatings—Various types of flocking and "glitter" may be applied to polystyrene foam for special effects. The materials are bonded to the foam with a suitable adhesive. In general, the clear, resin-solvent type proves satisfactory.

Preliminary investigation has shown that the vacuum metalizing process of decorating is entirely feasible. It is understood that the process is competitive costwise with other methods of decoration but the initial equipment cost may be a deterrent.

7. APPLICATIONS

Extruded cellular polystyrene on the market since the mid-forties has paved the way for many of the present day applications for rigid foam plastics. It continues to be a pace setter in the development of new markets because it is low in cost, it is readily available in a variety of products tailored for specific end uses, it is easily fabricated and possesses an excellent combination of properties.

The major markets for extruded polystyrene foam may be considered as insulation, panels, buoyancy, packaging, floral display and novelty, and electrical. The insulation markets may further be broken down into refrigerated rooms (freezers, coolers), buildings insulated for comfort, pipes and tanks, transportation, and appliances (See Section V—Foamed Plastics in Construction and Section VIII—Foamed Plastics for Insulation).

Low temperature insulation

Low temperature insulation was the first major market for extruded foams. Extruded polystyrene foam with its inherent resistance to water and water vapor overcame the problems caused by water and ice existing in conventional insulations. This characteristic along with its excellent insulating and structural properties led to rapid acceptance in all fields of low temperature insulation. Freezers and coolers in the dairy and meat industries, sharp freezers, storage and cooler rooms in the fruit producing and distributing fields and refrigerated locker plants are examples of this market. Refrigerated spaces may take on many forms and shapes but most are rooms constructed of masonry block or brick. In the use

Figure XII-4, *wall, ceiling and floor of a freezer room insulated with extruded polystyrene foam boards. The floor will receive a concrete slab, the side wall and ceiling will be plastered with a portland cement plaster.*

Figure XII-5, *43 ft diameter sphere for storing ammonia at 15°F insulated with 4 in. precut extruded polystyrene foam boards.*

of cellular polystyrene boards to insulate these rooms, an accepted method of applying the boards is to bond the first layer horizontally to a clean level wall with a suitable adhesive. Subsequent layers are then adhered to the previous layer, and if needed, held in position with treated wood skewers until the adhesive has set. The joints of the layers should be staggered so as to prevent moisture migration (Fig. XII-4). A two-coat plaster system or other finish is recommended to protect the foam from impact damage.

Fully insulated self-supporting partitions between coolers and freezers can be constructed with layers forming a sandwich between plastered skins. Substantial savings in space and cost of insulation result from this free standing partition.

Tanks, vessels and pipes operating below 150°F are insulated with polystyrene foam, either in the form of boards or specially cut pipe covering or lagging. Suitable adhesives and banding are used to apply the precut pieces; the foam is then covered with a weatherproof coating (Fig. XII-5).

Extruded polystyrene foams find widespread use as low temperature insulation in the transportation field: insulated truck bodies, railroad cars and ships. Its light weight is very significant when used as insu-

Figure XII-6, *polystyrene foam boards with "as extruded" skins being used as horizontal perimeter insulation under the floor slab of a house. The required cutting to fit around projection is easily accomplished with extruded polystyrene foam.*

Figure XII-7, *Type F extruded polystyrene foam boards with scoring for easy field fabrication to various widths.*

lation in transportation.

Comfort insulation

Comfort insulation applications are those in which the insulation is used to economically maintain a comfortable temperature within a building. Extruded cellular polystyrene has economically competed with lower cost fibrous insulations where use could be made of the foam's structural properties and water resistance. Three specific areas of applications are perimeter insulation, masonry wall insulation and roof insulation.

Perimeter insulation is primarily used in slab on grade buildings where the foundation walls are insulated by placing extruded polystyrene boards either horizontally or vertically against the footings and held in place by back fill (Fig. XII-6). The inherent resistance of extruded polystyrene foam to water and soil micro-organisms is very important in this application. Because of the demand for this type of insulation a special extruded polystyrene foam (Type F) is being produced in a range of thicknesses to accommodate various climatic conditions. This material has an extruded skin and is prescored to permit fast, easy installation, eliminating the need for cutting and fitting (Fig. XII-7).

Extruded polystyrene foam is an excellent insulation and plaster base for solid masonry construction. The boards are bonded with a portland cement mortar to the masonry walls and then plastered directly. The cut surface cells of the foam make an ideal base for the application of all types of plaster (Fig. XII-8). Extruded boards can also be applied to masonry walls and then a "dry wall" type of gypsum board can be applied to the foam and treated in the regular manner by painting (Fig. XII-9). The polystyrene foam boards in both of these cases eliminate the need for other types of insulation and furring strips.

The use of extruded polystyrene foam boards is growing rapidly as roof insulation. The Type F board having an extruded skin is used in this application by a variety of techniques. The water-vapor resistance properties of the polystyrene foam insure an insulated roof deck having a constant thermal conductivity. Several techniques have been developed for applying polystyrene foam on roof decks. These are primarily concerned with methods of applying the hot bitumens used in the conventional built-up roofs (Fig. XII-10). Since polystyrene foam is a thermoplastic, the foam must be protected from these materials or special care must be taken to prevent melting the foam.

Panels (sandwich construction)

Extruded polystyrene foam boards are playing an important role in the development of and use of panels in the building industry (Fig. XII-11). A high strength to weight ratio, ability to be bonded to various facing materials plus the insulating characteristics previously discussed make them ideal as a core material in this fast growing applica-

Figure XII-8, gypsum plaster applied directly to extruded polystyrene foam boards. The boards were bonded to a masonry block wall with portland cement mortar.

Figure XII-9, adhering "dry wall" board to extruded polystyrene foam previously bonded to a masonry wall.

EXTRUDED EXPANDED

tion. The primary disadvantage of polystyrene foam in this application is its relatively low heat distortion point. Thus, panels with total polystyrene foam cores have problems in meeting certain building codes and fire regulations. It has, however, been used in a wide variety of panel applications with many different facings ranging from concrete and steel to wood and plastic.

Glazing

A new light-transmitting cellular polystyrene copolymer foam having large cells has been introduced. This is the product described as Type G. It is expected that this product will find widespread use in skylights and other light-transmitting applications requiring translucency with good thermal insulation and the possibilities of decoration. It may be used between sheets of transparent plastic or glass (Fig. XII-12).

Form liners

An interesting architectural development involves the use of cellular polystyrene foam as form liners in the on-site casting of "thin shell" concrete roofs. By bending the extruded cellular polystyrene boards to the proper shape and fastening them temporarily to wooden forms it is possible to use the form simultaneously as a nonremovable foam board, thermal insulation and vapor barrier in one operation (Fig. XII-13). This technique eliminates the necessity of bonding insulation to the concrete roof after pouring and removal of the forms. The interior finish can be applied to the exposed surface of the polystyrene foam in the same manner as previously described for plaster base applications. This technique has been used on domes, barrel vaults, folded plates, hyperbolic paraboloids, and other shapes.

Figure XII-10, extruded polystyrene foam boards being applied to a metal roof deck with hot asphalt as the adhesive.

Figure XII-11, load-bearing sandwich panel as walls and roof in a house. The panels are 1/4 in. plywood faces bonded to a 2 in. extruded polystyrene foam core.

Figure XII-12, translucent window consisting of 1 in. of Type G extruded polystyrene copolymer foam between glass.

Figure XII-13, construction of hyperbolic paraboloid concrete roof using foam boards as form liners.

A modification of the form board technique utilizes wire supported extruded polystyrene foam for on-site construction of insulated structural sandwich panels. Reinforcing wire mesh is attached to the building frame and foam plastic insulation is placed against it. After the plastic foam is covered with additional wire mesh, mortar plaster is applied directly by spraying or troweling. When the facing materials have cured, the extruded cellular polystyrene remains as a permanent insulation vapor barrier.

Another unique application of the structural form board principle is in the construction of hyperbolic paraboloid roofs. This is the "off-set" wire concept developed at Purdue University under sponsorship of The Dow Chemical Company. In this technique, plastic form boards are placed between two networks of wires and serve as a temporary structural form for pouring the concrete and during cure. Once the concrete is cured the plastic foam remains permanently bonded to function as thermal insulation, water vapor barrier and base for interior decoration.

Buoyancy

Extruded polystyrene foam is 30 times lighter than water and since it is impervious to water it has been used extensively as a buoyancy medium in boats, rafts, buoys and other marine applications (Fig. XII-14). The use of extruded polystyrene foam in these applications eliminated two age-old problems inherent in air-tight chambers: punctures and corrosion. Special large sections of extruded polystyrene foam are produced and sold as "flotation" in making floating marinas, docks and life rafts.

Floral

Until the mid-forties, florists used moss as a base material in flower displays. Moss was dirty, hard to handle, and it was heavy, but it was the only thing available. As soon as extruded polystyrene was marketed, florists grasped its possibilities, and by 1947 it was already replacing moss as a floral base. Today it is the accepted "standard." It is clean, "featherweight," strong, and attractive. It can be cut into all kinds of shapes with a hot wire, coping saw, or penknife, and flower stems inserted in it will be held firmly in place.

With experience and ample chance to appreciate its beauty and workability, florists

Figure XII-14, large logs of extruded polystyrene foam support the floating dock and boat houses in this marina.

are extending its use into elaborate artistic displays. Extruded polystyrene is a fine artistic medium in its own right. Combine it with flowers and the possibilities are immense— trellises, bowers, seasonal scenes, period settings, local color effects, holiday ideas, and as many others as the florist can imagine.

Display and novelty

There are almost limitless artistic effects possible with extruded polystyrene. Extruded polystyrene has a crisp, snow-like appearance. It is simple to fashion it into three dimensional shapes and to color it with water colors or other suitable paints.

Anything from a simple decorative piece to a complete window display is readily possible. No other material is easier to "sculpt" and more attractive when finished. Counter exhibits, lifelike animals, holiday decorations, advertising signs and lures—all are easy to make with extruded polystyrene.

Packaging

The aesthetic qualities of extruded polystyrene are abetted by its structural strength to open yet another field, that of packaging. Delicate glass bottles, when packaged in extruded polystyrene, are protected against crushing and gain in sales appeal. Pharmaceutical items like anti-snake venom kits are protected in this way. For perfumes and cosmetics, the beauty of extruded polystyrene increases impulse buying. It is also practical as a packaging material for hardware, cutlery or tools.

Section XIII—EXPANDABLE POLYSTYRENE BEADS
PART I—MOLDING
By George C. Kiessling

I. DESCRIPTION OF EXPANDABLE POLYSTYRENE

Expandable polystyrene is the raw material for molding or extruding polystyrene foam. It consists of beads of polystyrene containing an integral expanding or blowing agent. These beads can be expanded into closed-cell foams ranging in density from ¾ to 20 lb per cu ft (Fig. XIII-1).

The polymer phase of expandable polystyrene is high molecular weight polystyrene containing 2000 to 3000 styrene (C_6H_5=CH=CH_2) units. From 5% to 8% of a low boiling point aliphatic hydrocarbon, such as pentane or petroleum ether, are incorporated into the polymer, which comes in the form of tiny spherical beads, 0.012 to 0.094 in. in diameter, or small cylindrical pellets measuring about 0.062 by 0.031 in. When the expandable beads thus prepared, weighing about 38 lb per cu ft, are heated above their softening temperature (190° to 200°F.), the internal pressure of the blowing agent causes the polymer to expand into a foamed structure. The degree of expansion can be controlled within the limits of 2 to 50 times the volume of the unexpanded beads.

Expandable polystyrene products are available in several different ranges of bead diameters. A typical large bead product, used for molding insulation and building panels, varies in bead diameter from 0.079 to 0.033 in. For molding packages, picnic coolers, and refrigerator components the medium bead product ranges from 0.047 to 0.023 in. diameter. A small bead type, varying from 0.033 to 0.016 in. in diameter, is used for molding insulated cups and other thin-wall items. In general, the bead size requirements for molding a foam article are determined in part by its density and in part by its minimum. wall thickness. Thus, a large bead product can be expanded to a low density (1 lb per cu ft) but it must be molded in heavy sections. A small bead product will have a higher density and can be molded into thinner sections.

Expandable polystyrene is available in two types. One type is used to make expanded polystyrene of Class 1 of ASTM D2125-62T: "Tentative Specification for Cellular Polystyrene," defined as "Natural or colored and not non-burning or self-extinguishing when tested in accordance with the Method of test for flammability of plastic foams and sheeting, ASTM D1692." The second type, often referred to as "SE" or "FR" type, is used to make expanded polystyrene of Class 2 of ASTM D2125-62T, defined as "Natural or colored and non-burning or self-extinguishing when tested in accordance with ASTM D1692." This Class 2 polystyrene foam may be described as "fire retardant" as defined by the National Fire Prevention Association in the "Handbook of Fire Prevention."

Expandable polystyrene in the form of pellets is used for both molding colored foam articles and extruding a variety of foam shapes, in a wide range of colors. These internally colored particles give deep color shades with uniform surface coloring and complete color penetration. Extrusion pellets contain special nucleating agents, in addition to the hydrocarbon blowing agent, to produce a uniform cell structure in the extruded sections and provide a smooth, satiny surface on the extrudate. The patented* additive system, normally a mixture of citric acid and sodium bicarbonate, can be modified to produce wide

*U.S. Patent 2,941,964

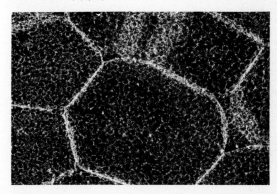

Figure XIII-1, cell structure of molded polystyrene foam of 1 lb per cu ft density.

variations in the cell size and rigidity of the extrudate.

Expandable polystyrene beads are manufactured by processes which combine suspension polymerization of styrene monomer with one of several procedures for incorporating the hydrocarbon blowing agent into the polystyrene beads. These procedures vary from incorporating the blowing agent into the monomer before polymerization to impregnating the beads in a pressure vessel, under conditions of elevated temperature and pressure, to force the hydrocarbon into the polystyrene beads.

In the suspension polymerization process, droplets of styrene monomer with catalyst are formed by controlled agitation in a reactor in the presence of organic or inorganic dispersants. Careful control of the process is necessary to provide the desired polymer bead size range, and control polymer molecular weight characteristics and blowing agent concentration. After cooling, the reactor product is washed to remove the dispersants, then dried. The beads are screened to remove oversize and undersize particles and to segregate the beads into different bead size products. In a final step, blending insures product uniformity. The beads are then packaged in shipping containers.

Expandable polystyrene pellets are manufactured by an extrusion process. Mixtures of expandable polystyrene beads, colorants, lubricants or nucleating agents are extruded in thin strands which are cooled and pelletized. The final pellets are usually screened to remove fines, blended and packaged.

In 1963 there were three commercial manufacturers of expandable polystyrene in the United States: (1) Koppers Co., Inc., Pittsburgh, Pa., (2) The Dow Chemical Co., Midland, Mich., and (3) United Cork Companies, Kearny, N.J. The total U.S. production capacity for expandable polystyrene was estimated at 75-million lb per year. In the remainder of the world, six other manufacturers of expandable polystyrene are reported: (1) Badische Anilin- & Soda-Fabrik AG, Ludwigshafen-am-Rhein, West Germany, (2) Shell Chemical Co. Ltd., London, Great Britain, (3) Sekisui Chemical Co., Japan, (4) Monsanto Chemical Co. Ltd., Great Britain, (5) BX Plastics Ltd., London, Great Britain, and (6) Brodr Sunde, Norway.

The properties of expandable polystyrene

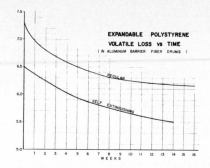

Figure XIII-2, loss of volatility with time.

which must be controlled to give satisfactory performance in the molding process are *volatile content* and *bead size*. For a given polystyrene base, the blowing agent concentration must be specified to assure suitable expandability and moldability for low density foam articles. For commercial expandable polystyrenes, the blowing agent concentration varies between 5 to 8% by weight. In some products small amounts of water are present in the expandable bead. Although concentrations of moisture below 0.5% by weight have no observable effect, higher amounts may have adverse effects on feeding the beads to continuous-type pre-expanders and may cause surface imperfections in the molded foam objects.

Because of a tendency to lose the volatile blowing agent, the shelf life of expandable polystyrene presents a problem to both raw material suppliers and expandable polystyrene molders. When stored at temperatures above 68°F or in containers which are not air-tight, the concentration of blowing agent in the expandable bead decreases slowly (Fig XIII-2). This volatile loss can adversely affect the expansion and molding of low density foams. Special containers with vapor barriers, lid gaskets and drum liners are used to minimize the volatile loss in storage and shipping. Since there is no control of environmental conditions during shipping and often in storage, the safe shelf-life for low density molding is limited to about 60 days. This is, of course, an extremely variable situation. With proper packaging and good control of storage conditions, shelf-life can be extended to several months. Several instances have been reported of expandable polystyrene over a year old being molded at densities of 3 to 5 lb per cu ft.

Blowing agent concentration is a factor in the expandability of expandable polystyrene.

Low concentrations of blowing agent will not allow a low density to be reached and may cause reduced production rates in the pre-expansion process. High concentrations of blowing agent may produce large cell expanded beads, which will tend to collapse and shrink during pre-expansion. This shrinkage raises the density of the foamed particles. Control of the amount of blowing agent in expandable polystyrene must be maintained within certain limits to give satisfactory expandability. This is not easy because of the variable shelf life described above, and because of the variety of end use requirements: density and processing equipment.

Expandability of expandable polystyrene is measured in terms of minimum bulk density achieved and time required to reach that density (time rate). In a continuous steam pre-expander, densities as low as 0.7 lb per cu ft can be reached. At a density of 1 lb per cu ft, production rates of 1000 lb per hr. have been reported, using a large expander with a tank capacity of 200 gallons.

The expandability of expandable polystyrene is also affected by the size of the beads. Because of their smaller surface-to-volume ratio, large beads retain the blowing agent longer than small beads and can be expanded to lower densities at faster rates. Bead size is usually expressed in terms of through, or on, a mesh number as defined in the U.S. Standard Sieve Series. Thus, a large bead product is typically through No. 8 mesh and on No. 16 mesh (8x16). A general purpose bead product is through No. 10 mesh and on No. 20 mesh (10x20). A medium product is through No. 16 mesh and on No. 30 mesh (16x30), while a small bead product is through No. 20 mesh and on No. 40 mesh (20x40). The chief criterion for selecting a bead size is the minimum wall thickness acceptable in the application. The decision is made by considering the actual diameter of the bead, when expanded, in relation to the critical dimensions of the object (Fig XIII-3).

The basic molding process for producing polystyrene foam objects from expandable polystyrene beads consists in heating the beads to a temperature from 200°F to 230°F. A uniform cellular structure is obtained and the polystyrene exhibits slight plastic flow. At that temperature, the surface of the expanding beads is somewhat sticky or tacky. As the cellular structure is being formed, internal

Figure XIII-3, enlarged view of polystyrene foam beads.

pressure builds up by vaporization of the blowing agent. This results in a huge volume increase and density decrease. The molding process takes advantage of this tacky bead surface and internal pressure buildup to fuse or weld the beads together into a relatively homogeneous foam.

Raw expandable polystyrene beads can be charged directly into a mold, expanded, and fused into the mold cavity, but this method has serious drawbacks. As some movement of the beads during expansion is necessary for filling the mold cavity, it is difficult to obtain uniform density in the molded article. Also, the molding of foam with a density below 3 lb per cu ft is extremely difficult.

A more satisfactory procedure is a two-step process which involves a pre-expansion of the raw beads to a density approximately equivalent to the density required in the molded article. Then the mold is completely filled with these pre-expanded beads, and they are fused together.

Molding of pre-expanded beads is performed in a closed mold which confines the expansion of the beads as they are heated so that they are pressed together on all sides. Fusing of the pre-expanded beads into a homogeneous molding is accomplished by injecting steam directly into the cavity, through small holes drilled into the mold from a steam chest which surrounds the cavity. As the foam particles expand, steam and water are expelled through the same perforations because of internal pressure buildup. The molded foam object is removed from the mold after this internal pressure has fallen off by cooling.

2. PRE-EXPANSION OF EXPANDABLE POLYSTYRENE

Expandable polystyrene can be pre-expanded by the application of heat from a variety of sources: (1) steam, (2) hot air, (3) radiant heater, (4) hot water and (5) oven. Steam is most commonly used because it is the cheapest and most efficient heat source readily available in most manufacturing plants. In the U.S. a continuous steam pre-expansion process is widely used. In this process, expandable polystyrene beads are fed continuously into the lower part of an upright drum at atmospheric pressure. A steam venturi aspirates the beads from an external hopper and delivers them into the drum where they are steam-expanded. Revolving agitators keep the beads in motion as they expand, preventing fusion inside the drum. The pre-expanded polystyrene beads overflow in a continuous stream from an outlet near the top of the drum and are conveyed to storage. Pre-expanded beads produced by this process are free-flowing and essentially dry after their transfer by air through a duct.

Steam is also used in another continuous process in which beads, spread on a conveyor belt, are passed through a steam chamber and then dropped off the end of the belt into a bin. Agglomeration of the pre-expanded beads into fused lumps or clusters may be a problem in this process.

A third process using steam involves the batch expansion of beads in a pressure chamber. Low steam pressures of 8 to 10 psi are used and the beads are agitated by a stirrer to prevent lumping. This method can be used to pre-expand to densities as low as 0.5 lb per cu ft.

Pre-expansion in air heated to temperatures of 210° to 240°F can be carried out using equipment similar to that employed for steam pre-expansion. Both continuous and batch processes have been successfully used. Commercial equipment for hot air pre-expansion is available. The chief disadvantage of using hot air is the slow rate of expansion because of the low heat capacity of air as compared to that of condensing steam. Reported advantages are a reduction in required aging before molding and shorter cooling time.

Expandable polystyrene was first pre-expanded commercially in the U.S. by radiant heat. The process is performed on a conveyor belt which passes a monolayer of raw beads under a bank of electric heating elements. The intense heat causes the beads to expand to densities as low as 2 lb per cu ft. This operation is relatively simple. Final bulk of the pre-expanded beads is controlled by the speed of the belt and the height of the heaters above the belt. The slower the speed, the lower the density of the product. As expansion occurs, the individual beads tend to sinter or fuse together. This lightly adhered material forms a lacy network which can be broken up at the end of the belt by rotating intermeshing rods or by feeding the lace directly into a blower and blowing them into storage. If the beads are fed onto the belt in excess, the lacy network may become too heavy and puff up high enough to touch the heaters and cause a fire. Attempting to produce too low a density by running the belt too slowly will cause bead shrinkage; this material will not mold properly because of excessive loss of blowing agent. One of the advantages of radiant heat pre-expansion is the very uniform density obtained. The chief disadvantage is a lower density limit of 2 lb per cu ft.

Hot water pre-expansion is used only where small amounts of expandable polystyrene are pre-expanded for experimental or laboratory applications. In this process, the raw beads are submerged in near-boiling water. As expansion occurs, the beads must be stirred to prevent them from sticking together. The natural buoyancy of the pre-expanded beads allows their removal from the surface when agitation is stopped. The pre-expanded beads must be thoroughly dried before measuring their density and before they can be molded satisfactorily.

Oven pre-expansion is also suitable for laboratory applications. For experimental work, densities of 2 lb per cu ft may be obtained by sprinkling a monolayer of beads on a tray and placing the tray in an oven at approximately 275°F. Expansion will require at least two minutes. Too heavy a layer on the tray will cause the expanding beads to agglomerate in a lacy network.

Control of the pre-expansion process is extremely important because any variation of density in molded polystyrene foam depends to a great degree upon the variation of density in the pre-expanded beads. Many problems in the molding process, such as shrinking, warping, and non-uniform surfaces, can be attributed to density variations of the pre-expanded beads. Good control of density during pre-expansion can be achieved by careful attention to the variables in the process. The method of measuring bulk density of pre-expanded beads must be carefully standardized and results must be correlated with density of molded items. Use of a large sample for bulk density measurements is preferred over a small sample. Good control of the steam temperature, pressure and quality is required. In the continuous steam pre-expander, a working steam pressure of 12 to 15 psig at the feeder is used. The actual pressure is not critical, but it is essential that the pressure remain constant during operation of the pre-expander. A change in steam pressure affects other variables such as the feed rate and the air-to-steam ratio. Fluctuating pressure may cause plugging in the bead feeder tube. The quality of the steam used for pre-expansion has generally no appreciable effect on the density of the expanded beads, but extremely wet steam may cause moisture build-up in the feeder tube and result in stoppage of the bead feed. On the other extreme, very dry steam may be too hot, and cause the expandable polystyrene beads to fuse together prematurely in the pre-expander. The usual practice is to add air to the steam in order to reduce its temperature. In some situations when it is not possible to add air to the steam, degrading the steam quality may overcome lumping and still allow low density to be reached. It is a good practice to equip a continuous steam pre-expander with a thermometer as near to the bead inlet as possible. This will allow the operator to maintain optimum conditions for different density requirements.

Safety precautions should be taken when increasing the feed rate to the pre-expander. Too high a rate can damage the machine: an ammeter will indicate the overload on the drive motor and by quick action it may be possible to forestall trouble. Opening the clean-out door will allow the pre-expander to dump its charge quickly. A less drastic measure is to stop the feed of beads to the funnel so that it will be emptied and allow the feed tube to draw in cold air. The cold air will instantly reduce the load on the stirrer. In returning to normal operation, cold air should be shut off gradually. If the stirrer has stalled, fusion can be reduced by: (1) stopping the steam flow instantly, (2) removing or opening the lid of the pre-expander drum, (3) pouring cold water into the drum, (4) opening the clean-out door in the side of the drum, (5) putting high velocity compressed air into the drum. If over-

working of the agitator occurs for any appreciable length of time, the motor may overheat, the stirrer drive may break, or the V-belt may slip. Complete stoppage of the agitator, whether due to overload or power failure, will allow the pre-expanded beads to fuse into a solid mass which would be extremely difficult to remove. It is wise to equip the pre-expander with automatic safety controls which would operate in case of power failure: they would stop the steam supply, cool the feeder assembly, inject cold water or compressed air into the machine.

An efficient method of recovering the lumps that may form in the machine is to pass them through a grinder, which will break them up into smaller particles; often individual pre-expanded beads can be recovered if the lumps are only lightly fused. These beads can then be mixed with the rest of pre-expanded beads for use in the molding process.

The use of an external additive on the beads, such as zinc stearate or a surfactant that tends to hold moisture on their surface may, to a certain extent, avoid lumping. These additives, however, may interfere with proper fusion in the molding process and in certain applications such as insulation board or picnic coolers may result in poor water-resistant properties. On the other hand, any material on the bead surface which tends to plasticize polystyrene at expansion temperature may also cause lumping: lubricating oil, waxes, mineral oil or condensed hydrocarbon blowing agent are examples of such materials. Blowing agent may condense on the surface when containers of expandable polystyrene beads are subjected to changes in temperature during shipping and upon delivery to the molder's plant. Many cases of lumping in fresh shipments were overcome by merely removing the lids from containers and allowing the beads to remain exposed to air. Lack of sufficient agitation in the tank and non-uniform movement of the beads in the feed tube may also result in lumping. Lumping can be reduced by using a larger pre-expander, reducing the bead feed rate or using large size beads. Generally, pre-expansion of low-density beads will result in more lumping than pre-expansion of a high-density material.

Currently there are three trends in the area of pre-expansion which bear watching. The first is the need for expanding beads at *increased rates* and to *lower densities*. Because of the rapid increase in molding capacity of expandable polystyrene in the U.S., many plants are struggling to keep costs down by faster pre-expanding. Improvements in continuous steam pre-expansion are expected to meet this requirement. Lower densities will also be obtained by new processes, but this may require development of improved batch techniques with greater control of expansion conditions. Pre-expansion to a density of ½ lb per cu ft requires excellent control of heating, agitation and cooling to avoid shrinkage or damage to the light, tender foam particles.

A second trend is toward more *uniformity* in the actual density of beads expanded in the continuous process. Experiments have shown that the residence time of expandable polystyrene beads in a continuous steam pre-expander can vary from one to twelve minutes while producing 1 lb per cu ft pre-expanded beads. In saturated steam @ 212°F a one-minute exposure of the beads results in a density of 1.4 lb per cu ft, while a twelve-minute exposure results in a density of 0.97 lb per cu ft (Fig XIII-4). Since this range of density also signifies a spread in bead diameter in the expanded foam particles, this can result in mold filling problems, particularly for critical thin-walled items. It is expected that improved batch pre-expansion techniques will be developed to correct this difficulty.

The third trend is the interest in *hot-air (or dry-heat) pre-expansion*. There have been several approaches to this type of process. One involves a batch technique method with a converted hot air clothes dryer. Another involves a continuous method with a venturi feeding system and hot air injected separately into an agitated tank. A third approach is a continuous process with screw-conveyor feed, and heating of the beads indirectly with steam in a heat-exchange. This last expander provides a small steam injection port for additional heat, for better performance at low densities. The hot air pre-expansion process has the advantage of producing bone-dry pre-expanded beads, which age very quickly and can be molded with shorter cooling cycles. Reduced aging seems to come from the absence on the bead surface of water which hinders air absorption into the cellular structure. Shorter cooling cycles probably come from the greater loss of blowing agent during hot air pre-expansion, because of longer exposure to heat in the dry process. Disadvantages of hot-air pre-expansion are the low production rates

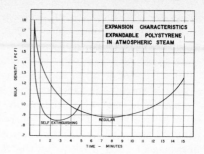

Figure XIII-4, expansion characteristics of polystyrene foam in steam at low pressure.

and the difficulty in obtaining a low density. Improvements in this type of process are anticipated. A worthwhile solution may come from a combination of steam and hot-air pre-expansion.

3. STABILIZATION OF PRE-EXPANDED FOAM PARTICLES

Fresh steam pre-expanded beads are moist, warm and pliable. Since a partial vacuum has been created within the cells of these particles, they deform very easily and shrink if subjected to mechanical or thermal shocks. This sensitivity to shrinkage is greater at low densities. In order to be suitable for molding into foam shapes without shrinkage or collapse, the pre-expanded beads must be aged or stored in well-ventilated bins to allow stabilization of pressure within the cells. The length of aging varies inversely with the density. Thus, 6 hours aging will normally be satisfactory for 2 lb per cu ft and higher, while 12 hours may be required for 1 lb per cu ft pre-expanded beads. If the beads are very wet, aging time must be extended. Normally, airveying (conveying by air) of the pre-expanded beads from pre-expander to storage bin will dry them sufficiently to avoid excessive aging time. There is evidence that aging can be shortened by hot-air drying of the beads during transfer or in the storage bin.

Accelerated aging may, however, shorten the usable molding life of the beads because of a more rapid loss of blowing agent at higher temperature: pre-expanded beads have a limited shelf life because of this loss of blowing agent. Since the rate of blowing agent loss is governed by the external surface area of the pre-expanded beads as well as by the storage temperature, small beads have a shorter shelf life than large beads. Normally, large beads stored at room temperature can be molded satisfactorily up to 3 weeks after pre-expansion while small beads have a shelf life of a few days only.

Efforts are being made to eliminate this stabilization step in the expandable polystyrene molding process. Its elimination will be a major contribution to the development of an integrated molding system. Hot air or dry pre-expansion shows promise as ways to speed up stabilization, but further development of these and other treatments are necessary.

4. MOLDING OF PRE-EXPANDED FOAM PARTICLES

The next step in processing expandable polystyrene is the molding process which generally consists of: (1) charging the pre-expanded beads into a mold, (2) heating the bead particles to fuse them together and complete expansion of the foam, and (3) cooling the molded foam until it is stable enough to be removed from the mold. There are several possible molding techniques which differ from one another in the way heat is introduced to the material. Selection of the best technique depends on a variety of factors, including the size, configuration, density and maximum thickness of the finished part, as well as the volume of required production. The possible molding techniques are briefly summarized in the following paragraphs. (See also Section III, Part 3.)

Steam chest molding

In this method saturated, low-pressure steam is introduced directly into the mold cavity through core box vents or small holes drilled through the mold walls from a steam chest. The mold itself consists of a double-wall cavity with the inner wall perforated. Single and multiple cavity molds of this type are usually held in hydraulic or air cylinder clamping presses. This method has become the most widely used molding technique for expandable polystyrene. Nearly all the commercial molding presses are designed for application of this method.

Autoclave molding

Articles can be successfully molded by exposing a filled, perforated mold to the steam chamber of an autoclave. The mold is cooled after its removal from the autoclave. Production rates can be reasonably high, with high mold costs.

Steam probe molding

For most foaming-in-place applications, sandwich construction and filling of large areas with thick sections, steam probes can be used to introduce the steam into the mold cavities. Aluminum, brass or copper perforated tubes are connected to a source of steam. For molding, the steam probe is inserted into the cavity filled with pre-expanded polystyrene beads and steam is injected into the material. The probe is then immediately withdrawn and the expansion of the foam fills the space previously occupied by the probe. Cooling is carried out in air, by immersion in water or by water spraying.

Conducted heat molding

This method involves the use of molds which do not provide for direct introduction of steam into the cavity from a steam chest. Heating of the pre-expanded material is accomplished by conduction of heat through the metal mold to the foam particles. This method is suitable for uniform thin wall moldings, such as cups; it is not recommended for molding foam thicknesses greater then $\frac{1}{4}$ inch.

High-frequency molding

It has been demonstrated that high-frequency dielectric energy is a suitable source of heat for molding pre-expanded beads. This technique does not utilize metal molds, but less costly plastic molds. When pre-expanded beads wetted with an additive that modifies their dielectric properties are exposed to a high-frequency field, expansion and fusion of the beads take place. This process offers several potential advantages over other techniques. It is a relatively clean process and yields a dry foam article. At present the biggest obstacle to the commercialization of high-frequency molding is the lack of suitable automated mold clamping and cooling systems.

Hot water molding

In this method, a self-clamped mold is immersed into hot water at a temperature of 208 to 212°F. The mold cavity must be perforated and vented to allow hot water to enter and heat up the pre-expanded foam particles. As the foam particles complete their expansion and fuse together, the water is forced back out of the perforations and vents. The hot water method cannot be used to mold polystyrene foam with densities below 3 lbs per cu ft, but the objects produced can have a much higher density.

Hot air molding

Hot air may be substituted for steam in molding expandable polystyrene by the steam methods described above. Its use, however, is not economical because of the longer heating times required. This method would have the obvious advantage of producing dry molded parts, but it is not a commercial technique because of the relatively high cost of hot air and the lower production rates of the process.

The commercial steam molding process

The greatest quantities of expandable polystyrene are processed today by the steam molding process. This method offers advantages of relatively low capital equipment and tooling costs and a capability for molding a wide range of polystyrene foam products. Commercial steam molding techniques are employed for molding large insulation blocks, 12 ft x 4 ft x 20 in, of 1 lb per cu ft density.

They are also employed for molding small hot-drink cups which weigh 2.5 grams each, have a foam density of 4.5 lb per cu ft and a wall thickness of 0.080 in. Molding of picnic coolers, packaging and refrigeration components, building panels and flotation equipment is carried out with steam (Fig XIII-5).

The steam chest molding method is also widely used because it can be performed automatically. The ready availability of automatic processing equipment is one of the major reasons for the continuing rapid growth of expandable polystyrene molding (See Section III, Part 3).

Although the equipment requirements for molding expandable polystyrene will vary with the type of foam product being molded, certain basic processing equipment is required. This equipment includes: (1) steam boiler, (2) pre-expander, (3) pre-expanded bead transfer system, (4) storage bins, (5) holding presses, (6) molds, (7) trimming and finishing equipment and (8) other auxiliary equipment such as scrap grinders, vacuum cleaners, etc. The capital investment in equipment and building area will depend upon the production capacity

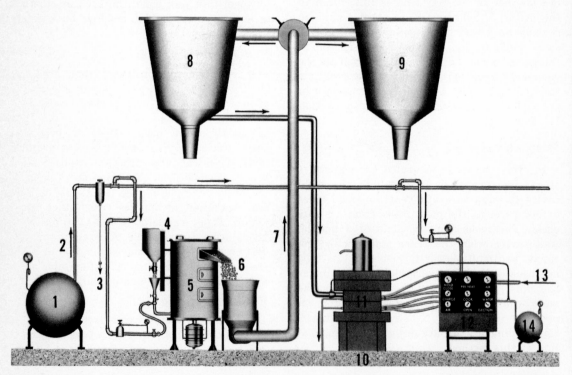

Figure XIII-5, flow diagram of the polystyrene bead molding process. Key: 1) Boiler; 2) Steam; 3) To sewer; 4) Raw beads; 5) Pre-expander; 6) Pre-expanded beads; 7) Airveying system; 8) Pre-expanded bead storage bag; 9) Storage bag; 10) Molding press; 11) Mold; 12) Molding controller; 13) Water; and 14) Air.

of the operation and the type of foam products being manufactured. The molding cycle used in the steam molding process consists of: (1) preheating, (2) filling, (3) fusion, (4) cooling and (5) ejection (Fig XIII-6).

Preheating

Successful molding of 1 lb per cu ft foam usually requires a preheated mold. At higher densities preheating is optional, but it offers the advantage of reducing the formation of steam condensate during fusion. When water collects on mold cavity walls in significant quantity, it interferes with the heating of the pre-expanded foam particles and prevents good fusion. Preheating is also recommended when surface appearance is important. A hot mold surface gives a smoother, more glossy appearance to the molded object. If the mold is preheated to too high a temperature, foam parts may stick to the metal surfaces. Preheating tends to lengthen the overall molding cycle, because of the additional time required for heating and cooling.

Filling

Mold cavities are completely filled with pre-expanded beads of a bulk density equal to the foam density desired in the finished part. There are several methods of mold filling: (1) gravity filling, (2) blow filling, (3) vacuum filling and (4) pressure filling.

Gravity filling is used for very large molds such as those used for molding insulation blocks. The pre-expanded beads are simply dropped into the box-like mold from an overhead bin until it is filled. Single and multicavity molds can be filled by gravity if the complete volume of the mold cavity is in the lower chest of a vertical press and there is a flat plate for the top. To obtain a good molded product, molds should be completely filled before fusion. Mold configurations or core obstructions sometimes cause the material to form voids. A positive fill may be achieved by the aid of pneumatic, hydraulic or electromagnetic *vibrator packers* suitably attached to the mold.

Blow filling is the technique most widely used in the commercial molding of expandable polystyrene. Blow filling is the conveying of pre-expanded beads into a mold by the use of compressed air. The stream of air passes through a venturi device and pulls the beads along with it into the mold. The air must be

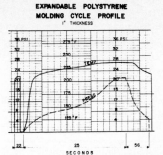

EXPANDABLE POLYSTYRENE
MOLDING CYCLE PROFILE
I" THICKNESS

Figure XIII-6, molding cycle curve.

bled or vented from the mold as fast as it flows in. Improper mold venting may cause unfilled corners or voids. The holes incorporated in a mold for steam injection are usually suitable for air venting. If a corner of a mold is incompletely filled, drilling a vent hole in this corner will allow the air to escape. The air pressure used for mold filling depends on the design of the mold and its vents. Too high an air pressure will cause eddy currents in the mold and prevent complete fill of the cavity. Too low an air pressure will not provide enough force to push the pre-expanded beads into all parts of the mold cavity. In molding higher density foam, the weep holes and rough lands of the molds can serve as vents for blow filling. Since the molding of densities below 2 lb per cu ft requires relatively tight molds to obtain good fusion, it is necessary to provide means other than holes for venting. This venting is provided by *cracking,* or opening the mold a fraction of an inch during the blow filling operation. Modern molding machines are equipped with devices to stop the mold closing action at a cracked position to allow proper venting. When filling is completed, the mold is closed. Advantages of blow filling over gravity fill methods are: (a) more uniform part densities are obtained since the operator is not a factor in the operation; (b) mold filling is much faster; (c) since the mold is filled in the closed position, flash is eliminated; (d) spillage and waste are kept to a minimum; (e) thinner wall sections and more complex parts are possible.

Vacuum filling of molds is carried out with a vacuum applied through the steam chest or a screened aperture with an aspirator or industrial vacuum system. Industrial vacuum systems capable of developing a vacuum of at least 75 in. of water can be used.

Pressure filling is used to fill molds which cannot be vented enough for successful filling with aspirators. A pressure vessel with a conical bottom is filled with pre-expanded beads, closed and then filled with air to a controlled pressure. When a tube from the vessel to the mold is opened, a very dense stream of beads is pushed by the air pressure into the mold. This system requires less mold venting than does the blow filling method. Filling must be shut down intermittently to refill the vessel with beads. High air pressure tends to pack the beads in the mold too tightly resulting in a product of excessive density. Unless means are provided to control air pressure in the vessel, the pressure will drop as the level of beads drops. This may result in non-uniform filling and variations in part weights. This method is not recommended.

Fusion

Once the mold is filled with pre-expanded beads and tightly closed, steam is injected into the mold cavity to effect further bead expansion and fuse the foam particles to each other. The fusion step is probably the most critical one of the cycle. The techniques and conditions used in fusing pre-expanded polystyrene beads into a polystyrene foam object have a significant effect on the overall length of the molding cycle and the physical appearance and properties of the molded foam. Chief factors to be considered are quality of the steam and steaming conditions used in cooking or fusing the foam.

The dryest possible steam should be used to fuse expanded foam particles. Wet steam introduces water into the mold cavity which intereferes with fusing. Wet steam also lengthens the fusion step because of the time required to heat up the water which collects in the mold. Water tends to increase the cooling portion of the cycle and the amount of moisture entrapped in the molded foam. The quality of the steam should be controlled by using short steam lines with as few fittings as possible, insulating or lagging the steam lines, installing sufficient steam traps or steam separators to remove entrained moisture and providing air vents at the ends of steam mains.

To obtain a well-fused polystyrene foam molding, it is necessary to drive out air and condensate in the mold and then to develop steam pressure and temperature within the mold to complete the expansion and fusion of the beads. The steaming part of the cycle should be carried out as rapidly as possible to avoid collection of excessive amounts of condensate and to obtain a fast cycle. Densities below 2 lb per cu ft should be cooked rapidly, for a few seconds only. Higher densities will tolerate a much slower cooking cycle. If the steaming cycle is too long, the foam will shrink and collapse because of overheating. If the steaming cycle is too short, the pre-expanded

Table XIII-1—Typical Properties of Molded Expandable Polystyrene

	Density, lb per cu ft					
	1.0	2.0	3.0	4.0	5.0	6.0
Tensile strength, psi						
(speed—0.05 in./min)						
@ −25°F	30	60	81			
@ 73°F	33	49	67		128	
@ 160°F	30	50	68			
Ultimate elongation, %	4	5	3	2		
Compressive strength, psi						
(speed—0.05 in./min)						
@ −25°F	18	41	46			
@ 73°F	19	29	45		92	
@ 160°F	12	26	38			
Flexural strength, psi						
(speed—0.10 in./min)						
@ −25°F	41	73	107			
@ 73°F	45	72	100		260	
@ 160°F	36	69	100			
Compressive set, %						
(speed—0.05 in./min)						
after 10% compression	2.3		3.8			
after 20% compression	5.4		9.8			
after 30% compression	10.3		17.7			
after 40% compression	14.3		24.3			
Thermal conductivity, Btu/hr-sq ft-°F/in.	0.258	0.242	0.243	0.244	0.246	0.251
Deflection, inches						
@ 125°F for 2 hr	0.004	0.005		0.009		0.006
@ 125°F for 6 hr	0.021	0.022		0.010		0.007
@ 125°F for 14 hr	0.023	0.025		0.014		0.011
@ 175°F for 2 hr	0.134	0.100		0.059		0.099
@ 175°F for 6 hr	0.197	0.144		0.094		0.122
@ 175°F for 14 hr	0.207	0.144		0.094		0.121
Water vapor transmission, grams/24 hr/meter²	11.8	8.2	5.0		3.5	
Dielectric constant,						
60 cps			1.19			
1 mc			1.02			
Dissipation factor,						
60 cps ± 10⁻⁴			6			
1 mc ± 10⁻⁴			6			
Dielectric strength, vpm						
short time			48			
step-by-step			49			
Volume resistivity, ohm-cm × 10¹³			3.8			
Noise reduction coefficient,						
plain surface			0.24			
perforated			0.25			

beads will not be adequately fused. When fusion of the foam inside the mold has been completed, the foam itself will seal off the steam entry ports. This event is signaled by a build-up of steam pressure in the mold steam chest, and indicates the completion of the fusion step. In automatic molding, the steaming cycle is controlled either by a timer, or by a device which reacts to a preset back pressure in the steam chest. When no preheating is used in the molding process, it is usually advantageous to leave the drain line valves open for the first few seconds of steaming. This allows most of the condensate to be blown from the chest rather than forced into the mold cavity where it would hinder fusion.

When steaming has been completed, there are significant variations in the temperatures throughout the foam, which cause a density gradient in the molded object. This density gradient can be minimized by molding with the lowest steam temperature that will give an adequate quality of fusion.

Cooling

Cooling the molded foam so that it can be removed is usually accomplished by circulating water through the steam chest or by spraying water on the mold cavity walls by means of nozzles inside the chest (Fig XIII-7). Since polystyrene foam is an excellent thermal insulator, cooling is usually the longest step in the molding cycle, and may require several minutes. Higher density foam requires more cooling time than foam of a lower density, and thicker sections need longer cooling than thin sections. If the mold is opened before the exterior of the molded foam has hardened or before the interior is sufficiently cool, post-expansion is caused by the inability of the cooled outer foam layers to hold the internal expansion pressure in the center of the molded foam. The molded object should be removed from the mold only after the foam has cooled sufficiently to reduce this internal pressure to the point where it can be retained by the hardened outer shell. The cooling time depends upon steaming temperature and thickness of the molded foam. The presence of water in molded foam increases the cooling time because moisture in the mold cavity must also be cooled.

A very promising technique for reducing cooling time in the molding of expandable polystyrene is the use of vacuum applied to the mold steam chest. The vacuum draws out

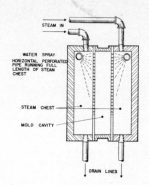

Figure XIII-7, diagram of typical polystyrene bead mold.

steam and moisture from the foam and speeds up cooling. In addition, the vacuum pulls the foam tighter against the mold surface and thereby improves heat transfer and gives better support to the foam structure at a stage when the hot foam is particularly sensitive to collapse and shrinkage. Other techniques which tend to reduce cooling time involve treatment of the pre-expanded beads to lower the quantity of blowing agent needed. Lowering the amount of residual blowing agent in the pre-expanded beads results in a reduction in pressure buildup in the mold cavity during fusion. The lower the internal pressure, the quicker it can be contained in a cooled foam shell. One technique for lowering blowing agent concentration is simply to age the pre-expanded beads in storage bins for several days: the volatile blowing agent is weathered away. Another technique consists of crushing individual, freshly pre-expanded beads and then re-expanding such flattened beads to the desired density. The re-expanded beads are finally molded in the usual fashion. This crushing treatment yields pre-expanded beads that mold extremely well at cooling times which are 40% to 60% of normal times. The chief drawback to the crushing process is that it requires extremely close control of all variables in the process. Commercial equipment is not yet available for using the crushed-bead technique.

Ejection

There are several possible ways of removing molded foam objects from mold cavities, such as: (1) manually lifting out the finished part, (2) floating the foam part out by blasting compressed air between the piece and the mold wall, (3) applying air pressure through the steam chest, (4) applying air pressure through an air ejection header system (this is sometimes necessary for cavity molds where it would be difficult to maintain air pressure on a steam chest), (5) using air-actuated or mechanically-actuated large-area knockout plugs, and (6) using mechanical stripper plates.

Molded foam pieces will tend to stick in the mold cavities if the foam is insufficiently cooled and continues to exert a post-expansion pressure upon the mold surface. If too high a steam temperature is used, sticking of the foam to the hot metal surface may occur. The use of Teflon-coated molds or of a silicone spray release agent may be desirable to facilitate removal of finished object.

5. MOLDING OF FOAMED POLYSTYRENE INSULATION BLOCKS

At present, one of the largest single uses of foamed polystyrene is for insulation board. Foam blocks as large as 12′ x 4′ x 20″ are molded from expandable polystyrene and cut into board or sheet for thermal insulation. Expanded polystyrene board is a commercial low-temperature insulation for cold-storage space, refrigerator display cases, industrial coolers, and low temperature piping. In refrigerated transportation, it serves as insulation in railway cars and truck trailers. In buildings, expanded polystyrene board is used as perimeter insulation, plaster base and roof insulation. Another current application is as aluminum siding backerboard. Generally speaking, the combination of thermal insulation property and mechanical strength of foamed polystyrene is used to advantage in the building and construction field.

Insulation board of foamed polystyrene is cut from large foam blocks of about 1 lb per cu ft density: although most of the general molding principles apply to block molding, the use of low-density material requires certain specialized techniques.

Beads slightly under 1 lb per cu ft are produced by steam pre-expansion. Since the expansion rate at this low density is relatively slow, most block-molding operations require a large size pre-expander (200-gallon size). Even minor variations in density are undesirable for block molding and extreme care should be taken to prevent shrinkage of the pre-expanded beads. Sudden thermal or physical shocks immediately after pre-expansion are a primary cause of shrinkage and should be avoided. Low density pre-expanded foam particles should not be passed directly through a fanner-blower since the fresh pre-expanded beads will increase in density upon impact with the fanner-blower impeller. The use of warm air to transfer the beads from pre-expansion tank to aging bins helps to prevent shrinkage and also tends to speed up the stabilization period. For block-molding 1 lb per cu ft pre-expanded beads should be aged at least 12 hours between pre-expansion and molding. Stabilization of pre-expanded beads is normally carried out in storage bins constructed of open weave canvas or wire screening, as it is important that these bins be well ventilated. Generally, indoor storage bins are used; for outdoor storage, precautions should be taken to keep the ventilated bins at approximately room temperature.

Mold design for block-molding must permit minimum cycle time for technical and economic reasons. The less mold metal to be heated, the drier the fusing steam will be in the mold cavity because steam condensation will be minimized. The drier the pre-expanded beads at the moment of fusion, the lower the steam pressure required. Designing the mold with the least amount of metal will also minimize the cooling time required.

Both batch and continuous molding processes are used for the commercial molding of foam polystyrene insulation blocks. In the batch process, a stationary mold is used, consisting of an open rectangular frame enclosed between two perforated steam chests. When closed, the steam chests are clamped tightly against the frame. For opening, the steam chests are unclamped and the frame drawn from between them. Final step is to remove the foam block from the frame. The top of the mold is usually hinged for gravity filling. In most commercial molds, steam chests cover the sides of the block as well as the two larger faces. The steam passages between the chests and the mold cavity should be of ample size, and may be holes, slots, core box vents, or screens.

It is desirable to expel as completely as possible all air in the chests and in the beads charged in the mold cavity. If air becomes trapped in some portion of the mold cavity, it may prevent access of steam to that portion and retard fusion. If air becomes mixed with steam, the mixture contains less heat energy than straight steam at the same pressure. Air may be driven out with low-pressure steam, with the drain lines open. Cooling of the fused block can be accomplished by water spray or water cascade on the mold walls. The drain outlets from the steam chest must be so located as to provide rapid and complete drainage of the condensate and cooling water. A specially-designed pressure gauge built into the mold will measure the expansion pressures and indicate completion of the cooling cycle; this will prevent post-expansion or excessive shrinkage. For a reasonable production rate with minimum manpower, the mold must be equipped with automatic devices to control steam and water, load the mold, lock it and unload it quickly. Several commercial designs of block-molds are currently available with varying degrees of automation. In the continuous process for molding foam polystyrene insulation blocks, pre-expanded polystyrene beads are fed continuously into a space formed by four continuous metal conveyor bands. In the first section, the bands are perforated so that steam may be introduced from steam chambers fitted wih adequate seals. The beads are fused in the first section. As the foam block moves forward, it is cooled in the second section and finally cut to the required lengths.

6. AUTOMATIC MOLDING

In recent years, foamed polystyrene has gained wide acceptance in an ever increasing variety of applications which take advantage of its unique combination of properties: (1) high strength-to-weight ratio, (2) excellent thermal insulation, (3) outstanding shock absorbency, (4) good moisture resistance, and (5) broad chemical inertness. It is used to package a multitude of industrial, consumer and military items. In a great variety of packaging applications, it has demonstrated outstanding savings in over-all packaging costs through: (1) elimination of damage, (2) lower shipping weight, and (3) reduced package assembly labor. In addition, the eye appeal, product identification and re-use features of foam packages are extra dividends which help sell the product inside (Figs XIII-8 and XIII-9).

Large quantities of expandable polystyrene are also used for molding foam picnic coolers, insulated beverage jugs, and ice buckets (Fig XIII-10). The good insulation and lightweight characteristics of polystyrene foam are used to advantage in these containers which are used to transport food and beverages and to keep them cool. Such items are being used in ever increasing numbers by the outdoor sports-

Figure XIII-8, molded foam package for watt-hour meters.

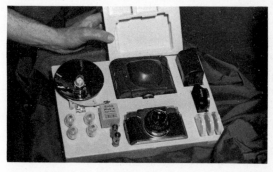

Figure XIII-9, molded polystyrene foam package for camera shipment and display.

Figure XIII-10, molded polystyrene foam picnic cooler.

Figure XIII-11, molded polystyrene foam hot drinking cup.

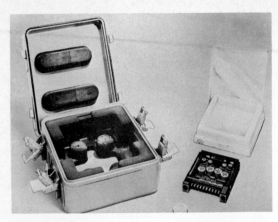

Figure XIII-12, molded package of polystyrene foam for shipment of delicate electronic equipment. Volume is 70% of previous aluminum case, weight is substantially lower and cost is about $35 below original package. Courtesy General Electric Ordnance Dept.

man, the traveler, the vacationer and the family on an outdoor picnic. Year-round uses have also appeared when the coolers are used as storage bins and packing cases. In a wide variety of color combinations, the insulated coolers and picnic chests are marketed in most retail variety, hardware and drug stores at popular prices.

An outstanding example of the growth of the molded expandable polystyrene market is the foam hot drink cup. From essentially zero in 1960, this application has grown to over two billion cups in 1964. Strong, lightweight foam cups are competitive with coated hot drink paper cups in cost and outperform them in heat retention and comfort characteristics (Fig XIII-11).

In all three of the above foamed polystyrene application areas, one of the chief reasons for success in the market is the development of fast, automatic molding equipment which can produce good quality foam articles at high production rates. The increased efficiency of newly developed machines has enabled molders to reduce manufacturing costs and bring the advantages of molded foamed polystyrene to the home and the industrial plant.

Automatic molding machines are available for processing polystyrene foam using an automated molding process. With this type of equipment which uses timer control of the molding cycle elements, polystyrene foam parts can be molded in continuous production with a minimum of labor. In the automatic molding

process, preheating of the molds, blow filling of the pre-expanded polystyrene foam beads into the mold cavities, fusion of the foam article, cooling of the mold, opening of the molds and ejection of the molded foam item are controlled by a system of timers and electrically operated switches.

The majority of modern steam molding machines are designed with horizontal operation of the machine clamp. If automatic ejection of the molded item is desired, the use of a horizontal acting clamp is almost mandatory. In all expanded polystyrene molding involving foam articles with variable cross sections and deep draws, careful attention must be paid to the design of the metal mold. Each new mold is usually a separate problem. Design of the molded part itself must be carefully considered to avoid problems of insufficient fill and poor steam distribution during fusion. Frequently, the establishment of the molding procedure for a new mold involves trial and error work to vary both the actual design of the metal mold itself and the molding variables in the molding process.

In molding foam packages and items such as picnic coolers and insulated jugs, medium and large diameter expandable polystyrene beads should be employed. In molding thin-wall items such as cups, small diameter beads should be used. In most thin-wall items, bead size is very critical and care must be taken to eliminate both oversize beads and undersize fines in the raw material used. Control of the density of the pre-expanded bead is extremely important because the diameter of the pre-expanded particle varies with its density. If a filling problem is encountered, frequently it can be overcome by the use of slightly higher density beads.

Extremely fast cycles have been obtained by the use of automatic molding equipment designed to produce thin-wall (0.080 to 0.100 in.) molded cups and containers. Over-all molding cycles of 10 to 15 seconds have been achieved on multi-cavity machines. The design of such equipment has been primarily proprietary information, but with the increased availability of commercial cup molding machines, the development of this technology should continue at a rapid pace.

One of the chief limitations of molded polystyrene foam is its relatively soft surface, particularly at low densities. The material is easily scarred and marred in normal handling. Coatings may be applied to the foam to improve this condition. Thermal stability of polystyrene foam is relatively good to temperatures of about 175°F. Above this temperature, the foam will soften and become distorted. Even with these limitations, the advantages of foam polystyrene make it an exciting material which is finding new uses every day. These new uses take advantage of the following:

1) Closed cell structure, 2) Controllable density, 3) Low thermal conductivity, 4) Low water absorption, 5) Low water vapor transmission, 6) Good resistance to impact, 7) Excellent energy absorption, 8) Good dielectric properties, 9) High strength-to-weight ratio, 10) Good resistance to cold embrittlement,

11) Chemical resistance, 12) No toxological effects.

Along with the development of new processing techniques, these advantageous properties give polystyrene foam excellent prospects for continual growth. Development of techniques for molding foam at densities below 1.0 lb per cu ft are expected. It will be possible to combine automated molding with continuous production lines. This combination is required to achieve success in high volume packaging applications and will allow expandable polystyrene foam products to challenge other established materials in the billion dollar packaging market.

PART II—BEAD EXTRUSION

By Vern Gliniecki

1. HISTORY

Polystyrene foam was first extruded directly from expandable beads on a commercial basis in 1959. Previously processing of this material was confined to steam chest molding. The most significant advantages of extrusion processing of foam are that it is a continuous rather than a batch operation and that the material is in a convenient form for further treatment.

A variety of foam products have been made by extrusion, including film, sheet, rod and tubing. Of these, film and sheeting show by far the greatest potential and overall interest.

Primary development efforts have been directed toward packaging, cushioning and decorative applications where advantage is being taken of the outstanding properties of polystyrene which include low thermal conductivity, water and grease resistance, dielectric properties, high strength-to-weight ratio, and favorable economics.

Much of the initial interest in extruded polystyrene foam was directed toward thin film laminations. Early field contacts were with paper and packaging firms where the concept of combination with paper was tried out. Various end uses were projected and many were investigated in detail, (Figs. XIII-13, XIII-14 and XIII-15). First success-

Figure XIII-13, hot drink cups and laminated picnic plates thermoformed from extruded expandable foam sheet.

Figure XIII-14, typical of other types of products produced from extruded expandable polystyrene sheet are these ribbons, bows, and record jackets.

ful commercial applications include hot drink cups, ribbons and bows, disposable plates, candy box liners and decorative-cushioning overwrap. These are now well established techniques and show a steady growth. In each instance the foam is laminated with paper or another plastic (U.S. patent 2,917,217).

Significant progress has been made since expandable polystyrene foam was first extruded from beads. Much better control over density, thickness, orientation, cell size, and surface finish is now possible. This improvement is due to better resins, newly designed equipment, and added processing knowledge.

2. DEVELOPMENT OF THE MATERIAL

Granulation

Expandable polystyrene was first available in the form of small spherical beads. The spherical shape worked quite well for steam chest molding, but not too well for extrusion, mostly because of feeding irregularities ranging anywhere between substantial surging to a complete stop of feed. The development of expandable pellets has essentially eliminated feeding problems. It also helped to supply the consistency required to extrude an item as critical as foam sheet.

Nucleation

The extrusion process for foam sheet would not be practical without nucleating agents to help control cell size. Without such additives, the extrudate is a rather viscous gel and the cell formation that occurs is large and non-uniform. As a result, the extruded surface is irregular and lacks appeal.

Nucleation has become a subject of much patent activity. A number of United States patents have been issued for the use of substances usually incompatible with polystyrene, yet capable of acting as nucleators. Various mechanisms are involved; however, the desired effect is usually accomplished by one of the following:

1. Carry-over of air into the melt and partial breakdown of cohesive forces.
2. Complete incompatibility of small sized particles.

Table XIII-2—Typical Properties of Film and Sheet Extruded from Expandable Polystyrene											
	MD	TD	MD	TD	MD	TD	MD	TD	MD	TD	MD	TD
Thickness, mils	3.5		9.0		11.5		17.5		35.0		50	
Density, lb per cu ft	7.4		8.8		6.4		7.7		5.2		6.6	
Tensile strength, psi (speed—0.5 in./min.)	880	640	750	570	920	440	320	340	600	380	340	420
Ultimate elongation, %	8.0	8.8	5.3	6.0	5.0	5.6	2.1	2.0	5.4	9.1	1.8	2.0
Tensile elastic modulus, psi (speed—0.5 in./min.)	9,970	5,240	7,480	4,950	9,380	2,990	3,930	5,110	5,250	2,900	5,050	4,380
Elmendorf tear resistance, g./mil	3.5	3.8	9.9	11.7	10.5	23.6	N.A.	N.A.	N.A.	N.A.	N.A.	N.A.
Folding endurance, cycles at 0.7 kg	88.5	3.5	149.0	30.0	N.A.	N.A.	N.A.	N.A.	N.A.	N.A.	N.A.	N.A.
Burst strength, psi	4.5		11.6		14.0		7.1		30.9		26.4	
Abrasion resistance wear index, mg loss/1000 cycles	310		100		46		115		33		69	
Water Absorption, lb/ sq ft (submerged, 10 ft water depth, 48 hr)	0.002		0.002		0.001		0.005		0.002		0.003	
Water vapor transmission, g/24 hr/100 sq in. at 73.4°F and 50% RH at 95°F and 90% RH	7.0 22.6		4.1 10.2		3.7 11.6		3.0 7.5		1.8 4.6		0.9 2.9	

MD—Machine Direction. TD—Transverse Direction. N.A.—Not Applicable.

3. Chemical reaction in which water or gas is driven off, by means of hydrates which release their water or other compounds which decompose to form gas or water at extrusion temperatures.

The most versatile nucleating system in current use is a combination of sodium bicarbonate and citric acid (U.S. patent 2,941,-964). This system enables a wide variety of cell sizes to be formed, including the very small cells which provide the best surface finish. The smaller cells are also a contributing factor toward lower densities. If, however, larger cell foam is needed because of fabrication requirements, other nucleators can be used. Calcium silicate additives (produced under the name of Silene by Columbia Southern, a division of Pittsburgh Plate Glass Co.) provide a medium-large cell structure that works well for foam parts requiring any combination of deep draws, greater rigidity or higher density (Fig. XIII-16).

Nucleation additives can be incorporated in the expandable granules or blended on the surface. The type and amount of additives used control quite closely the cell size formation. Requirements for large, medium, or small size cells require different proportions; therefore non-nucleated material is usually provided so that the processor may custom-blend to achieve the desired cell size. Additives are tumble-blended approximately 20 minutes to achieve proper distribution. Material so treated should be utilized within a few days to avoid moisture pickup that may occur with some of the nucleators in powder form. Nucleation additives may be a combination of sodium bicarbonate and citric acid, Silene (see above), or other easily available materials.

Figure XIII-15, expandable polystyrene foam film can be embossed to provide a variety of decorative or functional patterns.

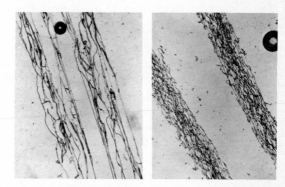

Figure XIII-16, cross section of extruded expandable polystyrene, showing both large and small cell structures.

3. DEVELOPMENT OF THE EQUIPMENT

Polystyrene foam sheet can be extruded on conventional equipment at some sacrifice in quality and output rate. Modifications in design can be made to correct such limitations. The parts that require attention are the extruder, the die, and haul-off. (Fig. XIII-17)

Extruder

For most requirements a 2½″ extruder is satisfactory for through-put rates up to 150 lb per hour. One such extruder can usually turn out enough foam to keep several forming machines operating full time. Larger extru-

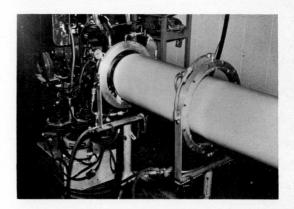

Figure XIII-17, overall view of foam sheet extrusion train.

ders (3½" and 4½") quite often do not offer significant advantage in output rates over the 2½" size because screw design for the larger extruders has not been finalized.

Due to the need for extruding expandable polystyrene at fairly low temperatures (250° to 260°F), a long barrel extruder is preferred. Ratios of 24 to 1 and 30 to 1 (barrel length to screw diameter) provide the close temperature control that is required for a low density foam extrudate. Additional flexibility can be obtained by coring the front cylinder zone and circulating either low pressure steam or cooling water.

Screw

The typical polystyrene screw which develops good mixing does not always work well for extruding expandable polystyrene foam. To ensure a high quality product, low screw speeds must be maintained to avoid excessive frictional heat. Otherwise melt temperatures rise, ruptured cells occur, density increases and surface finish is impaired. The low output rate for good quality foam has prompted considerable effort to concentrate on screw design. Screws that work with foam are generally useless for most other materials. The primary characteristics are extra depth in the feed section, i.e., up to ⅝" constant pitch on about 2 or 2½", followed by increasing root diameter between the feed and metering sections.

The delivery end of such screws has openings ranging between 150 and 180 thousandths of an inch, resulting in overall compression ratios between 2.5 to 1 and 3 to 1. For the purpose of good flow, large radii are used in the forward flights (½") and the nose sections are designed with a substantial taper (45°). The feed and compression zones are approximately seven flights long.

In instances where compression ratios of 2 to 1 or less have been tried, the output was higher, but objectionable surging occurred and the foam was not of satisfactory quality: it exhibited gauge variations and surface irregularities.

Die

Polystyrene foam sheet can be made by extruding a freely blown bubble or by using a mandrel to size the extrudate. Each method has advantages and disadvantages. For the thinner films past experience dictates the use

of a bubble process; whereas, for thicker sheet a sizing mandrel has proven to be more satisfactory.

The ordinary flat sheet die has not proven suitable for extruding expandable polystyrene foam because three dimensional expansion that occurs through foaming cannot be controlled. As a result, tubular type dies have been used almost exclusively. Such dies are further classified as straight-through or offset feed types. Here again end use requirements dictate which is to be used. The thinner films which are usually made by the freely blown bubble process are conveniently extruded with straight feed dies. In contrast, thicker sheet usually made with the aid of a sizing mandrel is more readily adapted to offset feed dies. In selecting a die for foam extrusion, allowances must be made for the advantages and disadvantages of each type.

1. The straight-through die can cause troublesome weld line problems. Due to the relatively low foam extrusion temperatures, i.e., approximately 250°F., manifold sections of proper length are used to allow reknitting of the foam passing by the spiders. These are well streamlined metal arms used to attach the central yoke to the die body.

2. The offset die can cause problems in controlling thickness. Material flowing over the central yoke must reknit on the bottom. Due to low extrusion temperature and because of greater travel, less material reaches the underside of the die. Hence, a thin spot may occur.

In extruding foam sheet in thicknesses (40 mils and higher) where a sizing mandrel may be advantageous, an offset tubular type die has proven most versatile. This design allows attachment of a support bracket for the mandrel without undue deflection of the central yoke. In addition, provisions are easily made for "on-the-run" adjustment of orifice opening. This in turn allows different sheet thicknesses to be made without machine work and without extreme changes in takeaway speeds which are undesirable as excessive orientation can be induced into the foam. The importance of low orientation is evident when the sheet is intended for further processing such as vacuum or pressure forming. Upon heating, the internal stresses in the foam tend to release and the sheet may tear or fail to draw properly, especially for deep parts.

Special die design features which have proven useful for foam extrusion are large manifold sections and short land lengths. These prevent large pressure drops within the die and enable foaming to occur after exit from the orifice. This is most desirable from a quality standpoint: low densities are possible and surface finish is at an optimum. Sharp edges at the orifice are an additional aid to good surface finish.

The size of the die to select depends upon the extruder capacity and/or sheet width requirements; for a 2½″ extruder, a tubular die 4″ to 6″ in diameter can be used. Sheet up to 54″ wide can be made depending upon blow-up ratio, i.e., mandrel size or bubble diameter.

Sizing mandrel—Bubble diameter

In extruding foam sheet some stretching must be done to eliminate folds and wrinkles that occur through expansion. Material initially at a bulk density of 60 lb per cu ft expands suddenly to a 5 or 8 lb per cu ft foam. The three dimensional expansion is best taken up by stretching over a mandrel or blowing a bubble. Expansion ratios from 2.5 to 1 to 4 to 1 are usually sufficient to compensate for the expansion. Higher blow-up usually results in excessive orientation which can become a problem in subsequent fabrication.

For the thinner foam films, a bubble process can be used which requires inflation air and restrictors to maintain constant sizing. Actually, sufficient force is generated by the entrapped blowing agent to inflate the bubble; however, additional air is used for cooling and restrictors are used to control overall blowup and prevent variation. In this manner control over sheet thickness and web width is good, although some wandering may be experienced.

The use of a sizing mandrel for thicker sheet provides other benefits in addition to constant sizing. Most significant of these is better cooling of the extrudate at the proper time which is immediately upon exit from the die. Large volumes of air can be utilized to equalize temperatures between inner bubble and outside. Then, the foam has a much more uniform and better appearance on both surfaces.

Materials suitable for mandrel construction include wood and the light metals, aluminum or magnesium. The metals are often preferred

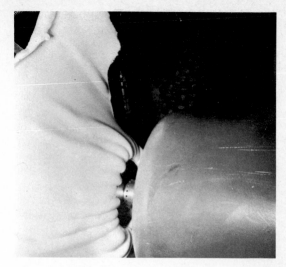

Figure XIII-18, close-up of foam expansion, showing wrinkling at the die orifice.

because of good thermal conductivity and light weight, the advantages thereof being no deflection at the point of attachment to the die (central yoke) and easy transfer of frictional heat generated by sheet sliding past the mandrel. Good temperature control is easily and inexpensively obtained with cooling water.

Metal mandrels are usually constructed by rolling flat sheet stock, approximately ⅛″ thick, into an open tube of a specified diameter and length. The front section is plugged with 2″ thick plate (round leading edge) to provide rigidity and enable cooling coils to be inserted. The rear mandrel section is left open except for criss-cross bracing. Positioning of the mandrel is easily accomplished by drilling centrally located holes in the front plate and rear brace. Then a rod can be inserted to allow attachment to the central yoke of the die and to a support stand. In this manner, the mandrel can be moved horizontally as the need arises. During startup, clearance is required and the mandrel is moved out of the way; whereas for steady state operation it can be moved into place close to the die so that wrinkles in the extrudate can be taken up. (Fig. XIII-18).

Mandrel length depends primarily upon output rates, i.e., linear velocity and sheet thickness. Sufficient heat transfer must occur to make the sheet dimensionally stable and prevent necking down and accompanying shrinkage. Mandrels over 36 inches in length are cumbersome and awkward to handle. Any additional cooling, if required, can better be obtained with an auxiliary air ring than by using longer mandrel sections.

Slitting station

Tubular foam sheet requires slitting before windup. In the free bubble process it is usually done after passage through the nip rolls. In mandrel sizing the extrudate is slit just past the mandrel, but before the nip rolls, to enable passage by the support stand without interference. The foam can be slit into multiple sections or, if the need arises, a full width section can be made. In the latter case, slitting is done on the bottom and the tube is gradually opened with the aid of a spreader. The spreader can be aluminum or stainless steel sheet shaped to form an elliptical profile. The shape is dictated somewhat by distance between mandrel and nip rolls. Usually a space of 15 to 20 feet is allowed to reduce wrinkling tendencies and improve overall handling behavior.

Haul-off

For foam sheet extrusion, special or modified takeaway equipment is required. Otherwise the necessary control over extrudate thickness density and orientation cannot be achieved. A suitable design would provide adequate width to process at least a 48″ wide web. The nip rolls should also have features which allow the necessary control over the properties of the extrudate. These include:

1. *Density*
   Tandem soft rubber rolls (25 durometer hardness), 10″ in diameter or larger, each individually driven and tiltable to provide additional wrap around, enable minimum roll pressures in haul-off, for low density foam. The nip rolls, one stationary and the other actuated by pneumatic cylinders, should have positive adjustment stops and controls for pressure adjustment on each side.

2. *Output rate*
   Depending upon the extruder capacity and the thickness required, various takeaway speeds will be needed. Variations between 5 and 300 feet per minute should be provided. This is usually accomplished in two steps, first a 10 to 1 speed ratio for normal use, then a special drive-all transmission unit that will increase the basic speed to the desired maximum rate.

3. *Orientation*
   It is generally desirable to make foam sheet with low orientation, especially if further processing is intended. Control is exercised by varying takeaway speed and blowup ratio to the extent that thickness is controlled and folds or creases are eliminated. Orientation, however, is not confined entirely to processing conditions, i.e., machine and cross-direction dimensions. There is another type of orientation, around the cells. As yet, no means have been devised to measure it, although the end effect is known. For example, large cell foam fabricated under the same conditions as small cell foam is more readily formed into deep parts. This difference is attributed to a lesser amount of cell orientation.

   The usual method of measuring orientation is to record shrinkage after exposure to a certain temperature, for example 1½ hours at 275°F. Experimentation has shown that foam sheet having free shrinkage approximately 60% in the machine direction or less is most desirable for forming. As shrinkage in the machine direction approaches 75% or more, forming becomes more difficult. In contrast, cross machine shrinkage rarely exceeds 45% and usually does not have a strong effect on forming unless blowup ratios in excess of 10 are used.

4. *Other*
   The haul-off should also have provisions for static electricity elimination, edge guidance, auxiliary slitting, and wrinkle control. The Mount Hope roll assembly, an eccentric roll sometimes referred to as a banana roll because of its shape, may help to control wrinkling of film during windup.

Windup

Foam sheet windup equipment can be included with the haul-off or be independent from it. The latter is a more versatile arrangement. Depending upon width requirements one or more separate webs can be wound at the same time on the same shaft. Due to the light weight of foam sheet, most conventional winders must be modified. Hollow shafts and magnesium core holders can be utilized in handling and removing foam from the core. A versatile windup design can handle a 48″ wide sheet, or multiple widths thereof. Rolls as large as 60 in. are possible on cores 8 in. dia.

4. PRODUCT CONTROL

In some of the uses that have developed

for polystyrene foam, the materials it was likely to replace were inexpensive. In other instances, a new development was being sought. But in every case, economics were a prime consideration. To compete effectively, low density foams are required. In addition, a uniform, consistent product must be made. And efficient use of the scrap must be possible.

Density

A prime requisite of extruded foam sheet is low density. Control over this variable is possible, by a combination of several means:

1. Blowing agent level is not as critical an item in controlling density as was originally expected. Foam in the neighborhood of 5 lb per cu ft is easily made with commercially available expandable styrene, even after long storage.

2. Temperature of the extrudate just prior to its exit from the die is a significant factor in density control. For 5 lb per cu ft foam the temperature should be approximately 250°F at output rates in the range of 75 to 100 lb per hour. For faster rates, up to 150 lb per hour, slightly higher temperatures are necessary because of reduced inventory time.

3. Nip roll pressure also has a significant effect on density.

Roll pressure	Density, lb per cu ft	Thickness, mils
0	5.5	250
20	7.0	150
25	8.0	80
30	10.5	55
40	11.5	50

4. Takeaway speeds within a range that allows good quality foam have no appreciable effect on density.

Travel ft per min	Density, lb per cu ft	Thickness, Mils
8	6.7	150
10	6.9	80
12	6.7	70
15	6.9	60
20 (inadequately cooled, no good)	9.6	35

5. Extruder speeds within a range that allows high quality foam have no appreciable effect on foam density. When excessive speed is reached, temperatures rise, the surface becomes rough and density increases.

Extruder rpm	Output rate, lb per hour	Density, lb per cu ft
30	50	7.4
40	75	7.4
45	100	7.8
60	150	8.4 (Surging— broken cells, no good)

When high-speed screws, designed especially for foam, are used, much higher rpm's are possible, i.e., up to 75 rpm and 200 lb per hour outputs. The foam made in this manner has a shorter inventory time and must be heated to higher temperatures, such as 275°F. Such foam is usually of lower density.

6. Die temperature affects foam density only insofar as it influences stock temperature. Best results have been noted at settings of 260°F to 270°F.

7. Foam sheet density is modified by subsequent processing. Original 6 lb per cu ft foam sheet can be reduced to 3 lb per cu ft during a forming process. If draws are not very deep, a 100% or greater increase in thickness is possible.

5. SCRAP UTILIZATION

A factor that has a strong bearing on the success of foam sheet is the effective utilization of scrap. Many of the uses for foam in packaging require fabrication into parts of various shapes. This may result in as little as 10%, or as much as 40% scrap. This material must be utilized in some manner to make economics favorable, although it is very lightweight and difficult to process on conventional equipment. A preliminary step-grinding is required. The foam scrap should be ground into a fluff-like composite resembling corn flakes. In this form, it is more suitable for reprocessing.

Direct use of ground scrap

The simplest and least expensive means of utilizing scrap foam is direct re-extrusion of the ground fluff. Volumetric mixtures of two parts fluff to one part virgin granules have been used without any sacrifice in output rate. The scrap addition, 10% by weight, has some effect on appearance, i.e., occasional lumps are formed, but these usually are not detectable after forming.

Repelletizing

The next most logical step in handling foam scrap, especially if large amounts are generated, is a repelletizing process. This is done primarily to redensify the foam for subsequent reuse.

Originally hopes were held to recover the residual blowing agent for reuse by blending with new feedstock; however, studies indicate that very little can be expected. Foam sheet immediately after extrusion contains approximately 4% blowing agent. This amount decreases in time. For a 100-mil thickness:

Time interval after extrusion	Percent blowing agent retained
0 hour	4.0
1 hour	4.0
1 day	3.0
1 week	2.2
1 month	2.0
6 months	0.7
1 year	0.3

Making use of left-over foam as soon after extrusion as possible looked promising initially; but by grinding much of the residual blowing agent is lost. At best 1% can be retained compared to 3.5% to 4% initially.

This matter of residual blowing agent is significant, because of its effect on density and fabrication conditions. A plasticizing effect is imparted to the foam and reduced temperatures are required for further extrusions. Consequently, the use of pelletized scrap as diluent material causes some difficulty at the usual foaming temperature, and homogenous melts cannot always be obtained.

The re-extrusion of scrap pelletized foam is painfully slow on conventional equipment. Rates in excess of 25 lb per hour cannot be obtained on 2½″ extruders. Specialized equipment is available, which markedly improves output.

Conical extruders have processed repelletized material having a bulk density in the range of 2 to 3 lb per cu ft at rates above 300 lb per hour. Such equipment is fairly expensive. A less costly approach would involve the use of hopper stuffers which are also effective.

At this time the most effective use of scrap foam appears to be a small combination extruder-pelletizer for making fine granules and feedback thereof at rates of approximately 25%.

6. ECONOMIC FACTORS

The cost of fabricated foam parts depends upon a number of factors including costs of equipment, material and material handling. All the equipment has been mentioned previously with the exception of a forming machine. Either a vacuum or pressure former can be used effectively. A pressure former allows forming and trimming in one step. In addition, there are other advantages including better detail, faster cycles and a high ratio of material utilization. (See Part III, this Section).

Total capital expenses for a complete line would run approximately $75,000. In addition, material and conversion costs must be considered. These, however, vary from company to company and area to area; therefore, direct quotations on costs can be misleading. Rough approximations based on sensible assumptions indicate foam items can often be made competitive with paper.

Foam items	Size	Sheet thickness, mils	Cost, $ M units
Meat trays	5½″x8″x1¼″	60	7.00
Apple trays	12″x20″	100	22.00
Hot drink cups	8 oz. capacity	100	7.00
Egg cartons	13″x8″x1½″	125	15.00

Each of the above applications is promising for foam, although the unit cost may be initially higher than for currently used material. Many plus factors are evident, however, including improved resistance to grease and moisture, better cushioning and a more pleasing general appearance.

EQUIPMENT SUPPLY SOURCES FOR POLYSTYRENE EXTRUSION

Company	Components*
Black-Clawson Company Dilts Division Fulton, N.Y.	A, B, D
Danson Barnett and Associates Ltd. Don Mills, Ontario, Canada	F
Davis Standard Division of Crompton and Knowles Corp. Mystic, Conn.	A, B, D

*Code:
  A = Extruder
  B = Screw
  C = Die
  D = Take-off
  E = Windup
  F = Auxiliaries

Company	Components*	Company	Components*
Egan (Frank W.) Co. Somerville, N.J.	A, B, C	Modern Plastics Machinery Corp. Clifton, N.J.	A, B, C, D
Essex Plastics Machinery Co. Peabody, Mass.	D, E	Mt. Hope Machinery Co. Taunton, Mass.	F
Fife Manufacturing Co., Inc. P. O. Box 9815 Oklahoma City 18, Okla.	F (Edge Guidance)	National Rubber Machinery Co. Akron 8, Ohio	A, B, C, D, F
Gloucester Engineering Co. Sargent Street Gloucester, Mass.	A, B, C, D, F	Prodex Corporation Fords, N.J.	A, B, C, D, F
Goulding Manufacturing Co. Saginaw, Mich.	D, F	Reifenhauer U. S. Sales Corp. New York, N.Y.	All (Package Unit)
Hobbs Manufacturing Co. Worcester, Mass.	E, F	Sterling Extruder Corp. Lansdale, Pa.	A, B, C, D
Johnson Manufacturing Co. Inc. P. O. Box 87 Chippewa Falls, Wis.	B, C, D, E, F	Simco Company Linden, N.J.	F
Mitts and Merrill Inc. 109 McCoskry Street Saginaw, Mich.	F (Grinding)	Waldron Hartig Box 791 New Brunswick, N.J.	A, B, C, D

PART III—THERMOFORMING
By Vern Gliniecki

1. DESCRIPTION AND TECHNOLOGY

Polystyrene foam sheet, available with a smooth soft surface and in a variety of thicknesses, can be thermoformed into many shapes. Such finished items retain all the desirable properties of the original sheet and can have additional built-in features, including shock absorbence, rigidity, surface detail, etc. These

Figure XIII-19, some thermoformed products made from expandable polystyrene sheet.

are both functionally useful and visually attractive in packaging applications.

This ability to thermoform foam successfully is a significant advancement, that has been made possible by the combination of controlled cell size formation and thinner sheet sections. Previously, extruded polystyrene foam with larger cells and thicker, as described in Section XII, could not be formed economically or with good detail.

Technology

Thermoforming is a process whereby plastic materials are heated to the softening point and then shaped to some specific form by means of vacuum, drape, plug assist, matched mold, or pressure forming techniques (Fig. XIII-19). The art is highly developed even though a relatively short time has lapsed since suitable forming equipment became available. Most of the early developments were made with sheets of high impact polystyrene, and many of the principles and techniques still apply.

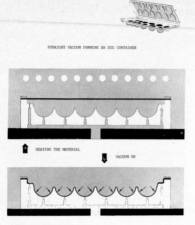

HEATING THE MATERIAL

VACUUM ON

a heat

b DRAPE

c vacuum on

Figure XIII-20, straight vacuum forming is an excellent fabrication method for shallow parts (those with a depth up to ½ shortest outside horizontal dimension).

Figure XIII-21, drape forming produces more nearly uniform wall thicknesses to depths equal to shortest horizontal dimension.

Vacuum forming

Vacuum forming was the first and most successful method for thermoforming plastics. All other methods are some modification of that technique. Essentially, the process requires a clamping frame to hold samples of required size and minimize shrinkage during the heating cycle. This frame is usually attached to a movable carriage so that the plastic sheet can be transferred to a heating station and quickly returned to the mold for forming. Atmospheric pressure on the heated sheet forces their entry into evacuated female cavities or their draping over male molds (Fig. XIII-20).

Drape forming, a slight modification of straight vacuum forming (Fig. XIII-21), is usually resorted to when deep draws are required. Heated sheet is draped over a male mold and the underneath air space evacuated so that the desired contour is formed. Quite often, a changeover to drape forming eliminates webbing problems encountered in straight vacuum forming.

Plug assist forming (Fig. XIII-22) combines the best features of straight vacuum and drape forming. This technique is a valuable aid in making parts of uniform wall thickness, especially with deep draws. The process, limited to female cavities, involves the use of a movable plug to assist material entry into the cavity. As the plug is depressed, compressed air from underneath first forces a

billowing of the material about the plug. This prevents contact of the sheet with the cavity lip which would result in drag and uneven material distribution. The plug stops near the bottom of the mold; then the underneath air is evacuated to allow the desired shape with all surface details.

In forming foam to relatively deep draws, the plug assist technique is usually necessary to provide uniform distribution of material along the sidewalls. The plug is most effective when heated to a temperature of approximately 125°F. Furthermore, the plug should be moved rapidly toward the bottom of the cavity allowing only slightly more clearance than the sheet thickness. The plug's overall dimensions will vary considerably depending upon the part that is being made.

Matched die forming is a continuation, or extra stage, of plug assist forming. A pair of matched molds form the softened sheet into desired shapes without the use of additional vacuum or air pressure. Positive clearance can be maintained to ensure constant thickness and good detail on both the inside and outside surface of formed parts. Another advantage is faster cooling since both sides of the sheet come into contact with the mold. Matched molds are limited in depth of draw and draft angles and shallow parts only should be attempted. They are good for forming foam sheet into parts requiring a lot of detail.

Pressure forming is a variation of the usual means of forming plastics, but air pressure is

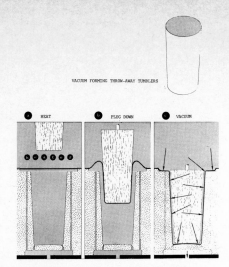

VACUUM FORMING THROW-AWAY TUMBLERS

● HEAT   ● PLUG DOWN   ● VACUUM

Figure XIII-22, plug assist forming.

used instead of vacuum. The normal sequence of operation consists of clamping the sheet material between a solid heating platten and the mold. The sheet is heated by conduction until properly softened. Then compressed air forces the heated sheet into the mold cavity. Vacuum can be used to evacuate the mold of entrapped air, or vented molds can be provided to ensure good detail. The advantages of pressure forming are: fast cycles, trimming in place, good utilization of material and fine detail. But it can be applied best to parts with shallow draws and higher density foam.

In pressure forming foam sheet and foam laminates, there are advantages in pre-heating to reduce overall cycle time. The foam should be unwound and conveyed past sandwich-type heaters for partial softening, prior to final contact heating on solid plattens.

Various other techniques have been devised to form and shape parts including slip forming, reverse draw forming and air-cushion forming. These, however, have not proven altogether suitable for forming polystyrene foam because of the low elongation of this material and the short heating cycles required.

2. DETAILS OF OPERATION

Heating

The heating of polystyrene sheet material prior to forming can be achieved either by convection, conduction, or radiation methods. Convection heating, such as is encountered in air circulating ovens, provides good and uniform heat distribution, but is much too slow for practical purposes. Heating by conduction,

usually referred to as platen or contact heating, is faster but still has limitations. Radiant heating has become the most popular means of bringing plastic sheet to its forming temperature. Radiant heaters are usually electrically-heated sheath-wire calrod units which convert source energy into heat. The intensity of the heating increases with electrical input and is measured in watt density. Temperatures range between 500°F and 1700°F and are easily controlled to the desired level with proportioning controllers. These controllers are usually timers which govern on and off time of the heaters, or rheostat-type switches.

In forming polystyrene foam sheet or polystyrene sheet-foam laminates, low temperatures are required as the heating of these products is delicate. Fractions of a second of excessive heating time can overheat or even completely destroy the foam structure.

Heat intensity output is usually defined as watt density per square inch of area. For foam and foam laminates, a range of 10 to 20 watts per square inch is usually satisfactory. The foam should be heated on both sides when the sheet thickness exceeds 40 mils, or if the foam is laminated to another plastic, or if the draw ratio is greater than 0.3. The draw ratio is the depth or height of the hollow in the piece compared to the smallest cross section of the opening.

Heaters should be located at least four inches above and/or below the foam sheeting to avoid localized overheating. If the optimum in uniformity is desirable and the forming equipment is devoted entirely to foam, expanded type porcelain or ceramic radiators, having embedded nichrome heating elements, can be substituted for calrod heaters.

Cooling

Foam cools very rapidly after forming. Regardless of the method selected, either vacuum or pressure technique, the cooling cycle lasts only a few seconds. Therefore, in forming foam sheet or foam sheet laminates, machine movement must be rapid to enable instant shaping after heating. Even so, some auxiliary heating is sometimes required to keep the foam at required temperatures during its transfer from the heating station to the forming station.

After forming, the foam is a thicker, lower density, material. Depending upon the depth of draw and the foam's original properties, the expansion can be as great as 100%, with a corresponding 50% decrease in density.

The shrinkage of polystyrene foam sheet after forming is dependent upon cell size and fabrication conditions. However, for design purposes, it can be assumed to be approximately 50% greater than for non-foamed polystyrene.

Trimming

Polystyrene foam sheet and foam sheet laminates can be trimmed with a variety of tools, including shears, circular saw, cutting press, and blanking dies. Surprisingly, large shearing forces are required for knife-edge trimming because of the compressible nature of foam. Therefore, attention has been given to razor blade and hot wire techniques. No single method, however, is suitable for all applications and often a combination of trimming techniques is required, especially if the parts have large perimeters.

Decorating

Polystyrene foam sheet can be decorated by conventional methods of spray painting, silk screening, and printing. Foam can also be vacuum-metallized successfully. The quality of finish and detail possible depends upon surface texture. The small-cell structure foams usually are the easiest to decorate. A sheet can be pre-decorated and then thermoformed into tray-type containers without delamination or significant distortion. Polystyrene paints and inks should be used, however, to ensure good adhesion and avoid solvent attack.

Assembly

Foamed articles can be adhered together in a number of ways including heat, impulse, ultrasonic sealing, solvent or adhesive sealing. The seals are effective but not particularly durable. Care must be taken to avoid brittleness rupture or cell collapse from high heat or high voltage. So far, the best results have been obtained with impulse-type seals using a small high-resistance nichrome wire to supply the heat to the bond or joint, under pressure. Solvent sealing is also effective but requires more time.

Scrap recovery

The matter of effective recovery of the foam scraps is important in determining costs of formed foam items. In some applications, the residual web after forming can amount to as much as 40% scrap. This question is discussed more completely in Part II, this section.

Design consideration

In designing molds for foam sheet articles, due consideration must be given to streamlined geometry: sharp corners, small angles, and severe drafts should be avoided. Selecting the type of foam sheet is also important: thin or thick sections, soft or hard texture, large or small cell sizes, and high or low orientation levels. Each type can, and usually does, show advantages for specific applications. Low orientation is preferred for vacuum forming and relatively larger cell sizes are more suited for deeper draws. A foam with a uniform size of cells is always easier to form than one with a random pattern of cell sizes.

Forming in line immediately after extrusion has not been very successful with foam sheet. This is attributed to a condensation of the residual blowing agent in the individual cells. As a result, a partial vacuum develops inside the cells. A certain time is, therefore, required to allow air to diffuse through the cells until equilibrium, that is atmospheric pressure, is re-established. Afterwards, the sheet will expand better with the application of heat, because of the mixture of air and blowing agent in each cell. This time varies depending upon extrusion conditions, but need not exceed 24 hours.

Conventional forming equipment can be used to thermoform polystyrene foam sheet, but refinements and specific modifications in design have proven useful. Most equipment suppliers are aware of these requirements and can provide the proper equipment.

PART IV—INJECTION MOLDING
By R. J. Bender

A relatively new technique for the forming of cellular polystyrene, applicable to objects where aesthetical appearance is greatly desirable, is injection molding. The starting material is not the pre-expandable spherical bead, as in other techniques described in this Section, but cylindrical pellets, or granules, supplied by The Dow Chemical Co. under the tradename of "Frostwood" resin. The pellets are melted, at a temperature of from 400 to 475°F, instead of being simply heated to saturated steam temperature at near atmospheric pressure, and fused, as is the case with expandable beads. So, strictly speaking, the finished product here is no longer an entirely cellular, or foamed, plastic. It has a characteristic light-density foamed core, with good thermal insulating properties, surrounded by a hard, high-density skin, with a swirled surface finish resembling a fine-grained, hardwood burl. It can be colored, by using from 25 to 75 grams of pure pigment per 100 lb of resin.

Great care must be given to proper venting during the injection process, to allow release of a substantial portion of the initial gaseous blowing agent.

Specific precautions should be used in expandable polystyrene injection molding, such as: 1) prepositioning of the ram, forward of feed opening, to minimize loss of blowing agent during heating; 2) shot size at least 50% of equipment rated capacity to maintain acceptably low overall density; 3) gravimetric, rather than volumetric, feeding for better uniformity of successive parts; 4) valve-type nozzle to prevent drooling; 5) precompression, in order to get maximum injection speed. Adequate venting of mold cannot be overemphasized. Mold temperatures are kept at 100 to 150°F to avoid condensation of the released blowing agent on the mold walls. Release agents, especially silicones, ruin the finish, and should be used only for the first few shots, until the cycle is well established. They are replaced with large, blunt, ejection pins, which

Figure XIII-23, three components of this ice bucket are injection molded of expandable polystyrene to give the unusual surface effect of wood, as well as some physical and chemical properties obtained only in injection molded thermoplastics. The expandable polystyrene components include the main body, the carrying handle, and the handle to the lid. The lid, itself, is molded of styrene-acrylonitrile.

Table XIII-3—Typical Chemical Resistance of Injection Molded Expandable Polystyrene

Inorganic acids,	
Weak	E*
Strong	E
Strong, oxidizing	F
Organic acids,	
Weak	E
Strong	G
Alcohols	E
Aldehydes	N
Amines,	
Aliphatic	E
Aromatic	N
Caustics	E
Esters	N
Foodstuffs	N
Glycols,	
Polyglycols	E
Polyglycol ethers	N
Hydrocarbons	N
Insecticides	N
Ketones	N
Oils	N
Pharmaceuticals	E
Salts	E

*Key:
E—Excellent—Unaffected in any way for duration of test.
G—Good—Very slight discoloration.
F—Fair—Moderate discoloration, possible dimensional or weight change.
N—Not Recommended—For one or more of several reasons, the resin is not recommended for applications in which these environments are liable to be encountered.

Figure XIII-24, expandable polystyrene resin for injection molding is made in a form that differs from conventional expandable polystyrene beads. Although the production of beads (right) is more costly than the cylindrical granules (left) used for injection molding, the beads are used for most expandable polystyrene applications because they facilitate filling the molds through long filling systems. In conventional expandable polystyrene molding, the resin is heated only to a point where expansion takes place and the individual beads fuse together. In injection molding, on the other hand, the pellets are actually melted in the cylinder prior to injection into the mold. This gives the characteristic foamed core surrounded by a hard, high-density surface skin. Since most conventional injection molding equipment is designed to handle granules, the resin is supplied in this form.

do not hurt the surface of the plastic.

While the finished objects of injection-molded expandable polystyrene have the appearance of wood, their properties are approximately those of pure polystyrene.

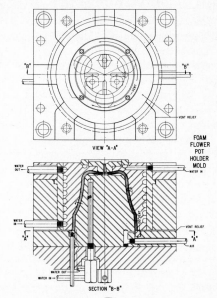

Figure XIII-25, this is the design of a prototype mold used to establish processing techniques for injection molding expandable polystyrene—it is not the mold used to make the ice bucket described in Fig XIII-23. This particular mold layout is presented to show the importance of adequate venting. Courtesy Dow Chemical Co.

PART V—POLYSTYRENE FOAM PAPERBOARD LAMINATE
By Dr. R. G. Fordyce

1. INTRODUCTION AND PROPERTIES

The continuous extrusion of sheets of closed-cell polystyrene foam sandwiched between two linerboard facings became commercial in 1959, following several years of joint development by Monsanto Chemical Co. and St. Regis Paper Co. The process is quite flexible: board thickness, foam density, size, shape and distribution of cells, and type of paper facings can be varied within wide limits. These variations substantially affect the properties of the finished product.

Foam characteristics other than its density have an important bearing on board properties. For example, the flat crush stress-strain curves perpendicular to the facing are quite different,

depending on whether the foam core is extruded or produced from expanded beads. In the latter case, the foam is much more resilient, and the bead product may not be used for embossed signs or displays, because it will not take and hold permanent compressive set. Even a superficial comparison between polystyrene foams made by extrusion and from expanded beads reveals significant structural differences.

Dimensional stability and effect of moisture.

Polystyrene laminate boards increase their dimensions (length and width) on exposure to high humidity. They also show a net change (shrinkage) over a single cycle. The net dimensional change becomes less with repeated cycling and, ultimately, the process becomes completely reversible.

This phenomenon must be given careful consideration in view of the practical use of the product. For example, very severe warpage results if a free panel of styrene foam laminate is coated on one side with a water-base paint, whereas the use of a non-aqueous paint or lacquer produces no such effect. Similarly, an aluminum-foil-faced laminate embossed sign may warp with ambient humidity changes, unless suitably countermounted or otherwise treated on the reverse side. There again, the severity of exposure conditions governs the degree of response.

Panels held securely in place by nails, staples or adhesive on wooden framing members, develop *shrinkage forces* as they attempt to respond dimensionally to ambient changes.

Flexural strength.

Flexural strength is determined on an Instron Model TM compression tester with a center-loading flexural jig. A sample 3 in. wide and 15 in. long is suspended across a 12 in. span and load is applied at 1 in. per minute at the center until the sample fails. The load and deflection at the elastic limit and yield point are obtained from the stress-strain curve.

The stiffness factor, EI, is a number combining load, deflection, and span length into a single value:

$$\text{Stiffness, EI} = \frac{Pl^3}{48Y}$$

where P = load, l = span length and Y = deflection at load P.

The effect of direction (MD or CMD), foam density, gauge and linerboard weight is significant. As may be expected, gauge has an exponential effect. The effect of heavier weight linerboard is more pronounced at lower gauges. Foam density, for example 2 versus 4 lb per cu ft, has some effect. And boards have much greater flexural strength in the MD than in the CMD direction.

The following strength data have been measured at standard conditions for a ¼ in. thick board with styrene foam density of 4 lb per cu ft and linerboard on both sides:

Tensile strength (parallel to surface) 918 psi MD
Tensile strength (perpendicular to
surface) 3250 psf
Apparent stiffness 235,000 psi MD
Modulus of elasticity 100,000 pai CMD

Water vapor transmission

The following data were obtained according to ASTM E96-53T, Procedure A:

Water vapor transmission rate (WVTR), gram per 100 sq in. per 24 hr at 100°F and 95% RH

Board ⅛ in. thick; foam @ 4 lb per cu ft   7.3
Board ¼ in. thick; foam @ 2 lb per cu ft   10.7
Board ¼ in. thick; foam @ 4 lb per cu ft   4.8

Chemical resistance

Styrene foam core is highly resistant to water, acids and alkalis. It is attacked, however, by certain solvents, notably aromatics (benzene), ketones (acetone), esters (amyl acetate), and chlorinated hydrocarbons (Ethylene dichloride). The wide-spread use of these laminates for containers for shipping bottled nitric acid is an interesting example of the chemical resistance of the styrene core laminate compared to an all-cellulosic fiber boxboard.

Embossibility

Detailed contoured shapes can be reproduced on the laminate flat surfaces by die-pressing at room temperature with moderate pressure. This property reflects the ability of the styrene core to take and hold permanent compression set.

Insect, mould and rodent resistance

Termites will consume the kraft paper liner but cannot penetrate the styrene core. Cockroaches and cereal insects do not survive on the laminate in absence of food. Moulds survive and grow only when appropriate ambient moisture and temperature conditions exist. Mice can penetrate the laminate only where there is an exposed edge on which to gnaw.

Thermal characteristics

Styrene foam laminates are recommended for continuous service up to 175°F, but not beyond. As presently manufactured, these laminates will not ignite spontaneously at temperatures below 500°F in the absence of a flame ignition source; they will burn if a flame is applied. Near future developments are expected to bring about production of self-extinguishing grades.

2. PRINCIPAL APPLICATIONS AND FABRICATION TECHNIQUES

Graphic arts applications

Embossed three-dimensional designs are possible by compressing specific areas of the board. The skilful use of printed design and color tone emphasizes the three-dimensional effects. Polystyrene foam laminates have over the chipboard materials, commonly used for signs and displays, the advantage of being thicker, structurally stronger and lighter. The weakening effect of absorbed moisture is confined to the linerboard facings, whereas the entire thickness of a solid fiber product can be affected.

Trays properly fabricated from the laminated boards hold water indefinitely, and this ability has been effectively used in displays.

Printability is another attribute in this market, and boards with coated bleached kraft facings were developed specifically to provide a good printing surface.

The methods and equipment used to fabricate point-of-purchase signs and displays are similar to those used for paper products. The first step is the placement of the advertising message on the surface of the board. Two principal methods are used: (1) mounting, for which the natural kraft surfaced products are normally used, and (2) printing, for which coated white products are selected.

Die cutting and scoring of foam paperboard laminates can be done on standard flat bed or rotary equipment such as Thompson-National, Sheridan or Miehle presses. Normally, 3-point steel rule is used for die cutting, either with a double bevel or double-double bevel. To maintain a full thickness edge in die cutting, that is to avoid compression of the foam, a serrated edge die rule should be used. Its action is similar to that of a saw blade; the preferred type is 2 or 3 point rule with 10 to 12 teeth per inch.

Embossing of foam laminates is done easily and cold in commercial presses. Dies can be constructed of steel rule, masonite or hardboard, metal or Dycril printing plates. The process of preparing Dycril photopolymer plates produces fine detail which can be transferred to the laminate surface. Maximum depth of etching in a Dycril plate is 0.040 in.

Cutting of foam laminate boards is easy, with rotary slitters. Guillotine cutters are not widely used, to avoid compression of the edges and ragged cut. Rotary or band saws do a neat job, but provision should be made to remove the dust: small particles of foam or paper tend to adhere to the surfaces as a result of electrostatic charges. Vacuum systems and brushes are used in combination; occasionally air blasts are useful.

Container applications

The combination of light weight and thermal insulating properties makes this material very useful for air shipments. In the case of shipments containing dry ice the relatively low transmission rate of carbon dioxide vapor through polystyrene foam laminates results in appreciable cost savings.

Millions of polystyrene foam laminate boxes have been fabricated using standard box-making equipment. Just as there are optimum conditions for making boxes from various fiberboards, there are optimum conditions for fabricating foam laminate containers.

Scoring method has a decided effect on the resistance of the container, especially stacking strength and rough-handling resistance. Laboratory tests have proven that maximum compression and scoring strengths are obtained by using three-point scoring for flap scores and V-to-flap scoring for body scores.

Manufacturer's joint, of the taped, glued and stitched types, can all be used satisfactorily with polystyrene foam laminates. Glued and stitched joints are stronger than taped joints, as is usually the case. It is recommended that a fast tack glue be used, since the impervious foam core in the laminate reduces the adhesive drying rate slightly. It is also recommended that the joint area be crushed prior to joining, to allow more uniform stacking of knocked-down boxes. For strapping polystyrene foam paperboard laminate boxes, it is recommended that glass reinforced pressure sensitive tape or flat fiber strapping be used.

Construction applications

The newest, fastest growing and potentially most important market areas for polystyrene foam laminates lie in the building industry. Since 1961, these boards have been used as a sub-roof board for mobile homes, because of good barrier characteristics against heat, moisture and vapor, a very good strength-to-weight ratio, acoustical benefits and ease of handling. Many satisfactory installations have been made in residential construction. The board has been used as a wooden floor underlayment, as backerboard for drywall construction and for ceilings: since batten strips are required for good appearance over joints in ceilings, this type is probably limited to playrooms and dens.

Section XIV—POLYETHYLENE FOAM
PART I—LOW-DENSITY POLYETHYLENE FOAM
By J. S. Laing

1. HISTORY

Polyethylene polymers are of great commercial interest because their unique properties provide an answer to many design bottlenecks. Sales of polyethylene now have reached in the U.S. nearly 2-billion pounds per year, and growth is continuing at a rapid pace. The versatility of the polymer is seen in its availability as extrusion coating materials, molding resins, sheeting, film, and more recently, in expanded form, as polyethylene foam.

In 1941 a first U.S. patent No. 2,256,483, was issued to E. I. du Pont de Nemours & Co. for a composition of expanded polyethylene. Much effort was expended since to provide a commercially acceptable manufacturing process and the first success was obtained by Bakelite Division, Union Carbide Corp., in the form of expanded polyethylene granules. Later, rods, blocks and some shapes of expanded polyethylene became available through American Agile Co., Cleveland, O. Sheets and tapes of expanded polyethylene were offered by Ludlow Papers, Inc., Needham Heights, Mass. These foams were primarily in the 10 to 30 lb per cu ft density range and their properties and uses have been well reported. More recently 2 lb per cu ft pre-expanded polyethylene planks, of various sizes and shapes have been developed by an extrusion process at The Dow Chemical Company, covered by U.S. patent No. 3,067,147.

Low-density polyethylene foam can be formed by mixing a foaming agent with the molten polymer under high pressure. The foaming agent expands under reduced or atmospheric pressure with simultaneous cooling. As the foaming agent expands the individual cells are formed. The degree of expansion and the cell structure can be controlled by careful cooling or partial crosslinking of the polyethylene by means of ionizing radiation.

2. PROPERTIES

Low-density polyethylene foam (2 lb per cu ft) retains all of the common properties of solid polyethylene and in addition offers the advantage of weighing only about one-thirtieth as much as the solid material. This low-density foam is earning acceptance in many areas because of the following combination of properties:

Chemical stability, strength and toughness, flexibility over a wide temperature range, low

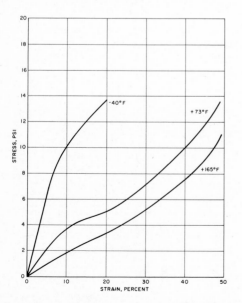

Figure XIV-1, compressive stress-strain of low density polyethylene foam at various temperatures.

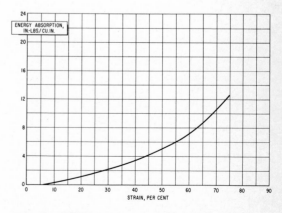

Figure XIV-2, energy absorption for low-density polyethylene foam.

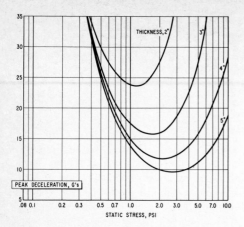

Figure XIV-3, dynamic cushioning of low-density polyethylene foam from a 12" drop height.

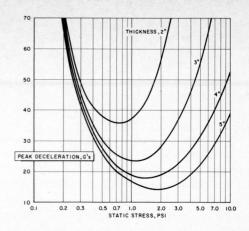

Figure XIV-4, dynamic cushioning of low-density polyethylene foam from an 18" drop height.

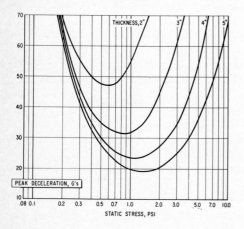

Figure XIV-5, dynamic cushioning of low-density polyethylene foam from a 24" drop height.

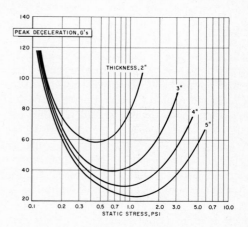

Figure XIV-6, dynamic cushioning of low-density polyethylene foam from a 30" drop height.

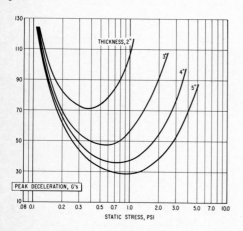

Figure XIV-7, dynamic cushioning of low-density polyethylene foam from a 36" drop height.

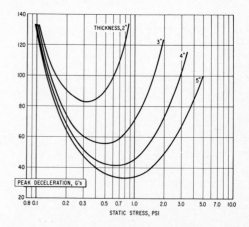

Figure XIV-8, dynamic cushioning of low-density polyethylene foam from a 42" drop height.

water absorption, low moisture vapor transmission, light weight, good insulation value, no odor, no toxicological effects and it is easily fabricated.

It has a natural white color and good cushioning property (energy absorption) over a wide range of temperatures.

Table XIV-1 lists typical property values for

Table XIV-1—Properties of Low-density Polyethylene Foam

	Test procedure	Property
Density, lb per cu ft	ASTM D 1622-59T	1.8-2.6
Water resistance:		
Capillarity	—	None
Adsorption, lb per sq ft	Military spec. MIL-P-40619	.1
Water vapor permeability, Perm-in.	ASTM E96-53T Procedure E	0.40
Buoyancy, lb./cu ft		55
Resiliency, % rebound	Bashore	30-35
Tensile strength, psi	ASTM D-1623-59T	20-30
Thermal conductivity, Btu. in./hr sq ft °F @ 70°F	Heat flow meter	0.35-0.40
Maximum temperature for continuous use, °F	—	160
Heat aging at 140°F:		
Volume change in seven days, %	—	1
Dielectric constant, at 10^9 cps	ASTM D1673-59T	1.05
Dissipation factor, at 10^9 cps	ASTM D1673-59T	0.0002

low-density polyethylene foam.

Static loading properties

Fig XIV-1 is a typical stress-strain curve for low-density polyethylene foam.

The energy absorbed by low-density polyethylene foam at any particular point can be determined on the curve by calculating the area under the curve up to that point. The value "energy absorption" expressed in in.-lb per cu in. can then be plotted as shown in Fig XIV-2.

Dynamic loading properties

Typical deceleration-load data for low-density polyethylene foam are presented in Figures XIV-3 through XIV-11. These were obtained at room temperature. Material thickness of 2,3,4, and 5 in. at drop heights ranging from 12 to 48 in. are given. These curves graphically illustrate the peak deceleration of a known weight dropped from various heights impacting the foam over a given area. For more detailed information on dynamic cushioning principles refer to Section VI: Foamed Plastics in Packaging.

Since low-density polyethylene foam is a thermoplastic material, it is stiff at low tem

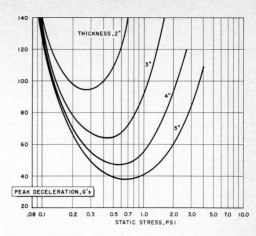

Figure XIV-9, dynamic cushioning of low-density polyethylene foam from a 48" drop height.

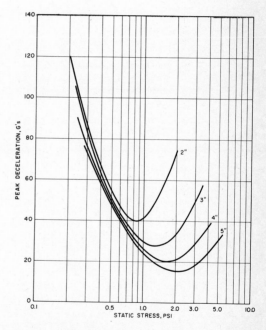

Figure XIV-10, dynamic cushioning of low-density polyethylene foam from a 30" drop height at —65°F.

peratures and becomes increasingly flexible at higher temperatures. Fig XIV-1 shows the static stress-strain relationship for the material at —40°F, 73°F and 165°F. Figures XIV-10 and XIV-11 illustrate the dynamic cushioning properties of low-density polyethylene foam at —65°F and +155°F for a 30 in. height of drop.

Compressive creep and set

All foamed plastics tend to creep under load; that is, they lose a portion of their original thickness when subjected to static load conditions over a period of time. Some materials are more subject to creep under load than others. Creep characteristics are important because they affect the cushioning ability of the material, particularly over extended periods of time. The designer uses this information for increasing the thickness of the material to compensate for creep effect. Figures XIV-12 and XIV-13 illustrate the creep characteristics of low-density polyethylene foam under varying load conditions and at various temperatures.

Compression set — the amount of thickness

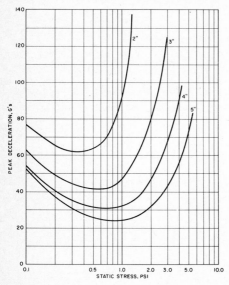

Figure XIV-11, dynamic cushioning of low-density polyethylene foam from a 30" drop height at 155°F.

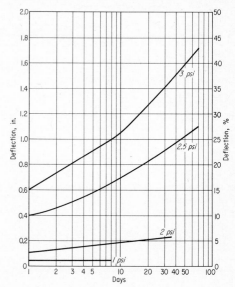

Figure XIV-12, compressive creep of low-density polyethylene foam (4" x 4" x 4" sample) at 73°F.

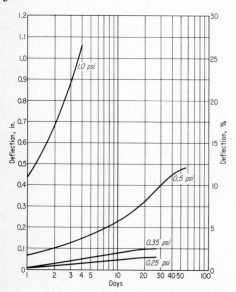

Figure XIV-13, compressive creep of low-density polyethylene foam (4" x 4" x 4" sample) at 155°F.

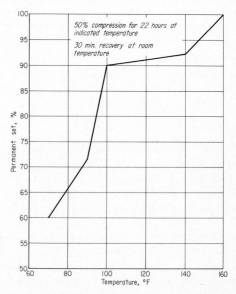

Figure XIV-14, permanent set of low-density polyethylene foam. 50% compression for 22 hours at indicated temperature; 30 min recovery at room temperature.

the material fails to regain after a given specified load has been removed — is also important in determining the performance of any cushioning material. Compression set is doubly important when the cushion is to be reused, and material that undergoes too much permanent set cannot economically be reused. Low-density polyethylene foam performance is shown in Figures XIV-14 to XIV-16 for various loading conditions and temperatures.

Chemical resistance

Polyethylene foam is exceptionally resistant to most solvents and chemicals at room temperature. The material shows no effects from contact with fuel oil and heavier hydrocarbons, but exhibits swelling when submerged for some time in gasoline. Acids and alkalis normally do not affect the material, but strong oxidizing agents may eventually cause degradation, especially at high temperatures. At temperatures above 130°F, it is susceptible to attack by various solvents.

Low-density polyethylene foam is chemically neutral and contains no water-soluble constituents.

Burning characteristics

Presently there are no low-density polyethylene foams that can be classified as flame retardant. The commercially available product has a burning rate of about 2.5 in. per minute as determined by ASTM D-1692-59T. It does not readily start burning from sparks or short circuits as the material will melt away, creating a void around the heat source.

3. FABRICATION

Mechanical methods

Low-density polyethylene foam is easily fabricated with conventional power tools. However, its flexibility makes the choice of fabricating tools more difficult than for rigid foams. Power tools with blades or bits having a slicing action give the best results.

Sawing—Bandsaws with scalloped blades and foam rubber slab splitters are used successfully for cutting and trimming this foam. Bandsaws with toothed blades and circular saws may be used, but should be operated with as high a peripheral speed as practical.

Sheets of low-density polyethylene foam may be fabricated from round stock using the veneering technique employed by the plywood industry. Round pieces of stock are placed in a rotating chuck and thin sheets of foamed plastic are peeled off with a cutting blade parallel to the axis of rotation. Sheets in thicknesses of 1/16″ to ¼″ have been fabricated from 6″ diameter round stock.

Routing—Router bits with spiral cutting blades are the most satisfactory. However,

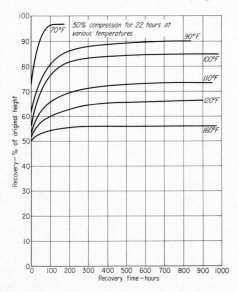

Figure XIV-15, recovery of low-density polyethylene foam. The samples were compressed 50% for 22 hours at the various temperatures and allowed to recover at room temperature.

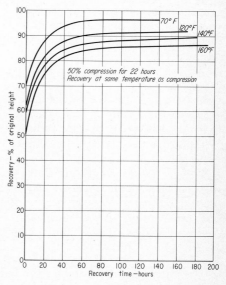

Figure XIV-16, recovery of low-density polyethylene foam, compressed 50% for 22 hours. Recovery is at the same temperature as compression.

Figure XIV-17, fabrication of low-density polyethylene foam with a bandsaw.

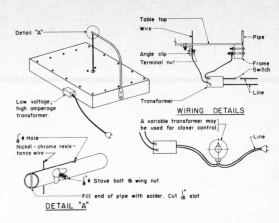

Figure XIV-18, hot wire cutting equipment.

straight blade router bits and dado blades may be used with high peripheral speeds.

Die cutting—Metal shear type steel rule dies may be used with excellent results in the fabrication of gaskets and seals from polyethylene foam. The cutting blade should be rigid and a sharp cutting edge should be maintained.

For parts requiring close dimensional tolerances, it may be necessary to age sliced stock for several days to allow it to become dimensionally stable before die cutting. The slicing operation tends to relieve stresses which are inherent in low-density polyethylene foam with the result that sliced stock may be dimensionally unstable during the stress relaxation period.

Sawdust in mechanical fabricating operations

Sawdust produced in the mechanical fabrication of plastic foams is not considered a health hazard but it may present certain problems. Sawdust in contact with the skin can be rather annoying, particularly if the worker is perspiring. It is also irritating if allowed to come in contact with the eyes. Employee comfort should be maintained by proper control of fabrication conditions: a pneumatic sawdust removal system at the point of cutting is recommended.

Hot wire cutting

Low-density polyethylene foam, a thermoplastic material, softens and melts when heated. This property is utilized in its fabrication by hot wire cutting, which involves the melting of the cell structure. A hot wire cut surface is different in appearance from that of a mechanically cut surface, because of the formation of a thin layer of plastic over the cell structure as it is melted by contact with the heated wire. This effect may be desirable because of the added strength afforded by the thin covering layer of solid plastic.

Feed rates in hot wire cutting vary substantially from one lot of material to another. They are generally lower than those in mechanical cutting. Multiple wires, spaced as desired, are therefore utilized in production operations whenever possible. Factors affecting feed rate in hot wire cutting are: temperature of the wire, thickness and density of the foam, cell size. The feed rate must be low enough to prevent distortion of the wire or wires which would result in uneven cuts. Automatic feeding devices are required to obtain flat, level surfaces on long, straight cuts. Some smoke is produced during a hot wire cutting operation and should be removed from the immediate area by proper ventilation or an exhaust system.

Plane surfaces may be cut with a taut, small diameter wire. The wire may be spring loaded to maintain a taut condition. Curved surfaces require a heavy wire or a ribbon formed to the desired shape. Symmetrical objects may be fabricated by rotation of either the foam or the formed wire. Electrical-resistance-heated metal dies may be used for cutting complete shapes from the foam in a single operation.

The individual components of a conventional

hot wire cutting assembly are readily obtainable items, and the principle of operation is simple. A low voltage current is applied to a nickel-chrome resistance wire, and heats it in proportion to the current applied and the resistance of the wire. Temperature control of the wire may be obtained with a variable voltage transformer in conjunction with a low voltage-high amperage transformer. Amperage and voltage drops per foot of wire for various sizes are listed in Table XIV-2 to

Table XIV-2—Wire Sizes and Current Requirements for Hot Wire Cutting

Size of wire	Voltage drop, v/ft	Amperes
No. 35	13 to 15	1.44 to 1.74
No. 25	6.2 to 8.6	3.0 to 4.0
No. 20	4.4 to 5.6	6.4 to 8.0
No. 15	2.5 to 4.0	12 to 18
No. 10	2.0 to 3.5	24 to 36
¼″ x ⅛″	1.5 to 2.0	75 to 110

Note: These are not minimum and maximum figures. They are intended only to assist in determining the size transformer to be used with each size wire. The transformer voltage output should be equal to the voltage drop of the cutting wire. Its current rating should be equivalent to the value stated in the table.

assist in determining the size transformer required.

Molding

Contoured molds may be used in shaping low-density polyethylene foam. The foam may first be mechanically cut to the approximate shape of the mold. Molds should be heated to a temperature of 250 to 350°F for the forming operation and subsequently cooled to stabilize the formed part and facilitate its removal from the mold cavity. Molds may be cored for better internal cooling or may be submerged into a coolant such as cold water. Coating the mold surfaces with "Teflon" greatly aids release of the polyethylene after cooling.

Sheets of polyethylene foam may be vacuum-formed to various shapes. The process is similar to that used for forming other heated plastic sheet. Heating is best accomplished on both surfaces of the sheet, keeping the heaters at about 12″ from the sheet.

Heated augers or rods may be used in coring low-density polyethylene foam. Tools should be heated to about 350°F to penetrate the foam by melting it.

4. HEAT BONDING

Parts made of low-density polyethylene foam may be joined by heat fusion. A hot plate heated to about 350°F is ideal for this operation. The surfaces of the two pieces of foam to be joined are heated simultaneously until softening begins. The pieces are then quickly joined under moderate pressure and an excellent bond forms as the foam cools. Coating the heating surface with Teflon will aid in the release of the polyethylene.

Sheets of the foamed plastic may be heat-sealed with special heat-sealing equipment. Satisfactory seals have been made by using half-cylinder brass bars with electric heating elements. At temperatures of 280 to 310°F sealing time will vary according to the thickness of the sheet. The use of glass matt reinforced Teflon cloth over the sealing bars will prevent sticking of the polyethylene to the bars. The diameter of the sealing bars may vary, but one inch diameter is considered a minimum for adequate seal strength.

5. ADHESIVES AND COATINGS

Adhesive bonding

Low-density polyethylene foam is inert to solvents; adhesives containing solvents can be used without fear of dissolving the foam. But the smooth skin surface of extruded foam presents a difficult bonding problem with the majority of available adhesives. Pressure-sensitive rubber-emulsion adhesives and rubber-solvent contact adhesives give the best results for bonding the smooth skin surface of the foamed plastic to itself or to other materials.

The cut surface of low-density polyethylene foam is not as difficult to bond as the smooth skin surface, since the cellular structure of the foam increases the contact interface between adhesive and foam and provides a certain degree of mechanical adhesion. The cut surface of the material may also be bonded to itself or to other materials with pressure-sensitive rubber-emulsion adhesives or rubber-solvent contact adhesives. When properly used these adhesives form bonds with strengths exceeding the tensile strength of the foam.

Low-density polyethylene foam is a closed cell foam and the bonding of it to nonporous materials with drying adhesives presents a drying problem. For this reason, pressure-sensitive and contact adhesives are more satisfactory.

Coatings

Low-density polyethylene foam is flexible and most applications for which it is used will

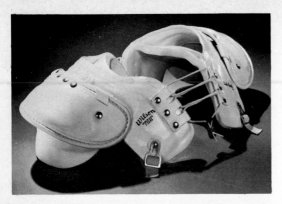

Figure XIV-19, low-density polyethylene foam is used as a cushioning material for football shoulder pads. Courtesy Wilson Sporting Goods Co.

utilize its flexibility. Consequently, the coatings applied to it will necessarily be elastic in nature.

Because printing inks adhere poorly to untreated polyethylene foam, it has been necessary to develop surface treating techniques in order to decorate the foam satisfactorily. There are two general categories of treatment: chemical and physical. Both have the effect of polarizing the surface of the foam, making it receptive to ink. These two general categories are broken down into four principal methods of treatment.

Chemical treatment may be chlorination or oxidation. Physical treatment may be a differential heat treatment or an electronic treatment. Since all of these processes are costly their commercial use for polyethylene foam is very rare.

A colored polyethylene film may be laminated to the surface of the foam as a decorative coating. This is accomplished with heat and slight pressure followed by cooling to form an integral colored skin. Vinyl film may also be bonded to the foam with a suitable contact adhesive to serve as a decorative coating.

Certain commercial elastomeric coatings may also be applied to low-density polyethylene foam as decorative or weather-resistant coatings. Coatings based on "Hypalon", synthetic elastomer produced by E. I. du Pont de Nemours & Co., have proven especially satisfactory for that purpose.

Hard surface coatings such as polyester and epoxy resins can be cast directly on the surface of low-density polyethylene foam. Re-inforced with glass fiber cloth, these coatings result in slightly flexible panels with hard, tough skins.

6. APPLICATIONS

Agricultural

Because low-density polyethylene foam has excellent cushioning properties, is tough and won't absorb water, it has found many uses in the field of agriculture. It has been used as padding to prevent bruising of cattle and chickens. It has also been used as a liner for loading hoppers in fruit and vegetable operations.

Athletic

Low-density polyethylene foam has found many applications as cushioning protection in athletic equipment. Football shoulder pads (Fig XIV-19) have been lined with the material. The foamed plastic has also been used as wall padding and wrestling mats in gymnasiums.

Buoyancy

Because of its closed-cell structure and natural resistance to water, the foam will maintain a buoyancy factor of at least 55 lb per cu ft. This, combined with toughness and flexibility, suggests its use in such personnel floatation items as water ski belts, buoyant jackets, marine toys and swimming aids, and for various kinds of buoys, floats and boat fenders.

Industrial

Another active use is for gasketing. The foam adjusts itself to any inaccuracies of the mating surfaces and with its non-wicking closed-cell structure provides an excellent seal against liquid or gas leakage. Polyethylene foam, in addition, has good solvent resistance.

Packaging (See also Section VI—Foamed Plastics in Packaging)

Various packaging applications require a material which is flexible, yet has enough rigidity to give continued support to the object packaged. Low-density polyethylene foam's closed cell structure has a myriad of cushioning bubbles to protect package contents from an abrupt jarring blow; after a blow, this shock-absorbent material gently eases the contents back to their original position. Polyethylene foam is non-corrosive, contains no water and absorbs none. Fabricators have found that this material can be easily fabricated to desired shapes to provide an economical packaging media.

Thermal insulation

In many types of refrigerated equipment, a flexible insulation can be used to reduce fabrication and labor costs. This equipment includes tanks, heat exchangers, line strainers and other nonstandard devices. Low-density polyethylene foam is economical to install and is an excellent insulator for these applications. It can be held in place by banding or with pressure-sensitive rubber-based adhesives. For outside work a surface coating is recommended to protect the insulation from the sun. Its resistance to chemicals and solvents suggests its use in trouble spots where corrosive atmospheres or spillage degrade other insulations.

PART II–FOAMED HIGH-DENSITY POLYETHYLENE
By H. J. Pazinski

1. GENERAL INFORMATION

Foamed polyethylene which has been expanded to a density of 0.46 (30 lb per cu ft) or higher is termed high-density foam. These foams can be produced from conventional high-pressure, low-density polyethylenes (0.916-0.927 specific gravity) or from low-pressure, high-density polyethylene (0.941-0.965).

Foamed polyethylenes are used in many contour and film and sheeting applications because of low cost, light weight and buoyancy characteristics. They come in the form of extruded rods and disks cut from rods or stamped from sheets for such applications as spacers, floats, cap liners, and bumpers. For wire and cable insulation, they have low dielectric constant in addition to the above advantages. They make a low capacitance material for insulation in high frequency applications, such as coaxial and video pair cables. Foamed polyethylenes are also used as jacketing for buoyant type cable.

By far, the most common method for the preparation of high-density polyethylene foams is by extrusion. Blow molding and injection molding are difficult and require very precise techniques. In the extrusion of wire and cable insulation and for contour foams, the cell structure is unicellular—that is, it consists of independent cells. In film and sheet extrusion, the die and head design will produce an end product consisting of interconnected cells.

Prior to 1958, all of the foamed polyethylene insulation was based on high-pressure or low-density polyethylenes (0.916-0.928 specific gravity). Their physical and mechanical properties limited their applications.

The introduction of the high-density or linear polyethylene resins in the 0.941 to 0.946 range provided a material tougher and more rigid than the conventional low-density resins. Because of the increase in density of the polymer, a product is obtained with improved tensile strength, higher hardness, higher deformation resistance, better abrasion resist-

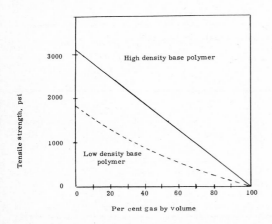

Figure XIV-20, tensile strength vs. gas content.

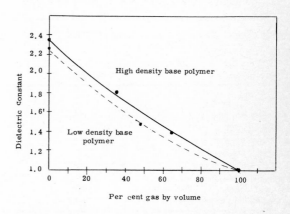

Figure XIV-21, dielectric constant vs. gas content.

ance, and higher modulus. To the fabricator of cellular products, these resins provide a means of making foamed, lightweight objects with physical and mechanical properties nearly equal to that of the solid low density polyethylene. New areas of applications such as miniature coaxial cables, contour and structural designs were opened up. This is all accomplished by proper choice of resins, blowing agent, foamed density, design and proper tooling for fabrication of the end products.

Because of the difference in dielectric constants, solid polyethylene is generally used with a 0.012 in. wall thickness on #19 AWG bare copper wire single-conductor telephone cable, while a thickness of only 0.009 in. of cellular high-density polyethylene foam is satisfactory for equivalent electrical performance. This results in a saving in weight—the weight of solid polyethylene insulation on such a cable is 3.8 lb per mile, that of the cellular product only 1.92 lb per mile. Such a difference results in substantial advantages in the handling and the installation of the cable.

2. RESIN REQUIREMENTS

Base resins available to the industry vary in density as well as in melt indices (from .01 to 10 or higher). These parameters dictate, to a degree, the processability, the mechanical, physical and electrical properties of the resins and good judgment is necessary to choose the proper resin for a particular cellular application. Often specification requirements, economic considerations or type of processing equipment narrow the selection. In various specialty areas, newly designed polymers are required, as standard resins are not adequate.

Low-melt-index resins result in foams with

improved mechanical and physical properties, but they are more difficult to process. The high-melt-index resin offers improved processing characteristics but poorer properties.

Wire and cable and contour applications now utilize foamed products based on both high- and low-density resins. Comparative properties of the solid base high and low density resins are shown on Table XIV-3.

Foamed polypropylene has also been manufactured and tested. Its mechanical properties

Table XIV-3—Comparative Properties of Solid Polyethylene Resins*

Properties	ASTM method, or special test	High-density polymer	Low-density polymer
Density @ 23°C, g/cc	D-792-50-A	0.947	0.920
Melt index @ 44 psi, grams in 10 min.	D-1238-51T	0.2	0.3
Hardness @ 23°C, Durometer "D"	D-676-55T	58	45
Vicat softening point, °F	D-1525	121	97
Torsional stiffness, psi @ 23°F	D-1043-51	100,000	23,000
Deformation under load, %	WC-75/B/3		
@ 110°C		0	20
@ 120°C		0	100
@ 130°C		33	—
Tear strength, psi	D-732-46	3000	2400
Tensile strength, psi	D-412-51T	3400	2200
Elongation at break, %	D-412-51T	250	625
Abrasion resistance		175	70
Brittle temperature (F_{20}**), °C	D-746-55T	−95	−100
Dielectric constant @ 1 mc	D-150	2.34	2.27
Dissipation factor @ 1 mc		0.0002	0.0002
Dielectric strength, vpm	D-119	550	550

*The physical, mechanical and some of the electrical properties of the foamed polyethylenes decrease with decreasing foam density (Fig. XIV-20 and XIV-21).
**20% failures.

Table XIV-4—Solid versus Cellular Properties

Property	Solid polyethylene	Foam from low density resin	Foam from high density resin	Foam from high density resin
Density @ 23°C, g/cc	0.92	0.50	0.48	0.65
Hardness, durometer "D"	45	39	49	51
Tensile strength, psi[1]	2100	600	1800	2800
Elongation, %	600	300	350	390
Scrape abrasion[2]	20-30	1-2	10-15	20-30
Dielectric constant @ 1 MC	2.28	1.50	1.53	1.7
Dissipation factor @ 1 MC	.0002	.0002	.0006	.0006
Compression loading, psi	1300	300	450	580
Dielectric strength, vpm	550	190	190	250
Flexural modulus @ 23°C, psi	22,000	14,000	60,000	—

[1]Properties measured on 2/64" wall insulation #14 AWG wire.
[2]Properties measured on 8 mil wall insulation #19 AWG wire. Comparisons based on equal wall thickness. Tests give number of strokes required to short an insulated wire scraped longitudinally over the machined edge of a square tool steel bar, with a 2 lb load hanging on wire.

are superior to those of high density polyethylene foam, but its low-temperature brittleness make it somewhat less attractive. Cellular polypropylene is being evaluated in various fields of application.

From the preceding data, one can choose any particular resin and by proper foaming, tailor, within limitations, a cellular product possessing the desired properties. (Table XIV-4).

3. BLOWING AGENT

In the preparation of high-density foams, a number of chemical blowing agents can be used. They vary widely in decomposition temperature and amount of gas evolution. In certain applications such as wire and cable, residue products which are polar in nature will have adverse electrical properties and cannot be used. Additives also affect the decomposition temperature range.

For high density foams, chemical blowing agents in a content range of 0.3% to 2.5% by weight are generally used. Chemical blowing agents are preferred to other types because of the ease of dispersion and minimum equipment modifications necessary.

Some of the typical blowing agents that can be used are azodicarbonamides, azobisisobutyronitrile dinitrosopenta methylene tetramine, and p,p'-oxybis (benzene sulfonyl hydrazide).

4. EQUIPMENT REQUIREMENTS

The high density foams can be produced on conventional extrusion equipment. A long-barreled 20:1 L/D ratio extruder with a metering type polyethylene screw is recommended to provide good, uniform mix of the polymer as well as uniform temperature of extrudate. This, in turn, will result in a uniform liberation of gas or a uniform foamed product. Any variations, due to poor heating controls or cycling of the heaters, will manifest itself in the end product. The die and head should be streamlined to prevent hang-up. Minimum land lengths are recommended.

The object of the operation is to obtain a thorough and uniform mixture of the blowing agent in the polymer. The temperature is adjusted to the decomposition of the blowing agent. The blowing agent liberates gas, which is held in the polymer by the pressures developed during the extrusion operation. As the extrudate emerges from the die, the pressure is released and the gas cells are formed.

Expansion of the polymer will occur from the time it leaves the die until it hardens by cooling in the air or in water. Adjustable cooling troughs which can use either hot or cold water, or just air cooling, are recommended. This method is widely used in wire and cable insulation, to control the diameter at a desired level of capacitance. In heavy wall insulation, all three media are used in succession to prevent the insulation from collapsing or going out of round.

Thus, the production of high density foams depends on:

1. Blowing agent concentration.
2. Viscosity of compound leaving die.
3. Temperature of compound leaving die.
4. Rate at which the material is cooled.

Extruder temperature profiles recommended for high density foams (compared with those for extrusion of solid polyethylene) are shown in Table XIV-5.

Extruder temperatures may vary with the type of extruder and screw. The use of additives in the polymer can be used to change the processing temperature profiles—they may either give a lubrication action or accelerate decomposition temperature of blowing agent.

In wire insulation, the conductor temperature must be controlled to obtain proper cell structure, density and adhesion. If the conductor is cold, the insulation surrounding the conductor will freeze and will not form cells. This results in lower density and poor elongation properties.

Table XIV-5—Comparative Extrusion Temperature Profiles

	Barrel temperatures, °F				Compound temp., °F	Screw temp., °F
	Rear	Middle	Front	Head		
High density foam						
0.92 density polymer	250	270	310	300	305	90
0.96 density polymer	290	320	400	390	395	90
Solid polymer						
0.92 density polymer	380	380	400	400	420	neutral*
0.96 density polymer	450	450	450	450	440	neutral*

*Neutral means that no external heat or cooling is applied to screw.

Section XV—FOAMED VINYL PLASTICS
By Arnold C. Werner and William M. Smith

1. MANUFACTURE

Vinyl foams are made by a number of different techniques, producing a wide variety of cell constructions, degrees of softness or rigidity. As many qualities can be controlled, vinyl foams are suitable for a large number of diverse applications.

Mechanical technique

One mechanical technique of which the *Elastomer process* and the *Dennis process* are examples involves foam formation by dissolving a gas under pressure in the plasticizer portion of the plastisol, then allowing the system to rapidly come to atmospheric pressure. This results in the dissolved gas coming out of solution as dispersed bubbles throughout the plastic, thereby foaming the liquid plastisol which is then fused. This foam is characterized by a fairly large but uniform cell size, medium to low density and presence of interconnecting cells. Plastisols so foamed may be cast onto a moving belt and fused with heat for the production of foam slabs, or cast into molds to make seat cushions and other items. Although it is possible to cast foam sections several inches thick by using this technique, fusing them is difficult because of the self-insulating nature of the foam.

A second technique, called *the Vanderbilt process*, involves the mechanical whipping of air into a plastisol in a machine such as an Oaks foamer (Fig XV-1). This process requires a specially compounded plastisol, one that possesses special rheological and surface tension properties.

The key to the process lies in the use of a proprietary surfactant, called "Fomade," which enables the plastisol to mechanically entrain air and retain it in tiny discrete bubbles with sufficient stability as it is pumped, poured, spread and finally gelled prior to fusion (Fig XV-2). Fomade (manufactured by R. T. Vanderbilt Co.) also contains a vinyl stabilizer so no further stabilization is usually required.

As a result of exposure to intense mechanical agitation, copious quantities of air are incorporated as tiny bubbles into the liquid plastisol. The type of foam produced by the Vanderbilt process has an interconnecting cell structure; the cells are very small and cannot be seen with the unaided eye. Density values are in the medium range, somewhat higher than those developed by the Elastomer technique.

Chemical blowing technique

Most vinyl foams are produced today by the chemical blowing agent technique. Chemically blown foams may be classified into those developed under pressure and those developed at atmospheric pressure:

Foaming under pressure—Confining the vinyl under pressure and heat decomposes a

Figure XV-1, internal view of Oaks Foamer. Courtesy E. T. Oaks Corp.

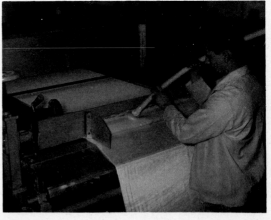

Figure XV-2, spread coating of foam by the Vanderbilt process. Courtesy R. T. Vanderbilt Co., and Middletown Rubber Co.

blowing agent so that when brought back to room temperature and atmospheric pressure, it is uniformly distributed throughout the vinyl mass in the form of very fine cells which are not connecting. When enough blowing agent is used, and when the plastic is subsequently heated to its softening point, the gas under pressure in each cell expands the plastic mass many times until an equilibrium is reached. The cells do not connect with each other and density is low. This type of foam is best suited for flotation stocks such as fish net floats, life preservers, boat bumpers, etc. It is available in commercial quantities from several manufacturers who market their products in a variety of shapes and sizes for fabrication into the final product. Density values may vary from 3 to 14 lb per cu ft with hardness values ranging from relatively soft to semi-rigid depending on the end use requirement.

Here is one technique by which pressure-molded vinyl foam is produced:

1) Fill mold with polyvinylchloride (PVC) plastisol, or slab stock, containing a blowing agent.

2) Confine in press using several thousand pounds pressure and metal gaskets to hold PVC in mold.

3) Elevate press temperature to 350°F (by steam or electricity) to decompose the blowing agent and fuse the vinyl. Since the gas and vinyl are confined under pressure throughout this fusion step, the temperature at which the gas decomposes is not important, and low temperature or high temperature blowing agents may be used.

4) After sufficient press time has elapsed to effect complete decomposition of the blowing agent, the press is cooled down so that the vinyl temperature is reduced to or near room temperature. The gas is now distributed throughout the plastic mass in minute bubbles, each one under pressure. The plastic is sufficiently cool and immobile to keep the gas confined under pressure until its expansion, and the molding may be removed from the press.

5) The partially-expanded molding is then placed in boiling water or in a forced-air circulating oven at about 200°F for post expansion. This modest amount of heat softens the plastic so that it will expand under the influence of the pressurized gas present in each cell. Expansion will continue until the gas pressure expands in each cell to equilibrium with atmospheric pressure.

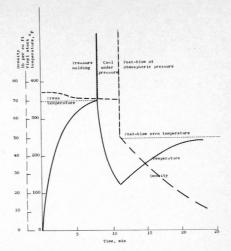

Figure XV-3, pressure-molded foam pressure and density versus time.

Fig XV-3 describes this process in terms of time, temperature, and foam density.

One of the problems involved in the use of pressure-molded foams is their tendency to shrink in service. This may result from the foam's effort to revert to its higher density, a typical manifestation of "plastic memory." To overcome this, an annealing cycle, where the foam is kept at 150°F for several hours to slowly dissipate its internal strains, is sometimes helpful.

An interesting technique has been developed to produce an expanded, unplasticized vinyl foam using acetone as a temporary plasticizer. Another technique, involving also the use of acetone, allows for the development of a solid vinyl skin where the foam is in contact with the metal mold. This is said to eliminate the need for applying a vinyl lacquer wear surface over the foam object.

Foaming at atmospheric pressure—Most chemically blown vinyl foams are expanded at atmospheric pressure. They utilize both high and low decomposition temperature blowing agents. Depending on the formulation and processing conditions, these foams have medium density, medium size cells partially or completely connecting.

Chemically blown foams use a blowing agent dispersed as a finely divided solid throughout the liquid plastisol. Blowing agents with micron-size particles may be dispersed on a paint mill, ball-milled, or simply stirred into a plastisol under high shear for thorough dispersion. The most common technique is to prepare the blowing agent as a concentrated paste (produced by milling into a suitable plasticizer) and then mixing this paste into a plastisol compound. The plastisol may then be poured into a mold, or more often, cast onto a paper or fabric substrate. Then it is passed through a fusion oven where, at a definite temperature, the blowing agent decomposes to form a gas which develops a cellular structure in the plastisol.

Plastisol gelation & fusion

Certain temperatures are more propitious than others for the activation of the blowing agent and the development of a satisfactory foam.

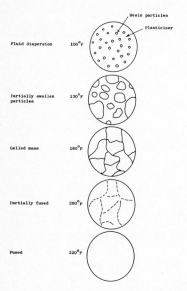

Figure XV-4, plastisol gelation and fusion.

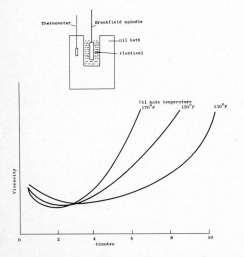

Figure XV-5, plastisol gelation viscosity versus time and temperature.

At room temperature, a plastisol is a dispersion of PVC particles in a plasticizer, each particle approximately a micron in diameter. Other formulating ingredients are generally present (e.g. stabilizers, pigments, fillers, etc.) in both liquid and powder form. As heat is introduced into the system during the fusion process, the plasticizer begins to penetrate into the PVC particles, thereby swelling them as shown in Fig XV-4. These swollen PVC particles contact each other, increasing plastisol viscosity, then developing into a dry gelled mass, lacking mobility or cohesiveness. Depending on the formulation, this gelled state will develop when the plastisol reaches a temperature in the 150-240°F range. Fig XV-5 shows the relationship between time and temperature in the gelation process.

As more heat goes into the plastisol, bringing it through the gel region, the resin dissolves in the plasticizer and a fused product ensues. It is thermoplastic and has high strength when cooled back to room temperature. The fusion temperature may start at about 300°F, depending on the types of resin and plasticizer used. Solvating plasticizers and copolymer resins tend to lower the fusion temperature to approximately 280°F. With a PVC homopolymer resin optimum physical properties occur near 350°F (Fig XV-6).

Being thermoplastic, the vinyl compound develops a degree of mobility as the fusion temperature range is reached. In this hot melt state, the vinyl compound develops measurable viscosities, many times the viscosity levels associated with a plastisol at room temperature. Fluidity increases as the temperature increases and until thermal degradation of the polymer occurs.

In order to develop a cellular structure during this change of temperature, the vinyl mass must be sufficiently fluid for the blowing agent to expand. But at the same time, it must be sufficiently cohesive to retain the gas, produced by the blowing agent, in uniformly sized and dispersed bubbles.

Pre-gelation foaming (low temperature)

A low temperature blowing agent, such as "Nitrosan," liberates its gas in the 190-220°F range. In this system, decomposition of the blowing agent occurs prior to the gelation of the plastisol. This requires high-molecular weight plastisol resins, slow gelling plasticizers, and, when necessary, various additives to retard gelation. Generally, copolymer plastisol resins and plasticizers such as dioctyl phthalate (DOP), tricresyl phosphate (TCP), etc. are not quite suitable due to their low temperature gelation action.

Plasticizers, such as didecyl phthalate (DDP) and polymeric types are better suited. Barium and calcium petroleum sulfonates are known to retard gelation and improve cell structure, and are therefore recommended as additives.

Gelation and fusion occur in rapid succession as the plastic mass continues to be exposed to fusion temperatures. Foams produced in this fashion are characterized by an open cell construction, relatively fine cell size and

medium to low density, depending on the quantity of blowing agent used.

Post-fusion foaming: high temperature

At least two blowing agents are available which decompose at temperatures within the fusion range of the plastisol (Table XV-1). Today, azodicarbonamide (AZ) is most commonly used.

The decomposition temperature range of vinyl systems based on azodicarbonamide is shown in Fig. XV-7. These system foam well within the hot-melt temperature range of PVC. The ability of PVC to expand at these temperatures depends also on the hot melt state (viscosity) of the plastic.

The hot-melt viscosity of a vinyl is decreased with:

1) higher plasticizer content

Table XV-1—Blowing Agents for Polyvinyl Foam

Blowing agent	Chemical composition	Gas volume per gram of blowing agent	Average decomposition temp. in vinyl	Typical applications	Supplier
Nitrosan (formerly BL-353)	N,N'-di-methyl-N,N'-dinitroso tere-phthalamide	125 cc	200°F	Atmospheric foam	E. I. duPont de Nemours & Co., Inc.
Celogen	p,p'-oxybis-(benzene-sulfonyl hydrazide)	110 cc	310°F	Extrusion	Naugatuck Chemical Co.
Unicel ND	Dinitroso-penta-methyl-ene-tetramine	96 cc	340°F	Pressure blowing*	E. I. duPont de Nemours & Co., Inc.
Celogen-AZ	Azodicar-bonamide	225 cc	350°F	Extrusion	Naugatuck Chemical Co.
Kempore R-125	Azodicar-bonamide	225 cc	350°F	Inj. molding Blow molding	National Poly-chemicals
Lucidol ADA	Azodicar-bonamide	225 cc	350°F		Lucidol Div., Wallace and Tiernan, Inc.
Azepor	Azodicar-bonamide	225 cc	350°F	Calendering Coating	Parco Chemical Co.
Celogen-BH	p,p'-oxybis-(benzene-sulfonyl semi-carbazide)	145 cc	370°F	High-temp. extrusion	Naugatuck Chemical Co.
Expandex 177	Barium azo-dicarboxylate	177 cc	450°F	Roto-casting	National Poly-chemicals

*Useful for industrial and other applications where the odor is not a problem.

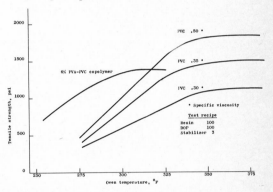

Figure XV-6, tensile strength of plastisol foams versus temperature and resin type.

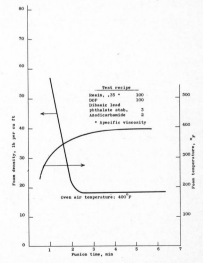

Figure XV-7, foam density and temperature versus fusion time for vinyl systems blown with azocarbonamide.

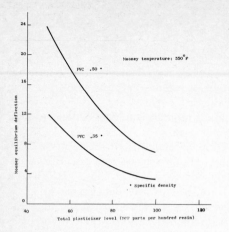

Figure XV-8, hot-melt flow as a function of plasticizer content and PVC molecular weight.

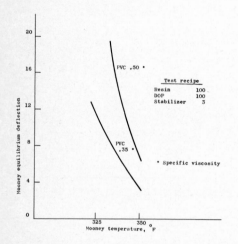

Figure XV-9, hot-melt viscosity as a function of temperature and PVC molecular weight.

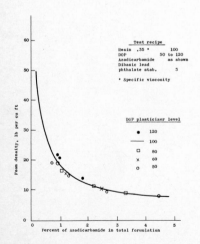

Figure XV-10, vinyl foam density versus blowing agent content and plasticizer level.

2) lower molecular weight PVC resins (Fig XV-8)

3) lower viscosity plasticizers (monomeric versus ploymeric)

4) higher blowing temperature (Fig XV-9).

The blowing agent content determines the final foam density. Fig XV-10 shows that 1% concentration of AZ is the most efficient: higher concentrations have little effect in reducing density.

Lower molecular weight resin is significantly more capable of producing good quality foam, over a wider range of formulating conditions (various blowing agent and plasticizer concentrations).

Early development work with AZ revealed that the addition of a number of chemical compounds (such as stabilizers for vinyls) are effective in causing a more rapid evolution of gas in the decomposition temperature range. Recent studies have confirmed these findings, and a number of proprietary vinyl stabilizer-activator materials are currently available.

Lead stabilizers are excellent activators for AZ, but they must be used cautiously because of lead's sulfur-staining characteristics. Barium-zinc activator-stabilizers are used because they do not cause sulfur-staining. A comparison of the activating influence of these materials on AZ is shown in Fig XV-11. Normally, rapid AZ activation is desirable in plastisol systems to reduce the length of time in the oven or to increase production rates.

Post-fusion foaming: low temperature

A number of conditions may exist where the azodicarbonamide system is not satisfactory

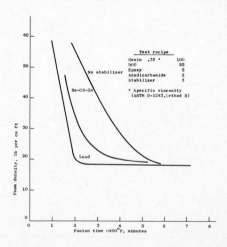

Figure XV-11, comparison of the activation action of various stabilizers.

because of its high temperature-time requirements. Some of these conditions may be:

1) Need for faster production rates with
existing equipment,

2) Limitation on maximum oven temperatures,

3) Coating of heat-sensitive substrates such
as synthetic fabrics, asphalt-saturated felt, or
paper.

For these cases, it is possible to develop
plastisol foam compounds based on a slightly
lower temperature blowing agent such as
"Celogen OT" (Table XV-1). Due to its lower
decomposition temperature, or its more rapid
decomposition rate at the same temperatures,
greater formulating restrictions are placed on
the formulator. The plastic mass must still be
sufficiently fluid for expansion at these lower
hot-melt temperatures. The use of reduced
molecular weight PVC homopolymers and
copolymers becomes mandatory, with this type
of blowing agent.

Half as much gas is developed with Celogen
OT as with AZ and it is necessary to double
the quantity of OT to produce equivalent densities (See Fig XV-12 and XV-13).

Fig XV-14 shows the use of copolymers and
reduced molecular weight homopolymers with
OT at laboratory oven temperatures in the
300° to 350°F range. The use of the copolymer
assures better density and completeness of
fusion.

2. FABRIC-FOAM LAMINATION

The most successful use of chemically-blown

vinyl foam is for foam-fabric laminates (patented Roggi process). These have been developed during the past few years into a popular
"fabric" for the manufacture of winter jackets, snowsuits for children, hats, shoes, boots,
handbags, belts, and upholstery stocks for
home and auto. In each case they simulate
various grades of leather.

Although the vinyl foam-fabric laminate de-
rives most of its strength from the fabric,
the physical properties of the vinyl portion are
important. The influences of plasticizer level
and type on the physical properties of vinyl
films are well known. The influence of resin
molecular weight on the physical properties of
the vinyl film is also well-documented. These

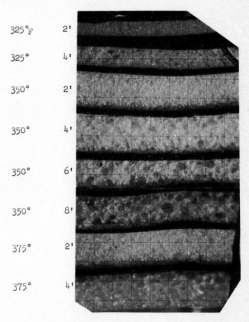

*Figure XV-13, micro-photographs showing cell
structure of foams blown with Celogen OT.*

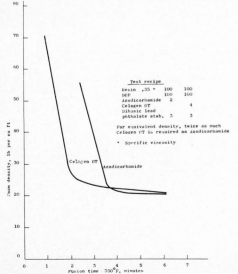

*Figure XV-12, foam density versus fusion
time for different blowing agents.*

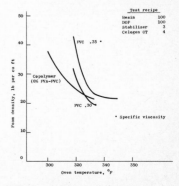

*Figure XV-14, foam density versus oven tem-
perature for various formulations blown with
Celogen OT.*

influences are equally valid for a cellular vinyl product.

Ultimate tensile strength, elongation and tear strength of plastisol foams based on a variety of molecular weight PVC resins and copolymers are shown in Fig XV-15. Foam strength is virtually independent of oven temperature, provided there is sufficient heat to develop adequate fusion and foaming.

These data also show that foam strength increases with increasing resin molecular weight. But with a high molecular weight resin, there is less latitude in the choice of foaming temperature.

In evaluating foam strength *per se*, it was noted that great care must be exercised in measuring foam density and then adjusting the physical property values accordingly: i.e. adjust values downward for higher densities and vice versa when evaluating a series of samples.

Foam density may vary as much as 5 to 10 lb per cu ft without significant change in the hand of the foam-fabric laminate. However, a variation of 5 lb per cu ft could create a 50% change in foam strength of a 20 lb per cu ft product. The influence of resin molecular weight on physical properties is negligible compared to the influence of such factors as foam density, plasticizer type and level.

Foam laminates via plastisol technique

One of the popular techniques is shown schematically in Fig XV-16. A release paper is first coated with an expanded plastisol skin coat. This compound may consist of a blend of monomeric and polymeric plasticizer and may be applied to a thickness of about 8 mils. This is partially fused in an oven with forced convection air to withstand the mechanical strain of subsequent operation. Overfusion of the skin would result in poor adhesion of the subsequent foam layer and would not allow the paper to be used for several passes through the oven. The paper and a partially fused skin plastisol is returned to the coating head where a plastisol, containing blowing agent, is applied to the vinyl skin. Then, the fabric is applied on the foam plastisol, prior to its entry into the final fusion oven.

As the laminate, now consisting of release paper, vinyl skin coat, unblown plastisol (containing blowing agent), and fabric, pass through the oven, fusion and foaming take place. After leaving the oven, the paper is pulled away and reused, if possible. Subsequent steps may involve embossing, printing, and top coating with a vinyl- or vinyl-acrylic-based solution coat for gloss and slip.

It is also possible to flux the plastisol containing the blowing agent first, then apply the fabric with a plastisol adhesive coat, and finally fuse and foam the laminate in a final oven pass. This latter technique is more costly.

Foam laminates via calender techniques

The technology of preparing a chemically-

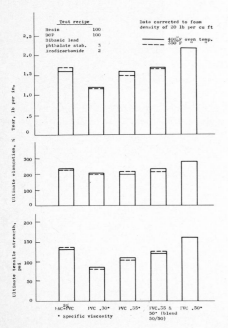

Figure XV-15, physical properties of vinyl foams as a function of resin molecular weight.

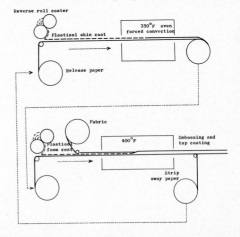

Figure XV-16, schematic representation of plastisol foam-fabric laminating and finishing line.

blown foam for processing through a calender is similar to the plastisol technique, but a few considerations are peculiar to calendering. First, the lowest decomposition temperature of the blowing agent must be kept above calendering roll temperatures, to prevent premature decomposition of the blowing agent on the calender. In this respect, AZ has been particularly useful.

A foam vinyl sheet tends to "pucker" when nearing expansion temperature, a phenomenon related to the mechanical orientation of the film during the calendering process. When the calendered film is laminated to a fabric prior to foaming, the mechanical anchorage of the film to the fabric minimizes puckering, but stress relaxation through the foam may be detected as a loss in cell quality.

In general, the time-temperature-density relationships for calendered foams are similar to those for plastisol systems (Fig XV-17). Slightly more AZ is required in a calendering formulation to achieve the same foam density as would be developed in a similar plastisol system. For example, 2 parts of AZ develops a calendered foam density of 28 lb per cu ft compared with 20 lb per cut ft for a plastisol system (Fig XV-10).

Vinyl foam-fabric laminates may also be manufactured by producing two vinyl films, by conventional calendering techniques—one vinyl film to be used as skin layer and the other vinyl film sheet containing blowing agent to be used for the foam layer. These two layers are then combined with fabric and the blowing agent is activated. The sequence of operations may be:

1) First combine unblown foam sheet with fabric:
   a) through bottom calender nip (this technique is restricted to those calenders where the bottom rolls travel at the same rate);
   b) on an embossing unit in tandem with the calender;
   c) or in a subsequent operation using a laminator and an adhesive plastisol tie coat.
2) Then combine the skin coat with the unblown foam-fabric laminate:
   a) on a laminator (all three lamina, skin, unexpanded foam and fabric, may be combined simultaneously in this fashion);
   b) by applying a reverse-roll-coated plastisol skin coat to the unblown foam.

A pass through a forced air convection oven activates the blowing agent thus producing the cellular portion of the construction. Subsequent steps may involve embossing and top coating as in the plastisol system (Fig XV-18).

Another technique involves the development of foam prior to application of the top film. By laminating a vinyl film to the foam after it has been blown, it is possible to have a completely bubble-free protective film covering the laminate.

Vinyl foam laminates are being produced in large quantity on both calendering and spread-coating (plastisol) equipment. The selection of the particular mode of operation is generally based on the equipment the company has on hand. Some features of each technique are worth noting. Calender processing is traditionally favored for large continuous runs, and foam laminates should be no exception. This is partly due to the lower cost of calender-grade resin compared with plastisol resins.

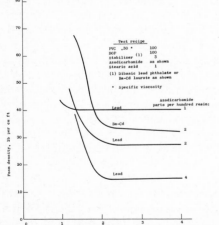

Figure XV-17, calendered foam density in relation to azocarbonamide concentration and stabilizer selection.

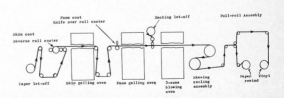

Figure XV-18, calendering of two vinyl layers.

However, calendered foam laminates require the installation of an oven to produce foaming, a piece of equipment which is not normally part of a calendering operation.

Plastisol coaters are relatively inexpensive to install, compared to calenders, and are more flexible with respect to short runs, style and color changes, etc. Furthermore, lamination of highly plasticized stocks to fabric may be more conveniently done with plastisol equipment.

3. EXTRUDED FOAM

Vinyl foam can also be produced by the extrusion process, of which two different systems are in use.

The first is a technique similar to calendering—that is, it involves fluxing the compound (containing the high-temperature azodicarbonamide blowing agent) at a temperature below the activation temperature, and then pelletizing the compound for later extrusion. When extrusion is performed, the temperature of the compound is held below the activation temperature. The extrudate, supported either by a core material or on a belt, is post-expanded in line, cooled and wound-up.

The second method employs a pre-fluxed compound which has been cubed or pelletized. The blowing agent is added to this by tumbling, and may be either the high-temperature azodicarbonamide or the low-temperature "Nitrosan." The mixture is fed into the extruder where conditions are maintained so that the blowing agent completely decomposes. The foam is immediately cooled as it leaves the die.

Figure XV-19, unicellular vinyl foam jacket with filler, covering primary insulation of electric cable.

This technique which calls for foaming during extrusion and having the extrudate issue as a uniform foam is a delicate process. A number of extruder conditions must be met, such as:

1) Sufficient heat and pressure must be developed in the extruder so as to decompose the blowing agent and then maintain the gas in a dissolved state in the plasticizer.

2) The barrel and screw must fit together with reasonable tolerance to prevent gas from leaking through the feed end.

3) The compound must be formulated so that it will extrude satisfactorily at the high temperatures at which blowing takes place.

4) The hot-melt viscosity of the vinyl must be sufficiently high to prevent surging from the extruder as a result of internal gas pressure.

It has been found desirable to extrude vinyl foam in such a way that an outside skin of unblown vinyl covers a blown vinyl core section. This means that a gradient of low to high density vinyl must be developed from the center to the outside surface of the extrudate. This may be done by keeping the die temperature considerably lower than the stock temperature so that the outside surface of the extrudate is sufficiently cool to prevent its expansion even though dissolved gas is present throughout the entire cross-section of the extrudate. In practice short or no die land length is beneficial to prevent tearing of the outer surface of the vinyl, especially for softer stocks. At slow extrusion rates, tearing of the skin becomes more critical since the foam structure is exposed to tearing by friction.

Applications for extruded cellular vinyl are mostly in the wire and cable industry. Of particular importance is the use of vinyl foam as a cable filler, cable jacket, and primary insulation. Cable fillers, the material used to fill the space between the insulated wires and the cable jacket, often consist of natural fibers which are sensitive to moisture and susceptible to fire and fungus attack. Extruded cellular vinyl is successfully overcoming these limitations. Blown vinyl cable filler is prepared by extrusion over a filament. It is then wound with the insulated wires and passed through a crosshead extruder where the cable jacket is applied; the cable filler fills most of the void between the insulated wire and the cable jacket. Cellular vinyl is also used as a cable jacket (Fig XV-19). Here the insulated conductors are passed through a crosshead extruder where a cellular vinyl sheath is applied. This type of construction is particularly useful in building wire for outdoor and underground applications.

4. ROTATIONAL AND INJECTION MOLDING

Rotational casting of vinyl plastisols is a familiar process for the production of toys, automotive armrests, and sun visors. Either azodicarbonamide and the relatively higher temperature blowing agent, "Expandex 177" (decomposition temperature of 450°F), can be used, although the latter gives better results.

Conventional formulations are prepared. A measured amount is placed into the mold, and the mold is closed and heated while rotating in two planes simultaneously to distribute the plastisol uniformly on its internal surfaces. Temperature of the plastisol must be raised above the decomposition temperature of the blowing agent to obtain a cellular structure. Relatively low levels of blowing agent are used to prevent pocked surfaces.

High-density vinyl foam can be injection molded by methods commonly used for solid vinyl materials. Mold closure time is critical in forming a cellular injection-molded structure. By varying closure time and the amount of blowing agent (usually azodicarbonamide), the degree of expansion can be controlled. The longer the closure time, the higher the product density. A finished product having a solid skin and a highly cellular interior can be obtained only by careful control of closure time.

5. TESTING TECHNIQUES

In regard to foam testing techniques, two points merit mention. In the test casting of two different plastisols with the conventional casting bars on a substrate, such as release paper or a metal plate, it is quite possible for a heavier film to be deposited from one of the compounds. This is entireily due to rheological differences of the two materials. If both compounds expand to the same density, the thicker unexpanded coating will rise to a greater expanded height. This will give the mistaken impression that one compound is actually expanding more than the other. This situation, which is not uncommon, necessitates foam evaluations to be made on the basis of actual density measurements rather than by visual inspection of the samples.

Another point which merits emphasis is the reliability of the laboratory oven used for foam work. A glance at any of the density-time graphs in this section shows that actual foaming occurs in a relatively short time. Any lack of uniformity in the oven with regard to temperature and/or air velocity (in the case of a forced circulating oven) is a potential source of error when making density comparisons during the critical period of foam development.

6. FUTURE AREAS FOR VINYL FOAM

Vinyl foam-fabric laminate will continue to grow in the upholstery field. With the development of a dry-cleanable vinyl-foam-fabric laminate, an upsurge in the use of vinyl foam in the garment industry may be predicted. Use of vinyl foam will continue to grow, particularly in applications where the foam is laminated to many substrates other than fabrics: for example, for flooring and wall covering.

A *strippable* vinyl foam coating was recently developed by several companies. It is used principally in the automotive industry as masking coating, also for protection of metal surfaces during shipments. It is flame-retardant and provides a barrier against moisture. The liquid plastisol usually weighs 10 to 11.5 lb per gal, has a viscosity of 2000 to 10,000 cps, and cures in 1.5 min. at 450°F, in 5 min. at 360°F.

Section XVI—FOAMED PHENOLICS

By M. N. Paul

1. GENERAL DESCRIPTION AND PROPERTIES

Phenolic foam is a non-flexible, thermoset, interconnected (open) cell product having low cost, good dimensional stability, low "k" factor, and heat and flammability resistance.

Density control of the foam is achieved by proper resin selection from a family of foaming resins. The reactivity of the resins differs so that the amount of heat liberated in the reaction, and consequently the degree of foam expansion, can be selected according to need. Since internally generated heat produces the foaming action, these resins can be foamed-in-place in hollow cavities or produced in large "molds" for subsequent conversion to slab stock. A thin skin of high-density resin is always formed on the exterior of the foam where heat losses prevent vaporization of the blowing aid and water.

Foam is generated by acid catalysis in a solution of phenolic resin containing water, a blowing aid (isopropyl ether or methylene chloride) and a surfactant ("Tween" #40). Heat liberated by the rapid chemical reaction of the acid and phenolic resin vaporizes the blowing aid and water so that a foam is formed during resin polymerization. By the time the foam has attained maximum expansion, the resin has become a highly cross-linked, infusible, insoluble material. The elapsed time for the entire reaction to be completed ranges from thirty seconds to five minutes, depending on the formulation.

Physical strength

Because phenolic foam can be produced over a wide density range, the material exhibits a correspondingly wide range of properties. This is especially true with regard to its strength characteristics. Listed in Table XVI-1 are average values for phenolic foam at densities of two and four lb per cu ft.

Table XVI-1—Average Strength Properties

	Density of Foam	
	2 lb per cu ft	4 lb per cu ft
Compressive strength, psi	25	60
Flexural strength, psi	25	65
Shear strength, psi	14	30
Tensile strength, psi	20	42
Shear modulus, psi	400	750

These values represent average, ultimate strength data obtained on samples of core foam (no skin, uniform density). In the conversion of liquid resin to finished foam, the vertical rise of the foaming mass results in the elongation of individual cells. Consequently, phenolic foam has a "grain" similar to that of wood, and the strength will vary depending on whether a property is measured parallel or perpendicular to the foaming direction. This is shown in Fig. XVI-1 through 4, which graphically illustrate the variation of strength properties with foam density.

Thermal conductivity

"K" factor—the insulating value of phenolic

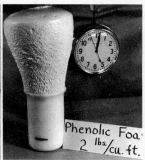

The rapid progression of the phenolic foaming action is illustrated in this sequence: (1) agitation of resin mix and catalyst; (2) pouring of the system; (3) initiation of foaming reaction after 15 seconds; (4) complete foaming after 55 seconds.

foam, as measured by ASTM C-177-45—varies with foam density (Figure XVI-5). For practical purposes, however, the "k" factor is minimum and essentially constant at about 0.2 over a density range of 1.5 to 3.0 lb per cu ft.

Dimensional stability at elevated temperatures

Phenolic foam is a tightly cross-linked, thermoset plastic, and its properties are relatively unaffected by heat and moisture.

Table XVI-2 shows that at least 90% of room-temperature strength is retained when the foam is tested at temperatures up to 250°F. Sandwich panels made with phenolic foam cores and "Masonite" facing skins, weather-tested according to ASTM D-1037-56T (which is an accelerated aging test involving six cycles with alternate water immersion steam spray, and hot 210°F and cold 10°F exposure), retained 90% of original compressive strength

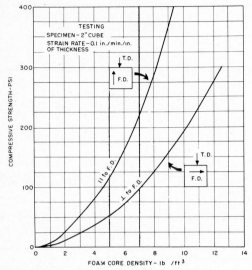

Figure XVI-1, compressive strength of HCl-catalyzed phenolic foam versus core density. Testing performed perpendicular and parallel to the foaming direction at room temperature (25°C).

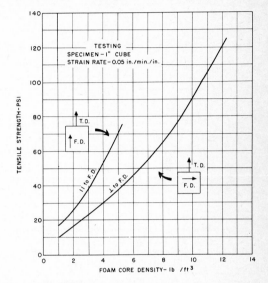

Figure XVI-2, room-temperature tensile strength of HCl-catalyzed phenolic foam versus core density.

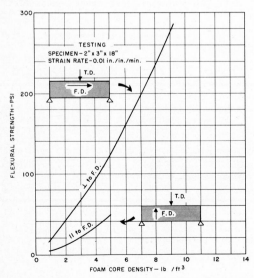

Figure XVI-3, room-temperature flexural strength of HCl-catalyzed phenolic foam versus core density.

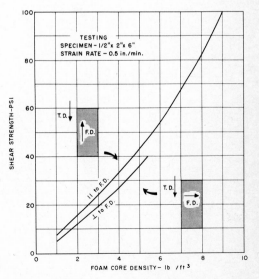

Figure XVI-4, room-temperature shear strength of HCl-catalyzed phenolic foam versus core density.

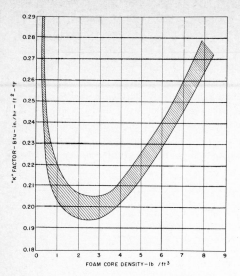

Figure XVI-5, thermal conductivity at mean temperature of 100°F versus phenolic foam density. Measurements made according to ASTM C-177-45 ("Guarded Hot Plate Method").

and showed no failures.

Slab foam, exposed for 16 hours at four different temperature levels (200, 250, 300, and 350°F), shrinks 0.014 in. per in. in length. No significant increase in shrinkage is obtained if the foam is subjected to a repeat 16-hour cycle. At temperatures above 400°F, however, dimensional stability falls off and shrinkage increases as exposure time increases. Comparative values appear in Table XVI-3.

Table XVI-3—Dimensional Stability of Core Foam* at Elevated Temperatures

	Temperature, °F				
	200	250	300	350	455
First 16-hr cycle					
Weight change, %	14.2	15.0	14.4	16.5	22.3
Length dimensional shrinkage, in./in.	0.007	0.014	0.014	0.017	0.037
Width dimensional shrinkage, in./in.	0.016	0	0	0.023	0.052
Second 16-hr cycle					
Additional length dimensional shrinkage, in./in.	0.004	0	0.004	0.001	0.013

Test samples were "neutralized", HCl acid-catalyzed foams of 1.6 lb per cu ft density. Slab dimensions were 9"x9"x2" thick. Foams wrapped in aluminum foil and placed in dead air oven for testing.

The thermal coefficients of expansion over several temperature ranges are shown in Table XVI-4.

Table XVI-4—Thermal Expansion Coefficients*

Sample	Test direction relative to foaming direction	Linear coefficient of thermal expansion, in./in./°C	Temperature range
Core (without skin)	perpendicular	0.34×10^{-5}	−27°C to 60°C
	parallel	0.53×10^{-5}	−27°C to 60°C
	perpendicular	0.67×10^{-5}	−27°C to 93°C
	parallel	0.92×10^{-5}	−27°C to 93°C
Skin (thin phenolic skin formed during foaming-in-place)	perpendicular	4.4×10^{-5}	−27°C to 60°C
	parallel	2.8×10^{-5}	−27°C to 60°C
	perpendicular	3.1×10^{-5}	−27°C to 93°C
	parallel	2.0×10^{-5}	−27°C to 93°C

Linear coefficients of thermal expansion were determined for 2 lb per cu ft density foam, with and without skin, for a 3½ inch span length in a direction both perpendicular and parallel to the foaming direction. Original span length was measured after conditioning samples at 200°F to constant weight and cooling down in desiccator to room temperature.

Moisture and moisture vapor absorption

Phenolic foam has an interconnected cell structure that will transmit moisture vapor

Table XVI-2—Physical Properties— Neutralized HCl-catalyzed Phenolic Foam Cores at Elevated Temperatures

Physical test and conditions	Test parallel to foam direction		
	Density, lb per cu ft	Strength, psi	Modulus of elasticity, psi
Compression			
73°F	4.13	47.2	3900
73°F*	3.64	52.9	4210
200°F	3.90	46.3	1540
250°F	3.69	44.4	1640
73°F	5.47	85.7	5940
200°F	5.41	79.2	2550
250°F	5.43	76.9	2480
Tension			
73°F	3.77	60.9	4350
73°F*	3.85	60.6	4930
200°F	3.93	54.0	2920
250°F	4.14	57.0	2970
73°F	5.62	88.0	6680
200°F	5.54	98.3	4390
250°F	5.47	96.1	4180
Shear			
73°F	3.59	27.0	502
200°F	3.72	25.6	499
250°F	3.74	25.2	384
75°F	5.37	41.4	658
200°F	5.46	41.3	600
250°F	5.39	43.5	549

Values are average of 3 tests. Remainder of data are averages of 5 tests each.

and slowly absorb water under conditions of total immersion. For applications in which resin is foamed in place, the outer "skin" significantly reduces the rate of water or moisture vapor absorption. Figures XVI-6 and XVI-7 show the volume percentage of water and moisture absorbed at various time intervals up to 1,000 hours. The moisture expansion coefficients for phenolic foam are given in Table XVI-5.

Table XVI-5—Moisture Expansion* Coefficients

Test direction relative to foaming direction	Linear change, in./in.	Testing Range	Water absorption (Volume %)
perpendicular parallel	-3.9×10^{-3} -2.5×10^{-3}	50% r. h. to dry	-0.07%
perpendicular parallel	2.4×10^{-3} 3.0×10^{-3}	50% r. h. to 95% r. h.	0.74%
perpendicular parallel	2.2×10^{-3} 4.1×10^{-3}	50% r. h. to total water immersion	19.8%
perpendicular parallel	2.2×10^{-3} 4.2×10^{-3}	50% r. h. to total water immersion	25.9%
perpendicular parallel	0.7×10^{-3} 4.2×10^{-3}	50% r. h. to total water immersion	31.0%
perpendicular parallel	0.7×10^{-3} 4.2×10^{-3}	50% r. h. to total water immersion	50.0%

*Linear changes in 2 lb per cu ft density foam without skin were determined for a 3½ inch span length in a direction both parallel and perpendicular to the foaming direction upon room temperature cycling from normal humidity to dry, high humidity, and high water contents. Original span length was measured after conditioning samples at 50% r. h. (relative humidity) and 23°C to constant weight.

Flammability resistance

Phenolic foam is rated as self-extinguishing when tested according to ASTM D-635-44. Because it is an organic material, the foam when subjected to flame will darken, char, and finally decompose (without melting), but will not propagate flame by itself.

Adhesion

When foamed in-place, phenolic foam adheres well to rough or porous surfaces such as plywood, paperboard, Masonite, cement, gypsum board, and similar materials. With such materials, the interface bond of the substrate and phenolic skin exceeds the core foam strength. On the other hand, adhesion to smooth impervious surfaces such as glass or metal is poor or non-existent, and a primer is required to achieve adhesion when foaming against such surfaces. Adhesives such as Armstrong D-253 (Armstrong Cork Company) and

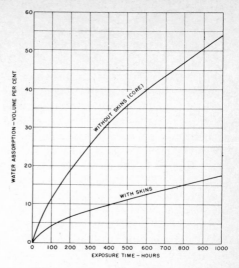

Figure XVI-6, water absorption versus time of total immersion in water at room temperature from 2 lb per cu ft density phenolic foam with and without skins.

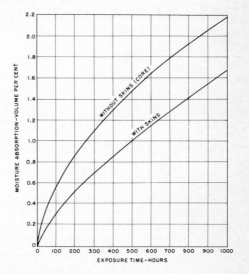

Figure XVI-7, moisture absorption at 100% RH and 23°C for 2 lb per cu ft density phenolic foam with or without skins.

EC-711 (Minnesota Mining and Manufacturing Company) have been used successfully to achieve adhesion. Phenolic foam slab stock may be adhered to other materials using a wide variety of adhesives including solvent type products. Essentially, any adhesive suitable for wood bonding will be satisfactory for phenolic foam.

Corrosion

Phenolic foams being prepared with acid

catalysts, it might be expected that they would have a high corrosion potential. This has not proved to be the case. Diluting of the acid in the resin system and subsequent isolation of the acid in the foam prevents corrosion. The most serious corrosion occurs when foam is generated in contact with a ferrous metal, using hydrochloric acid as the catalyst. Under these conditions, a protective coating (such as the adhesives mentioned, D-253 and EC-711) should be applied to the metal surfaces before foaming. Foams generated against non-ferrous surfaces will not cause corrosion, even after several years of service. Likewise, foams prepared in slab or molded form, subsequently installed on various surfaces have exhibited no corrosive effects.

Color

Phenolic foam varies from light yellow to light brown. This color gradually darkens on exposure to light. The foam may be colored by adding acid-stable pigments before foaming or by coating it with latex-, oil-, or water-based paints.

Sound absorption

Sound absorption of phenolic foam is quite good, and noise reduction coefficients (resonant tube method) range from 0.50 to 0.75.

2. FOAM FORMULATION AND PREPARATION

Ingredients

In addition to phenolic resin, there are three basic ingredients used in the formulation of phenolic foam:

● A *surfactant*, used in order to maintain foam integrity during the foaming process. "Tween" No. 40 is the recommended surfactant.

● A *blowing aid*, used to obtain a smooth, even foaming action, starting at a relatively low temperature when the low-boiling blowing aid is first vaporized. Without this ingredient, no foaming would occur until the boiling point of water is reached and foaming action would then be too violent. Isopropyl ether or methylene chloride are the recommended blowing aids.

● An *acid catalyst*, which initiates the resin polymerization reaction. Acids employed for this purpose include sulphuric/phosphoric, toluene sulfonic, hydrochloric, or phenol sulfonic.

A typical, general-purpose formulation might be:

Ingredient	Parts by weight
Foaming resin(s)	100
"Tween" #40	1
Blowing aid	6
Catalyst	8-13

Formulation variables

By varying the ratios of ingredients, changes in foaming characteristics and/or foam properties can be achieved. In terms of the basic ingredients, these may be categorized as follows:

● Surfactant—Use of the recommended quantity of "Tween" No. 40 results in a uniform, fine cell size distribution. A three-fourth reduction of the recommended quantity results in a coarse, thick, cell-wall structure. An increase up to fifty times the normal amount has a plasticizing effect during foaming and produces a tough, somewhat resilient, foam. Small variations are not significant.

● Blowing aid—Use of the recommended quantity of the blowing aid results in an optimum foam efficiency (lowest density for a given foam resin reactivity) and cell structure. Significant changes, from elimination to four times the specified quantity, results in rapid increases in foam density. Minor variations, up to 10%, are not critical.

● Acid type and amount—The type and amount of acid catalyst used is important in obtaining optimum foam expansion and minimum foam shrinkage. If less than the recommended amount is use, an insufficient rate of resin cure results which causes serious foam shrinkage. With more than the normal amount, the foam sets before vaporization of water and blowing aid is completed. This results in increased foam densities.

Control of foam properties

In addition to formulation variables, a number of conditions significantly affect foaming characteristics and foam properties. Proper control of these variables leads to optimum results in terms of process and product.

Density—Three phenolic foaming resins, each of which produces a specific foam density, are available for use. They are:

Resin	Density of foam obtained
BRL-2759*	1/3 lb per cu ft
BRL-2760*	1.8 lb per cu ft
BRLA-2761*	65 lb per cu ft

*Union Carbide designations.

To obtain intermediate foam densities, two of these products can be used in proper proportion. However, a number of other factors control foam density such as mass of material foamed, ratio of foam surface area to volume, temperature of mold or cavity in which foaming occurs, and the amount of restriction that is encountered by the foam when expanding.

Basically, conditions which remove heat from the foaming mass or increase back pressure on the foam will result in increased foam density. Thus, for a given foam formulation, minimum density and maximum uniformity would be obtained by foaming a large mass of material in an insulated open-top container. Maximum density and larger density gradient would be obtained by foaming a small mass of material in a cold metal mold having narrow cross sectional channels through which foam would have to travel.

Pot life—The time from addition of catalyst to onset of foaming is affected by the type and amount of catalyst employed, resins used, temperature of mix and catalyst when blended, and volume of ingredients involved. Pot life is longest when using "slower" catalysts (such as sulphuric/phosphoric), higher density foam formulations, pre-cooled ingredients and small mixes.

Cell size—The finer cell size foams are made using isopropyl ether as a blowing aid and sulphuric/phosphoric acid as the catalyst system. When properly formulated, however, all systems, regardless of blowing aid or catalyst used, should yield foams of uniform, relatively fine cell structure. Methods of producing a relatively large cell size are:

1. Reduction of amount of "Tween" No. 40.
2. Reduction of amount of catalyst.
3. Addition of water up to 15 pph of resin.

Skin control—The formation of a "skin" of higher density resin surrounding a foam core is due to the loss of heat which occurs at the foam surface. Depending on the specific application, the presence of this skin may or may not be desirable. Skin thickness can be minimized by carrying out the foaming operation so that heat loss from the foam is minimized. For example, when foam is generated in a cold metal container, a relatively thick skin is formed. Preheating the metal to 160-180°F markedly reduces skin thickness. Alternatively, the same formulation foamed in a wooden container will have a relatively thin skin due to the lower heat conductivity of the container wall.

3. APPLICATION POTENTIALS

Phenolic foam is a versatile material that exhibits a wide range of properties. Low "k" factor, low cost, and the characteristics of a thermoset material—heat, chemical and water resistance, dimensional stability and rigidity—are common over the entire density range. Structurally, the foam varies from a soft, easily crushed (non-resilient) material at ⅓ lb per cu ft to a hard, rigid, boardlike product at 10 lb per cu ft. In the low-density range (below 2 lb per cu ft), phenolic foam's dusty surface usually calls for an external skin or covering in order to achieve good handleability and minimize abrasion. Such a "skin" may take many forms—varying from a simple paint coating (which makes the foam non-dusting) to a paper, plywood, or metal skin, which permits it to take full advantage of the inherent strength of phenolic foam (Fig XVI-8).

Thermal insulation

Phenolic foam may be used for insulation as slab stock or as a foam-in-place material. There are numerous product fabrication techniques. For example, foam can be generated in paper containers so that a rigid packaged insulation of flat or curved foam is produced in a single operation. For foam-in-place applications, where handleability and structural strength are not important, the low densities attainable with phenolic foam result in minimum cost per unit volume. In filling very large cavities, hollow masonry walls for example, insulation can be foamed-in-place in batch portions. Foam to foam bonding is excellent.

Low-density phenolic foam (approx. 1 to 1.5

Figure XVI-8, some industrial applications for phenolic foam.

lb per cu ft) can be subjected to moderate localized crushing without impairing its "k" factor. This unique property offers a means of providing insulation around or in irregular structures where prefabrication of special insulation shapes would be prohibitively expensive. For example, low-density phenolic foam can be used to insulate honeycomb by simply pressing a slab of foam into the honeycomb. Each cell of honeycomb is thereby filled with insulation, and the "k" factor of the honeycomb is greatly reduced. In the case of a flat wall section which contains ribs, knobs or other irregular projections, slabs of foam can be used for insulation and will crush locally to accommodate surface irregularities.

Panel core

Phenolic foam's rigidity, temperature resistance, and dimensional stability are important assets when used in the fabrication of foam-core panels. The durability of such panels is excellent when tested according to ASTM D-1037-56T. In many cases of sandwich panel design, core rigidity is of greater importance than core strength and in these cases the relatively high shear modulus of phenolic foam, as shown in Fig XVI-9, allows core thickness, cost and weight to be significantly reduced. Sandwich panels utilizing phenolic foam cores can be fabricated by either laminating or foam-in-place techniques, depending on which method is the more economical for the specific type of panel under consideration.

Packaging

The ability to produce a cavity of the desired size and shape in phenolic foam by simply pressing an object, or a replica thereof, into the foam, makes this material suitable for packaging applications. This is true especially where a variety of objects, which differ in size and number from package to package, are concerned. Under these conditions, it is usually impractical to mold a wide variety of cavities. When using phenolic foam, each item "molds its own" shape in the foam by simply being pressed into it.

Handicraft

Because of its rigid nature, phenolic foam can readily be carved, cut, and shaped with simple tools. At a density of approximately 3 lb per cu ft the foam is well suited for use as an art medium and handicraft material. The ability to be rapidly and easily carved with a

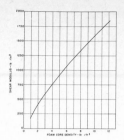

Figure XVI-9, shear modulus of hydrochloric acid catalyzed phenolic foam versus core density.

spoon, wooden spatula, dull knife, or other similar instruments, is an important advantage in the elementary, high school, and college art education field.

Vacuum-forming molds

Since phenolic foam has an interconnected cell structure, it offers unique properties in the field of vacuum-forming. At densities above 2 lb per cu ft, the compressive strength is sufficient to withstand vacuum-forming pressures. Consequently, for prototype work, a mold can be quickly carved from foam for producing new or experimental items. Alternatively, the foam can be completely encapsulated in a two shot vacuum-forming operation in order to produce a piece having a thermoplastic skin and a phenolic foam core.

4. HANDLING PRECAUTIONS

The three resins used to produce phenolic foam gradually age when stored at room temperature. This behavior results in an increase in (1) resin viscosity and (2) density of the foam prepared from a given formulation. A viscosity increase, however, is usually not an important consideration, and there is no general correlation between resin viscosity and foam density. A storage temperature of 40°F is recommended for this resin.

The acids used to catalyze phenolic foaming resins are all injurious to the skin, and the use of suitable protective clothing and face masks is essential when handling these materials. Isopropyl ether is flammable, and suitable precautions should be taken for storage and handling of this materials. Due to the evolution of formaldehyde from blowing aid during the formation of phenolic foam, provisions should be made to conduct foaming operation in a well-ventilated area so that personnel are not exposed to these fumes.

Section XVII—EPOXY FOAMS
PART 1—HISTORICAL DEVELOPMENTS

By John Delmonte

Epoxy resins may be readily foamed into useful structures, though the chemistry of the foaming process differs considerably from the reactions of other systems. The foamed epoxy resins introduced to industry have been of the rigid variety ranging in density from 2 lb per cu ft upward. Emphasis has been placed on the more rigid types of epoxy foam because the flexible systems which are capable of setting at low or moderate temperatures have a tendency to age-harden.

The economics of foam production have an important influence in the choice of materials. For a long time, the higher cost of toluene diisocyanate in urethane foam production justified an interest in some of the basic epoxy resin systems. More recently, lower cost of commercial grades of T.D.I. have reduced such interest. As matters stand, the selection of epoxy foams versus urethane foams will be predicated on the properties of the final product. There appears to be some merit in the superior chemical and heat resistance of some of the newly-developed epoxy foams.

Some of the first applications of epoxy foams appeared in the middle 1950's, when they were prepared and employed to reinforce laminated glass fiber structures. These foams reacted *in situ* and filled cubical volumes which in some cases measured 10 ft by 4 ft by 2 ft. The reaction mechanism involved a basic liquid epoxy resin system—diglycidylether of bisphenol A—reacted with a curing agent such as triethylene tetramine. To improve the efficiency of the foaming process, which relied on the exothermic nature of the reaction, water was added to the curing agent. This not only speeded up the reaction and contributed to a higher heat release, but it also increased the internal gas pressure, as the reaction temperature was well in excess of the temperature of boiling water. Additional processing aids included surface-tension-reducing agents.

Drawbacks to the epoxy foam system relying on exothermic reactions may be attributed to non-uniform heating. Portions near the walls of the container are at a lower temperature than the center, and this prevents uniform cell size. Furthermore, the center may reach temperatures in excess of 400°F, especially when the depth is over 12 in., resulting in a darkened or slightly charred core with a loss of physical properties.

Several years ago, blocks of low density epoxy foams measuring approximately 6 ft by 2 ft by 1 ft were produced. Various methods were available for producing such units, including heat cure. Aromatic curing agents, such as methylene dianiline, plus blowing agents may be used to cure such blocks in molds with heat externally applied. These foamed epoxy blocks were dimensionally stable and were used as reinforcement for plastics tooling and for buoyancy equipment. Plastics tooling often require space fillers to stiffen a structure, without adding too much weight, and foamed epoxy blocks may fill this need.

More recently, H. Chen and A. Nixon (ACS-F1195, April 1963) described some novel epoxy-boroxine foams distinguished by their heat resistance. Their system consisted of a standard liquid epoxy resin (diglycidylether of bisphenol A), a primary polyamine (e.g., pp'-diaminodiphenylsulfone) and trimethoxy boroxine. A highly cross-linked polymer is formed which liberates three moles of methanol per mole of boroxine. Excellent adhesion was reported as a characteristic of these epoxy resin systems. Epoxy boroxine foams remain

Figure XVII-1, epoxy foams can be easily sprayed as insulation over large surface areas, such as these storage tanks. Spray applications can be made with existing equipment—only minor modifications are needed. Courtesy Shell Chemical Co.

rigid at temperatures as high as 300°C. The diameter of cells varies from 0.1 to 0.5 mm. This system foams and cures without applied heat. Peak exotherm occurs between 5 and 10 minutes after mixing.

Other examples of successful epoxy foam products are the sprayed epoxy foams (Fig. XVII-1). As a two-component system, this foam requires equipment that will mix and spray rapidly. Data are reported below for "Epon Foam 175" of Shell Chemical Corporation:

Viscosity in centipoises at 77°F (resin)	5600
Viscosity in centipoises at 77°F (curing agent)	8200
Reaction time, seconds	5-20
Thermal conductivity, Btu/hr/sq ft/°F/in.	0.11-0.13
Density, lb per cu ft	1.7-2.0
Tensile strength, psi	26-31
Compressive strength, psi	13-17
Elongation, %	34-40

One development of epoxy foams consists of a liquid epoxy resin, room or elevated temperature curing agents, plus low density phenolic microballoon or glass microsphere fillers. There are considerable applications of these systems, called syntactic foams, in tooling and structures. Fig. XVII-2 shows an edge sealant to honeycomb core. These foams appear to be

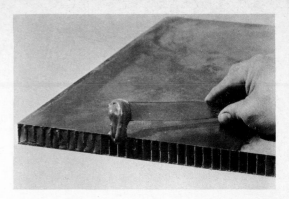

Figure XVII-2, low-density, thixotropic epoxy foam can be used as sealant for a honeycomb structure. Courtesy Furane Plastics Inc.

fulfilling important commercial needs.

The density range is 0.4 to 0.9 g per cc, higher than more conventional foams. Physical properties are good with compressive strengths of about 4000 to 5000 psi for a 0.7 g per cc density and lap shear to aluminum over 1200 psi. Densities above 0.75 to 0.80 g per cc are usually pourable; below that density, they are usually in a semi-paste consistency. Adhesion, as may be expected, is outstanding. They are being employed to stiffen thin skins of exotic metals used on missile and space structures.

PART II—PREFOAMED BLOCKS
By H. S. Schnitzer

Under present conditions of cost economics, one would use rigid epoxy foams only when absolutely necessary. Properly made, they offer dimensional stability, uniformity of density, top solvent and moisture resistance. In all other properties, and certainly in cost, other thermoset foams, particularly rigid polyurethane foam, can compete.

An example of an essential use of rigid epoxy foam is in a light-weight, self-contained, automatic "doppler" navigation system for the Thunderchief supersonic jet fighter-bomber (Fig. XVII-3). This device enables a pilot to set the co-ordinates of his starting point and destination, whereupon the system will indicate his course and distance to destination, his ground speed and drift over the terrain, his continual present position, the wind vector components, and alternate destination selec-

tion. Needed here was a flame-resistant dielectric "lens" that would be absolutely dimensionally stable under all foreseeable service conditions. It was done with rigid epoxy foam, cast-molded into blocks 1 ft x 2 ft x 6 ft, and machined to shape and dimension. Machining presents no problem, since the rigid epoxy foam has no grain and does not degrade even under fast fabrication.

Another place where this superior rigid foam has been found advantageous is as the base or core material for aircraft component checking fixtures, with which the accurate construction of specially-bent air foil frame, pipe, ducts, etc., can be gaged. The check points on these checking fixtures are the standards by which parts are judged, so the bases must be permanently dimensionally stable. Here 84 pounds of rigid epoxy foam replaced 800 pounds of steel in the fixture base. The base is carved out of and, in some cases, built-up in, rather thick sections of foam which are then covered with several layers of epoxy-glass cloth. The check fixtures are then cemented in place at the proper position, and the total unit is neat in appearance, rugged in construction, light in weight, has proven very satisfactory in use.

A further successful application is in making complicated patterns for foundry casting. The epoxy foam is shaped easily with knives, files, and sandpaper, which makes the construction of the pattern quite simple and saves man hours. The foam density of about 15 lb per cu ft makes the patterns quite rugged. Finishing is accomplished by rubbing the carved and sanded surface with a thick paste of plaster of Paris, and when this hardens it can be sanded smooth and given a coat of lacquer or any kind of paint presentable in surface.

Epoxy foam manufacture

The above applications are concerned with the epoxy foam and foaming methods developed by DeBell & Richardson. Other rigid epoxy foams have been developed for many other types of applications by other companies. They are being used for potting and encapsulation of electronic and electrical components, in aircraft structural applications, for spray-up, in some refrigerators and freezers as insulation.

The D&R type foams are made by taking a liquid epoxy resin, adding a chemical blowing agent which decomposes at a specific and controlled elevated temperature, adding a reactive curing agent and fillers if needed or wanted, and then cooking the batch to a predetermined level of viscosity, employing temperatures below the thermal decomposition point of the blowing agent. At a predetermined point in the "cook" of this mixture, an ingredient we refer to as a "trigger" is added which greatly accelerates the previously rather slowly advancing cure of the resin. This accelerated mix is then poured rapidly into a very sturdy preheated mold. Foaming here takes place very rapidly, and after displacement of the air the mold is clamped tightly closed. The exotherm now provides enough heat for the rapid expansion of the mass as well as cure of the composition, and the sturdy mold assures a uniform and even-textured foam.

Among the blowing agents used in making

Figure XVII-3, rigid epoxy foam "lens" for "doppler" automatic navigation system on Thunderchief jet fighter-bomber. The lens is fabricated from prefoamed block. Courtesy D&R Pilot Plants Inc.

epoxy foams are carbonates and bicarbonates of ammonium, sodium and potassium, various diazoamines and triazines, and several others, listed in the patents. Certain "secondary blowing agents" may be convenient to use, usually volatile liquids such as naphtha, toluene, n-propyl alcohol, etc.

Recently, Shell developed an epoxy foam system which uses vaporizable liquids as sole blowing agents, particularly the fluorocarbons of the type used extensively for urethane foams.

Aliphatic and aromatic polyamines seem to be the preferred reactive curing agents for epoxy foams.

The "trigger" material, a DeBell & Richardson contribution to the art, is a proprietary item of an undisclosed nature at this time.

Patent No. 2,739,134, dated March 20, 1956, was issued to Harvey L. Parry and Billee O. Blackburn, assignors to Shell Development Company; and Patent No. 2,831,820, issued April 22, 1958, to Arnold S. Aase and Luther L. Bolstad, assignors to Minneapolis Honeywell Regulator Company.

The foamed mass stays in the mold for up to 48 hours in the case of large blocks, during which external heat is applied to the mold surfaces to prevent too rapid a loss of heat from the outside surfaces of the foam which might lead to development of thermal stresses within the block as it cools. The center temperature in the mass of one of these large blocks has been found to be as high as 430°F by thermocouples. Since the block itself is a good insulator, maintaining the interior temperature of the foam at these high levels to effect a complete cure is simple. The biggest problems arise from maintaining a good cooling rate on the block so that it can be removed from the mold in reasonable time without leaving residual thermal stresses.

After removal from the mold, the block is trimmed with a band saw to remove the relatively high-density, thin skin of foam. This also serves to remove the parting films which are used on the interior of the mold to prevent sticking. The blocks are then ready for shipment to fabricators.

As compared to the isocyanate groups, which have to be watched carefully when there is humidity present, the epoxies are almost insensitive to moisture, so controls are easier. However, the lower reactivity of epoxy resin means that a harder push must be given at the start of the reaction.

Rigid epoxy foam properties

These foams may be produced at densities from below 4 lb per cu ft to well over 20 lb per cu ft.

Compressive strength—Varies from 60 psi at a density of 5 lb per cu ft to nearly 1100 psi at a density of 20 lb per cu ft. At a density of 13 lb per cu ft the compressive strength is 500 psi, with the compression modulus at this density between 11,000 psi and 12,000 psi.

Flexural strength—Varies from 200 psi at a density of 5 lb per cu ft to about 1000 psi at a density of 20 lbs per cu ft, with essentially a straight-line chart relationship. The flexural modulus, however, increases much faster. At 5 lb per cu ft density the flexural modulus is in the order of 2500 psi, while at 18 lb per cu ft it is up to at least 27,000 psi.

Tensile strength—Varies from about 50 psi at the 5 lb per cu ft density up to 500 psi at 18 lb per cu ft density. These foams are not produced for their tensile strength.

High-temperature behavior — Using diamines as curing agents, we get the best heat distortion resistances. Blocks of these foams have been exposed to oven temperatures up to 350°F for many hours, and there is no tendency to slump or melt in any way. There is a gradual change in color from the normal light cream to a dark tan-brown, but this color change also takes place on exposure to light, due to the amino groups present.

There is experience of a block of foam with a density of 18 lb per cu ft being exposed for 17 days at 250°F. During this period it lost 1.04% in weight, most of which occurred in the first few days. At the time shrinkage took place amounting to 2.5% in the linear dimensions, and again it was indicated that this shrinking took place in the early stages of the baking and then leveled off.

Warping does not occur when a block of rigid epoxy foam has been properly annealed; but when a block has been cooled unevenly, residual thermal stresses will be frozen in.

Behavior under load

To check behavior under load at elevated temperatures, blocks of foam were placed under a load of 20 psi and the amount of compression which took place at various temperatures was recorded. At slightly over 100°C (212°F) under this load, compression began. At any point above this temperature the lower density foams showed appreciable compression. At 4.2 lb per cu ft foam showed only 4% compression at 100°C, but it compressed to 44% at a temperature of 105°C (221°F) and kept on compressing as the temperature was raised. The higher density foams were much stronger under load at high temperatures. A 19-lb-per-cu-ft foam showed no compression at all at 105°C and only 8% compression at 120°C (248°F).

This deformation of the foam at high temperatures leads us into the possibility of postforming cured foams. Foams between 5-10 lb per cu ft density when raised to temperatures of between 250-300°F may be *compressed* at fairly low pressure to a fraction of their original volume. When cooled in the compressed state and removed from the press they will retain that compressed state at room temperature. If, however, the "molding" is again exposed to a temperature of 250°F, its plastic memory causes it to re-expand to its original shape and volume. The compressive strength of the re-expanded piece will be about 80% of the original compressive strength, indicating that the cell structure was not seriously damaged.

This moldability of prefoamed epoxy could lead to the avoidance of some difficulties of foaming in place. A rough cut block of foam can be heated, compressed, cooled, placed in a cavity, re-expanded by heating so that it will fill the cavity, then cooled again to make a shaped product. A smooth skin of a low-temperature curing epoxy or polyester can then be applied to the surface.

Fillers for epoxy foams

Care must be exercised in the addition of filler loadings to rigid epoxy foamable material. In the lower density foams the cell walls tend to be very thin and can be weakened by the inclusion of large amounts of fillers. In the higher densities, it is possible to use up to 20% of inert filler, but at densities of 5 lb per cu ft, 4% to 5% filler would be the maximum. Although fillers can provide some interesting properties, there is not much possibility of using them to save costs. Antimony oxide and chlorinated compounds must be added when it is desired to have a flame-resistant or self-extinguishing foam.

Chemical resistance

The rigid epoxy foams have remarkable chemical resistance. They are thermoset, resistant to all of the common organic solvents. These foams are unicellular, but in the lower densities the thin cell walls may permit some penetration by liquids into the exterior sections of the foams. A 1.5″ square cube of 5-lb-per-cu-ft foam, immersed in water for three weeks, had a weight increase of 116%. A similar piece of 10-lb-per-cu-ft foam increased 5% in weight. Both blocks quickly returned to their original weight when dried in an oven.

Section XVIII—FOAMED SILICONES
By Harold Vincent

1. HISTORY

Silicones are chemical compounds containing both organic and inorganic constituents. Individual molecules of these polymers contain organic groups joined to the basic siloxane (-Si-O-Si-) linkage. Developed commercially during World War II by Dow Corning, they have quickly found a place in practically every major industry. Silicones—as fluids, rubbers, or resins—are now produced by Dow Corning Corp., Union Carbide Corp., and General Electric Co. They are used as adhesives; additives for foams, plastisols, and paints; defoamers; brick and masonry treatments; cosmetic and polish formulations; greases; dielectric compounds, fluids, varnishes, potting materials; wire and cable insulation; paper coatings; release agents for molds; and in many other applications. Certain silicones are the most effective anti-foaming agents known and are used widely in the petroleum industry as anti-foaming additives.

Development work on silicone foams began in 1950 in an attempt to fill a need for a lightweight material which would tolerate long-term exposure to temperatures in the range of 400 to 700°F. The first foamable material was based on a silicone resin and was supplied in the form of a crumbled solid. The end-user melted the resin, added an amine catalyst and a nitrogen-evolving blowing agent, poured the mixture in place, and heated to foam and cure. Now there are four types of silicone foams available.

In 1953, the materials previously used were replaced by a series of premixed powders which melted and foamed when heated to a temperature above 300°F. These foams were stronger than the previous materials and densities ranged from 10 to 16 lb per cu ft. Although this type of foam could be used continuously at 650°F, numerous applications were encountered where either the relatively high densities or the heating to 320°F to activate the foam powder was undesirable or impractical. Also, many applications called for the use of resilient foams instead of the rigid foams produced by this method.

Several new types of silicone foaming materials are now available—including materials which foam at room temperature. These are two-component systems, that produce either rigid or resilient foams. They are prepared either by using a high-speed mixer for small quantities, or continuous mixers for larger pours. They can also be modified for spraying. These foams have densities in the range of 3 to 10 lb per cu ft.

Another form of foamed silicone is the silicone rubber sponge. This type of foam is prepared by mixing a chemical blowing agent into raw silicone rubber, then heating the mixture to a temperature which will decompose the blowing agent and vulcanize the rubber. As the blowing agent decomposes it forms bubbles of gas which form the cells of the sponge.

Additional data on silicone foams are given in Section VII.

2. ROOM TEMPERATURE FOAMING OF SILICONE RESINS

Silicone resins are available that expand at room temperature to give rigid and semi-rigid foams. These materials were developed pri-

Figure XVIII-1, catalyzed silicone resin is simply poured into forms and foamed in place without application of heat. Hot surfaces of this turbine, located in a petrochemical plant, had to be insulated to cut down danger of setting off flash fires.

marily as foam-in-place thermal insulation which would stand up under temperatures that decompose other foamed plastics. Both formulations expand to give foam densities in the range of 3.5 to 5 lb per cu ft. These foams are not only exceptionally heat stable, but they have good electrical properties as well. They can be used continuously at 650°F and intermittently at higher temperatures.

The unique properties of these silicone resin foams suggest their use as thermal insulation for high temperature plant process equipment as well as thermal insulation in the fields of aircraft, missile, automotive, atomic energy, and industrial ovens. Other suggested uses are potting and encapsulation of electronic components, electrical insulation, and (where minor strength requirements permit) as sandwich panels for lightweight heat-resistant structural members (Fig. XVIII-1).

Catalyzing

The resin component should be thoroughly stirred before the catalyst is added to insure a uniform distribution of the filler. To catalyze, add 7 parts of the catalyst to 100 parts of the resin, stir with a high-speed mixer for 15 to 30 seconds. Mixing by hand is not satisfactory, but foams of very good quality have been produced from both high-speed mixers and continuous mixers. Since the resin viscosity is in the order of 500 centipoises, the power of the mixer is not an important factor. The mixture should be poured into place within 60 seconds from the time of catalyst addition.

Expansion and curing

During the expansion period, a certain amount of hydrogen is evolved. Although the quantity of gas is small, adequate ventilation should be provided. Expansion is completed within 15 minutes after mixing the resin with the catalyst, but the foams stay soft for several hours. After ten hours, the foam is hard enough to cut and handle. This time can be reduced by heating the foam ½ hour at 200 to 250°F, two hours after expansion is complete. Foam density should be between 3.5 and 5.5 lb per cu ft depending upon the geometry of the cavity in which the material is foamed.

These foams have been expanded to a height of six feet with only a slight variation in density from top to bottom. Where the size of the cavity is too large for a single pour, successive pours can be made. In this instance three hours should be allowed between pours.

Table XVIII-1. Typical Properties of Room Temperature Foaming Silicone Resins

	Rigid	Semirigid
Density, lb per cu ft	3.5	3.5
Compressive strength, PSF		
at room temperature (R.T.)	900	280
at 500°F	72	—
at R.T., after 200 hr at 500°F	1152	500
at R.T., after 24 hr at 700°F	1020	320
Weight loss after 200 hr at 500°F, %	6.4	7.6
Volume loss after 200 hr at 500°F, %	8.3	9.1
Top continuous service temperature, °F	650	650
Water absorption, lb per sq ft surface area	0.284	0.284
Moisture vapor transmission, perm-inches	41.2	41.2
Thermal conductivity at 77°F, BTU/°F/hr/in./sq ft	0.281	0.281
Flame resistance, Lp 406 Method 2021-1	self-extinguishing	self-extinguishing
Dielectric constant at 10⁵ cps	1.09	1.10
Loss tangent at 10⁵ cps	.0028	.0103
Closed cells, % estimated	60	60

The exothermic temperature developed during expansion depends upon the size of the pour, but it rarely exceeds 120°F. This allows large batches of foam to be expanded in inexpensive cardboard or tar paper forms.

The typical properties of these foams are described in Table XVIII-1. The cell structure of silicone resin foams is small and uniform, and tests indicate that 60% of the cells are closed. The thermal conductivity is 0.281 Btu/in./°F/sq ft/hr. These foams are non-burning and give very low weight loss and dimensional changes when exposed to 500°F for over 200 hours. Although the compressive strengths of these materials are not impressive, no other plastic foam can withstand such high temperatures with such low volume and weight loss.

Newer room temperature foaming silicone resins are being developed. These materials do not contain solvents and can be handled within 15 to 30 minutes after foaming.

3. SILICONE FOAMING POWDERS

Silicone foaming powders are completely formulated, ready-to-use materials that produce heat-stable, non-flammable silicone foam structures. These materials require no additional mixing or catalyzing; and, since they are non-toxic, operators do not have to wear masks as protection against hazardous gases. Atmospheric pressure and humidity have negligible effect on foaming action.

These powders can be foamed into sheets and blocks and the structures can be carved or cut to practically any desired shape with conventional wood working tools. They are normally postcured to develop their best properties, but can often be cured in service. The after-cure is necessary to remove volatile by-products of the reaction from the foam. The slow cooling period for large masses of rigid foam is necessary because of the great difference in temperature that can exist between the center and outside of rapidly cooled foam. This temperature difference can produce stresses in rigid foam sufficient to produce cracks in the exterior.

The "after cure" procedure can be varied, but we recommend the following schedule:

4 hours at the expansion temperature (320°F),

plus 1 hour at 390°F,

plus 1 hour at 435°F,

plus 24 to 48 hours at 480°F,

plus slow cooling to room temperature (about 3 hours).

To some extent this "after cure" schedule depends on how thick a section is being cured. Thin slabs of foam will not need the careful step-up in cure temperature, nor the long cooling period.

Foamed structures made from these silicone materials are exceptionally heat stable, are resistant to thermal shock, and have excellent electrical properties. They may be used at elevated temperatures where other types of

foams fail in a relatively short time. Silicone foams have a uniform, multi-pore structure that is predominantly spherical and unicellular. These foams range in densities from 12 to 18 lb per cu ft. Typical properties are shown in Table XVIII-2.

Table XVIII-2. Typical Properties of Heat Expandable Silicone Resin Foams

| | Type of foaming powder | |
	Semirigid	Rigid
Density, lb per cu ft	14	16
Cell size, max diameter, in.	0.08	0.08
Compressive strength, psi		
at 77°F	200	325
at 77°F, after 200 hr at 500°F	190	210
at 500°F, after ½ hr at 500°F	25	70
at 500°F, after 200 hr at 500°F	45	80
Weight loss, %		
during expansion	1.3	1.0
after 1000 hr at 500°F	2.6	2.6
after 1000 hr at 570°F	4.2	4.2
after 72 hr at 700°F	5.2	5.2
Water absorption, % by wt.	2.3	2.1
Maximum continuous operating temperature, °F	650	650
Flame resistance	Does not burn	
Dielectric constant at 10^5 cps	1.25	1.26
Power factor at 10^5 cps	0.00102	0.00105
Thermal conductivity at 77°F, Btu in./°F/hr/sq ft	0.3	0.3

Applications

Silicone foaming powders have gained their widest acceptance in the aircraft and missile industries (Fig. XVIII-2). They provide thermal insulation and protect delicate equipment from thermal shock. The insulation may be applied:

(1) By foaming-in-place to encapsulate delicate instruments,

(2) By sawing prefoamed slabs into desired shapes,

(3) By foaming to shape in molds, then fitting the molded parts into place,

(4) By preparing light-weight, heat- and moisture-resistant sandwich structures.

These foaming powders are also finding applications in the auto industries where insulation must be applied in inaccessible places and must withstand high surface temperatures.

Surface preparation

When the silicone foaming powders are foamed in place and adhesion to cavity walls is of prime importance, special surface preparation is necessary. The cavity walls should be sanded lightly to remove gloss, and then brushed or sprayed with a silicone varnish.

Figure XVIII-2, magazine of aircraft oscillograph is protected by layer of silicone foam between mechanism and outer shell. Foam protects the device against both heat and shock.

Heating for three to four minutes at 300°F or allowing the varnish to dry for several hours at room temperature removes the solvent from the primer.

When the silicone foaming powders are foamed in blocks or sheets, the container or form in which they are cast should be coated with a silicone release agent. This compound can be wiped on the container with a cloth and should then be heated for 5 or 10 minutes at between 300 and 350°F in a well ventilated oven to remove the solvent.

Expanding and curing

Silicone foaming powders are expanded by heating to between 300 and 350°F in an air-circulating oven, or by using strip heaters, heat lamps or similar devices.

The time required for the powder to melt and expand to the maximum height is about 2 hours. To minimize shrinkage, however, the structure should be held at the expansion temperature for at least 4 hours. At this point the foam structure will be fairly rigid, and can be removed and formed to the desired shape before postcuring.

When silicone foams are used as thermal insulators, postcures are usually unnecessary because the foams will cure and become hard during use. A postcure is recommended when good compressive strength at high temperature is required. After being heated four hours at the expansion temperature (regular foaming), a typical foam should be cured progressively 1 hour at 390°F, 1 hour at 435°F and from 24 to 48 hours at 480°F. The foam should then be cooled one hour at 435°F, 1 hour at 390°F, and 1 hour at 150°F before removing from the oven. Total operation takes from 33 to 57 hours.

Preparing sandwich foams

Sheets or blocks foamed from the silicone foaming powders can be bonded to silicone glass laminates, to metals, or to silicone rubber to form sandwich structures. First spread a thin layer of silicone RTV adhesive on either bonding surface then fasten the surfaces together with a slight pressure and allow the silicone rubber adhesive to vulcanize at room temperature.

4. SILICONE RUBBER RTV FOAMS

There are a variety of RTV (room temperature vulcanizing) silicone rubber foams currently on the market. These have a low density and vary in resiliency. They expand and

Figure XVIII-3, fluid RTV silicone foam expands to seven times its original volume within five minutes after catalyzation. It sets to form a flexible foam.

vulcanize at room temperature and offer many of the advantages of silicone rubber, such as:

1. Resiliency over a temperature range of —100°F to 500°F
2. Excellent electrical properties
3. Excellent resistance to weathering, corona, ozone, moisture and other aging effects
4. Chemical inertness.

They offer advantages over solid silicone rubber in that they have a low density, are low in thermal conductivity and are soft or easily compressed. These materials may be used for

1. Vibration isolation or cushioning
2. Thermal insulation
3. Foam rubber parts

Catalyzing and mixing

One of the prime characteristics of the RTV silicone rubber foams is the ease with which they are produced. Foaming is accomplished by the addition of 5 to 6 parts of catalyst per 100 parts of base. The liquid catalyst can be easily mixed with the base material by various means. Although stirring by hand with a spatula will adequately mix the two components, a more uniform foam will be obtained if a high-speed laboratory mixer is used.

Both of these methods will tend to trap air pockets in the finished foam and the use of a continuous machine may be preferred for larger scale production. The foam should be poured into place within 60 seconds from the time of catalyst addition.

The catalysts used for this type of silicone foam contain stannous octoate. Containers should be kept tightly closed when not in use to prevent the loss of catalyst reactivity. For best results, catalyst in a container that has been at least half emptied should be transferred to a smaller glass container for further storage: catalyst stability is better when the air within its container is minimum.

Expansion and curing

Expansion begins immediately upon mixing the catalyst and the base material, and this expansion continues for approximately three minutes. Mixing should be vigorous for 15 to 20 seconds, and the catalyzed material should be poured into place within 30 to 60 seconds. The foam is strong enough to be handled within 5 to 10 minutes. Curing of the foam continues at room temperature and maximum strength is reached in about 24 hours. Very little heat develops during the expansion stage, and very little pressure is built up if the foam is not too confined (Fig. XVIII-3).

Varying application time

Cooling the base before mixing will slow down the reaction between base and catalyst. For example, at 0°F, the application time (time from catalyst addition to gelation) is about 90 minutes. Gelation time decreases if the base is heated.

Timing can also be controlled by varying the catalyst concentration. Below 6 parts of catalyst per 100 of base, the gelation time is lengthened. Conversely, raising the catalyst concentration above 6 parts per 100 speeds up the reaction and shortens the gelation time.

Molding

When expansion of catalyzed RTV silicone rubber foam is unrestricted, molds require little strength; cardboard and aluminum foil have proved satisfactory as mold materials. A rigid metal mold can be used if the casting is to be made to close tolerances, or if the foam is to be partially confined, to obtain a higher density. Confining the material so that expansion is limited causes pressure to be exerted against the sides of the mold. A press or suitable clamping devices can be used to keep sections of the mold together. The density of the finished foam depends upon:

1. The amount of RTV silicone rubber poured into the mold.

2. The rigidity and tightness of the mold.

When RTV silicone rubber foam is being molded under confinement, venting should be provided to allow the liberated hydrogen to escape. Gas trapped at the top or in corners of the mold will form pockets, preventing the foam from completely filling the mold.

Release

The use of a release agent is suggested. Normally, a 3 to 5% solution of household detergent in water will provide good release. Better release is provided by a saturated solution of candilla wax in toluene. Either solution may be applied to the mold by brushing, spraying, or wiping. The release agent should be allowed to dry thoroughly before applying the foam mixture.

Adhesion

To achieve adhesion between RTV silicone rubber foam and metal or other smooth surfaces, a primer is required. Suitable primers and instruction for their use are available from the suppliers of these foaming materials.

Flame retardant foam

A flame retardant masterbatch is available. This material can be added to the RTV silicone rubber foam in the ratio of 4 parts of RTV foams to 1 part of flame retardant masterbatch.

Silicone foam for encapsulation

One special RTV silicone foam is designed for processing by dip coating. It differs from other foams in that the gelation time is from

Table XVIII-3. Typical Properties of RTV Silicone Rubber Foam

Unfoamed base:	
Specific gravity	1.1
Viscosity, centipoise	10,000
Physical properties of foam:	
Density lb per cu ft	7 to 25
Closed cells, %	10 to 80
Thermal conductivity at 77°F,	
Btu in./°F/hr/sq ft	0.29 to 0.43
Compression-deflection:	
Load required for 25% deflection, psi	2
Load required for 50% deflection, psi	5
Thermal stability:	
Continuous operation, °F	300
Short term operation, °F	500
Electrical properties of foam:	
Electric strength, volts/mil	60
Dielectric constant, 10^5 cps	1.3
Dissipation factor, 10^5 cps	0.001
Volume resistivity, ohm-centimeters	9×10^{12}

30 to 60 minutes instead of 30 to 60 seconds. This allows the fabricator sufficient time to catalyze the foam and dip a large number of parts in it before the foam begins to expand. In this way a thin coating of a foam, normally from 0.015 in. to 0.065 in. thick, can be obtained on a variety of small parts. This will act as a cushioning medium to protect the part from stresses built up when the foam-coated part is later encapsulated in a solid plastic. Curing this type of foam is rather slow at room temperature, requiring 24 hours before it can be handled. Cure can be greatly accelerated by heating to about 150 to 300°F.

Properties of RTV foams

Some of the typical properties of these materials are shown in Table XVIII-3. Since there is a wide variety of RTV silicone rubber foams available, properties listed are not for any one type, but are an average typifying the group.

All of these materials are furnished as readily pourable fluids. Viscosity ranges from 1,000 to 30,000 centipoises, producing foams with densities ranging from 7 to 30 lb per cu ft. The cell structure of the foam follows the density closely. Low density foams are essentially all open celled; the higher density foams are predominantly closed celled. Thermal conductivity increases as the density increases, as does the load required to obtain a given deflection. Tear strength, tensile strength, and elongation also increase with higher density foams. All of the RTV silicone rubber foams remain rubbery from –100°F to 500°F. They can be used in continuous operation at 300°F and for shorter periods up to 500°F. The electrical properties listed are typical and do not vary greatly from one type to another, unless special fillers or additives are used.

5. SILICONE RUBBER SPONGE

Silicone rubber sponge is made by mixing a chemical blowing agent into unvulcanized silicone rubber. The mixture is then heated to a temperature which will decompose the blowing agent and vulcanize the rubber.

A chemical blowing agent for silicone rubber must not adversely affect the physical properties or appearance of the finished sponge, and it must be readily dispersible in the unvulcanized silicone rubber. Also, it should decompose to form a suitable gas at or near the vulcanization temperature. Two chemical blowing agents have been found to meet these general requirements, and to be other-wise suitable for silicone rubber sponges, Unicel ND and BL-353, both available from E. I. duPont de Nemours and Co. Several other companies produce blowing agents which might also prove useful in "sponging" silicone rubber.

Procedure

The unvulcanized silicone rubber must be milled both before and after the blowing agent is added. Thorough milling is particularly important after the blowing agent is added to insure good sponging. The silicone rubber and blowing agent mixture is sponged and vulcanized by one of the following methods:

1. *Cold forming method*—Preform the silicone rubber to approximately one-half the finished size by extruding or by pressing into shape in a cold press. Sponge the preform by heating it in an air circulating oven. Typical oven processing ranges from 10 to 30 minutes at temperatures of 300 to 400°F.

Continuous extrusions of small cross sections can be sponged in a hot air vulcanizing unit. However, this technique is not recommended for sections thicker than ½ in.

2. *Hot press method*—Load a silicone rubber preform into a mold preheated to the vulcanizing temperature, close the mold, and vulcanize. The mold temperature should be 240 to 250°F when BL-353 is used as blowing agent and 300°F when Unicel ND is used. The press times vary from 20 to 30 seconds for parts up to a 11/16 in. thickness, and 90 to 130 seconds for parts, ½ in. thick.

The part is removed from the mold and placed in an air circulating oven. The time and temperature depend on the type of silicone rubber stock and on the properties desired in the finished sponge. This information must be obtained from the silicone rubber supplier along with more precise information on the sponging operation.

Adjusting the density of the sponge

Increasing the amount of blowing agent or increasing the sponging temperature generally produces sponges having a lower density. Denser sponge can ordinarily be made by decreasing the amount of blowing agent or (when using the hot press method) by increasing the hot press interval.

Maintenance of uniformity

With silicone rubber stocks which show a tendency to crepe age, it may be necessary to mill the prepared stock just prior to fabrication to obtain good sponging characteristics.

"Crepe aging" is a technical term used in the rubber industry. Other terms used to describe the same thing are "development of structure" or "development of nerve." It's a reaction between the polymer and filler that proceeds slowly as the unvulcanized compound is shelf aged. It changes the compound from a plastic, workable material to a dry, crumbly, hard substance. Up to a point, crepe aging is reversible by working the compound on a rubber mill.

Flat sheet sponge will be more uniform in size and shape if it is quickly inverted and turned end for end after about $\frac{1}{3}$ of the oven sponging time has elapsed.

Silicone rubber sponge is used as blankets in heat sealing or bonding equipment for plastics or metal forming and in electrical or electronics applications as space fillers, bumpers, and check pools. These materials are useful in areas where thermal insulation or cushioning at extreme temperature is required.

Section XIX—CELLULAR MORTARS, PLASTIC SPHERES AND SMOKES

PART I—CELLULAR MORTARS

By M. N. Paul

1. WHAT ARE CELLULAR MORTARS?

Representing an entirely new concept in plastic foam, cellular mortars, or syntactic foams, differ from all other foams by deriving their cellular, or foam-like structure from pre-fabricated microscopic hollow spheres, marketed under the trade-mark "Microballoon."* Resembling fine red flour, these "Microballoon" spheres, which are made of phenolic resin, are mixed with either conventional polyester resins or epoxy resins to produce a low-density, high-strength material, which has been given the name cellular mortar.

Cellular mortar, because of its built-in sphere construction, has the unique advantage of being easily and conveniently "foamed-in-place." The chemical blowing reaction, normally required to obtain foam cellular structure, is avoided.

As a result of this unusual feature, cellular mortar has become of major interest as a sandwich core material in reinforced plastic boats. Because of the low density of syntactic foam, hull structures based on these materials can be made much stiffer, without significant loss of strength, than conventional laminated hulls of the same weight. If, on the other hand, weight is the determining factor, syntactic foams can be used to produce a light-weight hull without loss of stiffness.

In addition to boating applications, syntactic foam sandwich structures are used in the manufacture of various aircraft parts, and wherever high strength but relatively low-density cores are needed in reinforced plastic structures. Indicative of the excellent strength of sandwich constructions filled with syntactic foam is the fact that this type construction is under investigation as a substitute for poured concrete in thin-shell roofs. Further development with these foams is taking place in other areas of modern architecture where new design concepts require new materials.

Registered trade mark of The Standard Oil Company (Ohio).

2. GENERAL CHARACTERISTICS

When "Microballoon" hollow phenolic spheres are mixed with epoxy resin or conventional polyester resin, the resultant cellular mortar is puttylike in consistency. Consequently, it can be molded to shape, trowelled onto surfaces, and forced into cavities, as well as pressed easily into sandwich core structures.

When cured or hardened, cellular mortars derive their low density from the hollow phenolic spheres, and their high strength from the resin binder that holds the spheres together. Although cellular mortar can be made as low in density as 8 to 10 lb per cu ft, it is not as light as conventional foams. However, its considerably higher strength makes it an improved material for foam applications where both strength and light weight are requisite factors.

Because cellular structure is controlled via the phenolic spheres, cellular mortars have an advantage over conventional foams: they can be prepared free of voids, dense areas, and brittle skins. Another advantage of cellular mortar foam is the choice of different resin binders, which permits selection of the proper density and curing conditions for each application.

Spheres of phenolic resin used in cellular mortar are microscopic "bubbles" with an average diameter of 0.0017 inch. These spheres were originally developed co-operatively with The Standard Oil Company (Ohio) to reduce oil evaporation from cone-roof storage tanks. The spheres are filled with an inert gas, primarily nitrogen, which is contained by the walls of the resin sphere.

Table XIX-1—
Average Dimensions of Phenolic Spheres

Average particle size (dia.)	0.0017 inch
Size range (dia.)	0.0002 to 0.005 inch
Bulk density	3 to 5 lb per cu ft
Actual sphere density	12 lb per cu ft

Since these phenolic spheres have an ideal engineering shape, as contrasted with the polyhedral shape of the cells in a true foam, they greatly enhance the strength properties of cellular mortar. Average dimensions of these spheres are shown in Table XIX-1.

Preparation of mortar

The preparation of cellular mortar is a relatively simple procedure. Foams varying in density from 8 to 40 lb per cu ft can be economically and quickly produced by varying the proportion of resin binder to phenolic spheres. Phenolic Microballoons are somewhat hygroscopic and care should be taken to keep them dry during storage, lest difficulties occur in mixing. Since operating conditions which may affect the performance of cellular mortars vary considerably from plant to plant, this information can be offered only as a guide rather than a guarantee of foam performance.

The following formulations and procedures are typical of various kinds of cellular mortars. For purposes of comparison, formulations are presented for low- and medium-density foams using epoxy resins. If polyester resin is used, the specific proportions of resins, catalyst, and accelerator should be obtained from the polyester manufacturer. In general, a given proportion of "Microballoon" phenolic spheres to liquid resin will give approximately the same density of cellular mortar regardless of the resin binder used.

Composition	Formulation 1 Parts by wt.	Formulation 2 Parts by wt.
Epoxy resin ERL-2795	30.0	40.0
Epoxy hardener ERL-2793	7.5	10.0
Phenolic spheres BJO-0930	120.0	25.0
Foam density, lb per cu ft	8.6	21.0

Mixing: Add a weighed amount of polyester or epoxy resin to the mixing machine. A kneader-type machine is best for commercial operations, but a propeller-type mixer may be used for experimental-scale batches. With agitation, add separately the proper amounts of catalyst and accelerator for the polyester resin, or bardener for the epoxy resin. (It is *extremely important* that the catalyst and accelerator be added separately since combinations of peroxide and cobalt naphthenate are explosively reactive.) Gradually add the phenolic spheres and continue mixing until the components are well-dispersed. The resulting mixture will be a thick, puttylike mass, which then may be placed in a suitable mold and cured at room temperature. Temperatures up to 100° C can be used to accelerate cure.

When mixing small batches in a propeller-type machine, a point will be reached, before all the phenolic spheres have been added, when the machine is no longer effective. The final stages of dispersion can be performed by removing the formulation from the machine and hand kneading it in a polyethylene bag until smooth and uniform in appearance.

3. HANDLING CHARACTERISTICS

Field experience indicates that the best method of handling puttylike mixes of cellular mortar is with some form of heated trowel. Hot troweling imparts better flow properties to the mixture and makes it easier to form. Heated trowels have been successfully improvised by attaching a standard trowel or other shaped blade to an ordinary electric household iron or electric soldering iron.

Pot life, or working life, of cellular mortar mixes can be varied by altering the amount of catalyst or changing the hardener in foam formulations. In polyester cellular mortars, reducing the amount of catalyst increases pot

Table XIX-2—Physical Properties of Cellular Mortar

Binder	Density		Compression strength	Strength-to-weight
	lb per cu ft	g /cc	psi	ratio
Polyester*	10.5	.17	52	309
	12.5	.201	145	720
	18.7	.301	205	602
Epoxy	8.6	.139	86	620
	10.7	.173	159	920
	14.0	.226	218	960

*These tests made with a typical polyester resin serve only as an indication of the results that can be obtained.

Figure XIX-1, mold of boat hull, made of epoxy resin with glass cloth.

Figure XIX-2, a release agent is spread on the mold.

Figure XIX-3, a gel coat is painted over the release agent.

Figure XIX-4, outer skin of glass cloth is applied over the gel coat.

Figure XIX-5, glass cloth and resin are worked together with squeegee.

Figure XIX-6, cellular mortar is prepared: epoxy resin and phenolic microballoons are carefully mixed.

Figure XIX-7, cellular mortar is being applied upon the outer skin and carefully trowelled in.

life. In epoxy cellular mortars, the pot life decreases with larger volumes. A one-lb. mix of Formulation 2, for example, will have a pot life up to 40 minutes, while a 20-lb. mix will have a pot life of approximately 20 minutes. The pot life of epoxy foams can be increased by substituting an aromatic amine hardener for ERL-2793 in the following typical formulation:

Composition	Parts by wt.
Epoxy resin ERL-2795	54.7
Aromatic amine	10.3
Phenolic spheres BJO-0930	30.0
Foam density, lb per cu ft	21.0

Twenty pounds of the above foam will have a pot life of two hours. However, to cure the foam properly, an afterbake of two hours at 160° F or one hour at 180° F is necessary.

4. APPLICATIONS

The unique combination of properties offered by cellular mortars—light weight, high strength, and ability to be "foamed-in-place"—makes them excellent materials for many applications. Considerable activity in this area

Figure XIX-8, glass cloth is laid upon mortar to form inner skin.

Figure XIX-9, strong, lightweight boat is obtained after curing of hull and outfitting.

has centered around the use of cellular mortar —as a sandwich core material—in hull structures. Through the sandwich technique, a hull is formed by placing cellular mortar between an inner and outer layer, or "skin", of glass cloth.

Hulls so constructed have the strength and maintenance advantages of conventional reinforced plastic boats plus a great reduction in weight. A cellular mortar hull will be as stiff yet two to three times lighter than a laminated hull of the same thickness. This means that sandwich hulls filled with cellular mortar can be made up to three times as thick as laminated hulls, with an equivalent increase in stiffness

and strength, but with no increase in weight (Fig XIX-1 to XIX-9).

"Microballoons" are also used as low density fillers for compounds used for embedding electronic circuits, to make heat shields for manned spaceships, to prepare artificial wood for master model applications and numerous other areas. They are also used in seismographic dynamite and prosthetic devices.

PART II—PLASTIC OR GLASS SPHERES
By W. R. Cuming

Similar in appearance to the "Microballoons" described in Part I, and used for similar applications, "Eccospheres," a tradename registered by Emerson & Cuming, Inc., are also manufactured under license of Standard Oil Co. of Ohio. They can be made of glass or plastic materials (such as epoxy and polyesters) and even of copper and silver. They are monocellular, hole-free, spheres, with thin

walls but high compressive strength (Fig XIX-10).

Incorporated into mortars, casting resins (epoxies or polyesters) they produce a light foam having many desirable properties, such as high chemical and dielectric resistance, low dissipation factor. Their impermeability to water makes them attractive for flotation equipment.

Figure XIX-10, Eccospheres are hollow epoxy balloons, of several sizes; also shown (center) mixed as filler in a casting resin.

Table XIX-3—
Comparison of Some Characteristics of ECCOSPHERES

Properties	Type of Eccospheres		
	S I	EP-100	EP-250
Raw material	over 95% Silica	Epoxy	Epoxy
Diameter range	up to 125 μ	0.07 in. to 0.15 in.	0.13 in. to 0.18 in.
Bulk density, lb per cu ft	11	7.5	15.6
Average particle density, lb per cu ft	16.2	13.1	28
Mini. compression strength, psi	1000	500	2500
Dielectric constant, 10^2—10^{10} cps	1.16	1.10	1.25
Working temperature, °F	up to 2500	−70 to 325	−70 to 325

PART III—PLASTIC SMOKES
By Betty Lou Raskin

Foamed plastic smokes are a dispersion in air of some extremely low density, gas-filled, microscopic-sized, plastic particles. The smokes are prepared from foamable plastic compositions in a high temperature, high speed gas stream like that emanating from a gas turbine

or a jet aircraft. Invented at The Johns Hopkins University, foamed plastic smokes are the slowest settling smokes which have ever been synthesized. They have become popularly known as "holey smokes" because of the relatively high percentage of gas enclosed within the thin plastic walls inside each of the particles. As shown in the photomicrograph, the particles are spherical and *they are multicellular in structure, rather than balloonlike.* Like foamed plastics in bulk form, the particles can be synthesized from a variety of resins and expansion agents—in different colors, densities, resiliencies, and porosities. Open celled particles contain air; closed celled ones can be filled with many different types of gases, including helium. Some particles contain mixtures of open and closed cells (Fig XIX-11).

Foamed plastic smokes are the first synthetic smokes composed of gas-filled particles and they are the first smokes composed of spherical particles larger than about two microns in diameter. They can be used for special applications such as wind tunnel studies of model aircraft, smoke signals, theatrical effects, crop protection against frost, and as a floating projection screen.

The collected particles (obtained by putting particles collection equipment in the path of the smoke generator) can be used as low density fillers in various types of materials for

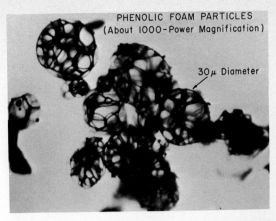

PHENOLIC FOAM PARTICLES
(About 1000-Power Magnification)

30μ Diameter

Figure XIX-11, as a contrast to the microballoons which are monocellular, these smaller phenolic foam particles (plastic smokes) are multicellular.

use in the insulation, filtration, construction, coating, and other industries. Exclusive worldwide rights to the commercial development of these smokes and collected particles have been acquired by The Dow Chemical Company.

Section XX—OTHER FOAMED PLASTICS

By R. J. Bender

PART I—UREA-FORMALDEHYDE FOAM

A plastic foam which may some day become a very successful and economic insulating material is *urea-formaldehyde* foam, or carbamide formaldehyde, as it is referred to in Great Britain where it was first developed for insulating purposes. The resin is the milky product of the reaction of urea pellets and liquid formaldehyde, cooked together several hours in the presence of proprietary additives.

In the U.S., urea-formaldehyde foam is being developed currently by two companies: Allied Chemical Co., and Infra-Insulation, Inc., Staten Island, N.Y.

One-shot, in-place foaming is performed by atomizing at the nozzle outlet of a gun a mixture of 50% resin and water, a mixture of about 5% foaming catalyst in water, and air at a pressure of 80 psi.

A 2 in. hose is used to lead the foam in the making from the gun nozzle to the cavities it is intended to fill. The foam consists of 80% closed cells, 20% open cells. It dries slowly in place. One cu ft of urea-formaldehyde resin will produce about 100 cu ft of foam.

Urea-formaldehyde foam has several advantages:

1) It is extremely light, can be prepared from 0.5 to 10 lb per cu ft.

2) Usual density for insulating applications is 1.1 lb per cu ft.

3) It has a low k-factor, about 0.208 at 70° F.

4) It has excellent sound-proofing qualities: a sound transmission class of 40 decibels.

5) It is inert chemically and resists the action of fungi and microbes.

Urea-formaldehyde, however, has some drawbacks:

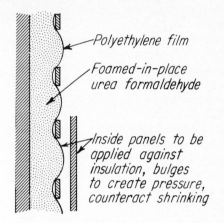

Figure XX-1

1) It has a relatively narrow limit of utilization from the temperature standpoint: Approx. from —20° F to a max of 120° F.

2) It has a very low mechanical strength.

3) It has a tendency to shrink while drying.

This tendency makes it necessary to use pressure for its application as wall insulant, so as to eliminate the formation of voids on the periphery of panels (Fig XIX-1).

According to the U.S. manufacturer, a 4-in. thickness of urea formaldehyde foam is equivalent to a 2-in. thickness of foamed-in-place polyurethane as insulant, but as it costs about one-fourth as much as urethane, the actual cost per sq ft of insulated wall is one-half that of an urethane-insulated wall. A two-in. thickness of urea formaldehyde foam costs about 33¢ per sq ft. This includes the cost of a sheet of polyethylene used to contain the insulation on one side while it is being applied, prior to the application of the inside panel (Fig XX-1).

PART II—CELLULAR CELLULOSE ACETATE

This rigid plastic foam is manufactured by the Strux Division of Aircraft Specialties Co., Inc., Hicksville, N.Y. and is essentially an extrusion product. It comes either in the form of boards, or as rods, 2¼ in. in diameter. Boards are ½ x 8 in., ¾ x 6 in. or 1 x 4 in. and the standard length is 6 feet, although

greater lengths can be extruded at extra cost.

The extrusion process results in a denser outer skin, which is removed by a pair of saws from the outer edges; top and bottom can also be dressed at a small extra charge.

Cellular cellulose acetate is a comparatively heavy foam: 6 to 8 lb per cu ft, and it is rather costly: $1.30 to $1.50 per lb. It is used mostly in sandwich form, bonded to metal, wood or glass, using polyesters, epoxies, polyurethane adhesive, or phenol-urea as bonds. Esters or ketones cannot be used. It has a wide range of temperature stability, from −70° F to 350° F. It has a thermal conductivity of 0.31 which does not make it an insulating material per se, but does not increase the heat transfer when used in a sandwich panel.

It has a low water absorption and a stable

buoyancy: after 14 days in water, one cubic foot of cellular cellulose acetate will support a weight of 52 lb with an initial buoyancy of 55 lb upon immersion. This makes it a desirable floating material.

Main applications of this foam have been for reinforcement in aircraft construction, for radome housings and gun port plugs.

Its good dielectric qualities—1.12 dielectric constant, 0.002 to 0.003 loss tangent—make it possible to use it for X-ray equipment.

PART III—FOAMED FLUOROCARBONS

Foamed fluorocarbons, such as FEP, are now being used by several manufacturers of wire and cable to insulate coaxial cable, chiefly for electronics. To the chemical inertness and resistance to low or high temperatures of fluorocarbon resins (from −100° F to 390° F) must be added the advantage of very light weight for the foamed product. The more foaming, the lower the insulation content required for the same result. Foaming occurs by introduction of a conventional blowing agent into the resin at the time of extrusion.

It appears that TFE cannot be blown as easily as FEP: the advantage that would accrue from using TFE would be a slightly

higher range of temperature stability, up to about 480° F. Times Wire and Cable, division of International Silver Co., and the Brand-Rex division of American Enka Corp., are experimenting in the field of foamed fluorocarbon insulation. The Surprenant division of International T. and T. Co. makes electronic wire of 0.05-in. diameter, and the dielectric constant of the foamed FEP insulation is about 1.6, compared to 2 or 2.2 for solid fluorocarbon.

The average density of foamed FEP is 1.14 lb per cu ft. The general idea is, obviously, to produce cables of very small diameters, with as much metal and as little insulating thickness as possible.

PART IV—FOAMED METHYL-METHACRYLATE

The Sekisui Chemical Co. of Osaka, Japan, is experimenting with foamed acrylic plastics, for the manufacture of structural sandwich panels. Foaming is being performed by an irradiation method—using acrylonitrile as base material. The main advantage claimed for this foam is its high temperature resistance—up to 400° F, about 100° F higher than the urethanes. It is said to have several times the

tensile strength of urethane foam, at a density of 2 lb per cu ft, also a high compression strength. Commercial production is imminent and cost supposed to be competitive with that of urethane. In the U.S., research on this type of product is being conducted by American Cyanamid Co. Dow Chemical Co. has developed a foamed methacrylate-styrene copolymer for use as translucent and insulated panels.

PART V—FOAMED ACRYLONITRILE-BUTADIENE-STYRENE

Under the name of "Expanded Royalite," U.S. Rubber Co. produces laminates formed by a combination of ABS sheet used for the outer skins, and several intermediate layers of foamed acrylonitrile-butadiene-styrene (ABS). A core of unicellular ABS gives rigidity to the sandwich, and layers of more flexible terpolymer substrate afford it high impact resistance. When heated to about 300° F, the blowing agent contained in the core and the substrate expands, while the skins keep their size.

This combination can be easily shaped by conventional thermoforming techniques, at a temperature of 300° F: drape forming, snap-back forming, positive bubbles, plug assist, reverse bubble, and combinations of these. Inexpensive reinforced epoxy molds can be used, much simpler than the dies and tools that would be required for metal parts. The parts are easily trimmed with ordinary tools.

Expanded Royalite is being used principally in the automotive industry for the manufacture of body components.

GLOSSARY OF TERMS
By R. A. Stengard

Cell size is the average cell diameter, in microns.

Closed cell content is the percentage in the foam of the closed non-interconnecting cells.

Compressive strength is the maximum compressive stress which a material is capable of sustaining. Compressive strength is calculated from the maximum load during a compression test and the original cross-sectional area of the specimen. It is expressed as lbs per sq in. (ASTM E6-61).

Dielectric constant of an insulating material is the ratio of the parallel capacitance of a given configuration of electrodes with the material as a dielectric to the capacitance of the same electrode configuration with a vacuum as the dielectric (ASTM D150-59T).

Dimensional stability is change in dimensions of a specimen on exposure to various environments. It can be expressed as a percent volume change or a linear dimension change. The linear change is preferable since most rigid urethane foams are not isotropic and exhibit different amounts of change on each axis.

Dissipation factor (also called loss tangent) of an insulating material is the ratio of the conductance of a capacitor in which the material is a dielectric to its susceptance. ASTM D150-59T. (It is also the tangent of the loss angle.)

Elastic limit is the greatest stress which a material is capable of sustaining without any permanent strain remaining after complete release of the stress. (ASTM E6-61).

Elongation is the increase in gage length of a tension test specimen usually expressed as a percentage of original gage length. (ASTM E6-61).

Flammability of a material has different meanings depending on the test method used. In general, it is a measure of the fire hazard of the material. Many and varied testing methods are used.

Flexural strength is the maximum stress in the outer fiber at the moment of crack or break (expressed as lb per sq in.). (ASTM D790-61).

Linear expansion coefficient is the ratio of the change in length per degree of temperature change to the original length.

Loss tangent (see dissipation factor.)

Mean specific heat is the quantity of heat required to change the temperature of a unit mass of a substance one degree, measured as the average quantity over the temperature range specified (ASTM C351-61).

Modulus of elasticity is the ratio of stress to corresponding strain below the proportional limit. (ASTM E6-61) Since rigid foams do not conform to Hooke's law throughout their elastic range, a "tangent modulus of elasticity is used—the tangent having the slope of the greatest part of the curve that follows Hooke's law (expressed in lb per sq in.).

Proportional limit is the greatest stress which a material is capable of sustaining without any deviation from the proportionality of stress to strain (Hooke's law). (ASTM E6-61)

Rigid urethane foams include a variety of foams having a wide range of properties. Densities range from 60 lb per cu ft to below 1 lb per cu ft and the properties change with density.

Rigid urethane foam has, in general, low elongation (<10%), and a low elastic limit (<10%). They can be crushed and will not recover if compressed beyond their elastic limit.

Semi-rigid urethane foam is a term often applied to low density (<2 lb per cu ft) rigid urethane foams and other foams having more flexibility than the heavier foams.

Shear strength is the maximum shear stress a material is capable of sustaining. Shear strength is calculated from the maximum load during a shear test and is based on the original dimensions of the cross-sections of the specimen (ASTM E6-61).

Solvent resistance is the percent change in volume, or the weight pickup of solvent per cu ft of foam, on immersion in a solvent.

Sound absorption is the fraction of the incident sound that is absorbed by the material.

Strain is a measure of the change, due to force, in the size or shape of a body compared to its original size or shape. Strain is a non-dimensional quantity, but it is frequently expressed in inches per inch. (ASTM E6-61).

Stress is the intensity at a point in a body of the internal forces or components of force that act on a given plane through the point. (Expressed as lb per sq in.). The stress is calculated on the original dimension of the specimen before it is tested. (ASTM E6-61).

Tensile strength is the maximum tensile stress which a material is capable of sustaining. Tensile strength is calculated from the maximum load carried to rupture during a tension test and the original cross-sectional area of the specimen (ASTM E6-61).

Thermal conductivity is the rate of heat flow, under steady conditions, through unit area, per unit temperature gradient in the direction perpendicular to the area. Thermal conductivity is usually expressed in English units, as Btu per sq ft per hr per deg F for a thickness of 1 in. This may be expressed mathematically as Btu-in per hr sq ft °F. (ASTM C168-56).

Water absorption is the amount of water a specimen picks up on total immersion in water over a specified time. Water absorption is usually expressed as lb water per cu ft of foam or as percent of the total foam weight.

Water vapor transmission, also called MVT (moisture vapor transmission), is the rate at which water will pass through a material. The rate may vary with the exposure conditions. Water vapor transmission is usually expressed as "perm-inches" which is the grains of water transmitted per sq ft per hr per in. differential of mercury for a 1 in. specimen thickness.

Yield point is the first stress in a material (less than the maximum attainable stress) at which an increase in strain occurs without an increase in stress. (ASTM E6-61).

Yield strength is the stress at which a material exhibits a specified limiting deviation from the proportionality of stress to strain. The deviation is expressed in terms of strain. (ASTM E6-61). Since low density rigid urethane foam exhibits a definite yield point, the yield strength is the stress at this point. High density rigid urethane foams do not exhibit a yield point so the yield strength is the stress at which there is a marked deviation from the proportionality of stress to strain. An off-set method can also be used (usually at a strain of 0.2 percent).

BIBLIOGRAPHY

FOAMED PLASTICS IN PACKAGING

BROWN, KENNETH, "Package Design Engineering", John Wiley & Sons, Inc. (1959).

HANLON, R. & HUMBERT, W., "Packaging with Foams", 18th SPE ANTEC (1962).

KERSTNER, O., "General Principles of Package Design", Northrup Aircraft, Inc., Report #57-187, (1957).

FOAMED PLASTICS IN SURGERY

"Silicone and Teflon Prostheses", *Annals of Surgery*, Vol. 157, No. 6, June 1963.

"Study and Use of Synthetic Materials as Subcutaneous Prostheses", *Plastic and Reconstructive Surgery*, Vol. 26, No. 3, Sept. 1960.

FOAMED PLASTICS IN ELECTRICITY

BOETTCHER, C. J. F., "Recueil des Travaux Chimiques des Pays-Bas", The Hague, Netherlands, Vol. 64, 1945, p. 47.

BRENNER, W., "Foam Plastics", *Materials in Design Engineering*, June 1956.

HARPER, C. A., "Electronic Packaging with Resins", McGraw-Hill (1961).

"Instrumentation for the Manufacture of Cellular Plastic Insulated Wires"; the Addison Electric Company Ltd., London, England; Ref. ARI/3.6.

"Measurements in Multipair Cables", J. T. Maupin; Bell Telephone Technical Journal, New York, N.Y. Vol. 30, July 1951, pp. 652-657.

"Properties, Economy and Extrudability of Cellular Insulation of Communications Cable," *Insulation*, Jan. 1962, p. 19.

WALLACE, WM. B., "Encapsulation Methods", *Product Engineering*, Nov. 11, 1963.

RIGID URETHANE FOAM

ABERNATHY, H. H., "Isocyanates and Their Reaction Products", *Rubber World*, Vol. 131, No. 6, p. 765 (March, 1955).

ARNOLD, R. G., NELSON, J. A., and VERBANC, J. J., "Chemistry of Organic Isocyanates", Elastomer Chemicals Department Report HR-2, E. I. du Pont de Nemours & Co., Inc. (January, 1956).

ARNOLD, R. G., NELSON, J. A. and VERBANC, J. J., "Organic Isocyanates—Versatile Chemical Intermediates", *Journal of Chemical Education*, 34 No. 4 p. 158 (April 1957).

CEAR, S., GRETH, G. G. and WILSON, J. E., "Formulation and Properties of Sorbitol Polyether-Based Rigid Urethane Foam", SPE Conference, Buffalo, New York (Oct. 5, 1961).

COOPER, W., PEARSON, R. W. and DARKE, S., "Isocyanate Reactions and the Structure of Polyurethanes", *The Industrial Chemist*, p. 121 (March, 1960).

CUNNINGHAM, R. E. and MASTIN, T. G., "Rates of Diisocyanates-Alcohol Reactions at Elevated Temperatures", *Journal of Organic Chemistry*, Vol. 24, pp. 1585-1587 (1959).

FRISCH, K. C. and ROBERTSON, E. J., "Advances in Technology and Uses of Rigid Urethane Foams", *Modern Plastics*, Vol. 40, p. 165 (October 1962).

GEMEINHARDT, P. G., DARR, W. C. and SAUNDERS, J. H., "Rigid Urethane Foams Derived from Crude Tall Oil", *I & EC*, Vol. 1, No. 2, p. 92 (Jan. 1962).

HARDING, R. H., "Determination of Average Cell Volume in Foamed Plastics", *Modern Plastics*, (June 1960).

JONES, R. E., "Rigid Urethane Foam-Process Variables and Test Procedures", *Plastics Technology*, p. 27 (Oct. 1961).

KNOX, R. E., "The Insulation Properties of Fluorocarbon Expanded Rigid Urethane Foam", Insulation Conference, SPI, New York City (April 26, 1962).

KNOX, R. E., "Frothing, a New Method for Producing Urethane Foams," *CEP* Vol. 57, No. 10 Tech. Manual (Oct. 1961).

KNOX, R. E. and STENGARD, R. A., "Molding Rigid Urethane Foam", Du Pont Foam Bulletin (Oct. 28, 1960).

KNOX, R. E., "Measuring the Thermal Insulating Effectiveness of Rigid Urethane Foam," Du Pont Foam Bulletin (Aug. 14, 1962).

LYON, C. K., GARRETT, VILMA H., and GOLDBLATT, L. A., "Solvent-Blown Rigid Urethane Foams from Low Cost Castor Oil-Polyol Mixtures", *Journal of the American Oil Chemists' Society*, Vol. 39, p. 69 (Jan. 1962).

MILLER, R. N., BAILEY, C. D., FREEMAN, S. M., BEALL and COXE, E. F., "Properties of Foams, Adhesives and Plastic Films at Cryogenic Temperatures", *Industrial & Engineering Chemistry Prod. R & D*, Vol. 1, No. 4, p: 257 (Dec. 1962).

MURPHY, E. B. and O'NEIL, W. A., "Infrared and Dielectric Analysis of Structural Polyurethane Foam", *SPE Journal 18*, p. 191 (Feb. 1962).

SAUNDERS, J. H., "The Relations Between Polymer Structure and Properties in Urethane", *Rubber Chem. & Tech. 33*, p. 1259 (1960).

SAUNDERS, J. H., "The Reactions of Isocyanates and Isocyanate Derivatives at Elevated Temperatures", *Rubber Chem. & Tech. 32*, p. 337 (1959).

SAUNDERS, J. H., "The Formation of Urethane Foams", *Rubber Chem. & Tech. 33*, No. 6, p. 1293 (1960).

SHKAPENKO, G., GMITTER, G. I. and GRUBER, E. E., "Mechaninsm of the Water—Isocyanate Reaction", *Ind. & Eng. Chem.* Vol. 52 No. 7, p. 605 (July, 1960).

STENGARD, R. A. and KNOX, R. E., "Improved Frothing Process for Rigid Urethane Foam", Du Pont Foam Bulletin (Aug. 25 (R) 1960).

STENGARD, R. A., "Low Temperature Properties of Urethane Foam", Du Pont Foam Bulletin (Sept. 19, 1960).

STENGARD, R. A., "Effect of NW/OH Ratio on the Properties of Rigid Urethane Foam", Du Pont Foam Bulletin (March 28, 1962).

STENGARD, R. A., "General Questions Often Asked About Rigid Urethane Foam", Du Pont Foam Bulletin (Mar. 1, 1962).

TENHOOR, R. E., "The World Market for Urethane Chemicals", *Chem. & Eng. News* (Feb. 4, 1963).

FLEXIBLE URETHANE FOAM

Allied Chem. Corp., National Aniline Research Notes RN-8, "Flexible Urethane Foam Self-Extinguishing Properties", (1961).

BARRINGER, C. M., E. I. duPont deNemours & Co., Bulletin HR-11, "Teracol 30, Polyalkyene Ether Glycol, a Resin for Urethane Products". March 30, 1956.

BOLIN, R. E., J. F. SZABAT, R. J., COTE, E. PETERS, P. G., GEMEINHARDT, A. S. MORECROFT, E. E. HARDY, and J. H. SAUNDERS, *J. Chem. & Eng. Data, 4*, 261 (1959).

BUIST, J. M., Proceedings International Rubber Conference, Washington, D.C., Nov. 1959.

DAVIS, S., J. M. McCLELLAN and K. C. FRISCH, Isocyanate Symposium, SPE, Minneapolis, Minn., Oct., 1957.

DWYER, F., J. M. KAPLAN, E. L. PIVER, JR., and H. STONE, 7th Annual Tech. Conf. of the SPI Cellular Plastics Div., N. Y., N. Y., April (1963).

EHLICH, A., and T. C. PATTON, Baker Castor Oil Co., Tech. Bull., "Castor Polyol Based Urethane Foam", July 18, 1963.

Farbenfabriken Bayer, Tech. Bulletin, "Spontaneous Ignition and Fire Behavior of Moltoprene T", Aug. 30, 1963.

HARDING, R. H., and C. J. HILADO, SPI Cellular Plastics Division Annual Technical Conference Proceedings, New York City (April, 1963).

HARRIS, R. F. and W. J. TOUHEY, JR., E. I. duPont deNemours & Co., Tech. Bull., "Resilient One-Shot Urethane Foams Using Freon-11 Blowing Agent", Sept. 27, 1961.

HARRIS, R. F. and W. J. TOUHEY, JR., E. I. duPont deNemours & Co., Tech. Bull., "Slab Production of One-Shot Resilient Polyether Foam", March 14, 1962.

HEISS, H. L., F. P. COMBS, P. G. GEMEINHARDT, J. H. SAUNDERS, E. E. HARDY, *Ind. Eng. Chem.*, *51*, 929 (1959).

KNOX, R. E., E. I. duPont deNemours & Co., Tech. Bull. HR-29, "Continuous Preparation of Urethane Foam Prepolymer", July, 1958.

Mobay Chem. Co., Interim Report "The Accelerated Testing of Urethane Foam for Mattress Application", TIB No. 60-F-24.

Mobay Chem. Co., TIB No. 74-F-28, "Flexible High Density One-Shot Polyether Urethane Foams".

Mobay Chem. Co., Tech. Data Bull., F-5 "Flexible Foams based on Mobay Experimental Polyester F-30", Oct. 19, 1956.

Mobay Chem. Co., TIB No. 75-F-29, "Methylene Chloride and Trichloromonofluoromethane (Refrig. 11) as Flexible Urethane Foam Blowing Agents."

Mobay Chem. Co., Interim Report on "Spontaneous Combustion of One-Shot Polyether Foam", August 29, 1960.

Mobay Chem. Co., Preliminary Tech. Info., "Urethane Carpet Underlay."

O'MEARA, A. L., E. I. duPont deNemours & Co., Tech. Bull., "Frothed One-Shot Resilient Urethane Foam", Oct. 22, 1962.

"Plastics Engineering Handbook", 3rd ed., Reinhold Publishing Corp., New York, 1960.

SANDRIDGE, R. L., P. G. GEMEINHARDT, J. H. SAUNDERS, *SPE Transactions, 3*, No. 2, April 1963.

SANDRIDGE, R. L., A. S. MORECROFT, E. E. HARDY, and J. H. SAUNDERS, *J. Chem. & Eng. Data, 5*, 495 (1960).

SAUNDERS, J. M., and K. C. FRISCH, "Polyurethanes: Chemistry and Technology", *Interscience Publishers*, New York, 1962.

SAUNDERS, J. H., S. STEINGISER, P. G. GEMEINHARDT, A. S. MORECROFT, and E. E. HARDY, *J. Chem. Eng. Data, 3*, 153 (1958).

STEINGISER, S., W. C. DARR, and J. H. SAUNDERS, *Rubber Chemistry and Technology*, Vol. xxxvi, No. 1, Jan., 1964.

TOUHEY, W. J. JR., and H. W. WOLFE, E. I. duPont deNemours & Co. Tech. Bull. "Effect of Temperature of Foam Intermediates on Properties of One-Shot Resilient Urethane Foam", July 28, 1961.

TUFTS, E., and W. J. TOUHEY, JR., E. I. duPont deNemours & Co., Tech. Bull., "Molding One-Shot Resilient Urethane Foam", Nov. 8, 1962.

Union Carbide Corp., Tech. Bull., "Niax Catalyst D-22 in Preparing Polyether Preploymers."

Union Carbide Corp., Silicones Div. Bulletin, "Silicone Surfactants for Polyurethane Foams", 1962.

WOLFE, H. W., JR., E. I. duPont, deNemours &

Co., Foam Bulletin, "Catalyst Activity in One-Shot Urethane Foam", March 16, 1960.

WOLFE, H. W., and E. TUFTS, E. I. duPont de-Nemours & Co., Tech. Bull. HR-27, "Urethane Foams from Polypropylene Glycols of Molecular Weight 2000", July, 1958.

FOAMED POLYSTYRENE

"ABS/Polystyrene Foam Panels Insulated Railroad Cars," *Plastics Design and Processing*, p. 21, October, 1961.

DOW, ALDEN B., "Ten-Year Performance of Plastics in Residences", *Performance of Plastics in Building*, Pub. No. 1004, Building Research Institute.

"Forming Thin Shells," Technical Bulletin No. 171-191, The Dow Chemical Company, Midland, Mich.

"A Guide to Design of Floating Structures with Styrofoam", Technical Bulletin No. 171-162, The Dow Chemical Company, Midland, Mich.

"Fabrication of Dow Foam Plastics", Technical Bulletin No. 171-175, The Dow Chemical Company, Midland, Mich.

"Adhesives and Coatings for Dow Plastics," Technical Bulletin No. 171-177A, The Dow Chemical Company, Midland, Mich.

"Low Temperature Insulation: Styrofoam," Technical Bulletin No. 157-201, The Dow Chemical Company, Midland, Mich.

"Styrofoam: Low Temperature Pipe Covering," Technical Bulletin No. 157-204, The Dow Chemical Company, Midland, Mich.

"Styrofoam: Expanded Polystyrene," Technical Bulletin No. 171-188A, The Dow Chemical Company, Midland, Mich.

"Styrofoam: Sandwich Construction," Technical Bulletin No. 171-144, The Dow Chemical Company, Midland, Mich.

"Building Insulation Products and Systems," Technical Bulletin No. 157-243, The Dow Chemical Company, Midland, Mich.

"Styrocel," Technical Bulletin No. 157-250, The Dow Chemical Company, Midland, Mich.

FUNKE, THOMAS, "Expanded Polystyrene as an Aid in Positioning", *The X-Ray Technician*, Vol. 27, pp. 190-192, November, 1955.

HANLON, R. G., and HUMBERT, W. E., "Principles of Foam Cushioning," *Modern Packaging*, Vol. No. 35, No. 10, p. 158, 1962.

KENNEDY, R. N., "Thermal Plastic Foams as Thermal Insulation in Roofs", Report of Conference—Plastics for Roof Construction, Building Research Institute-NAS-NRC, October, 1957.

McCUAIG, D. W., and McINTIRE, O. R., "An Expanded Polystyrene", *Modern Plastics*, March, 1945.

McINTIRE, O. R., and KENNEDY, R. N., "Styrofoam for Low Temperature Insulations", *Chemical Engineering Progress*, Vol. No. 44, No. 9, p. 727, September, 1948.

Manufacturing Chemists Association, Inc., "Plastic Foams—Storage, Handling and Fabrication," Safety Guide SG5, September, 1960.

WAIDELICH, A. T., "Plastics in Structural Panels," *Plastics in Building*, Pub. No. 337, Building Research Institute-NAS-NRC, pp. 51-56, April, 1955.

WALING, J. L., and GRESZCZUK, L. B., "Experiments with Thin Shell Structural Models", *Journal of the American Concrete Institute*, Vol. 32, No. 4, October, 1960.

ZIEGLER, E. E., "Foamed Polystyrene in Thin Shell Construction", *Structural Foams*, Pub. No. 892, Building Research Institute, 1961.

FOAMED POLYETHYLENE

The Dow Chemical Company, "Fabrication of Dow Foam Plastics", Midland, Michigan, 1961.

The Dow Chemical Company, "Packaging with Ethafoam", Midland, Michigan, 1963.

FOAMED POLYVINYL

MEYER & ESAROVE, "High Density Cellular Vinyl by Direct Extrusion", *Plastics Technology*, April, 1959.

VARENELLI, A. D., "Extruded Cellular Vinyl", *Wire & Wire Products*, July, 1961.

WERNER, A. C., "Formulating Polymeric Plasticizers in Vinyl Plastisol Formulations", presented at S.P.E. Philadelphia Section, February, 1962.

WOLSTENHOLME & ROGGI, "Rheological Study of Vinyl Calendering Compounds", *Modern Plastics*, 1960.

INDEX